PHYSICAL CONSTANTS COMMONLY NEEDED IN COMPUTATIONS

ELEMENTARY
MODERN PHYSICS

RICHARD T. WEIDNER

PROFESSOR OF PHYSICS

RUTGERS UNIVERSITY

ROBERT L. SELLS

PROFESSOR OF PHYSICS

STATE UNIVERSITY COLLEGE

GENESEO, NEW YORK

ALLYN AND BACON, INC.   BOSTON

PREFACE

Our aim in this second edition of *Elementary Modern Physics* remains as in the first—to treat the fundamentals of the physics of the twentieth century fairly rigorously, but at an elementary level. The text is intended primarily for use in the concluding portion of the general physics course for students of science and engineering, or as the basis for a separate course in modern physics. It is a companion to the authors' *Elementary Classical Physics* (Boston, Mass.: Allyn and Bacon, Inc., 1965), to which detailed references are made. The prerequisites, however, are merely an elementary knowledge of classical physics and of introductory calculus.

In view of the cordial reception that the first edition has received and, more especially, because we believe that its basic structure and strategy still represent an effective means of introducing non-classical physics, this revised edition is basically an updated, somewhat expanded, slightly more sophisticated and, hopefully, more felicitous version of the first one. Again, the text attempts to give a logically coherent and sequential account of the basic principles of the relativity and quantum theories, of atomic and nuclear structure, and of a few topics in elementary-particle, molecular, and solid-state physics.

We begin, after some preliminaries, with a simple treatment of special relativity, not only as the foundation of all later chapters, but particularly in anticipating the properties of the photon as a completely relativistic particle. The quantum effects are then introduced through the basic photon-electron interactions, and the wave properties of material particles are treated. With the basic principles of relativity and quantum physics developed, these are applied to atomic, nuclear, elementary-particle, and solid-state physics.

Apart from many minor changes intended to clarify, refine, and update the exposition and to bring matters of nomenclature and usage into conformity with present practice, the principal changes in the revised edition are these: Special relativity has been expanded to two chapters, the first on relativistic kinematics and the second on relativistic dynamics. Among new topics introduced in the chapters on relativity are space-time intervals, the light cone, the twin paradox, the energy-momentum four-vector, and the magnetic force as a relativistic effect. Discussion of wave mechanics and applications of the Schrödinger equation have been expanded; although the quantum theory of the hydrogen atom is still introduced through the admittedly defective, but pedagogically simple, Bohr theory, hydrogen wave functions are then given.   The separate chapter on x-rays has been eliminated; some simpler aspects of x-ray spectra are treated in Chapter 7 on many-electron atoms. Chapter 8 on instrumentation and accelerators has been expanded to include some of the newer devices. The treatment of elementary particles has been expanded substantially and placed in a separate chapter, which reviews the photon-electron interactions from the point of view of quantum field theory and Feynman graphs. Although the number of topics has been increased, we recognize that this is an introduction to modern physics and have made no attempt to be comprehensive and include every item of contemporary interest; this is patently impossible in any event.

Although some problems appearing in the first edition have been retained, most of the problems at the chapter ends are entirely new. Indeed, some minor topics, such as the focusing of charged particles by electric and magnetic fields, are dealt with only in problems. The more difficult problems are identified with an asterisk, and answers to all odd numbered problems are given in the back of the book. Summaries are also given at the chapter ends, as are references to other sources.

In its entirety this text provides enough material for a one- or two-semester course at the levels of the sophomore or junior year. The arrangement of topics is such, however, that it can be used for a shorter treatment without serious discontinuities; one might, for example, omit the latter sections of Chapters 2 and 3 on special relativity, large portions of Chapters 6 (Many-Electron Atoms), 8 (Instruments and Accelerating Machines used in Nuclear Physics), and 11 (Elementary Particles), and all of Chapter 12 (Molecular and Solid-State Physics).

We have benefited greatly from the comments and suggestions for improvements by many who used the first edition; unfortunately, we have not been wise enough or able, in our efforts to keep the length of the book from expanding inordinately, to incorporate them all. Our special thanks go to Dr. Arthur E. Walters, who assisted in many aspects of manuscript preparation and checked answers to problems, and to Mrs. Patricia B. Kinder, and Mrs. Maxine F. LaPiana, who typed the manuscript. We are also indebted to the editorial and production staffs of Allyn and Bacon for bringing this work to completion expeditiously.

Richard T. Weidner
New Brunswick, New Jersey

Robert L. Sells
Geneseo, New York

June, 1968

CONTENTS

FOUR
QUANTUM EFFECTS: THE PARTICLE ASPECTS OF ELECTROMAGNETIC RADIATION

FIVE
QUANTUM EFFECTS: THE WAVE ASPECTS OF MATERIAL PARTICLES

SIX
THE STRUCTURE OF THE HYDROGEN ATOM

SEVEN
MANY ELECTRON ATOMS

EIGHT
INSTRUMENTS AND ACCELERATING MACHINES USED IN NUCLEAR PHYSICS

NINE
NUCLEAR STRUCTURE

TEN
NUCLEAR REACTIONS

ELEVEN
THE ELEMENTARY PARTICLES

TWELVE
MOLECULAR AND SOLID-STATE PHYSICS

ELEMENTARY MODERN PHYSICS

O N E

SOME PRELIMINARIES

What is modern physics? How does it differ from, and in what ways is it similar to, classical physics? What central ideas of classical physics are carried over into twentieth-century physics, in which one encounters the very small and the very fast? Which of the classical ideas remain unchanged, and which must be modified or replaced? These questions and other important ones are dealt with in this introductory chapter.

1-1 The program of physics The program of physics is to devise concepts and laws that can help us to understand the universe. Physical laws are constructions of the human mind, subject to all the limitations of human understanding. They are not necessarily fixed, immutable, or good for all time, and Nature is not compelled to obey them.

A law in physics is a statement, usually in the succinct and precise language of mathematics, of a relationship that has been found by repeated experiment to obtain among physical quantities and that reflects persistent regularities in the behavior of the physical world. A "good" physical law has the greatest possible generality, simplicity, and precision. The final criterion of a successful law of physics is how accurately it can predict the results that experiments will yield. For example, our confidence in the essential correctness of the law of universal gravitation leads us to expect with almost complete certainty that, when the gravitational acceleration at the Moon's surface is measured there, it will be very close to 1.6 m/sec². We say that our certainty is *almost* complete, inasmuch as extrapolating from any law outside the range of its tested validity *may* predict results that come to be inconsistent with later experiment.

As physics developed, some early theories and laws were found to be inadequate with respect to phenomena for which they had not been tested. These have been supplanted by more general, comprehensive theories and laws, which more adequately describe phenomena in the new as well as in the old regions of investigation. Figure 1-1 shows the various regions of applicability of *classical physics, relativity physics, quantum physics,* and *relativistic quantum physics.*

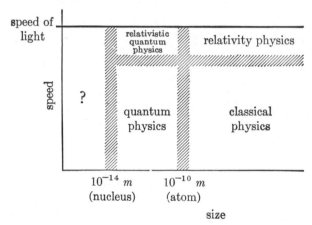

Figure 1-1. Regions of applicability of various physical theories.

Classical physics is the physics of ordinary-sized objects moving at ordinary speeds; it embraces Newtonian mechanics and electromagnetism (including the theory of light). For object speeds approaching that of light classical physics must be supplanted by relativity physics; for object sizes of about 10^{-10} m, approximately the size of an atom, classical physics must be supplanted by quantum physics. For subatomic dimensions and speeds approaching that of light only relativistic quantum physics is adequate. The limits of the several physical theories are not sharply defined; in fact, they overlap. Relativistic quantum physics is the most comprehensive and complete theoretical structure in contemporary physics. At dimensions of about 10^{-14} m, the approximate size of the atomic nucleus, different and perplexing phenomena appear; at present they are only partly understood.

The foundations of our understanding of atomic and nuclear structure lie in the two great ideas of modern physics, relativity theory and quantum theory. Both had their origins early in this century, a period in which improved experimental techniques first made possible the study of phenomena of small dimensions and high speeds and energies.

After reviewing some crucial aspects of classical physics we shall study the theory of relativity and the quantum theory and apply them to an analysis of atomic and nuclear structure. We shall be concerned with situations in which some familiar notions in physics may be inapplicable, situations in which classical physics is downright wrong. Does this mean, then, that all the time and effort spent in studying elementary classical physics is wasted, that one might better begin with relativity and quantum theory? Not at all! All results of experiment, however remote from our ordinary experience, must ultimately be expressed in classical terms, that is, in the classical concepts of momentum, energy, position, and time. Furthermore, we shall see that many of the concepts and laws of classical physics are carried over into the new physics.

1-2 The conservation laws of physics Both in classical and in modern physics nothing is more basic or simple than the conservation laws. In each conservation law the total amount of a certain physical quantity within a given system is constant, or conserved, provided only that the system as a whole is isolated from a specified external influence. For example, the total vector momentum of a system isolated from external forces is constant. Internal changes may take place within the boundaries of an isolated system through the mutual interaction of the particles within, but they have no effect on the total amount of the conserved quantity. Therein lies the power of a conservation law. We need not be concerned with the details of what goes on within the system—indeed, we may actually be ignorant of the internal interactions—but if the system is truly isolated, the conserved quantities remain unchanged. Thus, in classical physics we know that the total mass, energy, linear momentum, angular momentum, and electric charge going into a collision between two or more particles isolated from external influence is precisely the same as the total mass, energy, linear momentum, angular momentum, and electric charging coming out of the collision.

The conservation laws of classical physics are these: the laws of the conservation of mass, of energy, of linear momentum, of angular momentum, and of electric charge.

> *The law of mass conservation: The total mass of an isolated, or leakproof, system is constant.*

Despite changes that may occur in other quantities (e.g., energy, volume, and temperature) in a system the total mass is unchanged. This law may also be stated in the following form: mass cannot be created or destroyed; or, mass cannot be produced or annihilated.

The law of energy conservation: If no work is done on or by a system, and if no thermal energy enters or leaves the system as heat, the total energy of the system is constant.

Since all energy is ultimately either kinetic energy or potential energy, the law of energy conservation states that the sum of the kinetic energies of the particles and the potential energies of their mutual interaction in a system is constant. Thermal energy is merely the disordered mechanical energy of molecules or atoms in random motion on a scale so microscopic that the kinetic and potential energies of individual particles are not distinguished. (The *first law of thermodynamics* is merely the law of the conservation of energy expressed in its most comprehensive form, which includes heat, the transfer of thermal energy by virtue of a temperature difference.)

The law of linear-momentum conservation: When a system is subject to no net external force, the total linear momentum of the system remains constant both in magnitude and direction.

Newton's laws of motion are, of course, the foundation of classical mechanics, and it is useful to state these laws in the language of linear momentum.

(a) The momentum $p = mv$ of a particle subject to no net external force is constant.†

(b) When a body is subject to a net external force, the force equals the time rate of change of the linear momentum. In this form Newton's second law is sufficiently general to account for the motion of objects that accumulate or lose mass, as of a snowball rolling on snow or a falling raindrop losing water by evaporation. When the mass is unchanged, the force is simply the product of mass and acceleration, when $dm/dt = 0$:

$$F = \frac{d}{dt}(p) = \frac{d}{dt}(mv) = (v)\frac{dm}{dt} + m\frac{d}{dt}(v) = ma \qquad [1\text{-}1]$$

† A vector quantity is indicated by boldface type; its magnitude, by ordinary type.

This law has a profound consequence: if one knows the forces acting on a body and its initial position and velocity, it is possible, at least in principle, to predict in complete detail its future history, that is, to project precisely its position and velocity for all future times.

In the Système Internationale d'Unités (the rationalized meter-kilogram-second system of units), which will be used throughout this book, one newton is that force which acts on a mass of one kilogram to give it an acceleration of one meter per second squared.

> (c) When two bodies interact, the momentum imparted to one body during an infinitesimal time interval is equal but opposite to the momentum imparted to the second body during the same interval; therefore, the action and reaction forces, here both internal forces, are equal and opposite.

> *The law of angular-momentum conservation: When a system is subject to no net external torque, the total angular momentum of the system remains constant, both in magnitude and direction.*

Figure 1-2 shows the angular momentum L with respect to the point O of a particle of mass m and velocity v. The magnitude of the angular mo-

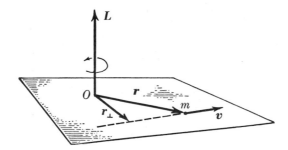

Figure 1-2. Angular momentum L of a mass point m about the point O.

mentum L is the cross product of the radius vector r and the linear momentum $p = mv$:

$$L = r \times p \qquad [1\text{-}2]$$

The direction of the angular-momentum vector L, as shown in the figure, is perpendicular to the plane containing the velocity vector v and the radius vector r. Its direction is given by the right-hand rule: rotate the vector r into the vector v through the smaller angle with the right-hand fingers, and the right-hand thumb will be in the direction of L. In magnitude the angular momentum of a single particle is given by

$$L = r_\perp mv$$

where $r_\perp$ is the component of r at right angles to v.

The torque τ about some chosen point is given by

$$\tau = r \times F \qquad\qquad [1\text{-}3]$$

or, in magnitude, by

$$\tau = r_\perp F$$

where $r_\perp$ is the component of r perpendicular to F; see Figure 1-3.

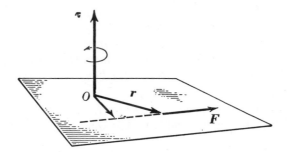

Figure 1-3. Torque τ of a force F about the point O.

When a system of particles is subject to no net external torque, its total angular momentum is constant. A single particle subject to a *central* force has a constant angular momentum with respect to a point at the force center.

The law of electric-charge conservation: The total charge of an isolated electrical system is constant.

Complete isolation is an idealization that can be only approximated and never perfectly realized, since any observation or measurement of a system necessarily interferes with it. For a simple example, consider what happens when the temperature of some thermally insulated liquid is measured with a simple mercury thermometer, which is initially not at the temperature of the liquid. When the thermometer is placed in the liquid, it is either heated or cooled by the liquid, and the liquid is, at the same time, either cooled or heated. The final thermometer reading is *not* the actual temperature of the liquid before the measurement was made: it is the temperature to which the liquid has been brought by reason of the insertion of the thermometer into it. Only if the liquid and the thermometer were at the same temperature before being brought into thermal contact with one another would the thermometer neither gain nor lose thermal energy, and only then would it indicate the true temperature of the body. But this cannot be known in advance and, if it were, the measurement would be superfluous.†️ Interference with a system through the very act of taking a measurement occurs not only in such simple instances as these; it occurs in all measurements. In short, a completely isolated system is one that can never be studied or observed, and we cannot study a system without violating its isolation. In classical physics, however, it is always possible, by exercising experimental ingenuity, to reduce the disturbances to such an extent that the system may be regarded as *effectively* isolated.

1-3 The classical interactions There are only two basic origins of force in classical physics, gravitational mass and electric charge; these give rise, respectively, to the universal gravitational force and to electromagnetic forces.

The attractive gravitational force F_g between two point masses m_1 and m_2 separated by a distance r is given by

$$F_g = Gm_1m_2/r^2 \qquad [1\text{-}4]$$

where G, the universal gravitational constant, is found by experiment to be 6.67×10^{-11} N-m^2/kg^2.

The forces between electric charges may be separated into two basic types: the electric force and the magnetic force. Coulomb's law gives the electric force F_e (also called the Coulomb force) between two point electric charges Q_1 and Q_2 at rest or in motion and separated by a distance r:

$$F_e = \left(\frac{1}{4\pi\epsilon_0}\right)\frac{Q_1Q_2}{r^2} = kQ_1Q_2/r^2 \qquad [1\text{-}5]$$

where $k = 1/4\pi\epsilon_0 = 8.99 \times 10^9$ N-m^2/C^2, and ϵ_0 is the electric permittivity of free space. The electric force F_e may be thought of as taking place through an electric field $\mathcal{E}$, defined as the electric force per unit positive charge. Thus, charge Q_1 creates an electric field of magnitude $\mathcal{E}_1 = kQ_1/r^2$ at the site of charge Q_2, and Q_2, finding itself in this electric field, is acted upon by an electric force of magnitude $F_e = Q_2\mathcal{E}_1 = kQ_1Q_2/r^2$.

The magnetic force arises when two electric point charges are *in motion* with respect to the observer. The magnetic interaction is conceived of as taking place through the intermediary of the magnetic field B. Thus, a

† Of course, if the heat capacities of the liquid and the thermometer were known with complete precision, it would be possible to correct for the heat entering or leaving the thermometer, but the heat capacities become known only if the specific heats of the materials are measured in some prior experiment. The prior experiment, however, if it is to give the specific heats without error, must involve a perfectly calibrated and corrected thermometer, and so on ad infinitum.

charge Q_1 moving at a velocity v_1 produces a magnetic field B_1 at the
location r of charge Q_2; see Figure 1-4. The magnetic field B_1 is given by

$$B_1 = \left(\frac{\mu_0}{4\pi}\right) Q_1 \frac{v_1 \times r}{r^3} \qquad [1\text{-}6]$$

where $\mu_0/4\pi = 10^{-7}$ Wb/A $=$ m, μ_0 is the magnetic permeability, and v_1 is
the velocity of charge Q_1; see Figure 1-4. Then, the magnetic force on

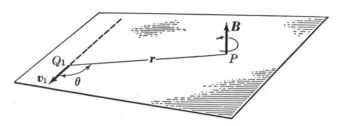

Figure 1-4. Magnetic field B at the point P, produced by the moving
charge Q_1.

charge Q_2 is given by

$$F_m = Q_2 v_2 \times B_1 \qquad [1\text{-}7]$$

where v_2 is the velocity of charge Q_2; see Figure 1-5.

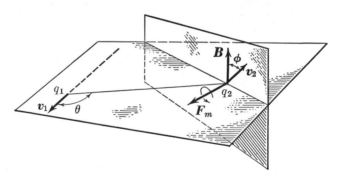

Figure 1-5. Magnetic force F_m on the moving charge Q_2, produced by the
moving charge Q_1.

In summary, the total force (excluding the gravitational force) on a
particle of charge Q and velocity v, situated at a point where the electric
field is $\mathcal{E}$ and the magnetic field is B, is given by

$$F = Q(\mathcal{E} + v \times B) \qquad [1\text{-}8]$$

The velocity-dependent force is the magnetic force F_m; the remaining force
is the electric force F_e.

1-4 Electromagnetic fields and waves Here we set down, without details of their origin, some important properties of electric and magnetic fields, their interrelations and, especially, the characteristics of classical electromagnetic waves.

Electric energy may be said to reside in an electric field established in space—in the region, for example, between the plates of a charged capacitor. The electric-energy density, or energy of the electric field per unit volume, is given by

$$u_e = \epsilon_0 \mathcal{E}^2/2 \qquad [1\text{-}9]$$

Similarly, the magnetic-energy density is given by

$$u_m = B^2/2\mu_0 \qquad [1\text{-}10]$$

Magnetic energy may, for example, be said to reside in the region between the poles of a magnet.

Not only does an electric charge create an electric field when at rest and, in addition, a magnetic field when in motion, but also a changing electric field creates a magnetic field (Ampère's law), and a changing magnetic field creates an electric field (Faraday's law). This is the origin of electromagnetic waves; an oscillating, and therefore accelerating, electric charge produces in space electric and magnetic fields, whose frequencies are the same as that of the electric charge. The fields constitute an electromagnetic field which, when detached from the electric charge that created it, travels through space at the speed of light c:

$$c = 1/\sqrt{\epsilon_0\mu_0} = 3.00 \times 10^8 \text{ m/sec} \qquad [1\text{-}11]$$

The instantaneous intensity I of an electromagnetic wave, the energy flow per unit time, through a unit area oriented at right angles to the direction of wave propagation, is given by

$$I = \epsilon_0 \mathcal{E}^2 c$$

The intensity is proportional to the *square* of the electric field (or of the magnetic field $B = \mathcal{E}/c$). An alternative form of this equation for the electromagnetic power per unit transverse area, one incorporating the relative directions of the energy flow and of the electric field $\mathcal{E}$ and magnetic field B, is this:

$$I = \mathcal{E} \times (B/\mu_0) \qquad [1\text{-}12]$$

The vector intensity I, also known as the Poynting vector, is in the direction of energy propagation; it is perpendicular to $\mathcal{E}$ and to B, which are themselves mutually perpendicular.

The existence of electromagnetic waves having the properties given above was predicted on theoretical grounds by James Clerk Maxwell in 1864.

Electromagnetic waves were first observed in the laboratory by Heinrich Hertz in 1887. The electromagnetic spectrum, ranging from long-wavelength radio waves to very-short-wavelength gamma rays, is shown in Figure 1-6. A representation of a monochromatic, plane, linearly polarized electromagnetic wave is given in Figure 1-7.

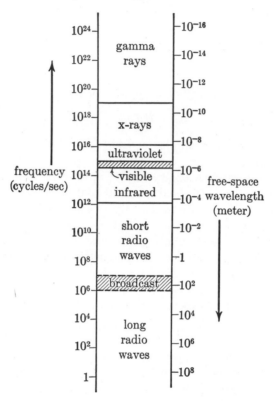

Figure 1-6. The electromagnetic spectrum.

When an electromagnetic wave is absorbed by the electrically charged particles in a material, the electric field does work on the charged particles. Because the charged particles are in motion, the magnetic field of the wave produces a magnetic force on them in the direction of the propagation of the wave. The radiation force F_r acting on a material that absorbs completely an electromagnetic wave that is incident upon it at right angles to the surface is given by

$$F_r = P/c \qquad [1\text{-}13]$$

where P is the power of the absorbed wave. Since an electromagnetic wave produces a radiation force, or radiation pressure, on a material that absorbs

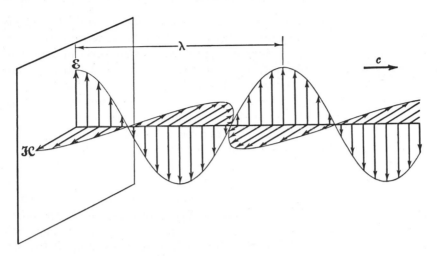

Figure 1-7. A monochromatic, plane, linearly-polarized electromagnetic wave.

(or reflects) the wave, one may attribute linear momentum to such a wave according to the relation

$$\text{electromagnetic momentum} = (\text{electromagnetic energy})/c \quad [1\text{-}14]$$

1-5 The correspondence principle Any theory or law in physics is, to a greater or lesser degree, tentative and approximate. This is true because applying a physical law to situations in which it has not been experimentally tested *may* show it to be incomplete or even incorrect. Thus, when we extrapolate from a theory to untested situations, we cannot be sure that the theory will hold. However, if a new, more general, theory is proposed, there is a completely reliable guide for relating this more general theory to the older, more restricted, theory. This guide is the *correspondence principle*, first applied to the theory of atomic structure by the Danish physicist Niels Bohr in 1923. We shall find it helpful to apply this principle in a broadened sense, using it to great advantage in relativity physics as well as in quantum physics.

> *The correspondence principle: We know in advance that any new theory in physics, whatever its character or details, must reduce to the well-established classical theory to which it corresponds when it is applied to the circumstances for which the less general theory is known to hold.*

Consider a simple, familiar situation that illustrates the correspondence principle. When we have a problem in projectile motion of relatively small range, the following assumptions are made: (a) the weight of the projectile

is constant in magnitude, given by the mass times a gravitational acceleration that is *constant* in magnitude, (b) the Earth may be represented by a
plane surface, and (c) the weight of the projectile is constant in direction,
vertically downward. With these assumptions a parabolic path is predicted, and we find excellent agreement with experiment, provided that the
projectile motion extends over only relatively short distances, but if we
try to describe the motion of an Earth satellite on the same assumptions,
very serious errors will be made. To discuss the satellite motion we must
assume, instead, that (a) the weight of the body is *not* constant in magnitude but varies inversely with the square of its distance from the Earth's
center, (b) the Earth's surface is round, not flat, and (c) the direction of
the weight is *not* constant but always points toward the Earth's center.
These assumptions lead to a prediction of an elliptical path and to a proper
description of satellite motion. Now, if we apply the second, more general,
theory to the motion of a body traveling a distance small compared to the
Earth's radius at the surface of the Earth, notice what happens: the weight
appears to be constant both in magnitude and direction, the Earth appears
flat, and the elliptical path becomes parabolic. This is precisely what the
correspondence principle requires!

The correspondence principle asserts that, when the conditions of the
new and old theories correspond, the predictions will also correspond; that
is, a new, general, theory will yield the old, restricted, theory as a special
approximation. We have, then, an infallible guide to the testing of any new
theory or law: the new theory must reduce to the theory it supplants. Any
new theory that fails in this respect is clearly defective in so fundamental
a way that it cannot possibly be accepted. Therefore we know that the
relativity and quantum theories *must* yield classical physics when applied
to large-scale objects moving at speeds much less than that of light. In the
next section we shall see another familiar example of the correspondence
principle.

1-6 Ray optics and wave optics There are two means of describing the
propagation of light: ray, or geometrical, optics and wave, or physical,
optics. Only wave optics is capable of explaining such phenomena as interference and diffraction. On the other hand, ray optics can satisfactorily
describe such phenomena as the rectilinear propagation, reflection, and
refraction of light. Wave optics is, of course, also able to account for these
phenomena. Therefore, wave optics is a comprehensive theory of light,
while ray optics is an adequate theory only in certain restricted situations.

The correspondence principle requires that the comprehensive theory
reduce to the restricted theory in the correspondence limit. Thus, wave
optics must become, in effect, ray optics in those conditions in which such
distinctive wave phenomena as diffraction and interference are unim-

portant. We know that interference and diffraction are clearly discernible only if the dimensions d of the obstacles or apertures that the light encounters are comparable to the wavelength λ of the light. When $\lambda \ll d$, the wave treatment gives the same results as the ray treatment. Symbolically we can write:

$$\text{Limit}_{\lambda/d \to 0} \text{(wave optics)} = \text{(ray optics)}$$

Figure 1-8 illustrates a situation in which we see the transition from conditions in which wave optics is required to the simpler conditions in

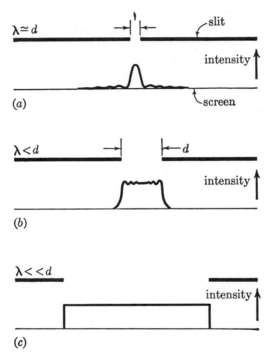

Figure 1-8. Distribution of intensity of monochromatic light passing through single slits of increasing width. Alternatively the screen is far from the slit in (a) but close to the screen in (b) and (c).

which wave and ray optics yield identical results. The figure shows the diffraction pattern of monochromatic light passing through a single parallel-edged slit for (a) a wavelength λ comparable to the slit width d, (b) a wavelength less than the slit width, and (c) a wavelength *much* less than the slit width. In the first diagram the wave disturbance is spread far into the geometrical shadow and has the characteristic alternating light and dark diffraction bands. In the second diagram the diffraction is less pronounced, and the light is concentrated mainly within the area bounded by the geometrical shadow. In the third diagram, where the wavelength is much less than the width of the slit opening, the intensity pattern is indistinguishable from that predicted by ray optics.†

Ray optics is concerned solely with the path of light, which may be represented as rays in the direction of light propagation. This suggests that a model for describing the character of light is the *particle model*. In such a model light is assumed to consist of small, essentially weightless particles, or corpuscles. This model is consistent with the observed facts that (a) in free space light follows a straight-line path in the manner of a stream of particles, (b) upon reflection light behaves like particles making elastic collisions with the surface, and (c) upon refraction in a transparent material, such as glass, the light behaves as if the direction of the particles abruptly changed at the interface, and (d) the intensity from a point source varies inversely as the square of the distance from it.

The most celebrated advocate of the particle theory of light was Sir Isaac Newton. He showed that, according to the particle concept, the speed of light in a refracting medium should be greater than the speed of light in a vacuum. Foucault, however, experimentally found the speed of light through water to be less than through air; the wave theory, of course, predicts a slower speed in a refracting medium. The Foucault experiment, together with the earlier work of Young and Fresnel on the interference and diffraction of light, convinced physicists that light consisted of waves, as was first proposed by Huygens.

Note that until the electromagnetic theory of Maxwell in 1864 physicists, although they knew light to consist of waves and thus could describe interference and diffraction, did not know what it was that was waving; that is, they did not know what the wave disturbance consisted of.

1-7 The particle and wave descriptions in classical physics In classical physics as well as in modern physics the ideas of particle and wave play a central role. We briefly summarize the characteristics of each.

An ideal particle can be localized completely. Its mass and electric charge can be identified with infinite precision, and the particle may be considered to be a mass point. Although we find that in Nature all particles have finite sizes, we may, under appropriate circumstances, regard them as mass points. For example, in the kinetic theory molecules are considered point particles, although their size is finite and they have internal

---

† Between (a) and (b) in the figure diffraction patterns may be complicated, some even showing a dark band at the center.

structures; similarly, stars are considered particles when we discuss the behavior of galaxies. In short, an object may be considered to be effectively a particle whenever its dimensions are very small relative to the dimensions of the system of which it is a part and when the internal structure of the particle is unimportant in the problem under consideration. Newtonian mechanics deals with ideal particles; given the initial position and velocity of a particle and a knowledge of the forces acting on it, we may predict in detail its future position and velocity.

The distinctive characteristic of a wave is its frequency or its wavelength. The simplest type of wave is strictly sinusoidal. Consider the electric field $\mathcal{E}$ of a perfectly monochromatic electromagnetic wave; its amplitude is $\mathcal{E}_0$, its frequency ν, and its wavelength λ. It travels in the positive X direction with a speed $v = \nu\lambda$. Then

$$\mathcal{E} = \mathcal{E}_0 \sin 2\pi(x/\lambda - \nu t) = -\mathcal{E}_0 \sin (\omega t - kx) \qquad [1\text{-}15]$$

where $\omega = 2\pi\nu$ and $k = 2\pi/\lambda$. Such a wave shows a sinusoidal variation of $\mathcal{E}$ in space for any fixed time; conversely, it shows a sinusoidal variation of $\mathcal{E}$ in time for any point x in space. Equation 1-15 requires that the electric disturbance extend over *all* possible values of x for all possible instants of time t.

An ideal wave, one whose wavelength and frequency can be known with infinite precision, cannot be confined to any particular region of space; rather, the wave must have an infinite extension along the direction in which it is propagated. It is a simple matter to show by a hypothetical experiment that if we are to measure and thereby know the frequency of a wave with complete accuracy, the wave must be infinite.

Suppose that we have a standard clock for measuring the number of wave crests that pass a fixed point per unit time. For simplicity, we imagine that the standard clock is an oscillator producing waves whose frequency is to be compared with that of some incoming wave. How can we state with complete assurance that the frequency of the incoming wave is precisely the same as the frequency of the wave generated by our standard clock?

We shall allow the two waves to interfere with one another, so as to produce beats. The number of beats per unit time equals the difference between the frequencies of the two waves. If the two waves are of precisely the same frequency, then we will detect no beats whatsoever. Now, if we observe the resultant amplitude of the two interfering waves over some *limited* period of time, we *may* find no appreciable change in this amplitude, but we *cannot*, on the basis of such a measurement, assert that there is none, for we might have found, if we had waited longer, that the combined amplitude of the two waves was decreasing or increasing (see Figure 1-9), which would indicate an incipient beat, or a difference between the fre-

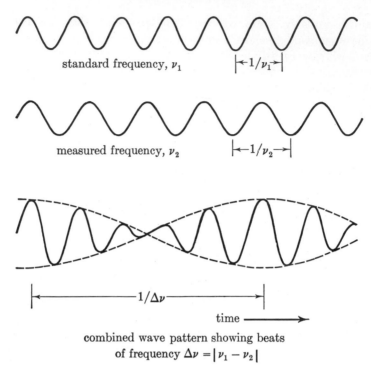

Figure 1-9. Beat pattern resulting from the superposition of waves of frequencies ν_1 and ν_2.

quencies. To be absolutely sure that no beats occur, that the frequencies of the two waves are precisely the same, we must wait for an infinite period of time. If, to measure the frequency with no uncertainty, we do wait for an infinite time, then the wave we measure will have traveled for an infinite time and have an infinite extension in space.

We now wish to determine how great is the uncertainty in the unknown frequency ν_2 when the beats it produces with a standard clock of frequency ν_1 are observed over a finite time Δt. If ν_1 and ν_2 differ by an amount $\Delta\nu$, then $\Delta\nu$ beats are observed per unit time; the time required to observe one complete beat is $1/\Delta\nu$ sec. On a conservative basis we may be confident of observing one beat if we make a measurement over a period of time Δt that is equal to the time needed for the occurrence of one beat; therefore we take $\Delta t \geq 1/\Delta\nu$, or

$$\Delta t \Delta\nu \geq 1 \qquad\qquad [1\text{-}16]$$

If the measured frequency differs from the standard clock's frequency by an amount $\Delta\nu$, then $\Delta\nu$ is a measure of the uncertainty in the measurement of frequency ν_2. It follows from Equation 1-16 that, if the frequency of a wave is measured over a very short time, the uncertainty in this frequency is large, and conversely. To have $\Delta\nu = 0$, Δt must be infinite.

A relationship giving the corresponding uncertainty in the wavelength can easily be deduced from Equation 1-16. Suppose that the wave has been observed only over the finite time interval Δt; then during this time the wave will have traveled a distance $\Delta x = v\Delta t$, where v is the speed of the wave. Therefore, it will have been observed only over the distance Δx,

$$\Delta x = v\Delta t$$

and, from Equation 1-16, $\Delta x \geq v/\Delta\nu$ [1-17]

but since $\nu = v/\lambda$

we have $\Delta\nu = v\Delta\lambda/\lambda^2$ [1-18]

We omit the minus sign, since we are concerned with the magnitudes only. Substituting Equation 1-18 in Equation 1-17 yields

$$\boxed{\Delta x\Delta\lambda^2 \geq \lambda^2}$$ [1-19]

If a wave is so observed that its extension in space is uncertain by an amount Δx, its wavelength will be uncertain by an amount $\Delta\lambda \geq \lambda^2/\Delta x$. As Equation 1-19 shows, $\Delta\lambda = 0$ only if $\Delta x = \infty$.

Our discussion on waves up to this point has been concerned only with monochromatic sinusoidal waves. Wave pulses, which are wave disturbances confined at a given time to some limited region of space, also can be propagated. Any pulse can be shown mathematically to be equivalent to a number of superimposed sinusoidal waves of different frequencies. It is for this reason that our analysis was carried out for a simple, monochromatic, sinusoidal wave. If we compute the number of waves of different frequencies that must be added together to give a completely sharp pulse, we find that *all* frequencies from zero to infinity must be included (see the analysis below). This agrees completely with what we have already found: if a wave pulse is confined to an infinitesimally small region of space, then we cannot determine what its wavelength is. Actually, we cannot speak of a single "frequency" for a pulse.

Wave Packets A monochromatic wave, traveling along the X axis with a velocity $v = \nu\lambda$, represented by

$$A = A_0 \cos 2\pi(x/\lambda - \nu t)$$ [1-20]

Here λ and ν represent the wavelength and frequency, respectively. The wave disturbance A is given as a function of both position x and time t and has the maximum value A_0. The quantity A_0 is the amplitude of the wave. For an electromagnetic wave A stands for the electric or magnetic field intensity, for a sound wave through air it represents the pressure, and for a transverse wave on a string it represents the transverse displacement. With the definition

$$k = 2\pi/\lambda \tag{1-21}$$

where k is the *wavenumber*, Equation 1-20 may be written in the form

$$A = A_0 \cos k(x - vt) \tag{1-22}$$

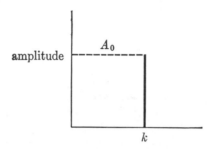

Figure 1-10. Frequency spectrum of a monochromatic wave.

Figure 1-10 shows the amplitude of a single monochromatic wave having a wave-number k, or wavelength $2\pi/k$, and Figure 1-11 shows A as a function of x at the particular time $t = 0$.

Let us now consider a collection, or packet, of monochromatic waves, all traveling at the same speed v (showing no dispersion) in the $+X$ direction. For convenience we imagine that all the waves have the same amplitude A_0 and that the wave packet includes all wavenumbers running from $k - \Delta k/2$ to $k + \Delta k/2$. Therefore, all waves lie within the band of width Δk, as shown in Figure 1-12. If $\Delta k = 0$, the band of waves becomes the single, monochromatic wave of Figure 1-10. Figure 1-13, showing the spatial extent of the wave packet at time $t = 0$, corresponds to Figure 1-11.

At the origin ($x = 0$), all the individual waves are in phase and add constructively, giving, therefore, a large resultant amplitude at this point. As we leave the origin in

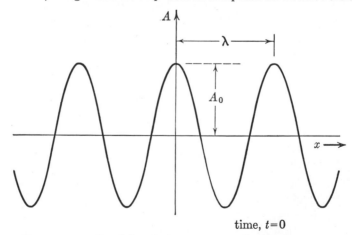

Figure 1-11. Spatial variation of a monochromatic wave.

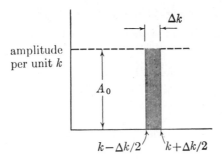

Figure 1-12. Frequency spectrum of a packet of waves.

either direction, the waves become increasingly out of phase, and the algebraic addition of the individual waves gives a resultant amplitude A, which rapidly approaches zero.

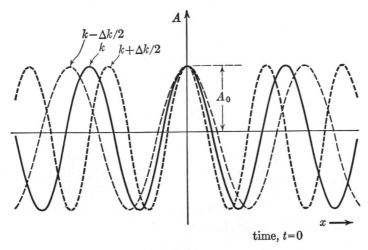

Figure 1-13. Spatial variation of a packet of monochromatic waves.

Using the principle of superposition, we now compute for any point x and any time t the resultant amplitude A composed of contributions of all monochromatic waves within the band Δk. We sum the individual contributions $A_k \, dk$ from $k - \Delta k/2$ to $k + \Delta k/2$. It is convenient to let $x - vt = x'$. Then Equation 1-22 becomes

$$A_k = A_0 \cos kx'$$

whore A_0 is now the amplitude per unit k.
The resultant displacement is given by

$$A = \int_{k-\Delta k/2}^{k+\Delta k/2} A_k \, dk = A_0 \int_{k-\Delta k/2}^{k+\Delta k/2} \cos kx' \, dk = (A_0/x') \sin kx' \Big|_{k-\Delta k/2}^{k+\Delta k/2}$$

$$= \frac{A_0}{x'} \left[\sin x' \left(k + \frac{\Delta k}{2} \right) - \sin x' \left(k - \frac{\Delta k}{2} \right) \right] \qquad [1\text{-}23]$$

We can simplify this by using the trigonometric identity

$$\sin (a + b) - \sin (a - b) = 2 \sin b \cos a$$

so that it becomes

$$A = (2A_0/x') \sin (x' \, \Delta k/2) \cos x'k \qquad [1\text{-}24]$$

The first three diagrams of Figure 1-14 show the separate factors of Equation 1-24 plotted against x', and the last two show the resultant wave A and the envelope of A^2 as a function of x'. Inasmuch as x' is equal to $x - vt$, Figure 1-14a is a "snapshot" of the intensity (proportional to the square of the amplitude) of the wave.

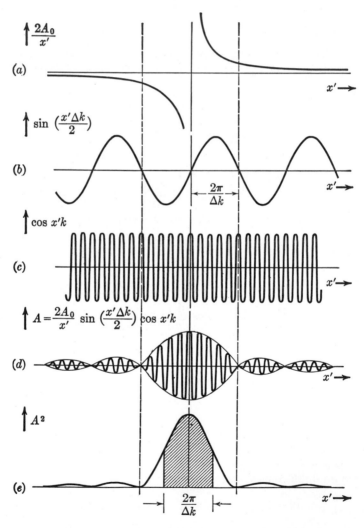

Figure 1-14. Spatial variation of the factors appearing in Equation 1-24 for a wave packet and the resultant wave A and envelope of A^2, all as a function of x'.

More than one half of the total energy of the wave packet is within the region $2\pi/\Delta k$ (the shaded area of Figure 1-14e is approximately three quarters of the total area under the curve). The uncertainty Δx in the width of the wave packet (at any instant of time) is at least as large as $2\pi/\Delta k$:

$$\Delta x \geq 2\pi/\Delta k \qquad [1\text{-}25]$$

We have introduced the wavenumber k merely for convenience in evaluating the integrals. To rewrite Equation 1-25 in terms of $\lambda = 2\pi/k$,

we start with $$|\Delta k| = 2\pi\,\Delta\lambda/\lambda^2$$

and Equation 1-25 becomes $$\Delta x\,\Delta\lambda \geq \lambda^2 \qquad [1\text{-}26]$$

This equation shows that, if $\Delta\lambda$ is small (that is, if the wave packet consists of almost monochromatic waves), then the spatial extent of the wave packet, Δx, becomes very large. On the other hand, if a wave disturbance is to be confined to a very small region in space, Δx, then $\Delta\lambda$ must be very large; that is, one must add together monochromatic waves over a wide range of wavelengths.

Waves and particles play such an important role in physics because they represent the *only two* modes of energy transport. We can transport energy from one point in space to a second point only by sending a particle from the first to the second site, or by sending a wave from the first to the second site. Particles and waves are the only means of communicating between two points. For example, we can signal another person by throwing an object at him (particle), calling to him (sound waves), motioning to him (light waves), telephoning him (electric waves in conductors), or radioing him (electromagnetic waves).

Only three interactions, or modes of energy transfer, are possible between particles and waves: (1) the interaction between two particles, (2) the interaction between a particle and a wave, and (3) the interaction between two waves. Two particles interact when they collide. An electric charge generating an electromagnetic wave is an example of the interaction between a particle and a wave. This wave can in turn interact, and give energy to, a second charged particle.† There is no interaction between two waves, and their combined effects at any point in space are governed by the *principle of superposition*, which states that one can superimpose two or more wave disturbances to find the resultant disturbance. Everyone has seen this: if two water waves travel, say, at right angles to one another on a pond, they interfere with one another at the point where and time when they cross, and then travel onward *as if* each wave were completely oblivious of the existence of the other. This behavior is in contrast to the behavior of two small, impenetrable particles, which cannot occupy the same spot at the same time. The superposition principle is, of course, the basis for treating all problems in interference and diffraction.

† See Weidner and Sells, *Elementary Classical Physics*, Sec. 41-4 (Boston: Allyn and Bacon Inc., 1965).

1-8 Phase and Group Velocities

When two sinusoidal waves of different frequency travel through a medium in the same direction at the *same* speed, the energy transported by the resultant wave also travels at the same speed as the individual component waves. But when waves of different frequency travel through the same medium at different wave speeds, the energy is transported at a speed—the group velocity—which differs from the phase velocity of either of the component waves.

Consider first sinusoidal waves of frequencies ν_1 and ν_2 traveling through a medium at the same speed. For simplicity we take the amplitude A to be the same for the two waves. The resultant wave form, at one instant of time, is found by superposing the component waves, as shown in Figure 1-15. (Note that Figure 1-15 is a snapshot of the component waves and their resultant as a function of displacement along the direction of wave

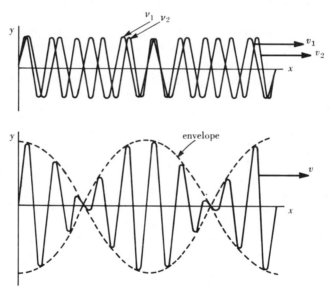

Figure 1-15. Two monochromatic waves of differing frequency and their resultant.

propagation; it looks like, but is not the same as, Figure 1-9, which shows the component and resultant oscillations at one point in space as a function of time.) The alternating constructive and destructive interference of the individual wave forms produces a slowly varying envelope. Since the energy of a simple harmonic oscillator is proportional to the square of the amplitude of oscillation, the energy carried by the resultant wave is concentrated in regions where the amplitude of the envelope is large. Thus, the speed with which the waves' energy is transported through the medium is the speed with which the envelope advances through space. But, for equal component wave speeds, the speed of the envelope—the so-called *group velocity*—is the same as the *phase velocity v* of either component wave. By the phase velocity is meant the speed with which a point on the wave of constant phase, such as a crest, travels along the propagation direction. By definition,

$$v = \nu\lambda = \omega/k$$

for a frequency ν, wavelength λ, angular frequency $\omega = 2\pi\nu$, and wave number $k = 2\pi/\lambda$. When waves of all frequencies have the same phase velocity, riding with the crest of one wave is like riding with the crest of any other wave, or with their resultant.

Now consider two sinusoidal waves of slightly different frequencies that travel through the same medium in the same direction, but with different phase velocities: $v_1 = \nu_1\lambda_1 = \omega_1/k_1$ and $v_2 = \nu_2\lambda_2 = \omega_2/k_2$. Such a medium is said to exhibit *dispersion*. A simple example is a refracting medium through which polychromatic light passes. We know that violet light travels through glass at a lesser speed than does red light (the refractive index for glass is greater for violet, than for red, light); consequently, white light passing through a prism of glass is dispersed into a spectrum.

It is easy to see that the group velocity v_{gr} differs from the phase velocity in a dispersive medium. Because one of the two sets of waves of different frequency travels faster than the other, riding on the crest of one wave is not the same as riding on the crest of the other wave, and a region of strong interference shifts as one wave gains on the other. The resultant wave envelope no longer remains locked to either component wave form. As Figure 1-16 shows, in a time t a crest of the wave of frequency ν_1 (or any other point of constant phase), advances a distance $v_1 t$, while a crest of the other wave advances a different distance $v_2 t$. During the same time the envelope shifts by an amount $v_{gr} t$.

A single sinusoidal wave traveling along the positive X-axis may be represented by $A \sin 2\pi(\nu t - x/\lambda) = A \sin (\omega t - kx)$. Then the resultant displacement y of two waves described above is given as a function of x and t by

$$y = A \sin (\omega_1 t - k_1 x) + A \sin (\omega_2 t - k_2 x) \qquad [1\text{-}27]$$

Using the trigonometric identity,

$$\sin \alpha + \sin \beta = 2 \cos \left(\frac{\alpha - \beta}{2}\right) \sin \left(\frac{\alpha + \beta}{2}\right)$$

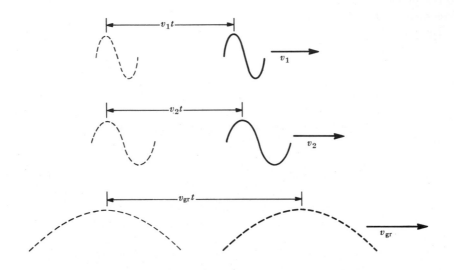

Figure 1-16. One wave advances at the phase speed v_1, a second mono-chromatic wave of different frequency advances at the phase speed v_2, and the envelope of their resultant advances at the group speed v_{gr}.

we may rewrite the resultant wave in the form:

$$y = 2A \cos\left[\left(\frac{\omega_1 - \omega_2}{2}\right)t - \left(\frac{k_1 - k_2}{2}\right)x\right]\sin\left[\left(\frac{\omega_1 + \omega_2}{2}\right)t - \left(\frac{k_1 + k_2}{2}\right)x\right] \qquad [1\text{-}28]$$

If the component waves differ only slightly in angular frequency and wave number, we may write

$$\omega = \frac{\omega_1 + \omega_2}{2} \quad \text{and} \quad k = \frac{k_1 + k_2}{2} \qquad [1\text{-}29]$$

where ω and k now represent average values. We may also write the differences as

$$d\omega = \omega_1 - \omega_2 \quad \text{and} \quad dk = k_1 - k_2 \qquad [1\text{-}30]$$

Using Equations 1-29 and 1-30, we write Equation 1-28 in the simpler form:

$$y = \left[2A \, \cos\left(\frac{d\omega}{2} t - \frac{dk}{2} x \right) \right] \sin \left(\omega t - kx \right) \qquad [1\text{-}31]$$

The equation for the resultant wave is comprised of two factors: the first (in brackets) represents the envelope, while the second represents an "average" component wave traveling with phase velocity, $v_{phase} = \omega/k$. The group velocity is that of the envelope, and we find it, as in the case of the phase velocity, by taking the ratio of the coefficients of t and of x. Thus,

$$v_{group} = d\omega/dk$$
$$v_{phase} = \omega/k \qquad [1\text{-}32]$$

The *group* velocity is the *derivative* of ω with respect to k, whereas the *phase* velocity is the *ratio* of ω to k. Writing ω as $v_{ph}k$, we have

$$v_{group} = \frac{d(v_{ph}k)}{dk} = v_{phase} + k \frac{dv_{ph}}{dk} \qquad [1\text{-}33]$$

If the phase speed is the same for all frequencies, and $dv_{ph}/dk = 0$, the phase and group velocities are the same. But, for a dispersive medium with a frequency-dependent phase velocity, the group velocity exceeds the phase velocity when $dv_{ph}/dk > 0$, and the group velocity is less than the phase velocity when $dv_{ph}/dk < 0$.

T W O

RELATIVISTIC KINEMATICS: SPACE AND TIME

The theory of special relativity, set forth by Albert Einstein in 1905, is fundamental to all modern physics and one of the greatest achievements of the human intellect. Despite the fact that it is often regarded as being esoteric and recondite, we shall find that its principal features arise in a natural way from the two fundamental postulates of relativity. The first postulate, *the principle of relativity*, is basic also to classical, or Newtonian, mechanics; the second postulate, *the constancy of the speed of light*, is at seeming variance with it and also with Postulate I, if the classical concepts of space and time are adhered to. It was the brilliant work of Einstein that reconciled the two postulates in a self-consistent theory of the physical universe, a theory which in many fundamental respects is quite different from that presented in classical physics. The theory of special relativity is not hypothetical or conjectural, inasmuch as a variety of experiments have firmly established its essential correctness.

Since relativity theory plays a major role in the study of atomic and nuclear physics, we shall discuss it in some detail. In this chapter we shall deal with relativistic kinematics, or the relativity of space and time, and in the next chapter with relativistic dynamics, or the relativity of momentum and energy.

2-1 The principle of relativity Let us first explore the meaning and consequences of Postulate I in the light of classical physics.

> *Postulate I, The Principle of Relativity: The laws of physics are the same, or invariant, in all inertial systems—that is, the mathematical form of a physical law remains the same.*

An *inertial system* is defined as a coordinate frame of reference within which the law of inertia, Newton's *first* law, obtains. A body that is subject to no net external force will move with a constant velocity if it is in an inertial system. A simple test of whether an observer is within an inertial system can be made by having him throw an object and then noticing whether this object travels in an undeviating path at a constant speed. It would do so only in a truly inertial system, and such a system can exist, strictly speaking, only in empty space, far from any mass. A reference, or coordinate, system attached to the Earth's surface may, however, be regarded as an approximately inertial system when the gravitational force on a body is balanced by a second force. Thus, an object sliding on a frictionless, flat plane on the Earth would move in a nearly † straight line with a nearly constant speed. The first postulate of relativity physics implies that all inertial systems are equivalent in that no one inertial system can be distinguished by any experiment in physics from any other inertial system, since the laws of physics are the same for all inertial systems.

To examine the full significance of Postulate I we must find the relationships between the spatial and temporal coordinates of one inertial system and the spatial and temporal coordinates of a second inertial system moving relative to the first.

2-2 Galilean transformations The equations in classical physics that relate the space and time coordinates of two coordinate systems moving at constant velocity relative to one another are called the *Galilean* (or *Newtonian*) *transformations*.

Consider two observers, 1 and 2, located in two separate coordinate systems, S_1 and S_2, respectively. System S_2 travels with a constant velocity v to the right with respect to S_1; conversely, S_1 moves to the left with a velocity $-v$ with respect to S_2. See Figure 2-1. For convenience we choose the X axes coincident and parallel with v, the velocity of S_2 relative to S_1; the positive directions of X_1 and X_2 are in that direction of v. We can speak only of the *relative* motions of S_1 and S_2. Each observer carries a meter stick

---

† The body will deviate from its straight-line motion because of the Earth's rotation about its axis.

and a clock to measure the location and time of a particle or object relative
to his own system. System S_1 is imagined to have an infinite number of
observers, one at each point in space. All these observers, at rest with
respect to one another, have identical meter sticks and synchronized clocks.
In a classical-physics system it is not difficult to synchronize these clocks
with one another, since, we assume, a signal can be sent from one point in
space to another at infinite speed. That is, when a clock at the origin of S_1
reads time t_1, all other clocks in S_1 read the same time t_1. For simplicity all
the many observers at rest in S_1 will be referred to as observer S_1. Similarly,
all of the many observers at rest in S_2 will be called observer S_2.

By specifying the location and time of some physical phenomenon, such
as the explosion of a small bomb, an observer describes an *event*. The space
and time coordinates of an event E (Figure 2-1), as described by observer S_1,

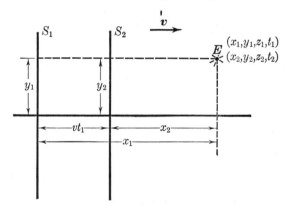

Figure 2-1. Space and time coordinates of an event E as measured by
two observers moving at a constant relative velocity v.

are $(x_1, y_1, z_1; t_1)$; the coordinates of the *same* event, as described by observer
S_2 are $(x_2, y_2, z_2; t_2)$. The space coordinates $x_1, y_1,$ and z_1 give the distances
of this event from the origin in the X, Y, and Z directions as measured by
the meter stick of observer S_1, and the time coordinate t_1 gives the time
of this event as measured by the clock of observer S_1.

We assume that observers S_1 and S_2 have synchronized their clocks and
compared their meter sticks when they were temporarily at rest with
respect to one another. System S_2 is then set in motion with respect to
system S_1, the clocks being set such that, when the origin of S_2 passes the
origin of S_1, both clocks read zero. When $t_1 = 0$, then $t_2 = 0$, and at this
instant $x_1 = x_2$. It is further assumed that the Y and Z axes of the two
coordinate systems are always respectively parallel.

From Figure 2-1 we can immediately write down the Galilean coordinate
transformations expressing the space and time coordinates as measured by

observer S_2 in terms of the coordinates as measured by observer S_1 for the same event:

Galilean
coordinate
transformations

$$
\begin{aligned}
x_2 &= x_1 - vt_1 \\
y_2 &= y_1 \\
z_2 &= z_1 \\
t_2 &= t_1
\end{aligned}
$$

[2-1]

That $y_2 = y_1$ and $z_2 = z_1$ follows from the fact that the relative motion between systems S_2 and S_1 is at right angles to these coordinates. To obtain the coordinates of system S_1 in terms of system S_2 we merely interchange subscripts and change v to $-v$; this is proper, because the labels 1 and 2 are purely arbitrary. Saying that S_2 moves with velocity v with respect to S_1 is equivalent to saying that S_1 moves with a velocity $-v$ with respect to S_2.

These classical transformation equations may seem completely axiomatic and self-evident, but it is crucial for us to appreciate the profound assumptions implicit in them.

The assumptions are that space is absolute and time is absolute in the following sense: the space interval between any two events is the same for all observers, and the time interval between them also is the same for all observers. From the point of view of the Galilean transformations the assumption of absolute space intervals means to us that, if observers S_1 and S_2 compare their meter sticks at the same time and find them to be of the same length, then they will always thereafter find them to be of the same length, regardless of their relative motion. The absolute nature of time intervals, as incorporated in the Galilean transformations, implies that if observers S_1 and S_2 have clocks that are synchronized and calibrated against one another initially, they will thereafter always agree, quite apart from their relative motion. Our everyday common-sense ideas of space and time are contained in, and expressed formally by, the Galilean transformation equations.

The velocity and acceleration transformations follow directly from Equations 2-1 by differentiation with respect to time. We define the X component of the velocity measured by observer S_1 as dx_1/dt_1, and for convenience we designate it by $\dot{x}_1$, the dot above the coordinate signifying the first derivative with respect to time. Similarly, we write the Y and Z velocity components as $\dot{y}_1 = dy_1/dt_1$ and $\dot{z}_1 = dz_1/dt_1$. The velocity components in system S_2 are $\dot{x}_2 = dx_2/dt_2$, etc. The acceleration is given by $\ddot{x}_2 = d^2x_2/dt_2^2$, etc., for observer S_2. It is important to grasp the exact meaning of the concept of velocity. We define dx_1/dt_1 as the limit of the distance traversed in the X direction, or dx_1 measured by the meter stick of observer S_1, divided by the time interval dt_1 measured by the clock of the same observer, S_1, both as the time interval approaches zero. It is meaningless to speak of dx_1/dt_2 etc., since the measurement of length and time for determining velocity must be made with respect to a *single* coordinate system. For the Galilean transformations this careful definition of velocity may not appear important, since time is regarded as absolute, $dt_1 = dt_2$, and therefore $dx_1/dt_2 = dx_1/dt_1$; we shall find later, however, that the coordinate transformations that satisfy the postulates of the theory of special relativity do not have such simplicity.

By differentiating Equations 2-1 we immediately obtain the velocity transformations, and the derivatives of these give the acceleration transformations:

Galilean velocity transformations

$$\boxed{\begin{aligned} \dot{x}_2 &= \dot{x}_1 - v \\ \dot{y}_2 &= \dot{y}_1 \\ \dot{z}_2 &= \dot{z}_1 \end{aligned}}$$

[2-2]

Galilean acceleration transformations

$$\begin{aligned} \ddot{x}_2 &= \ddot{x}_1 \\ \ddot{y}_2 &= \ddot{y}_1 \\ \ddot{z}_2 &= \ddot{z}_1 \end{aligned}$$

[2-3]

Equations 2-2 show that the velocity of a particle as measured in system S_2 is equal to the velocity of the same particle as measured in S_1 minus the velocity v of S_2 relative to S_1. Thus, velocities may be combined in accordance with the usual rules of vector addition. From Equations 2-3 we see that the corresponding acceleration components in two inertial systems, moving with respect to one another at a *constant* velocity, are equal.

2-3   Invariance of classical mechanics under Galilean transformations   To see more clearly the significance of Postulate I, the principle of relativity, let us consider two well-known physical laws of mechanics under a Galilean transformation: the conservation of linear momentum and the conservation of energy.

CONSERVATION OF LINEAR MOMENTUM   We suppose that an observer in system S_2 watches a head-on collision between two particles of respective masses m and M; see Figure 2-2a. Figure 2-2b shows the same collision as seen by an observer in S_1. As before, system S_2 moves to the right of system S_1 with a velocity v, and the velocities measured by the two observers are related by the Galilean velocity transformations, Equations 2-2.

The notation used in Figure 2-2 is this: the small letters and large letters refer to two particles of masses m and M, respectively, the subscripts 1 and 2 refer to the two observers, respectively, and the unprimed and primed velocities refer to velocities measured before and after the collision, respectively.

We now ask, "Is the law of conservation of momentum a good physical law in the sense that it satisfies Postulate I of relativity theory and, therefore, is invariant under a Galilean transformation?" To answer this question

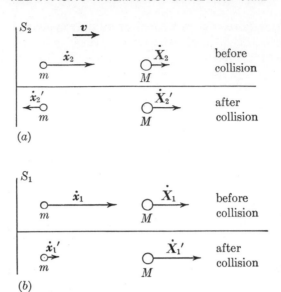

Figure 2-2. Collision of two particles as viewed by two observers moving at a constant relative velocity v.

we must see whether observers S_1 and S_2 will find the *same mathematical form* for the statement of the conservation-of-momentum law as each watches the same head-on collision of the masses m and M and measures the velocities with his own meter stick and clock.

For the observer in the inertial system S_2 the conservation-of-momentum law is written

$$\text{momentum before collision} = \text{momentum after collision}$$

Therefore,
$$m\dot{x}_2 + M\dot{X}_2 = m\dot{x}_2' + M\dot{X}_2' \qquad [2\text{-}4]$$

Using the Galilean velocity transformations, we can rewrite this equation in terms of the velocities measured by the observer in inertial system S_1,

$$m(\dot{x}_1 - v) + M(\dot{X}_1 - v) = m(\dot{x}_1' - v) + M(\dot{X}_1' - v)$$

which reduces to
$$m\dot{x}_1 + M\dot{X}_1 = m\dot{x}_1' + M\dot{X}_1' \qquad [2\text{-}5]$$

Equations 2-4 and 2-5 are of identical mathematical form; that is, they differ only in the subscripts 1 and 2. Therefore, an observer S_1 in some one inertial system and an observer S_2 in *any* other system that moves with a constant velocity with respect to S_1 would both agree that *momentum is conserved*. In short, the conservation of momentum law *is* a "good" law of classical mechanics. It must be noted, however, that the total linear momentum $m\dot{x}_1 + M\dot{X}_1$ before (or after) the collision as observed in S_1 is *not* the same as the total linear momentum $m\dot{x}_2 + M\dot{X}_2$ before (or after) the collision as observed in S_2, the total momentum being greater in S_1 in this example.

Invariance of Newton's Second Law   Let us show that Newton's second law of motion is invariant under a Galilean transformation. Consider two bodies, of respective masses m and M, that interact with one another as a result of some force, such as the gravitational force. If no net external force is applied to the system (the two bodies), the system is isolated, and the total linear momentum of the system must remain constant. For simplicity we assume that both masses lie on the X axis and move along it. Observer S_1 states this in the form

$$m\dot{x}_1 + M\dot{X}_1 = \text{constant}$$

Taking the time derivative of this equation gives

$$\mathrm{d}/\mathrm{d}t_1(m\dot{x}_1) = -\mathrm{d}/\mathrm{d}t_1(M\dot{X}_1) \qquad [2\text{-}6]$$

Because the force acting on a body is defined in terms of the rate of change of that body's momentum, the left-hand side of this equation is the force f_1 on m because of M, as measured in S_1, and the right-hand side is the force F_1 on M because of m, again as measured in S_1. Therefore,

$$f_1 = -F_1$$

which is Newton's third law.

Now considering the force acting on the mass m alone, we have

$$f_1 = \mathrm{d}/\mathrm{d}t_1(m\dot{x}_1) = m\ddot{x}_1 \qquad [2\text{-}7]$$

where it is assumed that the mass m has the same value in all inertial systems. In a similar fashion observer S_2 would write

$$f_2 = \mathrm{d}/\mathrm{d}t_2(m\dot{x}_2) = m\ddot{x}_2 \qquad [2\text{-}8]$$

Equations 2-3 show that $\ddot{x}_1 = \ddot{x}_2$, and therefore from Equations 2-7 and 2-8 it is seen that $f_1 = f_2$. From the invariance of Newton's second law and from the fact that the forces and acceleration are unchanged it immediately follows that, if S_1 is an inertial system, then S_2, which represents *any* coordinate system moving with respect to S_1 at a constant velocity v, is also an inertial system. From the point of view of Newton's second law all inertial systems, of which there are an infinite number, are equivalent and indistinguishable. Clearly, any coordinate frame of reference that is *accelerated* with respect to some inertial system cannot itself be an inertial system, because no longer does $\ddot{x}_1 = \ddot{x}_F$ hold.

We shall restrict our considerations to the *special* case, that of inertial systems moving with a constant velocity with respect to one another, and shall not discuss the more *general* case, in which one system is accelerated with respect to another. Thus our discussion will be confined to the theory of *special relativity*; the more general case of accelerated systems is treated in the theory of *general relativity*.

CONSERVATION OF ENERGY   To examine the invariance of the energy-conservation law under a Galilean transformation consider again the collision in Figure 2-2, assuming it to be perfectly *elastic* (although this might seem to rule out inelastic collisions, *all* collisions are elastic collisions at the subatomic level).

From the viewpoint of observer S_2 the conservation of energy law is written:

kinetic energy before collision = kinetic energy after collision

$$\tfrac{1}{2}m(\dot{x}_2)^2 + \tfrac{1}{2}M(\dot{X}_2)^2 = \tfrac{1}{2}m(\dot{x}_2')^2 + \tfrac{1}{2}M(\dot{X}_2')^2 \qquad [2\text{-}9]$$

This equation may be rewritten in terms of the velocities as measured by observer S_1 by using Equations 2-2, the Galilean velocity transformations:

$$\tfrac{1}{2}m(\dot{x}_1)^2 - m\dot{x}_1 v + \tfrac{1}{2}mv^2 + \tfrac{1}{2}M(\dot{X}_1)^2 - M\dot{X}_1 v + \tfrac{1}{2}Mv^2$$
$$= \tfrac{1}{2}m(\dot{x}_1')^2 - m\dot{x}_1' v + \tfrac{1}{2}mv^2 + \tfrac{1}{2}M(\dot{X}_1')^2 - M\dot{X}_1' v + \tfrac{1}{2}Mv^2$$

Using Equation 2-5, the invariance of the conservation-of-momentum law, we may cancel the terms involving v and, because the terms in v^2 also cancel, there remains

$$\tfrac{1}{2}m(\dot{x}_1)^2 + \tfrac{1}{2}M(\dot{X}_1)^2 = \tfrac{1}{2}m(\dot{x}_1')^2 + \tfrac{1}{2}M(\dot{X}_1')^2 \qquad [2\text{-}10]$$

Equations 2-9 and 2-10 are of identical mathematical form, differing only in the subscripts 1 and 2; therefore, the conservation-of-energy law is valid for all inertial systems.

We have found that *the laws of classical mechanics* (the conservation of momentum, Newton's laws of motion, and the conservation of energy) *are all invariant under a Galilean transformation. Thus, all inertial systems are equivalent in classical mechanics, and it is impossible by means of any experiment in mechanics to distinguish one inertial system from any other.* The invariance of the laws of mechanics, which has been formally proved here, is implicitly assumed in all elementary physics. For example, we are confident that a ping-pong game played on a moving train will follow the same physical laws for an observer fixed on the ground as for an observer traveling with the train.

We may draw another conclusion from the invariance of the laws of classical mechanics under a Galilean transformation, namely that the basic transformation equations confirm our assumption of the absolute character of space intervals and time intervals. Our analysis has also contained the assumption that the mass of a body is a constant and is completely independent of its motion with respect to an observer, so that it may be said that *the Galilean transformations and classical mechanics imply that length, time, and mass,* the three basic quantities in physical measurements, *are all independent of the relative motion of an observer.* As we shall see, the relativity physics of Einstein drastically revises this notion.

2-4 The failure of Galilean transformations One might well ask whether the laws of electromagnetism are invariant under a Galilean transformation. Inasmuch as Postulate I requires that *all* the laws of physics be invariant, the Galilean transformations are universally valid only if they also can be shown to be invariant under the transformations.

To examine this question we shall restrict our discussion to the propagation of electromagnetic waves, because this alone will enable us to analyze the invariance of classical electromagnetism, but first we shall consider a situation in mechanics.

Assume that a *sound* pulse is traveling to the right with respect to the medium transmitting it. The medium is assumed to be at rest in system S_1, and the velocity of the pulse, as measured in S_1, is $\dot{x}_1$. By "velocity" we mean its velocity with respect to the medium in which it is propagated, which in this example is air. For an observer in S_2 moving at a velocity v with respect to S_1 the measured (apparent) velocity by Equations 2-2 is $\dot{x}_2 = \dot{x}_1 - v$ (Figure 2-3). Therefore, the observer in S_2 measures a velocity of the sound pulse which is different from that measured by an observer in S_1.

We illustrate this by an example. A sound pulse from a cannon travels at 1,100 feet per second ($\dot{x}_1$) in still air with respect to the Earth (S_1). An observer in an airplane (S_2), moving at 400 feet per second (v) away from the source of the pulse, measures a velocity $\dot{x}_2 = \dot{x}_1 - v = 1,100 - 400 = 700$ feet per second. This is the velocity of the pulse with respect to *his* inertial frame (S_2). On the other hand, if the airplane approaches the source, then $v = -400$ feet per second and $\dot{x}_2 = 1,100 + 400$ feet per second, and the observer in S_2 measures the speed of the pulse as 1,500 feet per second. It follows that, in general, the measured speed of a sound pulse depends on the relative speed obtaining between the observer and the medium through which the pulse travels, and only when the observer is at rest with respect to the medium (here, air) will he find the measured speed to have the same value in all directions. *This result is confirmed by experiments with sound waves.* However, the measured velocity of the sound pulse in the system S_1, in which the air is at rest, *does not depend on the velocity of the source* of the sound. Of course, if a source of sound generates sinusoidal variations in the air pressure, rather than a pulse, the frequency and wavelength of the sound will, according to the Doppler effect, depend on the relative motion of the source and the medium, but the velocity of propagation of the disturbance will be independent of the source's relative motion.

We now turn to the completely analogous case of light. A pulse of light travels to the right with respect to the medium through which it is propagated at a speed $\dot{x}_1 \equiv c$ (Figure 2-3). The medium of light propagation historically was given the name *ether*. Because nineteenth-century physicists were firmly convinced that all physical phenomena were ultimately mechanical in origin, it was for them unthinkable that an electromagnetic disturbance could be propagated in empty space. Thus, the *ether* concept was invented. The only conspicuous property attributed to ether was that it

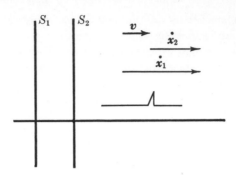

Figure 2-3. A pulse as viewed by two observers moving at a constant relative velocity v.

"carried" electromagnetic disturbances and that in an inertial system in which it was at rest, and in such a system alone, the speed of light was equal to c.

In terms of the Galilean transformations an observer at rest in S_1 measures the speed of the light pulse as c in the X_1 direction and also in *any other direction* in which the pulse might travel. Any observer at rest in another system S_2 measures the speed as $\dot{x}_2 = \dot{x}_1 - v = c - v$ when S_2 travels to the right; when S_2 moves to the left, he measures a different speed, $c + v$. This implies that the speed of light measured by any observer except one in S_1 depends on the velocity of the coordinate system with respect to the medium, the ether, through which the pulse of light is propagated. Therefore, the speed of light is certainly *not* invariant under Galilean transformations. In fact, if these transformations apply to light, then there exists in nature a unique inertial system in which the ether is at rest; in this system, and in this system alone, is the measured speed of light exactly c.

The essence of an experiment made to find and confirm the existence of the ether is simple: it is to measure the speed of light in a variety of inertial systems, noting whether the measured speed is different in the different systems and, most especially, whether there is evidence of a single, unique inertial system, "the ether," in which the speed of light is c. To perform such an experiment, however, is a far more difficult task than to perform one with sound waves because of the very high speed of light. In one of the most celebrated experiments of all time, in 1887, Michelson and Morley sought to find this unique inertial system. The experiment was simply that of determining whether there was a change in the measured speed of light as the Earth drifted through a conjectured ether in its axial rotation and its revolution about the Sun.

Let us analyze how the Michelson-Morley experiment, or its contemporary form with microwaves or laser beams, was an attempt to find the unique inertial system. It is assumed that the unique inertial system is the system S_1. The experimenter has no prior knowledge of whether he is at rest in S_1; hence, he must assume that he is, in general, in *any* system S_2, which moves with a velocity v with respect to S_1. When at some moment he is at rest in S_1, then S_2 is S_1, and the speed of light is measured as c, but six months later, when the Earth is moving in the opposite direction in its motion around the Sun, then S_2 will surely be in motion with respect to S_1, and the measured speed of light now will be different.

Because of the extremely large magnitude of c compared with the orbital speed of the Earth a measurement of the speed of light on Earth must, for practical reasons, be based on a measurement of the time interval required for a light beam to travel a known distance from some starting point to a reflecting mirror and back again. By measuring the time for a round trip one cannot measure the speed in a single direction; rather, one measures the *average* speed over the two opposite directions along a single line. The time for a trip from A to B and then back to A is the same as the time for a trip from B to A and then back to B. Clearly, then, one must compare time intervals for round trips along two *nonparallel* lines: the effect is a maximum when one compares the time intervals for lines parallel to the ether flow and those for lines at a right angle to it.

Consider a cylinder of length l which is at rest in system S_2 and aligned along the X_2 axis, the direction of relative motion of systems S_1 and S_2 (Figure 2-4, d to f). As before, S_2 moves to the right with a velocity v relative to the unique inertial system, S_1, the ether. While a light pulse travels to the right, an observer in S_2 measures the speed of the pulse as $c - v$, and the time required for the pulse to reach the right-end plate is $l/(c - v)$; after being reflected the pulse travels to the left with a speed $c + v$ relative to S_2 and reaches the left-end plate in a time $l/(c + v)$. Therefore, the time interval Δt_x for the light pulse to travel a complete round trip is

$$\Delta t_x = l/(c - v) + l/(c + v)$$

$$= \frac{2l/c}{1 - (v/c)^2} \qquad [2\text{-}11]$$

The sequence of events as seen by an observer in S_1 is illustrated in Figure 2-4, a to c.

Now consider the situation in which observer S_2 aligns the same cylinder along his Y_2 axis. The time interval required for the pulse to travel a round trip between what are now the bottom-end and top-end plates is designated by Δt_y. The sequence of events, as seen by observer S_1, is shown in Figure 2-5, a to c, and as seen by observer S_2, in Figure 2-5, d to f. From the point of view of observer S_1 only a light pulse that leaves the origin of system S_1 in the particular direction θ, necessarily traveling at the speed c, will reach the center of the top-end plate at A, as shown in Figure 2-5b. The pulse

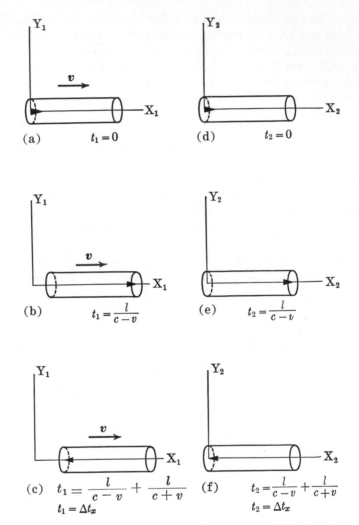

Figure 2-4. Time of flight of a light pulse as measured by two observers traveling at a constant relativity velocity v. The pulse moves parallel to v.

goes from O to A at a speed c in a time $\Delta t_y/2$, while the cylinder goes from O to B at a speed v in the same time.

Therefore $OA = c\Delta t_y/2$, $OB = v\Delta t_y/2$,   and $AB = l$

But $OA^2 = OB^2 + AB^2$

By substitution $(c\Delta t_y/2)^2 = (v\Delta t_y/2)^2 + l^2$

Solving for Δt_y gives, finally,

$$\Delta t_y = \frac{2l/c}{\sqrt{1 - (v/c)^2}}$$ [2-12]

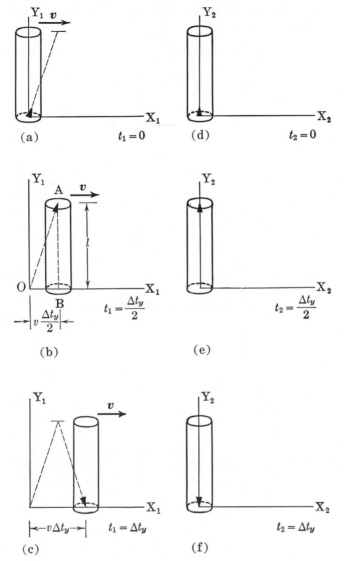

Figure 2-5. Time of flight of a light pulse as measured by two observers traveling at a constant relative velocity v. The pulse moves perpendicular to v, according to observer S_2.

Comparing Equations 2-11 and 2-12 shows that $\Delta t_x \neq \Delta t_y$; that is, the time taken by the light pulse in a round trip is *not* the same for the two perpendicular orientations. Of course, if the cylinder were at rest in system S_1, then v would be zero, and

$$\Delta t_x = 2l/c, \qquad \Delta t_y = 2l/c$$

Therefore, $\Delta t_x - \Delta t_y = 0$ when $v = 0$. When system S_2 is in motion with respect to system S_1,

$$\Delta t_x - \Delta t_y = (2l/c)\{[1 - (v/c)^2]^{-1} - [1 - (v/c)^2]^{-1/2}\}$$

It may be assumed that $v/c \ll 1$. The binomial expansion can be used (neglecting higher-order terms) to yield

$$\Delta t_x - \Delta t_y = (2l/c)[1 + (v/c)^2 - 1 - \tfrac{1}{2}(v/c)^2]$$
$$= (2l/c)(v^2/2c^2) \qquad [2\text{-}13]$$

Since the time for a round trip is approximately $\Delta t_x = 2l/c$, according to Equations 2-11 and 2-12, the maximum fractional change in the round-trip time interval for reorientation at $90°$ is, according to Equation 2-13,

$$\frac{\Delta t_x - \Delta t_y}{\Delta t_x} = \frac{v^2}{2c^2} \qquad [2\text{-}14]$$

The maximum speed v attainable on the Earth is the orbital speed of the planet Earth around the Sun, 3×10^4 m/sec. Substituting this value in Equation 2-14 shows that the fractional change in the round-trip time interval might be as large as 5×10^{-9}, or five parts in one billion! But Michelson and Morley were confident of being able to detect a change, should it occur, one hundred times smaller than this, that is, five parts in one hundred billion.

Using a precision optical instrument, the interferometer developed a few years earlier by Michelson, Michelson and Morley were able to measure indirectly the difference between Δt_x and Δt_y. This was accomplished by dividing a light beam into two separate beams that traveled at right angles to one another, were then reflected back along their respective paths, and were finally combined to form an interference pattern. Performing this experiment many times, at various times of the year and in various locations, Michelson and Morley always found that $\Delta t_x - \Delta t_y$ was zero; that is, the *result was always null*.†

This can have only one meaning: *any inertial system S_2 behaves as if it were the unique inertial system S_1*; or, the measured speed of light in *every*

---

† A number of workers have conducted similar experiments. Two particularly interesting ether-drift experiments are those of Essen and of Jaseja and his colleagues. The experiment made by L. Essen (*Nature*, Vol. 175, p. 793, 1955) is the microwave radio analogue of the optical Michelson-Morley experiment, in which short-wavelength radio beams replace the light beams, and beats between two resonant cavities at right angles to one another are observed rather than the interference between two light beams. The experiment made by T. S. Jaseja, A. Javin, and C. H. Townes (*Physical Review*, Vol. 133, p. A1221, 1964) compares the highly monochromatic infrared frequencies of two lasers, whose axes are perpendicular to each other. The precision of either of these experiments greatly exceeds that of the Michelson-Morley experiment.

inertial system is found to be the same, namely c, for all directions and for all observers. Therefore, there is no experimental evidence of a unique inertial system, or ether, inasmuch as *all inertial systems are equivalent for the propagation of light.* This fundamental assertion of the constancy of the speed of light for all observers is supported, not only by the Michelson-Morley experiment, but by a variety of other experiments, as we shall see.

2-5 The second postulate and the Lorentz transformations We may now write down the second postulate of relativity.

>*Postulate II: The speed of light in a vacuum is a constant, independent of the inertial system, the source, and the observer.*

This postulate, based on experiment, is obviously incompatible with the Galilean transformations, because these transformations require that the measured speed of light depend on the motion of the observer. Einstein observed the inconsistency between Postulate II and the Galilean transformations. Postulate II could not be relinquished, for it was an experimental fact. The Galilean transformations, despite their apparent success in classical mechanics and their obvious appeal to our common experience, had to be supplanted by less restrictive transformations, which would reduce to the Galilean transformations under appropriate conditions. How drastic such a change would be is demonstrated by the fact that our very ideas of space and time and their apparently absolute character are contained in the Galilean transformations.

Having seen that the Galilean transformations were fundamentally defective, Einstein sought coordinate transformation equations that would be in harmony with Postulates I and II, which state the invariance of physical laws under coordinate transformations and the invariance of the speed of light. The two postulates, which have been discussed separately thus far, may be regarded as a single postulate, in which the invariance of the speed of light is regarded as a fundamental physical law.

We shall find, as did Einstein in 1905, the transformation equations that satisfy the relativity requirements. These equations are known as the *Lorentz transformations*, because they were originated, in 1903, in his theory of electromagnetism, by H. A. Lorentz.

For simplicity let us consider motion in the X-Y plane only and the relative motion of two inertial systems along the X axis. Inasmuch as both the Z axis and the Y axis are perpendicular to the direction of relative motion of the two systems, the behavior along the one will be the same as that along the other. The most general type of transformation equations relating the space and time coordinates $(x_1, y_1; t_1)$ of an event, as observed in inertial system S_1, to the coordinates $(x_2, y_2; t_2)$ of the same event, as observed in inertial system S_2, must be of the form

$$x_2 = A_1 x_1 + A_2 y_1 + A_3 t_1 + A_4$$

$$y_2 = B_1 x_1 + B_2 y_1 + B_3 t_1 + B_4 \qquad [2\text{-}15]$$

$$t_2 = D_1 x_1 + D_2 y_1 + D_3 t_1 + D_4$$

where the twelve quantities $A_1, \ldots A_4 \ldots, D_4$ are constants, which are independent of the space and time coordinates but may depend on the relative velocity of one inertial system with respect to the other. We have assumed that Equations 2-15 are *linear* equations, involving the variables to the first power only, since only then would some single real event $(x_1, y_1; t_1)$ in S_1 correspond to a *single* real event $(x_2, y_2; t_2)$ in S_2, and conversely. Note that the time coordinate t_2 in S_2 now includes terms involving the spatial coordinates x_i and y_i of S_1, which cannot be precluded a priori. It is our task to find the values of the twelve constant coefficients $(A_1, \ldots, D_4)$. We shall obtain the simplest relationship between the space-time coordinates of S_1 and the space-time coordinates of S_2 by choosing the same orientations of the axes as those we chose for expressing the Galilean transformations (see Figure 2-1).

The components of the velocity of a particle as measured in the two inertial systems can easily be obtained from Equations 2-15. Defining the X and Y components of the velocity observed from system S_2 as

$$\dot{x}_2 \equiv \frac{\Delta x_2}{\Delta t_2} \qquad \text{and} \qquad \dot{y}_2 \equiv \frac{\Delta y_2}{\Delta t_2}$$

and those observed from S_1 as

$$\dot{x}_1 \equiv \frac{\Delta x_1}{\Delta t_1} \qquad \text{and} \qquad \dot{y}_1 = \frac{\Delta y_1}{\Delta t_1}$$

we obtain, using Equations 2-15,

$$\dot{x}_2 = \frac{\Delta x_2}{\Delta t_2} = \frac{A_1 \Delta x_1 + A_2 \Delta y_1 + A_3 \Delta t_1}{D_1 \Delta x_1 + D_2 \Delta y_1 + D_4 \Delta t_1}$$

By dividing both the numerator and the denominator of the right-hand side of this equation by Δt_1 we can express $\dot{x}_2$ in terms of $\dot{x}_1$ and $\dot{y}_1$:

$$\dot{x}_2 = \frac{A_1 \dot{x}_1 + A_2 \dot{y}_1 + A_3}{D_1 \dot{x}_1 + D_2 \dot{y}_1 + D_3} \qquad [2\text{-}16]$$

Similarly,

$$\dot{y}_2 = \frac{\Delta y_2}{\Delta t_2} = \frac{B_1 \dot{x}_1 + B_2 \dot{y}_1 + B_3}{D_1 \dot{x}_1 + D_2 \dot{y}_1 + D_3} \qquad [2\text{-}17]$$

Note that the denominators of these equations are identical.

We shall first apply some general conditions to the transformations, Equations 2-15, 2-16, and 2-17; this will reduce considerably the number of nonzero coefficients. Then we shall impose the experimental observation that the speed of light is the same in all inertial systems, to obtain the proper transformations of space-time events.

Transformations of Space-Time Events   Just as we did for the Galilean transformations (Equations 2-1 and Figure 2-1), we choose the $+X$ axis parallel to, and in the same direction as, the relative velocity v of system S_2 with respect to system S_1. This means that an observer in S_1 takes the origin of S_2 to be moving at speed v along the $+X_1$ axis; conversely, an observer in S_2 takes the origin of S_1 to be moving at speed v along the $-X_2$ axis.

We so set the clocks in S_1 and S_2 that, when the origin of S_2 passes the origin of S_1, both clocks read zero. Thus, when $t_1 = 0$, then $t_2 = 0$; the origins of S_1 and S_2 coincide at this time, and the space-time coordinates of the origin of S_2 as seen by observers S_1 and S_2 are as follows:

observer S_1 sees (0,0;0)

observer S_2 sees (0,0;0)

Using these values in Equations 2-15 gives

$$A_4 = B_4 = D_4 = 0$$

By our choice of origins coinciding at time $t_1 = t_2 = 0$ the three coefficients A_4, B_4, and D_4 are zero.

Next, let us consider the motion of system S_1's origin. As seen by observer S_1 the origin is, of course, always at rest: $\dot{x}_1 = 0$, $\dot{y}_1 = 0$. As seen by observer S_2 it moves along the $-X_2$ axis at speed v. Thus, $\dot{x}_2 = -v$, and $\dot{y}_2 = 0$. Using these values in Equations 2-16 and 2-17, we obtain

$$-v = \frac{A_3}{D_3} \quad \text{or} \quad \boxed{A_3 = -vD_3}$$

$$0 = \frac{B_3}{D_3} \quad \text{or} \quad \boxed{B_3 = 0}$$

Likewise, if we now consider the motion of system S_2's origin, we have $\dot{x}_2 = \dot{y}_2 = 0$ and $\dot{x}_1 = +v$, $\dot{y}_1 = 0$. Substituting these values in Equations 2-16 and 2-17 gives

$$0 = A_1 v + A_3, \quad \text{or} \quad \boxed{A_3 = -A_1 v}$$

$$0 = B_1 v + B_3, \quad \text{or} \quad \boxed{B_1 = -B_3/v = 0/v = 0}$$

The equation for y_2 in Equation 2-15 is now reduced to

$$y_2 = B_2 y_1 \qquad [2\text{-}18]$$

We now show that $B_2 = 1$. Consider two identical measuring rods, both of length L_0 when measured at rest in either S_1 or S_2. We fix one of the rods along the Y_1 axis in S_1 with one end at $y_1 = 0$ and the other end at $y_1 = L_0$. The second rod is fixed along the Y_2 axis between $y_2 = 0$ and $y_2 = L_0$. What does observer S_2 measure as the length of the rod fixed in system S_1? Since we know that the Y_2 coordinates of the ends of the rod do not depend on time (we showed that $B_3 = 0$), we can determine these coordinates at any time, and their difference will give the length as seen in S_2. Using Equation 2-18, we have, for the length L_2 of the moving rod as seen by observer S_2,

$$L_2 = B_2 L_0$$

Again, using Equation 2-18, we find that observer S_1 measures the length of the rod fixed in system S_2 as

$$L_0 = B_2 L_1$$

Now, the ratio of the length of the moving rod to that of the fixed rod, measured by observer S_2, must be the same as that measured by S_1; otherwise, we could distinguish between the inertial systems! Thus,

$$\frac{L_2}{L_0} = \frac{L_1}{L_0} \quad \text{or} \quad B_2 = \frac{1}{B_2} \quad \text{or} \quad \boxed{B_2 = +1}$$

Equation 2-18 then becomes:

$$y_2 = y_1$$

Notice that we discard the solution $B_2 = -1$, since that implies that the point $y_1 = L_0$ goes into the point $y_2 = -L_0$, which is not true. Inasmuch as the Z coordinate is similar to the Y coordinate, the Z components transform as

$$z_2 = z_1$$

Coordinates perpendicular to the relative velocity v of the two inertial systems are the same in both systems. This is nothing new.

What about the coefficients A_2 and D_2 in Equations 2-15? These are easily shown to be zero. First consider a rod of length L_0 parallel to the Y_1 axis from 0 to L_0 and at rest in system S_1. Then from Equation 2-16 we have

$$\text{lower end:} \qquad \dot{x}_2 = -v = A_3/D_3$$

$$\text{upper end:} \qquad \dot{x}_2 = -v = A_3/D_3$$

So, with respect to observer S_2 both ends move to the left at constant speed v.

Now, if $A_2 = 0$, then at time $t_1 = t_2 = 0$ a rod along the Y_1 axis will have $x_1 = 0$ and, according to Equations 2-15 and 2-18, observer S_2 will measure

$$x_2 = A_2 y_1$$

$$y_2 = y_1$$

See Figure 2-6. But by symmetry this cannot be so, since we must have symmetry about the axis of the relative velocity v. This will be true only if observer S_2 sees the rod perpendicular to v; therefore,

$$\boxed{A_2 = 0}$$

To show that $D_2 = 0$, consider two events in system S_1 occurring at the same X coordinate and the same time, say $x_1 = 0$ and $t_1 = 0$. Because they occur at the same time, they are simultaneous events from the viewpoint of an observer in that

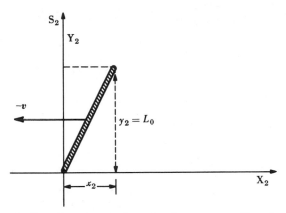

Figure 2-6. Coordinates x_2 and y_2 of rod as measured by observer S_2.

system. If one event occurs at the origin and the other at $y_1 = L_0$, then, according to the last equation of Equations 2-15, an observer in S_2 observes the event at L_0 to occur later than that at the origin at $\Delta t_2 = D_2 L_0$. Thus, events along the Y_1 axis (which are simultaneous in S_1) will, from the point of view of an observer in S_1, occur later than or earlier than $t_2 = 0$, depending on whether they occur above or below the Y axis. This again violates symmetry about the axis of v, unless

$$\boxed{D_2 = 0}$$

Substituting all the coefficients in Equations 2-15 and 2-16 we obtain the following (the Z coordinates are now included for completeness).

Coordinate transformations: Velocity transformations:

$$x_2 = A_1(x_1 - vt_1)$$

$$\dot{x}_2 = \frac{A_1(\dot{x}_1 - v)}{D_1\dot{x}_1 + A_1}$$

$$y_2 = y_1 \qquad \text{[2-19]} \qquad \dot{y}_2 = \frac{\dot{y}_1}{D_1\dot{x}_1 + A_1} \qquad \text{[2-20]}$$

$$z_2 = z_1$$

$$\dot{z}_2 = \frac{\dot{z}_1}{D_1\dot{x}_1 + A_1}$$

$$t_2 = D_1 x_1 + A_1 t_1$$

We have arrived at Equations 2-19 and 2-20 by using the homogeneity of space (the fact that a single event in one inertial system corresponds to a single event in any other inertial system) and by arguments from symmetry. There are now only two undetermined coefficients, A_1 and D_1.

Before we apply Postulate II to these equations, let us show that they reduce to the Galilean transformations when we assume that the time coordinate is independent of the spatial coordinates. For this the last equation of Equations 2-19 must have $D_1 = 0$ and $A_1 = 1$; then the four equations will reduce to Equations 2-1. As we have found, these particular values of the coefficients A_1 and D_1 are inconsistent with the second postulate of special relativity.

Let us now solve for A_1 and D_1, imposing the second postulate of relativity, the requirement that the speed of light be the same for all observers.

Imagine that observer S_1 shines a beam of light along the $+X$ axis. He measures its speed as c; that is,

$$\dot{x}_1 = c$$

A second observer, S_2, moving to the right with speed v relative to S_1, will, by the constancy of the speed of light, also measure the speed of this light beam as c. Substituting c for $\dot{x}_2$ in Equations 2-20 gives

$$c = \frac{A_1(c - v)}{D_1 c + A_1}$$

which gives

$$D_1 c^2 = -A_1 v,$$

$$D_1 = (-v/c^2)A_1 \qquad [2\text{-}21]$$

This equation reduces the unknown coefficients in Equations 2-19 to one, either A_1 or D_1. Let us take A_1 as the unknown. To obtain this coefficient we again use the constancy of the speed of light, but this time we suppose that S_1 projects the light beam along the $+Y_1$ axis; see Figure 2-7.

Observer S_1 will, of course, measure the speed as c (that is, $\dot{y}_1 = c$ and $\dot{x}_1 = 0$).

Observer S_2, moving to the right with speed v relative to S_1, will, by the velocity transformations of Equations 2-20, measure the velocity components $\dot{x}_2$ and $\dot{y}_2$ as

$$\dot{x}_2 = \frac{A_1(0 - v)}{A_1} = -v$$

$$\dot{y}_2 = \frac{c}{A_1} \qquad [2\text{-}22]$$

By the second postulate of relativity, S_2 must observe the light pulse to travel at the speed c, the same speed as that measured by S_1. Thus, the speed measured by S_2 must be

$$v_2 = \sqrt{\dot{x}_2^2 + \dot{y}_2^2} = c$$

Substituting Equations 2-22 into this equation gives

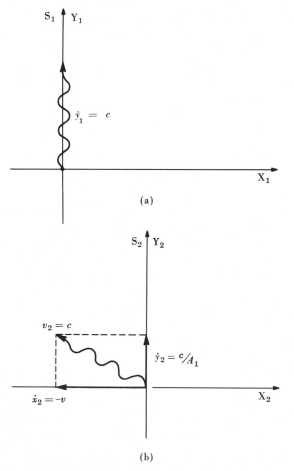

Figure 2-7. Light pulse as observed (a) by S_1 and (b) by S_2.

$$\sqrt{v^2 + c^2/A_1^2} = c.$$

$$A_1^2 = \frac{1}{1 - (v/c)^2}$$

$$A_1 = \frac{1}{\sqrt{1 - (v/c)^2}} \qquad [2\text{-}23]$$

Only the positive sign is taken for A_1, because a negative A_1, by Equation 2-20, would lead to a reversal in the Y and Z components of the velocity of objects seen from different inertial systems.

Substituting the values of A_1 and D_1 from Equations 2-21 and 2-23 in Equations 2-19 finally gives the Lorentz transformations for any space-time event:

Lorentz
coordinate
transformations

$$x_2 = \frac{x_1 - vt_1}{\sqrt{1 - (v/c)^2}}$$

$$y_2 = y_1$$

$$z_2 = z_1$$

$$t_2 = \frac{t_1 - (v/c^2)x_1}{\sqrt{1 - (v/c)^2}}$$

[2-24]

As in the Galilean transformations, Equations 2-1, to get the inverse transformation equations, giving x_1, y_1, z_1, and t_1, in terms of x_2, y_2, z_2, and t_2, we merely interchange the subscripts 1 and 2 and replace v with $-v$ in Equations 2-24 (see Problem 2-7).

The Lorentz transformations are the logical consequence of the experimentally established fact that the speed of light is a true constant of nature, independent of the motion of the source or observer and independent of the inertial system.

We have arrived at the unique transformations that meet the requirements of the two relativity postulates and that therefore supplant the Galilean transformations. By the correspondence principle (Section 1-5), we know that the Lorentz transformations *must* reduce to the Galilean transformations in that range of speeds in which the latter are known to be essentially correct. By comparing Equations 2-24 and 2-1 we see that the two sets of transformation become identical when $v/c \rightarrow 0$. Thus, when $v \ll c$, the Galilean transformations are an excellent approximation to the universally valid Lorentz transformations. The Galilean transformations are adequate for describing all low-speed phenomena. Mathematically, making $v/c \ll 1$ is equivalent to letting $c \rightarrow \infty$; therefore, we may regard the Galilean transformations as the correct coordinate transformations in a hypothetical universe in which the speed of light is infinite. We may write symbolically

$$\text{Limit}_{c \rightarrow \infty} \text{(Lorentz transformations)} = \text{(Galilean transformations)}$$

When the speed of an object is close to the speed of light, only the Lorentz transformations will apply. According to the Lorentz transformation for the time coordinate, Equations 2-24, the time coordinate (t_2) is no longer absolute; that is, it is no longer independent of the space coordinate (x_1). The clocks (t_1 and t_2) of observers in two different coordinate systems (S_1 and S_2) do not agree ($t_1 \neq t_2$).

It is obvious from the Lorentz transformation equations that no speed can exceed c. The quantity $[1 - (v/c)^2]^{1/2}$ appearing in them is real, rather than imaginary, only if $v < c$. If v were to be greater than c, this quantity would become imaginary, and a real event in one system would correspond to an imaginary and, therefore, unobservable event in another system. In the derivation of the Lorentz transformation relations it was assumed that there was one speed common to all observers, that of light. Now we see that this single speed c is, in fact, the maximum possible speed for any observer.

Moreover, as we shall see in later examples, a distinctive feature of relativity is this: two events that are simultaneous according to an observer in one reference frame are *not simultaneous* according to another observer in another frame. In other words, the simultaneity of events is relative.

The Lorentz transformations assure us that the speed of light, and only this speed, will be the same for all inertial coordinate systems. *The laws of electromagnetism then become invariant under a Lorentz transformation, and all inertial systems give an equivalent description of these laws.*

Using Equations 2-21 and 2-23 for D_1 and A_1 in the general transformations, Equations 2-20, we obtain the Lorentz velocity transformations:

Lorentz
velocity
transformations

$$\dot{x}_2 = \frac{\dot{x}_1 - v}{1 - (v/c^2)\dot{x}_1}$$

$$\dot{y}_2 = \frac{\dot{y}_1 \sqrt{1 - (v/c)^2}}{1 - (v/c^2)\dot{x}_1}$$

$$\dot{z}_2 = \frac{\dot{z}_1 \sqrt{1 - (v/c)^2}}{1 - (v/c^2)\dot{x}_1}$$

[2-25]

One surprising result of the Lorentz velocity transformations is that the Y and Z components of the velocity of a particle as measured in S_2 depend on the X component of the velocity as measured in S_1! As before, to obtain the velocity components measured in S_1 in terms of those measured in S_2 we simply interchange subscripts and replace v with $-v$ in Equations 2-25. Applying the correspondence principle to the Lorentz velocity transformations, we obtain the Galilean velocity transformations, Equations 2-2:

Limit (Lorentz velocity transformations)
$c \rightarrow \infty$
$\qquad\qquad\qquad\qquad$ = (Galilean velocity transformations)

Example 2-1   A fast car moves at a speed $c/2$ with respect to a man holding a lantern. A passenger in the car measures the speed of light reaching him from the lantern with his own meter stick and clock; in accordance with the relativity principle, he will measure the light's speed as c no matter what the direction of his velocity with respect to the lantern. Can we confirm this by using the Lorentz velocity transformations, Equations 2-25?

We shall test the invariance of c in the two simple situations in which (a) the car directly approaches the lantern and (b) the car moves perpendicular to the light signal it receives (from the lantern's point of view).

(a) Assume the car to be at rest in system S_2, which is traveling toward the lantern in S_1 with a velocity $v = -(c/2)$, as shown in Figure 2-8a. Since the light travels at

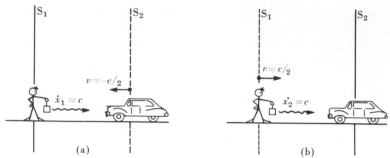

Figure 2-8. Velocity of light signal along $+X_1$ as observed (a) by S_1 and (b) by S_2.

a speed c with respect to the lantern, we have $\dot{x}_1 = c$ and, using Equations 2-25 to find $\dot{x}_2$, we have

$$\dot{x}_2 = \frac{\dot{x}_1 - v}{1 - (v/c^2)\dot{x}_1} = \frac{c - (-c/2)}{1 - (-c/2c^2)c} = c$$

Thus, the observer in the car, at rest in S_2, measures the speed of the light signal as c, too. Figure 2-8b depicts the situation as observed in system S_2.

We notice immediately from this example (as well as from the general velocity transformations, Equations 2-25, that the velocity of a particle measured in S_1 is no longer the vector sum of the velocity measured in S_2 and the relative velocity of S_2 with respect to S_1. For the example in Figure 2-8a the Galilean velocity transformations, Equations 2-2, would give

$$\dot{x}_2 = \dot{x}_1 - v = c - (-c/2) = (3/2)c$$

which *does* obey vector addition,

$$c + c/2 = (3/2)c$$

but is inconsistent with experimental results. Symbolically, under the Lorentz transformations we have, for the propagation of light in this example,

$$c + c/2 = c$$

(b) Now, assume that the car is again at rest in S_2 but is at a point along the positive Y_2 axis, as shown in Figure 2-9. The system S_2 is moving toward the lantern (which is at rest in system S_1) with a velocity $v = -(c/2)$. What velocity does an observer in the car measure for a light signal that, according to the observer holding the lantern in system S_1, travels along the $+Y_1$ axis at speed c? Figure 2-9a shows the motions of the car and the light signal as observed in S_1. According to the observer in S_1, the light signal travels at speed c along the $+Y_1$ axis: that is, $\dot{x}_1 = 0$ and $\dot{y}_1 = c$. Using the Lorentz velocity transformations, Equations 2-25, we get

$$\dot{x}_2 = \frac{\dot{x}_1 - v}{1 - (v/c^2)\dot{x}_1} = c/2$$

$$\dot{y}_2 = \frac{\dot{y}_1 \sqrt{1 - (v/c)^2}}{1 - (v/c^2)\dot{x}_1} = c\sqrt{1 - (1/2)^2} = \frac{c\sqrt{3}}{2}$$

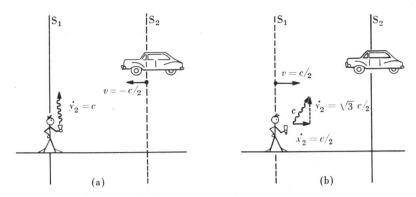

Figure 2-9. Velocity of light signal along $+Y_1$ as observed by (a) S_1 and (b) by S_2.

Thus, the observer in S_2 sees the light signal traveling toward him at an angle θ_2 relative to the $+X_2$ axis, determined by $\tan \theta_2 = \dot{y}_2/\dot{x}_2 = \sqrt{3}$; see Figure 2-9b. Solving for θ_2, we obtain $\theta_2 = 60°$.

To compute the speed of the light signal we must remember that in any one inertial system, say S_2, the resultant velocity v_2 of a particle traveling in any direction is still obtained by vector addition of the components in S_2; the speed is given by

$$v_2 = \sqrt{\dot{x}^2 + \dot{y}^2 + \dot{z}^2}$$

With $\dot{x}_2 = c/2$ and $\dot{y}_2 = c\sqrt{3}/2$ the speed of the light, according to the observer in S_2, is

$$v_2 = \sqrt{c^2/4 + 3c^2/4} = c$$

Again, both observers measure the same speed c for the light, as they must.

Just as we found in part (a), the velocity of the light signal measured in S_1 is not merely the vector sum of the velocity of the signal measured in S_2 and the velocity of S_2 relative to S_1. See Problem 2-9.

2-6   Length and time intervals in relativity physics

SPACE CONTRACTION   In classical physics the length of an object is the same for all observers, whatever their velocities with respect to it. Let us now examine the meaning of length in relativity theory according to the Lorentz transformations, remembering that only these transformations give a complete description of space and time.

Suppose that at some time observers S_1 and S_2 were at rest with respect to each other, compared their respective meter sticks, and agreed that both had the same length L_0. Then system S_2 is set in motion to the right with a speed v with respect to system S_1. Observer S_1 aligns his meter stick along the X axis, its left end at x_1 and its right end at x_1'; then from his point of view $L_0 = x_1' - x_1$. Similarly, observer S_2 aligns his meter stick along the X axis, the left and right ends at the points x_2 and x_2'; then from his point of view $L_0 = x_2' - x_2$. Each observer sees *his own* meter stick as having length L_0; this, of course, must follow from the fact that all inertial systems are equivalent and indistinguishable.

Now we ask, "What is the length of a moving meter stick, say S_2's meter stick, as measured by S_1?" First, we must recognize that even in non-relativistic physics it is essential to mark both ends of a moving object simultaneously. If one marked one end of a moving meter stick at one time and the other end at a later time, the distance between the two marks would not correspond to the length of the moving object; this distance could then assume any value, depending upon the time interval elapsing between the two marking operations. Inasmuch as observer S_1 must mark both ends of a moving object simultaneously, we must choose two events, $(x_1; t_1)$ and $(x_1'; t_1')$, representing the left and right ends of S_2's meter stick as measured by S_1, with $t_1' = t_1$. Equations 2-24 give the space-time coordinates $(x_2; t_2)$ and $(x_2'; t_2')$ of these same two events as measured by S_2 in terms of the events as measured by S_1. Because the meter stick is always at rest in S_2's system, the space coordinates x_2' and x_2 are independent of the times t_2 and t_2' at which S_2 measures them. Thus, it is not essential that the spatial measurements be made simultaneously in the system in which the object is at rest.

Using Equations 2-24, we have

$$x_2' - x_2 = \frac{(x_1' - x_1) - v(t_1' - t_1)}{\sqrt{1 - (v/c)^2}} \qquad [2\text{-}26]$$

with $t_1' = t_1$. The length of S_2's meter stick, as measured by S_2, is $x_2' - x_2 = L_0$; the length of this same meter stick, moving at speed v with respect to system S_1, but now as measured by S_1, is $x_1' - x_1 = L$. Therefore, Equation 2-26 becomes

$$\boxed{L = L_0 \sqrt{1 - (v/c)^2}} \qquad [2\text{-}27]$$

This relation shows the phenomenon of *space contraction*. Measuring the length of S_2's moving meter stick, S_1 finds it to be contracted by a factor $[1 - (v/c)^2]^{1/2}$ along the direction of the relative motion. This contraction is reciprocal; that is, observer S_2 finds the length of a meter stick of length L_0 at rest in system S_1 to be $L_0[1 - (v/c)^2]^{1/2}$. (We must recognize, however, that when S_2 marks the two ends of his own meter stick simultaneously, these two events are *not* simultaneous as observed by S_1.) Because the contraction is *not* in consequence of any physical disturbance (cooling, compression, etc.) but, rather, reflects the properties of space and time as contained in the Lorentz transformations, the phenomenon is known as *space contraction*. Since $y_1 = y_2$ and $z_1 = z_2$, there is no space contraction in a direction perpendicular to that of the relative motion. Clearly, the length of an object is *not* absolute but depends upon that object's relative motion with respect to the observer; it is a maximum when at rest in the observer's inertial system. We are accustomed to events in which v is very much less than c and in which, from Equation 2-27, L is therefore approximately equal to L_0.

Although the length of a moving object no longer has the same value for all inertial observers, there is one length that is invariant, namely, the length of an object at rest with respect to an observer. Thus, all inertial observers would agree that L_0 is properly the length of a given meter stick *when it is at rest in their respective inertial systems*. This length of an object, sometimes called the *proper length*, is an invariant property of an object.

Time Dilation Relativity physics shows that time, like length, is not absolute but, rather, depends on the relative motion of the observer.

Two observers, S_1 and S_2, while at rest with respect to one another, synchronize their respective clocks and agree that the interval between two events timed on their clocks is T_0. Now we imagine system S_2 to be moving at a speed v to the right with respect to system S_1. Observer S_1 keeps his clock at rest at a particular point x_1 in his system and measures the time interval T_0 as that time between the instants t_1 and t_1'. Similarly, S_2 keeps his clock at a fixed position x_2 and measures the interval T_0 as the time between the instants t_2 and t_2'. Thus each observer measures the time interval on his own clock to be T_0. We wish to find out how the intervals registered on the two clocks compare when *both* intervals are measured by observer S_2. From Equations 2-24 we see that the time interval $t_2' - t_2$ between any two events, as measured by observer S_2, is related to the space interval $x_1' - x_1$ and to the time interval $t_1' - t_1$ between the same two events, as measured by observer S_1, by the following:

$$(t_2' - t_2) = \frac{(t_1' - t_1) - (v/c^2)(x_1' - x_1)}{\sqrt{1 - (v/c)^2}} \qquad [2\text{-}28]$$

Now, observer S_2 wishes to measure the time interval on a clock that is at rest in inertial system S_1. Because all clocks at rest in system S_2 have been synchronized, it is not important where in S_2 the time of an event is measured. Therefore, we choose a clock at rest in S_1 at the point $x_1 = x_1'$ and consider the events $(x_1; t_1)$ and $(x_1; t_1')$. In the equation above the time interval $t_2' - t_2$ between the two events, as measured by observer S_2, is, then,

$$t_2' - t_2 = \frac{t_1' - t_1}{\sqrt{1 - (v/c)^2}}$$

Letting the time interval that observer S_1 measures with a clock at rest in his system be $T_0 = t_1' - t_1$ and the time interval, between the same events, that S_2 measures for the moving clock be $T = t_2' - t_2$, we obtain:

$$T = \frac{T_0}{\sqrt{1 - (v/c)^2}}$$ [2-29]

This relation shows the phenomenon of *time dilation*. For an example of the consequences of time dilation suppose that $v = 0.98c$; then $[1 - (v/c)^2]^{1/2} = 1/5$, and $T = 5T_0$. Therefore, if the time interval between two consecutive ticks on each of two identical clocks is T_0, the *proper time*, when both are at rest with respect to an observer, then, when one clock is in motion at $0.98c$ with respect to the other clock, the time interval between consecutive ticks of the moving clock will be $5T_0$ as measured on the resting clock. That is, the resting clock makes five ticks for every tick of the moving clock. We might say that moving clocks run slow, or "live longer." Again, this effect is reciprocal, in that each observer finds the other moving observer's clock to run slow.

For $v \ll c$ the relative time of relativity physics reduces to the absolute time of classical physics. Despite the fact that space contraction and time dilation strike us as being extraordinarily bizarre, there is direct and inescapable experimental evidence of time dilation in the decay of high-speed meson particles.

Whereas in prerelativity physics space intervals, time intervals, and the simultaneity of events are intuitively taken to be absolute, and the speed of light is regarded as relative, in the relativity physics of Einstein, because the speed of light is absolute for all inertial systems, the space intervals and time intervals and the simultaneity of events are relative.

In our everyday experiences we observe objects moving at speeds much smaller than the speed of light. Therefore, the distinctive relativistic effects embodied in the Lorentz transformations are not easily discerned. The following examples involving very high speeds will illustrate the unusual properties of space-time events in relativity physics.

Example 2-2 An interesting confirmation of the time-dilation phenomenon (Equation 2-29) is found in the decay of high-energy and, therefore, high-speed *muons*. These particles are produced in the decay of other unstable particles, called π mesons, which in turn are created in high-energy collisions of nuclei (these particles will be discussed in Sections 11-2 and 11-4). We shall find that the muon is identical with the electron except that its mass is approximately 207 times greater and that it is unstable, rather quickly decaying into other particles. The measured half-life of muons that are at rest with respect to an observer is 1.52×10^{-6} sec; that is, if 1,000 muons are at rest with respect to an observer, the observer will find only 500 muons surviving after 1.52×10^{-6} sec has elapsed. If, on the other hand, the muons are moving with respect to an observer, their lifetime will be dilated, and they will appear to this observer to live longer. According to Equation 2-29, this observer will measure a half-life T given by

$$T = \frac{T_0}{\sqrt{1 - (v/c)^2}}$$

where $T_0 = 1.52 \times 10^{-6}$ sec is the half-life in the inertial system of the muons, and v is the relative velocity between the mesons and the observer.

In the high-energy collisions between cosmic-ray particles from outer space (mostly protons) and nuclei in the atmosphere muons are produced, and some approach the Earth's surface with speeds very nearly c. For such particles time dilation will, therefore, be appreciable and readily observed.

Consider 1,000 muons approaching the Earth's surface at a speed of $0.98c$ from an altitude $L_0 = 2.23$ km, this height being measured by an observer fixed on Earth. We may think of this distance as being registered on a long, vertical post *fixed* to Earth; see Figure 2-10. As measured by the observer on Earth, the muons' half-life is $T = T_0/[1 - (v/c)^2]^{1/2} = 5T_0 = 7.60 \times 10^{-6}$ sec, and their flight time is $L_0/(0.98c) = (2.23 \times 10^3\,\text{m})/(0.98 \times 3.0 \times 10^8\,\text{m/sec}) = 7.60 \times 10^{-6}$ sec (the two are equal only because of our convenient choice of L_0). Therefore, of the original 1,000 muons at 2.23 km altitude only 500 will have survived decay upon reaching the Earth's surface.

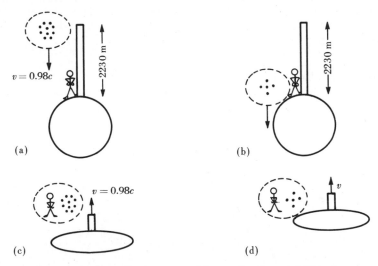

Figure 2-10. Muons and Earth approaching each other at $0.98c$. As seen by observer fixed on Earth: (a) 1,000 muons approaching Earth, (b) 500 undecayed muons arriving at Earth. As seen by observer traveling with the muons: (c) Earth approaching 1,000 muons, (d) Earth arriving at 500 undecayed muons.

How do these decay events appear to an observer moving with the decaying muons? He finds that half the muons decay in a time of $T_0 = 1.52 \times 10^{-6}$ sec. Moreover, he sees the Earth and vertical post approach him at a speed of $0.98c$. Because of the space-contraction phenomenon the Earth's distance from him is contracted (that is, the vertical post fixed to Earth is contracted). At the time that he counts 1,000 muons the Earth's distance from him by his measurements is only $(2.23\,\text{km})[1 - (0.98)^2]^{1/2} = 0.446$ km. Thus, the time of flight, according to him, is $(446\,\text{m})/(0.98 \times 3 \times 10^8\,\text{m/sec}) = 1.52 \times 10^{-6}$ sec. But this is just the decay half-life in the rest system of the muons; therefore, an observer in that system also will find 500 of the original 1,000 muons surviving when the Earth reaches the muons.

Although the two observers, one on Earth and one with the muons, disagree on the measurements of time and of length intervals, they both agree that 500 muons survive when the Earth and muons meet.

If our classical notions of space and time were valid, there would be no dilation of time, the observer on Earth would measure the half-life of the moving muons to be 1.52×10^{-6} sec, and the flight time would be $(7.60 \times 10^{-6})/(1.52 \times 10^{-6}) = 5$ times the half-life. Since only one half of the muons survive each half-life, the observer on Earth would then predict that $(1/2)^5 = 1/32$ of the original 1,000 survive to the surface. Thus, without relativistic effects he should find only 31 muons surviving. This is not in agreement with experiment. Time-dilation effects observed with high-speed particles give emphatic confirmation to relativistic physics.

See the film reference at the end of this chapter.

Example 2-3   In this example we wish to consider some specific events, namely the births and deaths of three men. In order that we may use the Lorentz coordinate transformations, Equations 2-24, we consider two inertial systems, S_1 and S_2, with axes aligned as in Figure 2-1; S_2 moves along the $+X_1$ axis at a speed of $0.98c$ with respect to S_1. We might think of S_1 as an inertial system in which the Earth is at rest and of S_2 as one in which a rocket ship is at rest.

At the time $t_1 = t_2 = 0$ observers in S_1 record the simultaneous births of three men: Jim, born at S_1's origin, John, born at $x_1 = +10$ light-years (one light-year is the distance a light pulse will travel in one year), and Dick, born at S_1's origin; see Figure 2-11a. Both Jim and John remain at rest in S_1 throughout their 70-year life

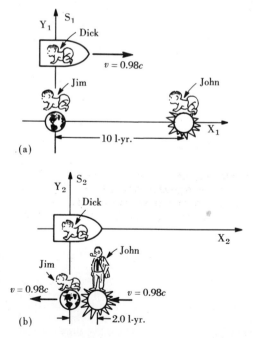

(a)

(b)

Figure 2-11. (a) The simultaneous births (a) of Jim, John, and Dick, as observed in system S_1 and (b) of Jim and Dick, as observed in system S_2. In (b) observers in S_2 find John to be 49 years old and 2 light-years from Jim and Dick. See Table 2-1.

span, according to the observers in S_1. Dick, on the other hand, is born and remains at rest in the rocket ship, which is at rest in S_2. With respect to S_2 Dick also lives exactly 70 years.

(a) According to observers in S_1, how long does Dick live?
(b) According to observers in S_2, how long do Jim and John live?
(c) According to observers in S_2, how far apart are Jim and John?

In this problem it will be convenient to measure time in years and distance in light-years. Velocity will then be measured in light-years per year. Thus, in these units the speed of light is simply one light-year per year, $c = (1 \text{ l-yr})/(1 \text{ yr})$, and the relative velocity of S_2 with respect to S_1 is $v = 0.98c = 0.98$ light-year per year. Obviously, expressed in these units, the velocity of any body will always be somewhere between 0 and 1.

Equations 2-24 relate the space-time coordinates of any event as measured from two inertial systems S_1 and S_2. In our problem of the Earth and the rocket ship there are six relevant events: the birth and death of Jim, the birth and death of John, and the birth and death of Dick. If we know the space-time coordinates of an event as observed in one of the systems, we can use Equations 2-24 to obtain the coordinates of the same event as observed in the other system. Table 2-1 lists the

Table 2-1

	SPACE-TIME COORDINATES	
EVENT	$S_1(x_1; t_1)$	$S_2(x_2; t_2)$ $v/c = 0.98$
Birth of Jim	(0 ; 0) given	(0 ; 0) computed
Death of Jim	(0 ; 70 yr) given	(−343 l-yr; 350 yr) computed
Birth of John	(10 l-yr; 0) given	(50 l-yr; −49 yr) computed
Death of John	(10 l-yr; 70 yr) given	(−293 l-yr; 301 yr) computed
Birth of Dick	(0 ; 0) given	(0 ; 0) computed
Death of Dick	(343 l-yr; 350 yr) computed	(0 ; 70 yr) given

space-time coordinates of the six events as observed in the two systems S_1 and S_2 and indicates which are given and which computed by Equations 2-24.

A sample calculation of space-time coordinates follows.

Consider the birth of John. Observers at rest in S_1 record the birthplace of John as $x_1 = +10$ light-years and the time of birth as $t_1 = 0$. Observers at rest in S_2 compute the location and time of John's birth by means of Equations 2-24:

$$x_2 = \frac{x_1 - vt_1}{\sqrt{1 - (v/c)^2}} = \frac{10 \text{ l-yr} - 0}{\sqrt{1 - (0.98)^2}} = 5(10 \text{ l-yr}) = 50 \text{ l-yr}$$

$$t_2 = \frac{t_1 - v/(c^2)x_1}{\sqrt{1 - (v/c)^2}} = 5\left(0 - 0.98\frac{10 \text{ l-yr}}{1 \text{ l-yr/yr}}\right) = -49 \text{ yr}$$

Observers in S_2 record John's birth as 50 light-years from the birthplace of Dick and Jim 49 years before the births of Dick and Jim.

Now, consider the death of John. According to observers in S_1 that event takes place at $x_1 = 10$ light-years and $t_1 = 70$ years. According to observers in S_2 by Equations 2-24, the event is,

$$x_2 = \frac{x_1 - vt_1}{\sqrt{1 - (v/c)^2}} = 5\left(10 \text{ l-yr} - \frac{0.98 \text{ l-yr}}{\text{yr}} 70 \text{ yr}\right) = -293 \text{ l-yr}$$

$$t_2 = \frac{t_1 - (v/c^2)x_1}{\sqrt{1 - (v/c)^2}} = 5\left[70 \text{ yr} - \left(\frac{0.98 \text{ l-yr}}{\text{yr}}\right)\frac{10 \text{ l-yr}}{(1 \text{ l-yr/yr})^2}\right] = 301 \text{ yr}$$

The other space-time coordinates are calculated in a similar manner.

With the use of Table 2-1 it is now easy to answer the questions asked at the beginning of this example:

(a) According to observers S_1, how long does Dick live? From the table we have

Life span of Dick according to observers S_1:

$$t_1 \text{ (death)} - t_1 \text{ (birth)} = 350 \text{ yr} - 0 \text{ yr} = 350 \text{ yr}$$

This is in agreement with the time dilation of moving clocks, Equation 2.29. For this example the lifetime interval of the moving man is increased by a factor of 5.

(b) According to observers S_2, how long do Jim and John live?

Life span of Jim according to observers S_2:

$$t_2 \text{ (death)} - t_2 \text{ (birth)} = 350 \text{ yr} - 0 \text{ yr} = 350 \text{ yr}$$

Life span of John according to observers S_2:

$$t_2 \text{ (death)} - t_2 \text{ (birth)} = 301 \text{ yr} - (-49 \text{ yr}) = 350 \text{ yr}$$

This too is in agreement with Equation 2-29.

(c) According to the observers stationed in S_2, how far apart are Jim and John at any instant? The locations of Jim and John must be determined at some *common time* t_2 in S_2. Since we know that John travels at a velocity of 0.98 light-years per year relative to S_2, let us for convenience find John's location at $t_2 = 0$, at which time we already know that Jim is at the origin. From Table 2-1 we see that John is born at $x_2 = +50$ light-years at time $t_2 = -49$ years. Then, 49 years later John will have moved to the left a distance $vt = (0.98 \text{ l-yr/yr})(49 \text{ yr}) = 48$ light-years. Therefore, at time $t_2 = 0$ John will be at the location

$$50 \text{ l-yr} - 48 \text{ l-yr} = +2 \text{ l-yr from } S_2\text{'s origin}$$

At this time Jim is at S_2's origin (and is just being born). Observed from S_2, John and Jim are, therefore, 2.0 light-years apart at the time $t_2 = 0$. This is different from their separation, 10 light-years, observed in the reference frame S_1 in which they are at rest. These distances are, of course, in agreement with the phenomenon of space contraction, Equation 2-27. Notice that at the time $t_2 = t_1 = 0$ observers in S_2 find John 49 years old when Jim and Dick are just being born; see Figure 2-11b. On the other hand, observers in S_1 find John, Jim, and Dick all being born simultaneously.

2-7 Space-time events and the light cone

Consider the sequence of space-time events in Example 2-3 as observed in the two systems S_1 and S_2.

It is useful to show the six space-time events in Table 2-1 on a space-time graph. In Figure 2-12 the events as observed in S_1 and S_2 are indicated on graphs of time t as ordinate versus displacement x as abscissa; note that in the usual graph the displacement is the ordinate and the time the abscissa.

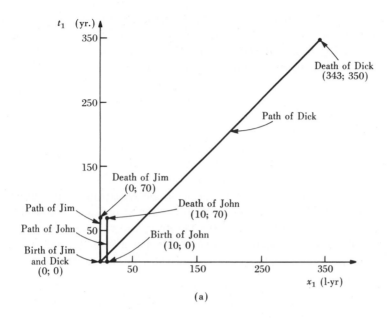

(a)

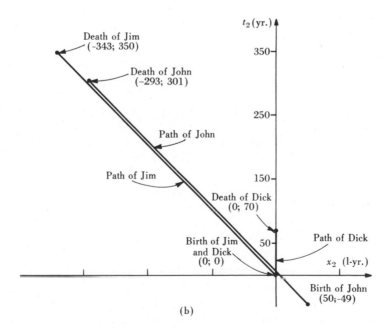

(b)

Figure 2-12. Space-time graph of events in Table 2-1 as observed (a) in system S_1 and (b) in system S_2.

On Figure 2-12a it is obvious that all events occurring along the same horizontal line are *simultaneous in system* S_1. Thus, all three births occur at the same time $t_1 = 0$, and the deaths of Jim and John are simultaneous events in S_1, occurring at the time $t_1 = 70$ years. Similarly, events along the same vertical line occur at the same location in space. For example, the births of Jim and Dick and the death of Jim all occur at the same point, $x_1 = 0$ light-years, and the birth and death of John occur at the same point, $x_1 = 10$ light-years.

The "path" representing the time sequence of events of a single object on a space-time diagram specifies the location x of the object as a function of time t. Inasmuch as the velocity of the object is defined as $\Delta x/\Delta t$, the slope, *measured with respect to the t axis*, of the space-time path gives the velocity of the object. Figure 2-12a shows that the paths of Jim and John are both vertical and the slopes zero; therefore, the velocities of both men are zero. On the other hand, the path of Dick is a straight line from the origin to the point ($x_1 = 343$ l-yr; $t_1 = 350$ yr). The slope, or velocity, is

$$v_1 \text{ (Dick)} = \frac{\Delta x_1}{\Delta t_1} = \frac{343 \text{ l-yr}}{350 \text{ yr}} = 0.98 \frac{\text{l-yr}}{\text{yr}}$$

Figure 2-12b is a space-time diagram of the *same* six events listed in Table 2-1, but now as observed in system S_2. From the point of view of observers in S_2 only two events are simultaneous, the births of Jim and Dick. The space-time path of Dick is now vertical, showing that Dick remains at rest in S_2. The space-time paths of both Jim and John have the same slope to the t_2 axis, corresponding to the velocity, -0.98 light-years per year.

All of the earlier conclusions concerning events can be read directly from these two figures.

Is there a limit to the magnitude of the slope of a space-time path? There is. Because of the second postulate of relativity we know that the speed of light is the *same* in all inertial systems and, moreover, that this speed is the *maximum* speed. Therefore, in any inertial system no space-time path can have a slope greater than c. If we choose units of length and time such that the magnitude of c equals 1, then the maximum slope is 1. Thus, the space-time path of a light pulse makes an angle of 45° with respect to the time axis. Figure 2-13 shows the space-time paths of two light pulses, one traveling along the $+X$ axis and the other along the $-X$ axis. At the time $t = 0$ both pulses are at the origin, at $x = 0$. The slope of each light pulse is, of course, $c = 1$ light-year per year. The slope of the space-time path of any particle can never exceed this. If we set the Y axis at right angles to the plane of the paper, the light paths now generate a light cone whose axis is the time axis; see Figure 2-14.

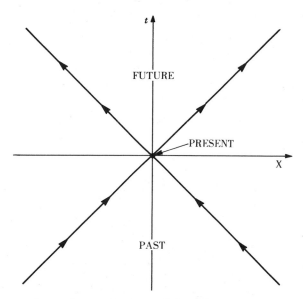

Figure 2-13. Space-time paths of two light pulses traveling on the X axis in opposite directions.

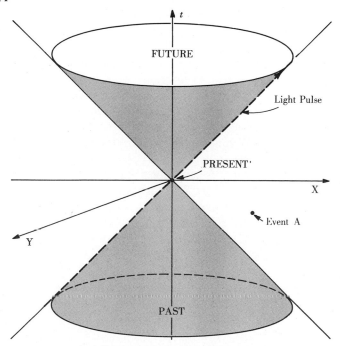

Figure 2-14. Light cone with time t along the axis of the cone. Axis Y is perpendicular to the plane of the paper, i.e., perpendicular to axes T and X.

Any event, say the event (0, 0), is limited in its ability to be influenced by something in the past ($t < 0$) or to influence events in the future ($t > 0$). In Figure 2-14 only events within the cone marked "past" can influence the present at the space-time origin; similarly, a present event can influence only events within the "future" cone. Events that fall outside the light cone of Figure 2-14, such as event A, cannot influence an event at the apex of the cone; for it to do so, the signal from A to the apex would have to travel faster than c. All events within the light cone can be causally related to an event at the apex; all events outside it cannot.

For an illustration of causally related events let us again look at the six events in Table 2-1. As our apex event we choose the simultaneous births of Jim and Dick, first as observed in S_1 and then as observed in S_2. From Figure 2-12a we can see that all the events except the birth of John could be causally related. There is no question that the birth of Jim influences his own death, and the same may be said of the birth and death of Dick. Since the death of John falls within the future part of the apex-event's cone, it, too, could be influenced by the event at the apex.

In Figure 2-12b, in which we observe events from the point of view of observer S_2, we again see that Jim's and Dick's births can be causally related to all the other events except John's birth. Even though John is born 49 years before Jim and Dick, he is 50 light-years away from them, and the fastest signal possible, that of light, would take 50 years to reach Jim's birthplace.

A question related to the discussion above is that of the sequence of events. If an observer S_1 sees an event A and then an event B, is it possible that in some other inertial system B precedes A? We shall see that it is indeed possible in some cases, but not in others. Does this mean that relativity theory does not preserve the causality of two related events with respect to all observers? We can use the Lorentz transformations to answer these questions.

Consider any two events in four-dimensional space-time. S_1 observes the two events shown in Figure 2-15a. We can always choose our space-time coordinates such that one of the events, say A, occurs at the origin (0, 0, 0; 0). The coordinates of event B we label ($x_1, y_1, z_1; t_1$).

The space-time coordinates of the two events A and B as measured by a second observer, S_2, are given by the Lorentz coordinate transformations, Equations 2-24. For simplicity we let

$$\frac{1}{\sqrt{1 - (v/c)^2}} \equiv \gamma$$

Then the coordinates observed by S_2 are as follows.

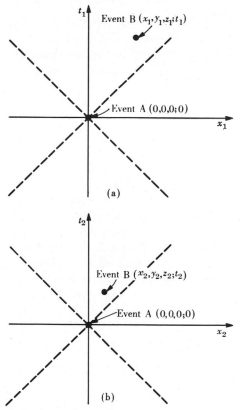

Figure 2-15. Two space-time events observed (a) from system S_1 and (b) from system S_2.

Event A:

$$x_2 = \gamma(x_1 - vt_1) = 0$$
$$y_2 = y_1 = 0$$
$$z_2 = z_1 = 0$$
$$t_2 = \gamma\left(t_1 - \frac{v}{c^2}x_1\right) = 0$$

Event B:

$$x_2 = \gamma(x_1 - vt_1)$$
$$y_2 = y_1$$
$$z_2 = z_1$$
$$t_2 = \gamma\left(t_1 - \frac{v}{c^2}x_1\right)$$

Figure 2-15b shows events A and B as observed in system S_2, which moves along the $+X_1$ axis at speed v. Event A is common to all inertial systems, having the coordinates $(0, 0, 0; 0)$. Therefore, space and time intervals between the two events A and B will be those of coordinates B alone. It is obvious that the spatial separations between the events are not the same, or invariant, in the two systems. Calling these L_1 and L_2, we have

$$L_1^2 = (x_1^2 + y_1^2 + z_1^2)$$
$$L_2^2 = (x_2^2 + y_2^2 + z_2^2) \neq L_1^2$$

Nor are the time intervals the same:

$$t_2 \neq t_1$$

Is there some interval, analogous to the separate space intervals and time intervals of Galilean physics, that is invariant under a Lorentz transformation? There is, in fact, such an interval, and we can easily find it by means of the Lorentz transformations. We recall that the Lorentz transformations were developed on the postulate that all observers measure the same constant speed c of a light signal. Therefore, if event A were to represent the start of a light pulse and event B the arrival of the pulse at the point (x, y, z) in space, then both observers S_1 and S_2 must obtain for light signals

$$x_1^2 + y_1^2 + z_1^2 = c^2 t_1^2$$
$$x_2^2 + y_2^2 + z_2^2 = c^2 t_2^2$$

or

$$x_1^2 + y_1^2 + z_1^2 - c^2 t_1^2 = 0$$
$$x_2^2 + y_2^2 + z_2^2 - c^2 t_2^2 = 0$$

All inertial observers measure the *same* value for the quantity $x^2 + y^2 + z^2 - c^2 t^2$ for the events connected by light signals: zero. Inasmuch as this quantity is a combination of the space interval and the time interval between two events, we might wonder whether it is an invariant quantity between any two events. Let us find out. For system S_2 the interval is $x_2^2 + y_2^2 + z_2^2 - c^2 t_2^2$. Using the Lorentz transformations, we can express all coordinates in terms of the coordinates in system S_1:

$$x_2^2 + y_2^2 + z_2^2 - c^2 t_2^2 = \gamma^2 (x_1 - v t_1)^2 + y_1^2 + z_1^2 - c^2 \gamma^2 [t_1 - (v/c^2) x_1]^2$$

Multiplying out the right-hand side, collecting terms, and recalling that $\gamma = 1/[1 - (v/c)^2]^{1/2}$, we obtain

$$\Delta S^2 = x_2^2 + y_2^2 + z_2^2 - c^2 t_2^2 = x_1^2 + y_1^2 + z_1^2 - c^2 t_1^2 \qquad \text{[2-30]}$$

Thus the quantity ΔS^2, called the *space-time interval*, is an invariant quantity, having the *same value in any inertial system*. As derived here, it is the space-time interval between any space-time event $(x_1, y_1, z_1; t_1)$ and the space-time event $(0, 0, 0; 0)$. There are three ranges of values for this interval, as follows.

$\Delta S^2 = 0$. In this case $x^2 + y^2 + z^2 = c^2t^2$, and the events are connected by light signals. All space-time points connected to the origin with $\Delta S^2 = 0$ generate the light cone. See Figure 2-16.

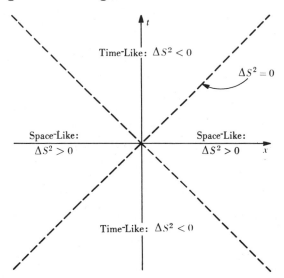

Figure 2-16. Regions of space-time for the space-time interval ΔS^2 greater than, equal to, and less than zero.

$\Delta S^2 > 0$. In this case $x^2 + y^2 + z^2 > c^2t^2$, and the region is said to be *space-like*. As mentioned earlier, events in this region are not causally related to the event $(0, 0, 0; 0)$, because signals would have to travel faster than c to make them so.

$\Delta S^2 < 0$. In this case $x^2 + y^2 + z^2 < c^2t^2$. This region is said to be *time-like*, and all events in it can be causally related to event $(0, 0, 0; 0)$.

What about causality? That is, if event B follows event A in one system, does it follow it in all other systems? Again let event A be $(0, 0, 0; 0)$ and B be $(x_1, y_1, z_1; t_1)$ as observed in S_1. Then in S_2 the time interval is given by

[2-24] $$t_2 = \gamma[t_1 - (v/c^2)x_1]$$ [2-31]

We can have t_1, x_1, and v with positive or negative values but, whatever their signs, we must also, by the invariance of the space-time interval, have

$$x_2^2 - c^2t_2^2 = x_1^2 - c^2t_1^2$$

If in S_1 event B follows event A, then $t_1 > 0$. Then by Equation 2-31 we shall have $t_2 > 0$ if $t_1 > (v/c^2)x_1$ or if, rewriting, $c^2t_1^2 > (v/c)^2x_1^2$.

Now, $v/c < 1$; therefore, for any time-like event ($\Delta S^2 < 0$) with $t_1 > 0$ we shall always have $t_2 > 0$; observers in all inertial systems always observe event B to follow event A. Similarly, in the time-like cone with $t_1 < 0$ we shall always have $t_2 < 0$; then event B precedes event A in all systems. Causality *is* preserved for events within the time-like region.

On the other hand, of events in the space-like region there is no unique ordering. For example, assume that in S_1 event B follows event A. Then $t_1 > 0$ and, by Equation 2-31, t_2 will be negative if $t_1 < (v/c^2)x_1$, or $ct_1 < (v/c)x_1$. This can, of course, occur in the space-like region; thus, whether or not there is a reversal of order depends on where the event is located in this region.

2-8 The Twin Paradox   Observers in different inertial systems observe the same event at different points in space and at different times. Correct descriptions of any series of events may be given in any one of the inertial systems; the different systems disagree only concerning the time and place of the events. For example, consider the inertial system S_1 in which the Earth and a relatively close star, 49 light-years from the Earth, are at rest. We wish to observe the aging of three people: two twins, Jim and Dick, born on the Earth, and John, born at the same time as Jim and Dick but on a planet near the star, 49 light-years from Earth. Note that all measurements are made, with respect to observers at rest in S_1, and all the immediately following statements apply to them.

Because of the finite speed of light signals the earliest age at which John can be aware of the twins' birth is 49 years, the time a light signal takes to travel from the Earth to the star. Similarly, the twins will be 49 years old before becoming aware of John's birth.

Let us now assume that, when all three men are 20 years old, Dick decides to take a rocket trip out to John's star. We assume that Dick very quickly accelerates to the speed $v = 0.98c$ with respect to S_1 and then continues at that constant speed toward the star; see Figure 2-17. Upon arrival he quickly decelerates and comes to rest. From relativity theory we know that all observers in S_1 will agree that Dick traveled at a speed of 0.98 light-years per year toward the star, covering the distance of 49 light-years in the time interval (49 l-yr)/(0.98 l-yr/yr) = 50 years. Thus, upon Dick's arrival at the star John will be 70 years old (20 + 50). At this

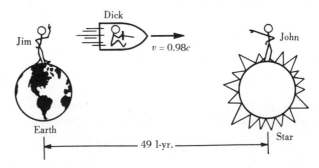

Figure 2-17. Dick's trip out to a star, observed from system S_1. See Table 2-2.

time Jim, of course, will be the same age, 70 years. On the other hand, both John and Jim will observe traveler Dick to be aging at only one fifth their rate, because he is moving at $0.98c$ relative to their reference frame S_1. Therefore, from their point of view Dick will have aged by only $50/5 = 10$ years in travel. Dick will then be $20 + 10 = 30$ years old when he meets John. Thus, from John's point of view traveler Dick will be 30 and John, his contemporary at birth, will be 70, when they meet. True, but strange.

The situation must be consistent from Dick's point of view. Let us see whether, upon meeting John, Dick also agrees that John will be 70 and he himself only 30. Until the age of 20 all three men agree that they are 20. Then Dick hops onto, say, inertial system S_2, which moves at $0.98c$ with respect to S_1. How do events look in system S_2? If at the time $t_1 = 0 = t_2$ Dick and Jim are at the same point in space, namely $x_1 = x_2 = 0$, then to find, from inertial system S_2, the location in space and time of the three men at this departure time and also at the time of the later meeting of John and Dick at the star we must use the Lorentz coordinate transformations, Equations 2-24. Table 2-2 lists the important space-time events as

Table 2-2

EVENT	SPACE COORDINATES AND AGE	
	As observed by S_1	As observed by S_2 $v/c = 0.98$
Separation of Jim and Dick:		
Location and age of Jim	(0 ; 20 yr)	(0 ; 100 yr)
Location and age of Dick	(0 ; 20 yr)	(0 ; 100 yr)
Location and age of John	(49 l-yr; 20 yr)	(9.8 l-yr; 340 yr)
Meeting of Dick and John:		
Location and age of Jim	(0 ; 70 yr)	(−9.8 l-yr; 110 yr)
Location and age of Dick	(49 l-yr; 30 yr)	(0 ; 110 yr)
Location and age of John	(49 l-yr; 70 yr)	(0 ; 350 yr)

seen by observers both in S_1 and in S_2, and Figure 2-18 diagrams them. Note that, for convenience, we have chosen the origin of the space-time diagrams (Figures 2-18) to be the event of the departure of Dick from Jim.

Notice in Figure 2-18a that, although from an observer S_1's point of view John was 20 years old and 49 light-years away from Jim and Dick at the time of Dick's departure, from Dick's point of view John's twentieth birthday was not simultaneous with Jim's departure from Dick but occurred 240 years earlier; see Figure 2-18b. Moreover, according to S_2, on John's twentieth birthday John was 245 light-years from the origin of system S_2. From system S_2's point of view (Figure 2-18b) John arrives at the origin 10 years after Jim's and the Earth's departure from Dick's rocket ship. Thus, Dick will be $100 + 10 = 110$ years old. According to system S_2 how old will John be when they meet? From John's birth until he meets Dick, S_2 observes John to have lived $340 + 10 = 350$ years; see Figure 2-18b. Inasmuch as John is moving with respect to S_2, he will age at only one fifth the rate observed in S_1; thus John's age when he meets Dick will be $350/5 = 70$ years, or the very same age we observed from John and Jim's viewpoint. Observers in both systems agree on the relative aging of the men in the two systems. Unfortunately, this simple one-way trip does not allow us to bring Jim and Dick back

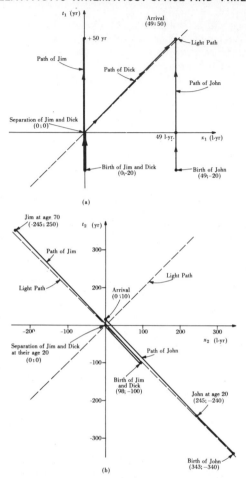

Figure 2-18. Space-time paths of Jim, John, and Dick as observed (a) from system S_1 and (b) from system S_2. See Table 2-2.

together again, so that each can directly observe the age of the other. An examination of that situation with a round trip introduces the famous "twin paradox."

We consider the two twins Jim and Dick born on Earth. At age 20 Dick hops onto a rocket ship traveling away from the Earth at a constant speed of $0.98c$. Upon reaching a star, which is 49 light-years from the Earth and at rest with respect to it, Dick stops, says a quick hello to John, and then hops back onto his rocket, which travels back to the Earth at $0.98c$. Arriving home, Dick quickly comes to rest and meets his twin Jim. The question: how old will each be when they meet? According to system S_2, Dick's age upon meeting John is 110 years. Since Dick is moving relative to system S_2 for the first 100 years, his age relative to inertial systems in which he is always at rest is $\left(\frac{100}{5}\right) + 10 = 30$ years.

First let us view the situation from Jim's reference frame. Jim is at rest in inertial frame S_1 and remains so throughout Dick's trip. From his viewpoint Dick travels a total distance of 98 light-years on the round trip; see Figure 2-19a. Since Dick's

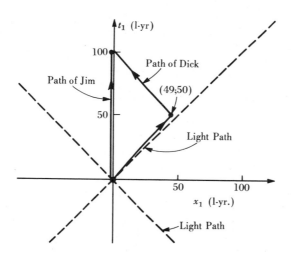

Figure 2-19. Space-time paths of Jim and John as observed from system S_1. See Table 2-2.

speed is $0.98c = 0.98$ light-years per year, the total time for the trip, according to Jim, is $(98\text{ l-yr})/(0.98\text{ l-yr/yr}) = 100$ years. When Dick returns, Jim will then be $20 + 100 = 120$ years old. On the other hand, during the trip Dick will not age as rapidly; because of time dilation he will, in traveling at $0.98c$, have aged only $100/5 = 20$ years during the entire trip. Therefore, when they meet, Dick will be only $20 + 20 = 40$ years old. From inertial system S_1 the two twins will not be the same age when they meet: the traveling twin will be the younger.

How do things look from Dick's viewpoint? We are tempted to argue that Dick's going out and back with respect to Jim and the Earth is completely equivalent to Jim and the Earth's going out and back, and the star's coming forward and receding, with respect to Dick. Then, because Jim and the Earth move out at speed $0.98c$ and come back at $0.98c$, we might argue that clocks on the Earth slow down and Jim ages at one fifth the rate of Dick. Finally, we might suppose that, when they are reunited, Dick would say that Jim is younger than he is. But this is just the opposite of what Jim, always at rest on the Earth, predicts. On their meeting Jim expects that Dick will be younger, and Dick expects that Jim will be younger. Clearly, both cannot be right, or else we have a paradox.

It is not difficult to locate the fallacy in the argument that led to the seeming paradox. It is, of course, true that we can use any one inertial system to describe behavior in the Universe: all inertial systems are equivalent in their description of physical laws, and one cannot distinguish one from the other. What about the reference system fixed to the Earth and the reference system fixed to the rocket? Does each actually qualify as a *single* inertial system in which one can make measurements, such as time and space intervals?

The system in which the Earth (and Jim) is at rest certainly qualifies as a single inertial system throughout the travel of Dick. We called this inertial system S_1. We therefore have confidence in Jim's prediction that, when his traveling twin Dick returns, the traveler will be the younger.

The system in which the rocket (and Dick) is at rest is, on the other hand, *not* a single inertial system throughout the travel period. During the first part of the trip, when Dick and the star are approaching one another, Dick and the rocket are at rest in an inertial system we call S_2, which moves at a constant velocity of $0.98c$ away from the Earth toward the star. Upon arrival at the star and immediately turning homeward Dick *changes inertial systems*, so that he comes back in still another, system S_3, which again moves at a constant velocity of $0.98c$ but *toward* the Earth. Note that the traveler Dick makes some space and time measurements in one inertial system, S_2, and some in a second, quite different, inertial system, S_3. Inasmuch as *special* relativity is restricted to inertial observers, that is, to observers who always remain in a single inertial system, it is not applicable to Dick's system. Since Dick's system is not a single inertial system throughout but, rather, an *accelerating reference frame*, one would have to use the theory of general relativity to analyze events in detail as seen from it. A detailed analysis applied to Dick's system would indeed show that Dick makes exactly the same prediction that Jim made from the inertial system S_1: that Dick (who did not remain in the same inertial system) would be younger than Jim (who remained in the same inertial system) when they were together again.

We can see that in still another way twins Dick and Jim are not equivalent. Suppose, for the sake of argument, that each spends his life inside a space ship. Jim's space ship remains on Earth all the while, and his experiences in it are pretty uneventful. On the other hand, Dick, whose rocket ship travels to a distant planet and back, has quite different experiences. Upon take-off, with the rocket's acceleration, Dick, together with other unattached objects within the rocket, is thrown against its wall as he changes inertial systems; he has a similar experience when the rocket arrives at the planet, slows down, and then speeds up in the opposite direction in still another inertial frame; finally, when he arrives back home at Earth, and his rocket again decelerates, he experiences a shock for the third time. Thus, when the twins are reunited and compare life histories, they find not only that their ages are quite different but also that Jim's existence has been quiet while Dick's has been punctuated by three shocks.

It is, of course, possible to describe the travels and aging of Dick and Jim, from the time that they part until they meet again, from the viewpoint of any single inertial system. For example, an observer always in inertial system S_2 would see the Earth and star always moving at velocities $0.98c$. Upon the parting of the twins he would observe the rocket ship and Dick to be at rest until the star arrived; then Dick and his ship would quickly accelerate and head toward the Earth at a speed somewhat *greater* than $0.98c$. When Dick caught up with Jim and the Earth, an observer in S_2 would find that Dick had aged less than Jim, just what an observer in S_1 would find. Of course, equivalent description would be made by an observer in the inertial system S_3.

2-9 Summary   Classical mechanics is invariant under the Galilean transformations and is in agreement with experiment for $v \ll c$.

The correct description of the physical universe is based on the principle of relativity: all the laws of physics, including that of the speed of light in vacuum, are invariant in all inertial systems under the Lorentz transformations.

The Lorentz coordinate transformations are:

$$x_2 = \frac{x_1 - vt_1}{\sqrt{1 - (v/c)^2}}$$

[2-24]

$$y_2 = y_1$$

$$z_2 = z_1$$

$$t_2 = \frac{t_1 - (v/c^2)x_1}{\sqrt{1 - (v/c)^2}}$$

No signal or particle can move at a speed exceeding the speed of light in vacuum.

Relativity physics is supported by the following experimental observations: the Michelson-Morley and related experiments concerning the invariance of the speed c, direct observation of time dilation in muon decay, and the observation that the speed of particles accelerated in high-energy particle accelerators never exceeds c. In the next chapter we shall find further support in the mass variation with speed and the equivalence of mass and energy.

The transition from relativity physics to classical physics can be written symbolically as:

$$\underset{v/c \to 0}{\text{Limit}}\ (\text{relativity physics}) = (\text{classical physics})$$

The transformation equations relating length and time intervals are the following:

	Relativistic form	Classical form
length:	$L = L_0 \sqrt{1 - (v/c)^2}$	$L = L_0$
time:	$T = T_0/ \sqrt{1 - (v/c)^2}$	$T = T_0$

BIBLIOGRAPHY

FILM   Friedman, F., F. D. Frisch, and J. Smith, *Time Dilation, An Experiment with Mu-mesons*. New York; Modern Learning Aids. By measuring the decay of cosmic-ray muons at two different elevations it is found that muons moving at $0.99c$ decay at only one ninth the rate of muons at rest. See *American Journal of Physics*, **31**, 342 (1963), for a report of this experiment.

Bohm, D., *Special Theory of Relativity*. New York: W. A. Benjamin, Inc., 1965. The first fifteen chapters contain a lengthy discussion of prerelativistic ideas of space and time and how experimental facts led to the Einsteinian relativistic views of these concepts. See Chapter XXVI for a graphical interpretation (Minkowski diagram) of relativity theory.

Feynman, R. P., R. B. Leighton, and M. Sands, *The Feynman Lectures on Physics.* Reading, Massachusetts: Addison-Wesley Publishing Co., Inc., 1963. On pages 15 and 16 a simple "light clock" is used to illustrate time dilation.

Ney, E. P., *Electromagnetism and Relativity.* New York: Harper and Row, Publishers, 1962. After a review of classical mechanics and relativity at the mathematical level of calculus in Chapter 1, Chapter 2 develops the theory of special relativity. Worked examples and problems help to illustrate the concepts.

Smith, J. H., *Introduction to Special Relativity.* New York: W. A. Benjamin, Inc., 1965. Special relativity is developed by means of only the mathematics of algebra. Chapter 6 is devoted to the "twin paradox" problem and its solution from slightly different viewpoints. The text has numerous examples and problems.

PROBLEMS

2-1　　Assume that in Figure 2-2 $M = 6m$ and $\dot{x}_2 = 2\dot{X}_2$. (a) What is the velocity of the center of mass of this system with respect to S_2? (b) What are the velocities of the two masses as measured by an observer in the center-of-mass system?

2-2　　From the center-of-mass coordinate system two objects of masses m and $2m$ are moving toward one another at velocities $+v$ and $-v/2$, respectively. They make a completely inelastic collision. (a) Calculate the total ordered kinetic energy before and after the collision and the increase in thermal energy resulting from the collision. (b) Do part (a) from the point of view of an observer moving at a velocity $+v$ with respect to the center of mass.

2-3　　Assume that the Earth is moving through the ether at 3.0×10^4 m/sec. A light pulse is sent *one* way from a source to a detector, which is a known distance from the source. The displacement vector from the source to the detector (both at rest with respect to the Earth) is parallel to the velocity of the Earth relative to the ether. According to the Galilean transformations, what are the transit times of the light pulse, as measured by an observer at rest with respect to the ether and by an observer at rest with respect to the Earth, when the distance between source and detector is (a) 3.8×10^2 m and (b) 3.8×10^8 m (distance to Moon)?

2-4　　Inertial system S_1 is at rest with respect to the medium through which sound pulses travel. The pulses are observed to travel at a constant speed of 1,100 ft/sec. A second inertial system, S_2, moves at a constant speed of 400 ft/sec along the $+X_1$ axis. With respect to this axis (a) in what direction would a sound pulse have to travel so that an observer in S_2 would also measure a speed of 1,100 ft/sec, and (b) in what direction would that observer find the pulse to be moving?

2-5　　*　A cylindrical tube 1.0 m in length has a light source at one end and a mirror at the other end. The tube, at rest in inertial system S_2, is perpendicular to the velocity $v = 10^{-4}c$ of S_2 relative to inertial system S_1; see Figure 2-5. An observer in system S_1 sees the source emit a light pulse in a direction parallel to the tube axis. Assuming that the ether is at rest with respect to S_1, how far will the pulse miss the light source upon its return to the lower end of the tube, according to an observer in S_2 (a) using the Galilean transformations, (b) using the Lorentz transformations.

2-6 * Assume that in the Michelson-Morley experiment (see Section 2-4) the length of the cylinders is 2.0 m and the wavelength of the light 5,000 Å. (a) If the speed of the Earth through the ether is 3.0×10^4 m/sec, what fraction of a wavelength shift will there be between the two beams when they recombine? (b) At what speed must the apparatus move through the ether to have the two beams recombine 180° out of phase with one another?

2-7   Solve algebraically for x_1, y_1, z_1, and t_1 in terms of x_2, y_2, z_2, and t_2 in Equations 2-24. This proves the statement that the inverse Lorentz transformations result from changing v to $-v$ and interchanging subscripts.

2-8   Protons leave a particle accelerator at a speed of $0.6c$ to enter and travel through an evacuated tube 1.0 m long, as measured by an observer at rest in the laboratory, and finally reach a detecting device. (a) How long does it take for a proton to travel from one end of the tube to the other according to an observer traveling with a proton? (c) What is the tube's length as measured by an observer traveling with a proton?

2-9   Train A travels east at $0.80c$ relative to a station; train B travels west at $0.98c$ relative to the same station. Find the following velocities (take east as positive); (a) train A relative to train B, (b) train B relative to train A, (c) the station relative to train A, and (d) the station relative to train B.

2-10 * Two space ships moving toward one another on a head-on collision course are separated by a distance of 4.0×10^{10} m, according to an observer on Earth. At this time, according to the observer, one of the space ships is coincident with the Earth. Relative to the Earth system both ships are traveling at the same speed, $0.98c$. (a) How much later do the two ships collide, according to the observer on Earth? (b) How much later do they collide according to an observer on the space ship coincident with the Earth at the initial separation?

2-11   A rigid rod is oriented at an angle of θ_1 with respect to the X_1 axis. What is the rod's orientation θ_2 as measured by an observer traveling at a speed v along the positive X_1 axis?

2-12 * A rod 1.25 m long is to pass through a window 1.00 m wide. More precisely, the rod of rest length 1.25 m, in motion as shown in Figure 2-20, passes

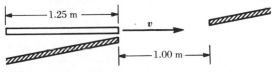

Figure 2-20. Rod passing through a window.

through an opening that is 1.00 m between edges when measured by an observer at rest with respect to the window. The rod's speed is such that the two ends of the rod coincide simultaneously with the two window edges, according to an observer in the reference frame in which the window is at rest. (a) What is the speed of the rod? (b) Now consider events from the point of view of an observer traveling with the rod. What is the width of the window opening relative to this observer? (c) From the point of view of an observer traveling with the rod do the two rod ends coincide simultaneously with the two window edges and, if not, which rod end, the leading or the trailing one, first coincides with a window edge? (d) What is the time interval between the two coincidences as measured by an observer traveling with the rod?

2-13 Train A travels east at $0.98c$ relative to a station; train B travels north at $0.98c$ relative to the same station. Find the velocity of train A relative to train B.

2-14 In the following an alternative derivation of the time-dilation relation is made. Suppose that a pulse of light completes a round trip along the axis of a cylinder, as shown in Figure 2-5. (a) What is the time interval T_0, measured by an observer at rest with respect to the cylinder, taken by the pulse in completing the round trip, in terms of the cylinder's length L and the speed of light c? (b) Suppose now that the cylinder is in motion at speed v, its axis at right angles to the direction of motion of an observer, who clocks the round-trip time of the light pulse. The observer realizes that the speed of the light pulse must be c. Derive a relation giving the round-trip time T in terms of L, v, and c. (c) Eliminate L in the two relations derived in parts (a) and (b) and find T in terms of T_0, v, and c.

2-15 Although the speed of propagation of electromagnetic waves is c for all reference frames, the frequency and wavelength of monochromatic waves differ from one reference frame to another; that is, there is a *relativistic Doppler effect*. A monochromatic wave traveling along the positive X_1 axis may be represented by the relation $y_1 = y_0 \sin 2\pi(\nu_1 t_1 - x_1/\lambda_1)$, where ν_1 and λ_1 are the frequency and wavelength measured by an observer S_1. The same wave, observed along the X_2 axis in reference frame S_2, must have the form $y_2 = y_0 \sin 2\pi(\nu_2 t_2 - x_2/\lambda_2)$. (a) Use the Lorentz coordinate transformations to find ν_2 and λ_2 in terms of ν_1, λ_1, and the relative speed v between the two reference frames. (b) Show that the relativistic Doppler effect reduces to the classical Doppler effect when $v \ll c$.

2-16 Distant galaxies have been found to be moving away from Earth with speeds as high as $0.81c$. (a) If the lifetime of a star, as measured by an observer at rest with respect to the star, is 50 billion years how long would the star live, according to an Earth observer, if it were moving at $0.81c$ relative to Earth? (b) An observer at rest with respect to this star observes light of wavelength 5,000 Å. What wavelength would this light have with respect to an Earth observer, and in what part of the electromagnetic spectrum would it fall?

2-17 (a) At what speed must a clock travel, relative to an Earth observer, to run slow by 1.0 sec in 1 yr (3.16×10^7 sec)? (b) By what factor does this speed exceed that of a satellite orbiting Earth close to its surface at 18,000 mi/hr?

2-18 A fast train moves at the speed $0.9c$ relative to Earth. Inside the train a fast runner moves at a speed $0.9c$ relative to the train. Assume that the directions of the two velocities are the same. What is the speed of the runner relative to Earth?

2-19 A professor gives an examination to two students. One student, S_1, remains at rest with respect to the professor; the other student, S_2, is moving at $0.98c$ with respect to the professor. After 50 min have elapsed on the professor's clock the exams are picked up. (a) From student S_1's point of view how much time does each have to do the exam? (b) From student S_2's viewpoint, how much time does each one have?

2-20 * A fast train traveling at a speed of $0.8c$ passes two posts fixed to the ground and adjoining the train tracks. The posts are separated by a distance of 125 m, measured by an observer on the ground. Observers on the ground find that the front and back ends of the train coincide simultaneously with the two posts as the train passes. (a) What is the length of the train according to an observer traveling in the train? (b) How long does it take, according to an observer on the ground, for the train to pass one post? (c) What is the time interval, measured by an observer standing at one point in the train, between the passing of the first and second posts? (d) What is the distance between the posts according to observers riding in the train? (e) The coincidence of the ends of the train with the two posts was simultaneous from the viewpoint of an observer fixed on the ground. Which end of the train, front or back, first coincided with a post, as according to an observer on the train?

2-21 (a) As seen by observer S_1, one explosion occurs at the location $x_1 = 0$ at the time $t_1 = 0$. A second explosion occurs at a near-by location a little later, at $x_1 = 1.0$ km and $t_1 = 1.0 \times 10^{-6}$ sec. What must be the velocity of a second observer S_2 relative to S_1 who observes both explosions to occur simultaneously? (b) A second set of explosions is seen by observer S_2 as follows: one explosion at $x_2 = 0$ and $t_2 = 0$ and a second at $x_2 = 1.0$ km and $t_2 = 1.0 \times 10^{-6}$ sec. Where and when are these events as observed by S_1?

2-22 A rod at rest in S_1 is aligned parallel to the X_1 axis and has a length L_0 when measured in S_1. (a) Derive the length of the rod as measured in system S_2, which moves at speed v along the $+X_1$ axis. (b) The ends of the moving rod, representing two events, must be simultaneous in S_2. What is the time difference between these same two events measured in S_1? (c) Suppose you had chosen as two events the ends of the rod, which were simultaneous in S_1, the system in which the rod is at rest. What would be the spatial difference and time difference between these two events as observed in S_2?

2-23 At the time $t_1 = 0$ a point light source at the origin of inertial system S_1 sends out a spherical wave of light. A second inertial system, S_2, moves along the $+X_1$ axis, as in Figure 2-1. Assume that the speed of S_2 relative to S_1 is $0.98c$. (a) After 1.0 sec has elapsed on S_1's clock locate the wave front and the position of the origin of S_2's reference frame. (b) After 1.0 sec has elapsed on S_2's clock locate the wave front and the origin of S_1's reference frame. (c) Repeat parts (a) and (b), using the Galilean transformations, taking the ether to be at rest in S_1.

2-24 * Two blinking lights (each blinking at 9.5×10^{-9} sec^{-1}), are at opposite ends of a 1.5 m rod. The rod and attached lights are placed along the X_1 axis and set in motion with velocity v along the $+X_1$ axis. (a) At what speed v must the rod be moving so that the two lights will be observed by S_1 to be blinking 180° out of phase with respect to one another? (b) With what frequency does either light blink, from S_1's viewpoint? (c) At what speed v must the rod be moving so that the two lights will be blinking

180° out of phase with respect to one another when viewed by a single observer at the origin? (d) What frequency does this single observer measure for each of the lights?

2-25 * Consider a square of sides of length L_0 and at rest in inertial system S_2. Two sides are coincident with the X_2 and Y_2 axes respectively. System S. moves at constant velocity $-v$ along the X_2 axis. (a) Locate the four corners of the object as observed in S_1 at the time $t_1 = 0$. (b) The events locating the four corners of the object in part (a) were simultaneous in system S_1. On the other hand, a single observer at the origin of S_1 would not see these events at the same time because of the travel time of light from the corners to the origin. At what times does a single observer at the origin see the four events of part (a)?

2-26 * A luminous cube has an edge length L_0 when at rest. A camera takes a photograph of the cube when the cube is traveling at a high speed v relative to it. It is far from the cube, which moves at right angles to the line joining cube and camera; see Figure 2-21a. We concentrate on the light that comes from cube edges A, B, and C and enters the camera during

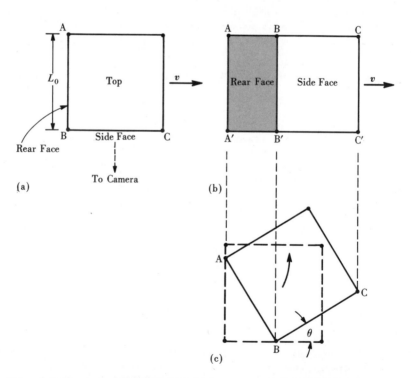

Figure 2-21. A moving cube being photographed at right angles to its direction of motion: (a) view from above, (b) the photograph of the side of the cube, (c) an interpretation of (b), in which the cube has been rotated.

the very short time the shutter is open for the photographic image. Light pulses that leave points A, B, and C simultaneously (in the reference frame of the camera) do *not* reach the camera simultaneously; light has a finite speed, and it travels farther from A than from B and C and, consequently, during the brief moment that the camera shutter is open light from the farther edge A enters the camera at the same time as light that has been emitted from edges B and C at a *later* time. The developed photograph appears as shown in Figure 2-21b; the rear face AB (rear with respect to the motion of the cube) is visible, while the side face BC is shortened by space contraction. Show that a person examining such a photograph might infer that the cube was not moving with high speed at right angles to the camera but, rather, was at rest after being rotated through an angle θ, as shown in Figure 2-21c, where $\sin \theta = v/c$. This illustrates a general effect; a high-speed object moving transverse to the observation point is seen to be *rotated*.

2-27 The linear density (number per unit length) of electrons in a certain wire conductor is λ_0 when no electric current exists in the wire and the electrons can be imagined to be at rest. When a current is established in the wire, the electrons drift along the wire at the drift speed v. Find the linear density λ of the drifting electrons in the wire in terms of λ_0, v, and c, as measured by an observer at rest with respect to the wire.

2-28 Monochromatic light passes through a single slit and produces a diffraction pattern on a distant screen, as shown in Figure 1-8a. The light source, slit, and screen are all at rest with respect to a first observer, who marks the locations of intensity zeros on the screen. Suppose that a second observer is in motion at a very high speed along the line in which the light travels from the source to the slit. (a) Will this observer find the intensity zeros to come at the marks made by the first observer? (b) Is the distance between the slit and observation screen changed? Now a third observer travels at a very high speed along the sheet containing the slit. (c) Does this observer find the intensity zeros at the locations marked by the first observer? (d) Is the slit width changed for the third observer?

2-29 A pion is an unstable elementary particle with an average lifetime of 3.7×10^{-8} sec (from the moment of its creation until it decays) as measured by an observer at rest with respect to it. (a) If an average pion travels a distance of 3.0 m during one lifetime, according to an observer in the laboratory, what is the pion's speed? (b) How long did this pion live, according to an observer in the laboratory? (c) How far did the pion travel between birth and death, according to an observer traveling with the pion?

2-30 Two observers A and B are both stationed at rest on Earth and separated by 2.94×10^3 m, as measured by meter sticks at rest on Earth. The clocks of A and B have earlier been synchronized and found to run at the same rate. A rocket passes along the line connecting A and B at a high speed. When the rocket passes observer A his clock reads zero (0.00×10^{-5} sec); when the rocket later passes observer B, B's clock reads 1.00×10^{-5} sec. (a) What is the speed of the rocket relative to the Earth as it passes from A to B? (b) What is the time interval, measured on a clock carried by an observer riding with the rocket, between the instants that A and B pass the rocket? (c) What is the distance between the locations of A and B as measured by meter sticks carried by an observer traveling with the rocket?

2-31 * There are some physical quantities which, within an isolated region of space, are conserved; that is, when viewed from some inertial system, the amount of the physical quantity within that region always remains the same. A familiar example of a conserved quantity is electric charge. Consider an isolated volume in which two equal, but opposite, charges are separated by a distance d and are at rest. Now, in this inertial system there is no violation of the conservation of total charge if the two charges disappear, are annihilated, *simultaneously*. At any instant of time the total charge within the volume is always the same: namely, zero. Show that, if total charge is to be conserved *in all inertial systems*, the two charges must be together ($d = 0$) at the time of annihilation. This is an example of a general principle concerning any conserved quantity; if a quantity is to be conserved in all inertial systems, then it must be locally conserved (conserved within any arbitrarily small volume).

2-32 * In the paradox of the twins (Section 2-8) Dick travels outward from twin Jim, visits John, then returns to Jim. (a) Sketch the space-time paths of Jim, Dick, and John from the viewpoint of the inertial system in which Dick is at rest on the outward leg of the trip. (b) According to an observer in this inertial system, when and where will Dick meet John, and when and where will Dick meet Jim on his return?

2-33 Triplets A, B, and C are born "simultaneously"' on Earth. A stays at home, while B travels immediately after birth to a near-by star 100 l-yr away at the speed of 0.8c, and C travels to another star 100 l-yr away at the speed of 0.6c. Upon reaching their respective destinations B and C reverse directions and return to Earth at the same respective speeds. (a) What is A's age when B returns? (b) What is B's age when he meets A? (c) What is A's age when C returns? (d) What is C's age when he meets A?

T H R E E

RELATIVISTIC DYNAMICS: MOMENTUM AND ENERGY

Relativistic kinematics, which deals with space intervals, time intervals, and velocities, all as summarized in the Lorentz transformations, has its basis in the fact that all measurements of the speed of light give the same constant c. Now, the special theory of relativity requires not only that fact but also that the laws of physics be invariant for all inertial observers. In this chapter, then, we shall consider relativistic dynamics, which deals with the mechanics of particles moving at speeds up to c and the appropriate relativistic forms for momentum and energy, and we shall require that the basic laws of momentum and energy conservation be invariant under the Lorentz transformations.

We shall first arrive at the relativistic relation for a particle's momentum and find that a particle's relativistic mass may be imagined to increase with speed. The relativistic relation for kinetic energy will show that we can attribute a change in a particle's kinetic energy to a change in its mass. Indeed, the general law of energy conservation becomes, through the equivalence of energy and mass, the law of mass-energy conservation. We shall examine the analogy between the invariant space-time four-vector and the momentum-energy four-vector and derive the transformation relations for energy and momentum components. Finally, we shall consider one important application of special relativity to electromagnetism (apart from the constancy of the propagation speed c of electromagnetic radiation); we shall find through a qualitative argument that the so-called magnetic force, ordinarily taken as a distinctive type of electromagnetic interaction between charged particles in motion, originates from the strictly electric, or Coulomb, force together with the requirements of relativity.

3-1   Relativistic mass and momentum   By analogy with the classical relation for momentum we take a particle's relativistic momentum p to be given by the relation

$$p = mv \qquad [3\text{-}1]$$

where m is the so-called relativistic mass. By definition, then, a particle's relativistic mass m is that physical quantity by which the velocity v must be multiplied to yield the vector quantity p such that the total momentum Σp of an isolated system is conserved. We know that the *classical*, or Newtonian, law of momentum conservation is invariant under a *Galilean* transformation, in which the momentum of a particle is taken to be its velocity multiplied by an *invariant* mass. Clearly, the classical relation for momentum *cannot* be invariant under a Lorentz transformation. Therefore, we must be prepared to find, in imposing the requirements of relativistic kinematics, as expressed in the Lorentz transformations, on the laws of dynamics for particles at high speed, that the relativistic mass is not an invariant quantity but, rather, depends in some fashion on the particle's speed.

In re-examining the law of momentum conservation for particles traveling at relativistic speeds we insist that the two basic postulates of the special theory of relativity be satisfied: the postulates that the physical laws be invariant for all inertial frames and that the speed of light be measured as the same constant by all observers or, equivalently, that the description of events in space and time be in accord with the Lorentz transformations. We know, of course, that whatever differences may emerge between the relativistic and classical forms of momentum, the relativistic momentum mv *must*, through the correspondence principle, reduce for low speeds to the familiar form $m_0 v$, where m_0 represents the particle mass at zero speed or, at least, a speed v much less than c, the speed of light.

Our strategy is as follows. We first consider an elastic collision between two identical objects which is so completely symmetrical that we may be assured that the law of momentum conservation is valid. We then examine the same collision from the point of view of another inertial observer and require the law of momentum conservation to be invariant.

Suppose that we have two particles A and B with the same mass m_0 when compared at rest. The particles are fired at one another in opposite directions at very high but equal speed so as to collide elastically, as shown in Figure 3-1a. The particles' velocities are equal in magnitude but opposite in direction both before and after the collision. Because of the symmetry of the collision we can be sure that the collision is observed in the center-of-mass reference frame, the inertial frame in which the system's total momentum is zero at all times. The collision appears even more symmetrical if we rotate the coordinate axes, as shown in Figure 3-1b, so that the velocities of both particles make the *same* angles with respect to the X_{cm} and Y_{cm} axes. Take the velocity component along X_{cm} of either particle to have the magnitude v_x. Then we can imagine particle A as having been thrown and then caught by an observer, whom we shall also call A, who travels to the right at the speed v_x and at a distance $\frac{1}{2}y$ below the X_{cm} axis. Similarly, we can imagine particle B to have been thrown and then caught by an observer B, who travels to the left at the speed v_x and at a distance $\frac{1}{2}y$ above the X_{cm} axis.

A third observer, one fixed with respect to the X_{cm}-Y_{cm} inertial frame and therefore different from observers A or B, can then assert, simply on the basis of symmetry, that both particles A and B were thrown *simultaneously*, collided at the origin, and then were caught *simultaneously* by the respective observers. In other words, the *time interval T_{cm}, as observed in the center-of-mass reference frame,* between the throwing and the catching of particle A is the *same* as that between the throwing and the catching of particle B.

Moreover, an observer in this center-of-mass reference frame can be certain that momentum is conserved in the collision; indeed, the total vector momentum of the system along any one direction must be zero. This implies that the change Δp_{yA} in the momentum component along the Y_{cm} direction for particle A before and after collision must equal in magnitude the change Δp_{yB} in the momentum component along Y_{cm} for particle B. Thus, the law of momentum conservation requires that

$$\Delta p_{yA} = \Delta p_{yB} \qquad\qquad [3\text{-}2]$$

Particle A travels a distance $\frac{1}{2}y$ along Y_{cm} before, and another $\frac{1}{2}y$ after, collision; all told, it travels a distance y in the time interval T_{cm}, so that the Y component of A's velocity is y/T_{cm}. The momentum change along Y_{cm} is twice the magnitude of the momentum component along Y_{cm} before or after collision. Therefore,

$$\Delta p_{yA} = 2m_A y/T_{cm}$$

where m_A is the relativistic mass of particle A. We also have

$$\Delta p_{yB} = 2m_B y/T_{cm}$$

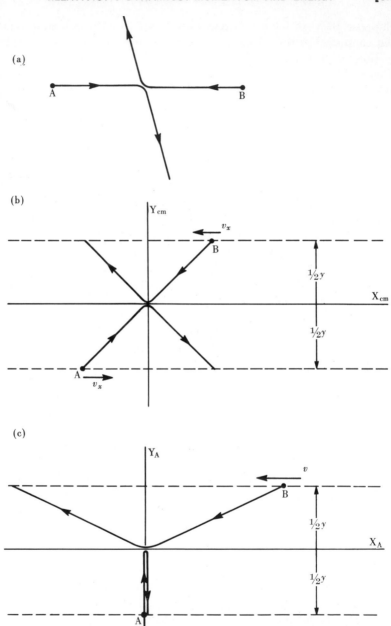

Figure 3-1. Identical particles A and B colliding elastically at equal speeds: (a) viewed by an observer in the center-of-mass reference frame; (b) same as (a), but with X_{cm} and Y_{cm} axes so oriented as to make the collision completely symmetrical for the observer in the center-of-mass reference frame (c) viewed by an observer moving along the X axis with A.

where m_B is the relativistic mass of particle B. Equation 3-2 then becomes, for an observer in the center-of-mass inertial frame,

$$m_A y / T_{cm} = m_B y / T_{cm}$$

Because of the symmetry of the collision we know that the two particles have the same relativistic mass: $m_A = m_B$.

If relativistic momentum conservation is to hold for *all* inertial frames, then Equation 3-2 must also be satisfied for any other inertial frame moving at constant velocity relative to that of the system's center of mass. For convenience we now examine the collision from the inertial frame in which observer A is at rest; see Figure 3-1c. The differences are as follows. Observer A now sees his particle A traveling back and forth along the Y_A axis and particle B traveling obliquely before and after the collision. We denote the velocity of observer B relative to observer A by v. Observer A, stationed at a point $\frac{1}{2}y$ below the X_A axis, sees observer B traveling to the left at speed v and at a distance $\frac{1}{2}y$ above the X_A axis. Note that the transverse distance y between the two observers A and B is the same in the new X_A-Y_A reference frame as in the earlier X_{cm}-Y_{cm} reference frame, since there is *no space contraction* at right angles to the direction of relative motion.

As measured by observer A, however, the time intervals between the tossings and the catchings of the two particles are *not* the same: particle A is thrown and caught at the *same* location in reference frame X_A-Y_A, but particle B is thrown from a location on the right and later caught at another location on the left. Recall this general relativistic feature of time intervals: if two events occur at the same location in one observer's reference frame, then the time interval between them is the proper interval T_0, but if they are observed from a reference frame traveling at a speed v, then the time interval between them is longer (dilated) and is given by

[2-29] $$T = T_0 / \sqrt{1 - (v/c)^2}$$ [3-3]

Thus, if we take the time interval between the tossing and the catching of particle A as observed by A to be T_0, then the time interval between the tossing and the catching of particle B *as observed by* A is T.

Seen by observer A, the sequence of events is as follows. First B throws particle B, then A throws particle A, then the particles collide, then A catches particle A, and finally B catches particle B. We have an example here of the general rule that events that are simultaneous in one reference frame (the tossing and catching of particles A and B in the X_{cm}-Y_{cm} reference frame) are not simultaneous in a second reference frame in motion with respect to the first.

In the X_A-Y_A reference frame shown in Figure 3-1c the changes in momentum along Y_A are, then,

$$\Delta p_{yA} = 2m_A y/T_0$$

$$\Delta p_{yB} = 2m_B y/T$$

Substituting these relations in Equation 3-2, to guarantee the invariance of momentum conservation, then yields

$$m_A y/T_0 = m_B y/T$$

and using Equation 3-3 gives

$$m_A = m_B \sqrt{1 - (v/c)^2} \qquad [3\text{-}4]$$

where m_A and m_B are the respective masses of the particles observed in the X_A-Y_A reference frame, and v is the speed of observer B relative to observer A. The time dilation and the relativity of simultaneity are derived from the Lorentz transformations. Therefore, Equation 3-4 must hold, if momentum conservation is to be invariant under the Lorentz transformations. Clearly, this equation cannot be satisfied unless m_A and m_B are different. If we recall that the two masses were taken to be equal when measured at rest with respect to an observer, it is apparent, as we anticipated, that the relativistic mass of a particle must depend in some way on its speed.

In the collision shown in Figure 3-1c *both* particles are in motion. To find out how the mass of a particle depends upon its motion with respect to an observer we now consider the special collision occurring when particle A is at rest in the X_A-Y_A reference frame. That is, we suppose that the Y components of the speeds of both particles A and B approach zero. Particle A is then at rest with respect to the reference frame X_A-Y_A, and we label its mass m_0, the *rest mass*. An observer at rest in X_A-Y_A now sees particle B approach and then recede along a single straight line, just making a grazing collision with particle A; see Figure 3-2. The speed of particle B is then just the speed v of observer B (with respect to which it is now at rest).

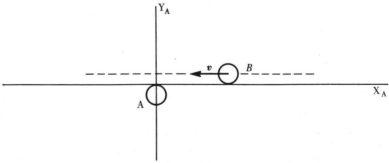

Figure 3-2. Collision of moving particle B, with particle A at rest, as viewed by observer A; derived from Figure 3-1c in the limit of zero transverse velocity component.

When at rest, particle B's mass was also m_0, but now, when it is in motion at speed v relative to an observer in X_A-Y_A, its mass is different, and we label its mass m. For the grazing collision with $m_A = m_0$ and $m_B = m$ Equation 3-4 becomes

$$m_0 = m\sqrt{1 - (v/c)^2}$$

$$m = \frac{m_0}{\sqrt{1 - (v/c)^2}} \qquad\qquad [3\text{-}5]$$

By the same token observer B sees his own particle B at rest with mass m_0 and particle A in motion at speed v with mass m. Any observer then finds that, if a particle has a rest mass m_0 when measured at rest with respect to him, then its mass when it moves at speed v is $m_0[1 - (v/c)^2]^{1/2}$. Figure 3-3

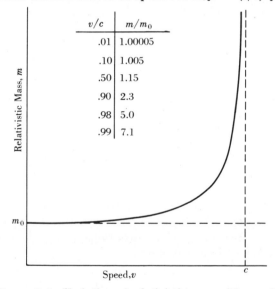

v/c	m/m_0
.01	1.00005
.10	1.005
.50	1.15
.90	2.3
.98	5.0
.99	7.1

Figure 3-3. Variation of relativistic mass with speed.

shows a particle's relativistic mass as a function of the particle's speed, as given by Equation 3-5. Clearly, m deviates markedly from m_0 only when the speed is comparable to the speed of light; for example, with $v/c = 1/10$ it exceeds m_0 by only 0.5 percent.

When it is said that a particle's mass depends on its speed, what is implied basically is that the relativistic momentum p of a particle with velocity v is given by the relation

$$\boldsymbol{p} = m\boldsymbol{v} = \frac{m_0\boldsymbol{v}}{\sqrt{1 - (v/c)^2}} \qquad\qquad [3\text{-}6]$$

where m_0 is a constant, independent of speed. Experiments with particles traveling at speeds approaching that of light demonstrate conclusively that Equation 3-6 correctly gives a particle's momentum at all speeds up to c. Of course, for low-speed particles, with $v/c \ll 1$, the relativistic momentum reduces to the classical form, $p = m_0 v$. Whereas in prerelativity physics space intervals, time intervals, and mass were regarded as absolute and the speed of light was regarded as relative to some unique inertial frame, the relativity physics of Einstein requires that, because the speed of light is absolute for all inertial systems, space intervals, time intervals, and mass (defined as the momentum-velocity ratio) be relative and depend on the relative motion between the object and the observer.

In relativistic dynamics we take the force F on an object to be the time rate of change of its relativistic momentum. Therefore, Newton's second law is written in the form

$$F = \frac{dp}{dt} = \frac{d}{dt} mv \qquad [3\text{-}7]$$

which may also be written

$$F = m \frac{dv}{dt} + v \frac{dm}{dt} \qquad [3\text{-}8]$$

In classical mechanics, when the mass of an object is constant, $dm/dt = 0$; then the two forms of Newton's second law, $F = (d/dt)mv$ and $F = m\, dv/dt = ma$, are equivalent. In relativistic dynamics, however, the two forms usually are not equivalent; this is so because the mass m varies with the particle's speed and, therefore, with time, if the *speed* changes with time. The general form, $F = dp/dt$, is always correct. It allows one to deal, even in classical mechanics, with situations in which a system's mass changes, for example, with that of a rocket.†

One very important situation, in which a particle's speed is constant while its velocity changes, is that of a particle traveling in a circular arc, under the influence of a force, toward the center of the arc. Because the force is radial and at right angles to the particle's motion, the particle travels at constant speed but with an ever-changing direction.

Consider a particle of relativistic mass m and electric charge Q moving with velocity v at right angles to a uniform magnetic field B. The magnetic force, which is perpendicular to the velocity and therefore causes the particle to move in a circle, has the magnitude

$$F = QvB$$

† For an exposition with examples of nonconstant mass and Newton's second law see Weidner and Sells, *E.C.P.* Sec. 9-7.

Because the particle moves with a constant speed, its relativistic mass is constant, and hence $dm/dt = 0$. Equation 3-8 then becomes $F = m\,dv/dt = ma$, where a is the centripetal acceleration with a magnitude v^2/r, r being the radius of the circular path; see Figure 3-4. Using this relation for the magnetic force, we have

$$QvB = mv^2/r$$

$$\boxed{p = mv = QBr}$$ [3-9]

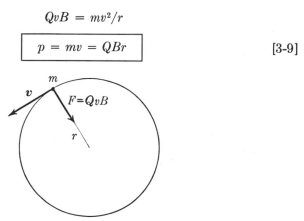

Figure 3-4. Motion of a charged particle in a transverse magnetic field.

It must be remembered that, although this equation is of exactly the same form as that obtained by the methods of classical mechanics, the mass m appearing in it is the relativistic mass, not the rest mass.

Equation 3-9 is the basis of a simple method of determining the relativistic momentum of a charged particle. In this method Q is known, B and r are measured, and p is computed from the equation. Inasmuch as v can be measured by using crossed electric and magnetic fields (Section 8-4), the relativistic mass m can be computed from Equation 3-9. This was essentially the method used by A. H. Bucherer (1909) and others to verify the variation of relativistic mass with speed, predicted by relativity theory.

Example 3-1. A particle of rest mass m_0 initially moves at speed $0.40c$. (a) If the particle's speed is doubled, how will its new momentum compare with its initial momentum? (b) If the particle's momentum is increased until its final momentum is ten times its initial momentum, how will its final speed compare with its initial speed?

(a) The initial momentum is given by Equation 3-6:

$$p_1 = \frac{m_0 v_i}{\sqrt{1 - (v_i/c)^2}} = \frac{0.40 m_0 c}{\sqrt{1 - (0.40)^2}} = 0.44 m_0 c$$

When the speed is doubled, the particle moves at speed $v = 2(0.40c) = 0.80c$, and the momentum becomes

$$p = \frac{m_0(2v)}{\sqrt{1 - (0.80)^2}} = 1.33 m_0 c$$

The ratio of the final momentum to the initial momentum is 3.0, whereas the ratio of the final speed to the initial speed is 2.0.

(b) The initial momentum of the particle is $p_i = 0.44m_0c$. The particle's momentum now becomes ten times as great, and the speed of the particle is again given by Equation 3-6:

$$p = 10(0.44m_0c) = \frac{m_0v}{\sqrt{1 - (v/c)^2}}$$

Rearranging and squaring, we have

$$(4.4)^2c^2 - (4.4)^2v^2 = v^2$$

$$v = 0.975c$$

The ratio of the speeds is $v/v_i = 2.4$, whereas the ratio of the momenta is $p/p_i = 10$.

3-2 Relativistic energy We now have expressions for relativistic mass (Equation 3-5) and relativistic momentum (Equation 3-6) and the correct form of Newton's second law of motion (Equation 3-7). We next ask, "What is the relativistic kinetic energy E_k?" To find this we define it, as in classical physics, as the total work done in bringing a particle from rest to the final speed v under a constant force F:

$$E_k = \int_0^s F \, ds = \int_0^s (d/dt)(mv) \, ds = \int_0^t (d/dt)(mv)v \, dt$$

$$= \int v \, d(mv) = \int (v^2 \, dm + mv \, dv)$$

To integrate we must remember that both m and v are variables, the dependence of one on the other being given by Equation 3-5. We shall find it simpler to express v in terms of m and then integrate with respect to the variable m. The expressions for v and dv can be obtained by rewriting Equation 3-5 in the form

$$1 - (v^2/c^2) = m_0^2/m^2$$

Differentiating, we have

$$-2v \, dv/c^2 = -2m_0^2 \, dm/m^3$$

Combining the two equations, we have

$$mv \, dv = (c^2 - v^2) \, dm$$

Substituting for $mv \, dv$ in the equation for the kinetic energy E_k, we then have

$$E_k = \int_{m_0}^m [v^2 \, dm + (c^2 - v^2) \, dm] = c^2 \int_{m_0}^m dm = mc^2 - m_0c^2$$

$$\boxed{E_k = (m - m_0)c^2} \qquad \text{[3-10]}$$

Thus, the relativistic kinetic energy is the increase in mass, arising from the particle's motion, multiplied by c^2. We see that the relativistic kinetic energy is markedly different from the classical kinetic energy. Furthermore, in relativity physics to say that a particle has kinetic energy is to say that its mass exceeds its rest mass. Of course, by the correspondence principle the relativistic kinetic energy must reduce to the familiar classical kinetic energy, $\frac{1}{2}m_0v^2$ for $v/c \ll 1$. To show that it does we expand Equation 3-10 by the binomial theorem:

$$E_k = m_0c^2\{[1 - (v/c)^2]^{-1/2} - 1\}$$
$$= m_0c^2[1 + \tfrac{1}{2}(v/c)^2 + \tfrac{3}{8}(v/c)^4 + \ldots - 1]$$
$$E_k = \tfrac{1}{2}m_0v^2 + \tfrac{3}{8}m_0v^4/c^2 + \ldots$$
$$\lim_{c \to \infty} E_k = \lim_{c \to \infty} (m - m_0)c^2 = \tfrac{1}{2}m_0v^2$$

It is important to recognize that the relativistic kinetic energy is *not* given by $\frac{1}{2}mv^2$, where m is the relativistic mass.

We have seen that an increase in the kinetic energy of a particle corresponds to an increase in its mass. This is true of energy in general: a change in the total energy of a system of particles corresponds to a change in the mass of the system. Equation 3-10 may be written more generally as

$$E_k = E - E_0 = mc^2 - m_0c^2 \qquad [3\text{-}11]$$

where E represents the particle's *total energy* and is given by

$$\boxed{E = mc^2} \qquad [3\text{-}12]$$

and where E_0 represents the particle's *rest energy* and is given by

$$E_0 = m_0c^2 \qquad [3\text{-}13]$$

In a system of particles the rest energy E_0 and rest mass m_0 are the system's total energy and total mass when its center of mass is at rest.

Equation 3-12 is the famous Einstein relation, which shows the equivalence of energy and mass, each being a different manifestation of the same physical entity. A particle at rest with respect to an observer has a rest mass m_0 and a rest energy m_0c^2. Because mass and energy are equivalent and interchangeable, we no longer have the separate laws of energy and mass conservation; rather, relativity physics combines these in a single, simple law, the conservation of mass-energy. This law holds in any inertial system, as does the conservation of relativistic momentum.

In physics the momentum is, in general, a more useful concept than the velocity (for example, we have the conservation of momentum but not the conservation of velocity). Therefore, it is often convenient to express the energy E in terms of p rather than v. We can eliminate v in the following manner. Squaring Equation 3-5 and multiplying both sides by $c^4[1 - (v/c)^2]$ gives

$$m^2c^4 - m^2v^2c^2 = m_0^2c^4$$

Substituting Equations 3-6, 3-12, and 3-13 for mv, mc^2, and m_0c^2 in this equation immediately gives the desired relation between E and p:

$$E^2 = (pc)^2 + E_0^2 \qquad \text{[3-14]}$$

Let us examine the relativistic equations under two limiting conditions, very low speeds and very high speeds.

$v \ll c$. This is the classical region, in which Newtonian mechanics is adequate, and the relativistic quantities reduce to their familiar classical forms, namely

$$m \approx m_0$$
$$p \approx m_0v$$
$$E_k \approx \tfrac{1}{2}m_0v^2$$

In this region the kinetic energy is much less than the rest energy; that is,

$$E_k \ll E_0$$

because

$$\frac{E_k}{E_0} = \frac{\tfrac{1}{2}m_0v^2}{m_0c^2} = \tfrac{1}{2}\left(\frac{v}{c}\right)^2 \ll 1$$

$v \approx c$. This represents the extreme relativistic region. Therefore, Equations 3-5, 3-11, and 3-14 become

$$m \gg m_0$$
$$E \gg E_0$$
$$p \approx E/c$$
$$E_k \approx E$$

If a particle has energy and momentum but has zero *rest* mass—a possibility that makes no sense from a classical viewpoint but is admissible in relativity theory—then the equations above are *exactly true*, and a zero-rest-mass particle must necessarily travel with the speed of light, c. That is, for a zero-rest-mass particle:

$$m_0 = 0, \qquad E = pc, \qquad E_k = E, \qquad v = c \qquad \text{[3-15]}$$

Conversely, if a particle with a nonzero energy travels with the speed of light, it *must* have a zero rest mass, since from Equations 3-5 and 3-13,

$$m = \frac{E}{c^2} = \frac{m_0}{\sqrt{1 - (v/c)^2}} \qquad \text{[3-16]}$$

If $v = c$, the denominator equals zero, and for a nonzero rest mass the energy of the particle would be infinite—an impossibility. However, if the rest mass is zero, the right-hand side of Equation 3-16 becomes 0/0, an indeterminate. The relativistic mass m may be found from Einstein's equation $m = E/c^2$, and it is finite even though m_0 is zero. The variations of energy (and, therefore, of mass, because $E = mc^2$) with speed for a proton, an electron, and a particle of zero rest mass are shown in Figure 3-5.

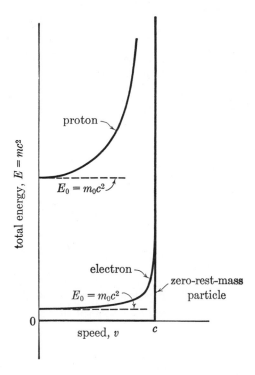

Figure 3-5. Total relativistic energy versus speed of three particles having different rest masses. (The rest energies are *not* to scale relative to one another.)

For the zero-rest-mass particle the relativistic energy E has a nonzero value only if the particle moves at the single speed c, but at this speed its energy (and mass) can have any value from zero to infinity. A zero-rest-mass particle has zero rest energy; therefore, its total energy is purely kinetic, as shown in Equation 3-15.

It is useful to examine the dependence of energy on momentum. The relativistic total energy E is shown as a function of the relativistic momentum p in Figure 3-6, following the equation

[3-14]
$$E^2 = (pc)^2 + E_0^2$$

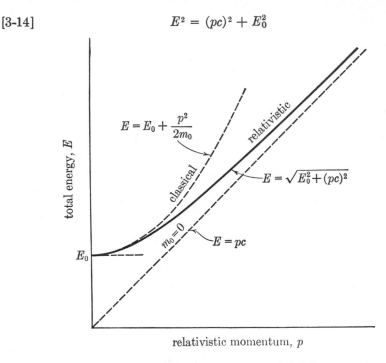

Figure 3-6. Total relativistic energy versus relativistic momentum of a particle.

For low speeds, or $v \ll c$, the relations $m \approx m_0$ and $p \approx p_0 = m_0 v$ hold. Therefore, in this, the classical region, the total energy is given by

$$E \approx p_0^2/2m + E_0 = \tfrac{1}{2}m_0 v^2 + E_0$$

On the other hand, for very high speeds the relation $E \approx pc$ holds, as shown in Equation 3-15. In the classical region the kinetic energy $E - E_0$ varies as the *square* of the momentum, whereas in the extreme relativistic region the kinetic energy $\approx E$ varies *linearly* as the momentum. It follows from Equation 3-14 that the slope dE/dp of Figure 3-6 is equal to the speed v of the particle.

3-3 Equivalence of mass and energy, and bound systems To illustrate the significance of the equivalence of mass and energy and the conservation of mass-energy we shall consider two situations: *unbound systems* and *bound systems*.

UNBOUND SYSTEMS   Consider a collision between two particles, each having a rest mass m_0. They are projected toward one another, each with speed v relative to an observer at rest in the center-of-mass reference frame. We assume the collision to be perfectly inelastic; thus, the two particles stick together to form a single particle, whose rest mass is designated M_0. We ask, "How is the final rest mass M_0 related to the rest mass m_0 of each of the incident particles?" From a classical-physics standpoint we should expect M_0 to equal $2m_0$, but we shall find that relativistically this is not so.

By the conservation of linear momentum we know that the total momentum must be zero. This follows from the fact that the total momentum is initially zero, the particles before the collision having equal but opposite momenta. Therefore, after the collision the amalgamated particles must be at rest.

The total energy of the two particles before the collision is $2mc^2$, where mc^2 is the rest energy plus the kinetic energy of each particle. In accordance with energy conservation the total energy of the two particles before the collision must equal the total energy M_0c^2 of the composite after the collision. Note that the total energy of the composite is entirely rest energy, since the center of mass is at rest. Thus, mass-energy conservation gives

$$M_0 = 2m_0/\sqrt{1 - v^2/c^2}$$

The rest mass M_0 of the composite body after collision is greater than the rest mass $2m_0$ of the incident particles. This is so because the energy that we observe as the incoming kinetic energy of the two particles becomes a part of the rest energy of the combined particles after the collision.

In this example the collision was observed from a reference frame in which the center of mass was at rest. In general, it is true that an observer in any inertial system also will find that the total relativistic momentum is conserved and that the total mass-energy is conserved (see Section 3-4).

Example 3-2.   Two satellites, each of rest mass 4,000 kg and traveling at a speed of 18,000 miles per hour with respect to an Earth observer, approach one another, collide, and stick together. Find the increase in the total rest mass of the system.

Because the satellites have equal but opposite momenta, the total momentum is zero; therefore, after the collision the composite object is at rest. Since total energy is conserved, all the kinetic energy of the incident satellites is converted into rest mass, and

$$\text{increase in rest mass} = \Delta m = 2E_k/c^2$$

where E_k is the initial kinetic energy of each satellite. The speed of each satellite, 18,000 mi/hr = 5 mi/sec, is much less than the speed of light, and we can use the classical expression for the kinetic energy, $E_k = \frac{1}{2}m_0v^2$. Therefore,

$$\Delta m = \frac{2E_k}{c^2} = \frac{2(\frac{1}{2}m_0v^2)}{c^2} = m_0\left(\frac{v}{c}\right)^2$$

$$\Delta m = (4{,}000 \text{ kg})\left(\frac{5}{186{,}000}\right)^2 \approx 0.003 \text{ g}$$

BOUND SYSTEMS   One of the most important consequences of Einstein's relativity theory arises in the binding together by some attractive force of two particles, A and B, to form a single system. To break the system into its separate components requires work, that is, the adding of energy to the system. Let the rest mass of the composite system be M_0 and the rest masses of the individual particles be m_{0A} and m_{0B}. We observe the bound system and the ensuing separation into A and B from the center-of-mass reference frame.

The breaking up of the bound system is shown symbolically in Figure 3-7, where E_b is the energy that must be added to the system in order to separate the particles completely. Because the energy needed to break the system is exactly equal to the energy binding the system, E_b itself is called the *binding energy* (the energies are equal in absolute value, opposite in sign).

$$E_b \quad + \quad \boxed{\begin{matrix} A \\ B \end{matrix}} \quad \longrightarrow \quad A \; + \; B$$

Figure 3-7. Symbolic representation of the splitting of two bound particles.

Now, applying the conservation of mass-energy to this situation, we have

$$M_0 + \frac{E_b}{c^2} = m_{0A} + m_{0B} \qquad [3\text{-}17]$$

If $E_b > 0$, then from this equation $M_0 < m_{0A} + m_{0B}$. That is, the rest mass of the bound system must be *less* than the sum of the rest masses of the individual particles when separated. This is in contrast with the situation of unbound systems, in which the rest mass of the composite *exceeds* the rest masses of the separated particles. In principle it is then possible to calculate the binding energy E_b if we know merely the rest mass of the system as a whole and the rest masses of its constituents. Only in the case of nuclear forces is the binding energy between particles great enough to produce a measurable mass difference.

We are free to choose the zero of *total kinetic and potential energy* of a system of particles—called the total mechanical energy E_m—at any convenient value. The most convenient value for particles that attract one another is zero when the particles are all infinitely separated and at rest.

When particles are *bound* to one another, the energy E_m of the bound system is *negative*, because energy must be added to the bound system to separate the particles completely and to bring the energy of the system up to zero. Figure 3-8 shows the relationships among rest masses, total relativistic energy, binding energy, and mechanical energy.

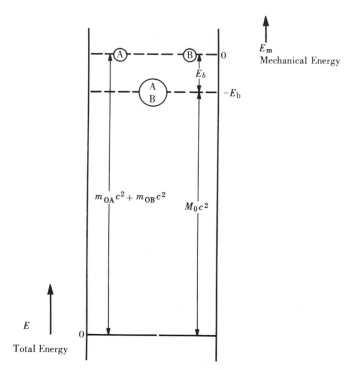

Figure 3-8. Energy-level diagram showing the energy of two particles when bound together and when completely separated from one another and at rest. The total relativistic energy is plotted on the left; the mechanical energy, on the right.

Example 3-3. The binding energy of an electron and a proton together, forming a stable hydrogen atom, is known experimentally to be 13.6 eV. This energy is called the ionization energy, since it is the energy that must be added to a hydrogen atom to separate it into two oppositely charged particles. The total mechanical energy of a hydrogen atom is -13.6 eV. By using Equation 3-17 it is possible to compute the difference between the mass of the hydrogen atom, $M_{0H} = 1.67 \times 10^{-27}$ kg, and the sum of the rest masses of the separated electron, m_{0e}, and proton, m_{0p}:

$$m_{0e} + m_{0p} - M_{0H} = E_b/c^2 = 13.6 \text{ eV}/c^2$$

The fractional change in the mass is

$$(E_b/c^2)/M_0 = \frac{(13.6 \text{ eV})(1.60 \times 10^{-19} \text{ J/eV})}{(1.67 \times 10^{-27} \text{ kg})(3.00 \times 10^8 \text{ m/sec})^2}$$

$$(E_b/M_0c^2) = 1.53 \times 10^{-8}$$

J here being joules. This fractional mass difference, slightly more than one part in one hundred million, is much smaller than the experimental fractional error in the measurement of the masses of the hydrogen atom, proton, and electron. Therefore, in a reaction in which the binding energy is *several electron volts*—and all *chemical* reactions are of this order of magnitude—it is impossible to detect directly a change in the total mass of the system. A change in mass can, however, be detected in *nuclear* reactions, in which the binding energy typically is *several million electron volts*.

3-4 Momentum-energy four-vector

Special relativity and the Lorentz coordinate transformations were constructed on this fundamental observation: the speed of light is invariant. All inertial observers measure the speed of a light beam as the same constant c. In this section we consider two other scalar quantities that are invariants: the magnitudes of the space-time four-vector and of the momentum-energy four-vector.

SPACE-TIME FOUR-VECTOR   First consider a displacement vector whose tail is located at the coordinate origin at the time $t_1 = 0$ in inertial system S_1. If at the same time the coordinates of the head of the vector are x_1, y_1, and z_1, we may write

$$l^2 = x_1^2 + y_1^2 + z_1^2$$

where l is the length of the vector. The quantities x_1, y_1, and z_1 represent the components of the vector along the three directions in space.

What are the space and time intervals that are measured by a second observer moving at some constant velocity $v \ll c$ and whose coordinate axes X_2, Y_2, and Z_2 do not necessarily coincide with those of S_1? By means of Galilean transformations similar to Equations 2-1 the length of the vector is found to be

$$l^2 = x_2^2 + y_2^2 + z_2^2$$

The time interval between the two events of locating the two ends of vector l is the same in S_1 and S_2, namely zero. The quantities x_2, y_2, and z_2 represent the components of the vector along the second coordinate axes. Although the distance x_2 is not, in general, the same as x_1 (nor are y_2 and y_1, or z_2 and z_1, the same), the length l is the same, or invariant, for any two inertial systems. Thus, for any displacement in three-dimensional Euclidean space we may write

$$\text{space invariant} = l^2 = x_2^2 + y_2^2 + z_2^2 = x_1^2 + y_1^2 + z_1^2 \qquad [3\text{-}18]$$

As stated above, the time interval between the two events of locating the two ends of vector l is the same in S_1 and S_2; similarly, under the Galilean transformations the time interval between *any* two events is invariant:

$$\text{time invariant} = \Delta t = \Delta t_1 = \Delta t_2$$

In Galilean physics space intervals and time intervals are separate invariants, but the speed of light is not an invariant. In Chapter 2 we found that we must use the Lorentz transformations rather than the Galilean transformations to guarantee the invariance of c, and in relativistic kinematics separate space intervals and time intervals must be replaced with a single space-time interval ΔS^2 relating any two events. This space-time interval is now the invariant quantity:

[2-30]   space-time invariant $= \Delta S^2 = x_2^2 + y_2^2 + z_2^2 - c^2 t_2^2$

$$= x_1^2 + y_1^2 + z_1^2 - c^2 t_1^2 \qquad [3\text{-}19]$$

The space and time coordinates $(x_1, y_1, z_1; t_1)$ of an event in one inertial frame are not necessarily the same as the space and time coordinates $(x_2, y_2, z_2; t_2)$ of the same event in a second inertial frame—the coordinates are, in fact, related by the Lorentz coordinate transformations—but the *space-time interval* between this event and another event, say an event occurring at the origin at $t_1 = t_2 = 0$, is the same, or invariant, in all inertial systems.†

Equations 3-18 and 3-19 are closely analogous; indeed, in relativity we may think of the four coordinates of an event (three in space and one in time) as being the *four* components of an invariant vector in space-time. We may take the four components of the space-time *four-vector* to be x, y, z, and ict, where $i = (-1)^{1/2}$; then, squaring each component and adding the squares yields Equation 3-19. (Of course, a four-dimensional vector with three real spatial components and one imaginary time component cannot be visualized; we are merely extending the formal properties of ordinary three-dimensional vectors into four-dimensional space-time.)

MOMENTUM-ENERGY FOUR-VECTOR   Now consider the basic relation of relativistic dynamics, giving a particle's total energy E and momentum p in terms of its rest energy E_0:

[3-14] $$E^2 = E_0^2 + (pc)^2$$

Although this equation was derived for motion along one direction only, it holds for any motion. Now p represents the magnitude of the total momentum of the particle and has, in general, the rectangular components p_x, p_y, and p_z, where $p^2 = p_x^2 + p_y^2 + p_z^2$. We may rewrite the momentum-energy relation in the form

$$-(E_0/c)^2 = p^2 - (E/c)^2$$

$$= p_x^2 + p_y^2 + p_z^2 - (E/c)^2 \qquad [3\text{-}20]$$

The left side of this equation depends only on the particle's rest mass, since $-(E_0/c)^2 = -(m_0 c)^2$. The *rest* mass m_0 and *rest* energy E_0 of any one

† It is, of course, arbitrary whether one chooses the space-time interval to be $x^2 + y^2 + z^2 - c^2 t^2$ or the other way around, $c^2 t^2 - x^2 - y^2 - z^2$. Both conventions are in use; we shall always use the interval as defined in Equation 3-19.

particle are always the same. Put differently, a particle's rest energy E_0 is invariant regardless of the inertial frame from which its momentum and energy are measured. Thus Equation 3-20, with an invariant quantity $-(E_0/c)^2$ on its left side, is of the same form as Equation 3-19. A particle's relativistic momentum components and energy are related to an invariant in exactly the same way as an event's space and time coordinates are related to an invariant space-time interval.

Just as in relativistic kinematics we think of the three space coordinates and one time coordinate of an event as components of a four-dimensional space-time interval, so too in relativistic dynamics we regard the three components of momentum and the one value of energy in any one inertial frame as combining to yield a *momentum-energy four-vector*. The components of this four-vector in the inertial frame S_1 are p_{x1}, p_{y1}, p_{z1}, and iE_1/c, of which the first three give the particle's momentum components along the X_1, Y_1, and Z_1 axes, respectively, and E_1 is the total energy of the particle in this inertial frame. Squaring the four components of the momentum-energy four-vector and adding yields Equation 3-20. Indeed, the fundamental assumption of relativistic dynamics is that the momentum-energy four-vector in *any* inertial frame yields the same invariant:

$$\boxed{\begin{aligned} \text{momentum-energy invariant} &= -(E_0/c)^2 = p_{x2}^2 + p_{y2}^2 + p_{z2}^2 \\ &- (E_2/c)^2 = p_{x1}^2 + p_{y1}^2 + p_{z1}^2 - (E_1/c)^2 \end{aligned}} \qquad \text{[3-21]}$$

Comparing the momentum-energy four-vector $(p_{x1}, p_{y1}, p_{z1}; iE_1/c)$ with the space-time four-vector $(x_1, y_1, z_1; ict_1)$, we see that we can construct one from the other by using the replacements

$$\begin{aligned} p_{x1} &\quad \text{for} \quad x_1 \\ p_{y1} &\quad \text{for} \quad y_1 \\ p_{z1} &\quad \text{for} \quad z_1 \end{aligned} \qquad \text{[3-22]}$$

$$iE_1/c \quad \text{for} \quad ict_1, \quad \text{or} \quad E_1/c^2 \quad \text{for} \quad t_1$$

The Lorentz coordinate transformations permit us to compute the space and time coordinates of an event in system S_2, given the corresponding space and time coordinates of the event in S_1; or conversely. We can construct corresponding transformation relations that give the momentum components and the total energy of a particle in inertial frame S_2 in terms of the momentum components and energy in another inertial frame S_1. Using Equations 3-22 in the Lorentz coordinate transformations, Equations 2-24, we find

$$p_{z2} = \frac{p_{x1} - v(E_1/c^2)}{\sqrt{1 - (v/c)^2}}$$

$$p_{y2} = p_{y1}$$

$$p_{z2} = p_{y1}$$

$$E_2 = \frac{E_1 - vp_{x1}}{\sqrt{1 - (v/c)^2}}$$

[3-23]

We see from the first equation that the X component of a particle's momentum as observed in S_2 depends, not only on the corresponding momentum in S_1 and the speed v of S_2 relative to S_1, but also on the particle's total energy E_1. Similarly, the last equation shows that the total energy in S_2 depends on the total energy in S_1, the relative speed v between the inertial systems, and the momentum along X in S_1.

The inverse transformations again result from interchanging subscripts 1 and 2 and replacing v with $-v$. Note that the velocity v appearing in Equations 3-23 is that of *inertial frame S_2 relative to that of inertial frame S_1.* The *velocity of a particle* that is being observed in S_1 or S_2 is *not* the same as the v appearing in Equations 3-23. The particle's velocity is given by the particle's relativistic momentum divided by its relativistic mass; in S_1, for example, the *particle's* velocity is given by

$$v_1 = \frac{p_1}{m_1} = \frac{p_1}{(E_1/c^2)} = \frac{p_1 c^2}{E_1}$$

[3-24]

To see how the momentum-energy transformation relations work, consider the following examples.

Example 3-4. A particle of rest mass m_0 and rest energy E_0 is moving along the positive Y_1 axis of S_1 at speed $0.6c$. (a) What are the particle's four momentum-energy components as observed in S_1? (b) What are they as observed in an inertial system S_2 that is moving along the positive X_1 axis at speed $0.98c$? (c) What are the particle's kinetic energies in S_1 and in S_2?

(a) Since the particle moves along the Y axis in S_1, then $p_{x1} = p_{z1} = 0$. By definition,

$$p_{y1} = m_1 v_{y1} = \frac{m_0 v_{y1}}{\sqrt{1 - (v_1/c)^2}}$$

$$= \frac{m_0(0.6c)}{\sqrt{1 - (0.6)^2}} = \frac{0.6m_0 c}{0.8} = \tfrac{3}{4}m_0 c$$

The total energy E_1 can be computed from Equation 3-24:

$$E_1 = \frac{p_1 c^2}{v_1} = \frac{(\tfrac{3}{4} m_0 c)c^2}{0.6c} = \tfrac{5}{4}m_0 c^2 = \tfrac{5}{4}E_0$$

(b) Equations 3-23 show that

$$p_{y2} = p_{y1} = \tfrac{3}{4}m_0 c$$

$$p_{z2} = p_{z1} = 0$$

For p_{x2} we obtain

$$p_{x2} = \frac{p_{x1} - vE_1/c^2}{\sqrt{1 - (v/c)^2}} = \frac{0 - (0.98c)(\tfrac{5}{4}E_0/c^2)}{\sqrt{1 - (0.98)^2}} = -6.1m_0 c$$

Finally, we find the energy in S_2 to be

$$E_2 = \frac{E_1 - vp_{x1}}{\sqrt{1 - (v/c)^2}} = \frac{(\tfrac{5}{4}E_0) - (0.98c)(0)}{\sqrt{1 - (0.98)^2}} = \tfrac{25}{4}E_0$$

(c) The kinetic energies in S_1 and S_2 are

$$E_{k1} = E_1 - E_0 = (\tfrac{5}{4}E_0) - E_0 = \tfrac{1}{4}E_0$$

$$E_{k2} = E_2 - E_0 = (\tfrac{25}{4}E_0) - E_0 = \tfrac{21}{4}E_0$$

Example 3-5. Two particles A and B, each of rest mass m_0, approach one another at equal speeds, collide, and stick together to form a third particle C, of rest mass M_0. How are m_0 and M_0 related? In Section 3-2 we treated this situation by assuming that mass-energy is conserved. Here we shall discuss the problem from the viewpoint of the invariance of the momentum-energy four-vector. We suppose that the particles are moving in opposite directions along the X_1 axis in system S_1. Then, when an observer in S_1 applies momentum conservation to this collision, we can write

$$p_{x1A} + p_{x1B} = p_{x1C} \qquad [3\text{-}25]$$

Observer S_1 is chosen to be in that reference frame in which the system's center of mass is at rest. Then the system's total momentum is not only constant but *zero* both before and after the collision:

$$p_{x1C} = p_{x1A} + p_{x1B} = 0 \qquad [3\text{-}26]$$

Now, if we assume the invariance of momentum conservation, an observer in another inertial frame S_2 must also find momentum to be conserved in this collision. From S_2's point of view,

$$p_{x2A} + p_{x2B} = p_{x2C} \qquad [3\text{-}27]$$

But the momenta as measured in S_1 and S_2 are related through the momentum-energy transformation equations. Using Equations 3-23 in Equation 3-27 we have

$$\frac{p_{x1A} - (v/c^2)E_{1A}}{\sqrt{1 - (v/c)^2}} + \frac{p_{x1B} - (v/c^2)E_{1B}}{\sqrt{1 - (v/c)^2}} = \frac{p_{x1C} - (v/c^2)E_{1C}}{\sqrt{1 - (v/c)^2}}$$

This equation may be written in the form

$$[p_{x1A} + p_{x1B}] - p_{x1C} = (v/c)^2(E_{1A} + E_{1B} - E_{1C})$$

When Equation 3-26 is used in this equation, the left side becomes zero, and the equation reduces to

$$E_{1A} + E_{1B} = E_{1C} \qquad [3\text{-}28]$$

An observer in system S_1 finds that according to this equation the total energy of the two particles A and B before the collision is the same as the total energy of the single particle C after the collision: in other words, total energy is conserved. Note especially that relativistic energy conservation came *as a result* of relativistic momentum conservation.

Equation 3-28 looks simple and obvious enough in expressing that the total energy of the two particles before collision is the same as the total energy of the single particle afterward, but note what is implied about the rest masses of the particles, m_0 for A and B and M_0 for C. If the *speed* of particles A and B is denoted by v_1, then

$$E_{1A} = E_{2B} = \frac{m_0 c^2}{\sqrt{1 - (v_1/c)^2}} \qquad [3\text{-}29]$$

Particle C remains at rest in S_1, so that its total energy is

$$E_{1C} = M_0 c^2 \qquad [3\text{-}30]$$

Putting Equations 3-29 and 3-30 into Equation 3-28, we have

$$\frac{2m_0 c^2}{\sqrt{1 - (v_1/c)^2}} = M_0 c^2 \qquad [3\text{-}31]$$

The rest mass M_0 of the composite particle C formed in this inelastic collision is *greater* than the sum $2m_0$ *of the separate rest* masses of A and B. This agrees with results given in Section 3-2.

3-5 Special relativity and the electromagnetic interaction The speed c of propagation of electromagnetic waves is a relativistically invariant quantity. Electric charge is also a relativistic invariant; that is, the magnitude of a particle's electric charge does not depend on the speed of the particle. The simplest and most compelling experimental evidence for electric-charge invariance is that an electrically neutral system of particles with equal but opposite charges remains electrically neutral quite apart from the speeds of the particles within it. Thus, a hydrogen molecule with two protons and two electrons, and a helium atom also with two protons and two electrons are both found to be electrically neutral to within one part in 10^{20} although the speeds of the component particles differ greatly for the two systems.

The electromagnetic interaction between a pair of electrically charged particles is customarily separated into two parts: the *electric* force, which always acts between any two charged particles whether each is at rest or in motion with respect to the observer, and the *magnetic* force, which acts between them only when they are both in motion relative to the observer. It is easy to see that the magnetic force between any two charged particles Q_1 and Q_2 can be turned off, so to speak, merely by a proper choice of reference frame. For example, if an observer rides in a reference frame that is at rest with respect to charge Q_1, he will measure no magnetic force between the two charges. First, the magnetic force on Q_2 due to Q_1 will be zero, because Q_1 creates no magnetic field at the site of Q_2 (or at any other point in space, since Q_1 is at rest). Second, even if Q_2 were moving with respect to the observer, there would be no magnetic force on Q_1 due to Q_2, because Q_1 is not moving. This simple example shows us that a magnetic force between two charged particles may exist for observers in some inertial systems but not in others. The first postulate of relativity, the invariance of the form of a physical law in all inertial frames, requires that the laws of electromagnetism be of the same form in all inertial frames. In this section we shall give a qualitative discussion of how electric and magnetic forces as viewed in different inertial systems are related.

Clearly, the magnetic interaction is intimately related to the choice of reference frame. Since special relativity deals with the transformation relations between reference frames, we expect that the appearance or non-appearance of the magnetic force between charged particles is basically a relativistic effect. It is easy to see, at least in a qualitative way, that

$$\text{magnetism} = \text{electricity} + \text{relativity}$$

In this view the magnetic interaction is not a separate and distinct type of fundamental force; rather, the so-called magnetic force originates from the strictly electric (or Coulomb) interaction and the requirements of special relativity.

To see the connection between magnetism, electricity, and relativity let us consider an example of what is usually described as a purely magnetic force. Two parallel, infinitely long, current-carrying conductors attract one another magnetically when the currents are in the same direction, and they repel one another when the currents are in opposite directions. In this situation an electric force is thought not to act between the two conductors, because each is taken to be electrically neutral. In the standard analysis of this situation we say that the moving charges in one conductor generate a magnetic field at the site of the other conductor, and the charges moving through the latter conductor are thereby acted upon by a magnetic force. This force is transmitted ultimately to the crystalline lattice of the solid wire through which the charges move.

Let us re-examine this situation from the point of view of special relativity. For simplicity we imagine that the current through each conductor results from there being equal amounts of free positive charges moving in the direction of the current and free negative charges moving in the opposite direction. We know, of course, that in metals the current results from the motion of free negative charges (electrons) only, but the physical arguments concerning the more symmetrical situation chosen here are simpler, and the results are similar to those one would obtain by assuming the motion of particles with only one sign of charge.

Figure 3-9 shows positive and negative charges moving through a lattice assumed electrically neutral. They produce an electric current to the right in each wire and, classically, this results in an attractive magnetic force be-

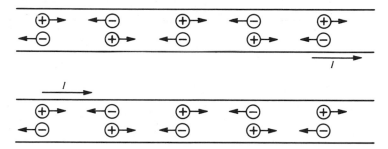

Figure 3-9. Positive and negative charges moving at equal speeds through two parallel conductors with electric currents in the *same* direction (to the right).

tween the two wires. Can we, by invoking special relativity, describe this effect in terms of an electric force only? As we shall see, the answer is yes, but only if we are very careful. First, we must recognize that we have not considered how a force transforms between one inertial frame and another. A force on a particle does *not* have the same magnitude for all observers, inasmuch as it is defined as the particle's momentum change per unit time interval, and both these quantities depend on the observer. We shall not derive the force-transformation relations in detail here but shall merely make use of the reasonable fact that, although the magnitude of a force may change in the transformation between one inertial frame and another, its direction does not change.

Let us focus on the net electric force on the positive and negative charges in one of the wires. In doing so we shall intentionally *exclude* any magnetic interaction, concentrating on electric forces alone and invoking the requirements of relativity.

To find the force on a *positive* charge we first must transform the system into an inertial system in which the positive charge is at rest; this is illustrated in Figure 3-10a. Notice that an observer in this frame finds the positive charges at rest; the distance between adjacent positive charges is indicated by D_0. On the other hand, the negative charges now are moving to the left at a higher speed than in Figure 3-9; because of space contraction the distance between adjacent negative charges is less than D_0, say D. The resultant electric force on a given positive charge is due to the other charges, both positive and negative, in the same wire and also to the positive and negative charges in the other wire. It is obvious that that component of the force which is due to the other positive charges in the same wire is zero,

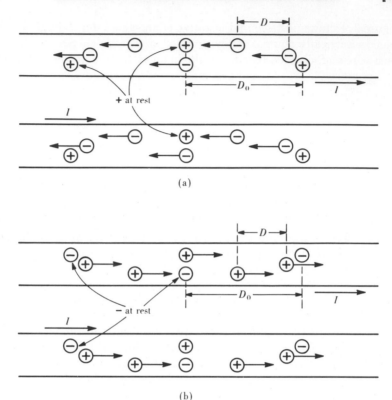

Figure 3-10. The conductors and charge carriers of Figure 3-9 but now as observed by (a) an observer at rest with respect to the positive charges and (b) an observer at rest with respect to the negative charges.

since there are equal numbers of uniformly spaced positive charges to the left and to the right, and that the same is true of that component which is due to negative charges in the same wire.

Now, what about the resultant force due to the charged particles in the other wire? Because of the contraction of the distance between adjacent negative charges there will be more negative charges per unit length than positive charges. Thus, from the point of view of a positive charge in, say, the lower wire the *net* charge of the upper wire is *negative*, and the chosen positive charge is attracted to the upper wire. Transforming back to the inertial system in which the wires are at rest (Figure 3-9) will still give an attractive force between the positive charge and the upper wire, although one of a different magnitude from that in Figure 3-10a. (In similar fashion a positive charge in the upper wire of Figure 3-10a finds the lower wire negatively charged, because of the contraction of the distance between the moving negative charges in it, and is therefore attracted to the lower wire.

We next consider forces on the negative charges. What kind of force, attractive or repulsive, from all the other charges will a negative charge in the lower wire of Figure 3-9 experience? To find this we follow the same procedure as before. First we view the charges from an inertial frame in which the chosen negative charge is at rest; then we transform back to the system in which the wires are at rest. Figure 3-10b illustrates the motion of the charges from a reference frame in which the negative charges are at rest. Again the negative charge experiences no net force from the positive and negative charges in the lower wire, because of equal numbers in both directions along the wire but, because of space contraction for the moving positive charges, it sees the other wire charged positively and is therefore attracted to it. (Similar arguments hold for negative charges in the upper wire.) Finally, transforming back to the reference frame in which the wires are at rest (Figure 3-9) still gives an attractive force between any negative charge and the other wire.

Both the positive and negative charges in one of the wires of Figure 3-9 are attracted to the other wire. These charges will then move across the width of their own wire until they arrive at the surface closest to the other wire but, because they are bound to the conducting wire, they cannot leave the surface; thus, the attractive force is transmitted to the entire wire. We have shown in a qualitative way that two wires carrying currents in the same direction attract one another *without* the action of a magnetic force, at least an explicit one.

Now consider a situation in which the currents in the two parallel, infinitely long, current-carrying conductors are in opposite directions. We again assume that the current in each wire is due to there being equal numbers of positive and negative charges moving in opposite directions but at the same speed. The motion of the charges, as observed in a frame in which the wires are at rest, is shown in Figure 3-11. We wish to find the forces acting on the positive and negative charges in, say, the lower wire.

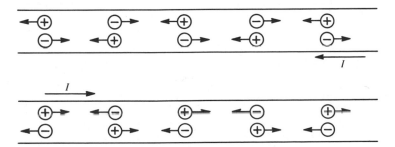

Figure 3-11. Positive and negative charges moving at equal speeds through two parallel conductors with electric currents in *opposite* directions.

To find the force on a positive charge we must first observe it from a reference frame in which this positive charge is at rest, as shown in Figure 3-12a. Note that the force on the positive charge due to all the other positive and negative charges *in the same wire* is zero, as we found before. Now consider the force due to the charges in the other wire. In the upper wire the negative charges are at rest, and the positive charges move to the left. Because of space contraction there is more positive charge per unit length than negative charge in the upper wire, and the chosen positive charge in the lower wire finds the upper wire positively charged; therefore, the two wires repel each other.

To find the force on a negative charge in the lower wire we transform to a frame in which this charge is at rest; see Figure 3-12b. Viewed from this frame, the upper wire has a net negative charge, and the chosen negative charge in the lower wire is repelled by it.

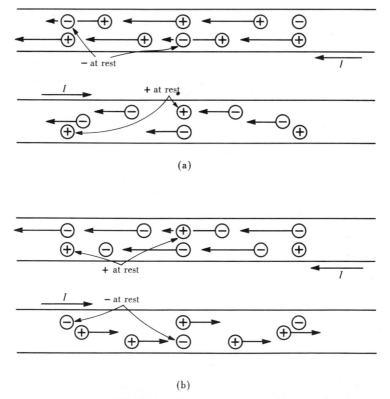

(a)

(b)

Figure 3-12. The conductors and charge carriers of Figure 3-11 but now as observed by (a) an observer at rest with respect to the positive charges in the lower conductor and (b) an observer at rest with respect to the negative charges in the lower conductor.

In short, the resultant force of one current-carrying conductor on another whose current moves in the opposite direction is a repulsive one. Once again we have arrived at the result without recourse to an explicitly magnetic interaction between electric charges.

Although the qualitative arguments given above were applied to a symmetrical situation in which equal numbers of positive and negative charge carriers moved in each wire, they hold just as well for any ratio of carriers. If all of the charge carriers were negatively charged, as they are in most ordinary metals, we should again find that currents in the same direction attract and currents in opposite directions repel. When currents are in the same direction, the negative charges are attracted by the other wire, and as a result there is an excess of negative charge on the surface nearest the other wire. This is in contrast with the situation shown in Figure 3-9, in which both positive and negative carriers move to the near sides of the wires in equal numbers with no net charge at the surface. By making use of this effect it is possible to determine the sign of the predominant carriers.†

3-6 Computations and units in relativistic mechanics The classical equations for the momentum and kinetic energy of a particle can be used only when the speed of the particle is much less than the speed of light; for high speeds the relativistic relations must be invoked. It is useful to have a rule of thumb for determining whether a computation in a problem can safely be treated relativistically or classically. Table 3-1 shows the conditions

Table 3-1

	For the condition	Error in relation below is no greater than 1 percent
Classical region	$E_k/E_0 < 0.01$ or $v/c < 0.1$	$E_k \approx \frac{1}{2}m_0v^2$ and $p \approx m_0v$
Extreme relativistic region	$E/E_0 > 7$ or $E_k/E_0 > 6$ or $v/c > 0.99$	$E \approx pc$

which, if fulfilled, lead to errors no greater than one percent in the computed momentum or energy. If the kinetic energy of a particle is a very small fraction of its rest energy, classical mechanics applies; on the other hand, if the total energy or the kinetic energy greatly exceeds a particle's rest

† See the description of the Hall effect in Weidner and Sells, *E. C. P.* Sec. 32-9.

energy, then the extreme relativistic relation $E = pc$ (which holds strictly only for $m_0 = 0$) can be applied.

For atomic and subatomic particles a convenient unit of energy is the electron volt or multiples of it:

$$\text{Kilo electron volt} = 1 \text{ keV} = 10^3 \text{ eV}$$
$$\text{Mega electron volt} = 1 \text{ MeV} = 10^6 \text{ eV}$$
$$\text{Giga electron volt}\ddagger = 1 \text{ GeV} = 10^9 \text{ eV}$$

From Equation 3-14 the corresponding unit for momentum is the electron volt divided by the speed of light, eV/c. When momentum is expressed in these units, the unit for pc is just the electron volt, eV. The speed of an atomic particle is most conveniently given in units of the speed of light, that is, as v/c. In these units the speed of any particle must lie somewhere between 0 and 1. These particular units (eV for energy, eV/c for momentum, and v/c for speed) simplify calculations in classical as well as in relativistic problems.

The classical kinetic-energy and momentum relations can be written in terms of a particle's rest energy $E_0 = m_0c^2$, its speed v/c, and the constant c, as follows:

$$E_\text{k} \text{ (classical)} = \tfrac{1}{2}m_0v^2 = \tfrac{1}{2}(m_0c^2)(v/c)^2 = \tfrac{1}{2}E_0(v/c)^2 \qquad [3\text{-}32]$$

$$p \text{ (classical)} = m_0v = \frac{(m_0c^2)(v/c)}{c} = \frac{E_0(v/c)}{c} \qquad [3\text{-}33]$$

For example, the kinetic energy and momentum of an electron (rest energy, $E_0 = 0.51$ MeV) moving with a speed of $(1/100)c$, for which the classical relations apply, are easily found to be:

[3-32] $E_\text{k} = \tfrac{1}{2}E_0(v/c)^2 = \tfrac{1}{2}(0.51 \text{ MeV})(10^{-2})^2 = 0.26 \times 10^{-4} \text{ MeV} = 26 \text{ eV}$

[3-33] $p = \dfrac{E_0(v/c)}{c} = \dfrac{(0.51 \text{ MeV})(10^{-2})}{c} = 0.51 \times 10^{-2} \text{ MeV}/c$

$\qquad = 5.1 \text{ keV}/c$

The masses of particles in atomic physics are frequently given in units of the *atomic mass unit* (unified), or "u." *One atomic mass unit is defined as 1/12 the mass of a neutral carbon atom (isotope 12).* Avogadro's number, 6.02252×10^{23}, gives the number of atoms in 12 g of atomic carbon. Therefore,

$$1 \text{ u} = \frac{1}{12}\left(\frac{12 \text{ g}}{6.02252 \times 10^{23}}\right) = 1.660 \times 10^{-27} \text{ kg}$$

‡ The energy unit BeV (billion electron volts) is also used to denote 10^9 eV. The GeV is preferred, however, because in European usage a billion designates a million million (10^{12}), not a thousand million (10^9).

The relation between the atomic mass unit, u, and the energy unit MeV is particularly useful. We find this from the general mass-energy relation, $E = mc^2$

$$E = mc^2 = (1 \text{ u})c^2$$

$$E = \frac{(1.660 \times 10^{-27} \text{ kg})(2.998 \times 10^8 \text{ m/sec})^2}{(1.602 \times 10^{-19} \text{ J/eV})(10^6 \text{ eV/MeV})}$$

$$E = 931.5 \text{ MeV}$$

Therefore,

> 1 unified atomic mass unit $= 1 \text{ u} = 931.5 \text{ MeV}/c^2$

This relation may be regarded as giving the basic conversion factor between mass and energy units. The rest energies of the electron and proton are:

> electron rest energy $= 0.51101 \text{ MeV} = 0.00055 \text{ u-}c^2$
>
> proton rest energy $= 938.26 \text{ MeV} = 1.00728 \text{ u-}c^2$

It is worth memorizing that the rest energy of an electron is approximately one half a mega electron volt, $\frac{1}{2}$ MeV, and that the rest energy of a proton is approximately one giga electron volt, 1 GeV. By convention, when a particle is described as, say, a 3.0 MeV particle, this means that the *kinetic* energy, not the total energy E, is three mega electron volts.

Example 3-6.   What is the speed of a 2.0 MeV electron? The kinetic energy E_k is 2.0 MeV, and the rest energy E_0 is 0.51 MeV. Because $E_k > E_0/100$, a relativistic calculation must be made. Equation 3-5 shows that

$$mc^2 = \frac{m_0 c^2}{\sqrt{1 - (v/c)^2}}$$

> $$E = \frac{E_0}{\sqrt{1 - (v/c)^2}}$$ [3-34]

This equation is often useful in relativistic computations. Solving for v/c gives

$$v/c = \sqrt{1 - E_0/E^2} = \sqrt{1 - E_0/(E_k + E_0)^2}$$

$$v/c = \sqrt{1 - (0.51/2.51)^0} = 0.98$$

Example 3-7.   What is the momentum of a 20.0 GeV electron? Table 3-1 shows that, because $E_k/E_0 = 20{,}000/0.51 \approx 40{,}000$, we can use $E = pc$ with an error of much less than 1 percent; therefore,

$$p = E/c = (E_k + E_0)/c = (20.0 + 0.0005) \text{ GeV}/c \approx 20 \text{ GeV}/c$$

3-7 Summary   The relativistic momentum of a particle is

[3-6] $p = mv,$ where $m = m_0/\sqrt{1 - (v/c)^2}$

In relativistic dynamics the total energy and the relativistic mass of a particle are related by the Einstein equation

[3-12] $E = mc^2$

A particle's kinetic energy is given by

[3-10] $E_k = E - E_0$

where $E_0 = m_0c^2$ is the rest energy of the particle.
    The dynamical quantity

[3-14] $(pc)^2 - E^2 = -E_0^2$

is invariant under the Lorentz transformations, having the same value in all inertial systems.
    The rest mass of a bound system of particles is less than the total mass of the separated parts by E_b/c^2, where E_b is the total binding energy.
    A particle's total energy and its momentum components transform from one inertial system to another in a manner analogous to that of the space-time Lorentz transformations:

$$p_{x2} = \frac{p_{x1} - v(E_1/c^2)}{\sqrt{1 - (v/c)^2}}$$

$$p_{y2} = p_{y1}$$

[3-23] $p_{z2} = p_{z1}$

$$E_2 = \frac{E_1 - vp_{x1}}{\sqrt{1 - (v/c)^2}}$$

Maxwell's laws of electrodynamics are Lorentz-invariant. The magnetic interaction between moving charges arises, according to special relativity, when a strictly electric interaction is transformed to another inertial system.

BIBLIOGRAPHY

Feynman, R. P., R. B. Leighton, and M. Sands, *The Feynman Lectures on Physics.* Reading, Mass.: Addison-Wesley Publishing Company, Inc., 1963. See Section 17-4 for a derivation of the Lorentz transformation equations for energy and momentum.

Leighton, R. B., *Principles of Modern Physics.* New York: McGraw-Hill Book Company, Inc., 1959. A brief description of relativistic electrodynamics and the electromagnetic four-vector potential is given in Section 1-8.

Purcell, E. M., *Electricity and Magnetism*. New York: McGraw-Hill Book Company, Inc., 1965. Chapter 5 gives an elementary but thorough development of electric fields as observed in different inertial systems. Relations for the electric force on a moving charge are also derived.

PROBLEMS

3-1 A satellite orbits the Earth (mean radius, 6.37×10^6 m) near its surface with a period of 84 min. By what percentage does the satellite's relativistic mass exceed its rest mass?

3-2 A uniform solid object is in motion at very high speed. (a) Does the object's density, defined as the relativistic mass per unit volume, depend on its speed relative to the observer? (6) If so, does the density increase or decrease with speed? (c) If the solid object is a cylinder, does its density at any given speed depend upon the orientation of the axis relative to the direction of motion?

3-3 * The pion is an unstable elementary particle with a rest energy of 140 MeV and a mean life of 2.55×10^{-8} sec. The mean life is the average time interval, measured in the reference frame in which the particle is at rest, between the creation of a pion and its decay into other particles. A track in a bubble-chamber photograph, showing the life history of a pion decaying in its mean life, has a length of 5.0 cm. The pion moves at essentially constant speed in producing the track. (a) What is the kinetic energy of the pion? (b) What is the pion's speed?

3-4 An electron circles the Earth (mean radius, 6.37×10^6 m) at the Equator, where the magnitude of the Earth's magnetic field is approximately 0.34 gauss. By what percentage does the electron's relativistic mass exceed its rest mass?

3-5 A polyenergetic beam of protons enters a uniform magnetic field of 0.667 Wb/m² perpendicularly to it. The beam is found to break up as a spectrum whose radii range from 10.0 to 1.00 m. (a) What is the range of momenta values (in units of MeV/c) of the proton beam? (b) What is the range of kinetic-energy values (in units of MeV)?

3-6 (a) What is the radius of curvature of a beam of 10 GeV electrons injected perpendicularly into a uniform magnetic field of 2.0 Wb/m²? (b) What would nonrelativistic physics predict for the radius of curvature? (c) What would be the radius of a beam of 10 GeV protons injected into the same field?

3-7 At the proposed high-energy accelerator to be built in Weston, Illinois, protons will be accelerated to energies as high as 200 GeV. (a) Find the speed of such protons. (b) If the final intensity of the proton beam is 10^{14} protons/sec, what is the minimum power (watts) necessary to accelerate the protons?

3-8 A charged particle is accelerated from rest by an electric potential difference. The particle then enters a uniform magnetic field of constant magnitude at right angles to the magnetic field lines. It is found that when the accelerating potential is increased by some factor, the radius of curvature of the particle's path in the uniform magnetic field also increases by almost the same factor. Show that the particle's speed after being accelerated by the electric field is nearly c.

3-9   What is the fractional difference in mass between a 1.0 g piece of copper at 0.0 °C and the same piece of copper at 100 °C? The specific heat of copper is 0.093 cal/g-C°.

3-10   It is now possible to accelerate electrons to energies of 20 GeV. (a) By what factor does such an electron's relativistic mass increase? (b) What is the percentage difference between the speed of light and the speed of a 20 GeV electron?

3-11   Because the electron and proton have the same magnitude of electric charge, the kinetic energies of an electron and a proton that are both accelerated from rest across the *same* electric potential difference are always exactly the same, irrespective of differences in the speeds of electron and proton. Across what minimum potential difference must an electron and a proton be accelerated from rest so that their momenta are the same to within 1 part in 100?

3-12   What are (a) the kinetic energy (in eV) and (b) the momentum (in eV/c) of a particle of rest energy 0.50 GeV moving with a speed of $v/c = 1/1000$?

3-13   The relation between a particle's total energy E, rest energy E_0, and momentum p may be represented by a right triangle with sides pc, E_0, and E. Draw such a triangle and mark the particle's kinetic energy for (a) $v/c \ll 1$ and (b) $v/c \approx 1$.

3-14   An electron has a momentum of 1.0 MeV/c: what are (a) its kinetic energy and (b) its speed? A proton has a momentum of 1.0 MeV/c: what are (c) its kinetic energy and (d) its speed?

3-15   What are the momenta of (a) a 1.0 GeV (kinetic energy) electron and (b) a 1.0 GeV (kinetic energy) carbon atom (rest energy ≈ 12 GeV)?

3-16   A particle's kinetic energy is 5 times its rest energy E_0: what are its (a) momentum and (b) speed, both in terms of E_0 and c?

3-17   A high-energy accelerator accelerates a beam of electrons through a total potential difference of 10.0 GeV. The average number of electrons striking the target is 12×10^{13} per second. (a) What is the average electron current? (b) What is the average force exerted on the target by the electron beam as the electrons are brought to rest?

3-18   A particle's speed is less than c by 0.010 percent. What are the particle's (a) kinetic energy and (b) momentum, both in terms of energy E_0 and c?

3-19 *   (a) What is the maximum speed possible of a particle whose kinetic energy may be written $\frac{1}{2}m_0v^2$ with an error in the kinetic energy of no greater than 1 percent? (b) What is the kinetic energy of an electron moving at this speed? (c) What is the kinetic energy of a proton moving at this speed?

3-20 *   (a) What is the minimum speed possible of a particle whose kinetic energy may be written as its total energy E and, therefore, as pc with an error in the total energy of no greater than 1 percent? (b) Under such conditions what is the kinetic energy of an electron? (c) Of a proton?

3-21 A particle of rest mass m_0 initially moves at speed $0.40c$. (a) If the speed is doubled, by what factor is the particle's kinetic energy increased? (b) If the particle's kinetic energy is increased by a factor of 1,000, by what factor is the speed increased?

3-22 The total intensity of radiation from the Sun at the Earth's surface is 8.0 J/cm²-min. Calculate the loss in the Sun's mass per second and the fractional loss in the Sun's mass in 10^9 years (approximately one tenth of the age of the universe) resulting from its radiation. The distance from the Sun to the Earth is 1.49×10^{11} m and the Sun's mass at present is 2.0×10^{30} kg.

3-23 A rocket ship having a final payload rest mass of 4×10^4 is accelerated to a speed of $0.98c$. (a) What minimum energy is required to accelerate the rocket ship to this speed? (b) How much equivalent mass does this represent? (c) What amount of nuclear fuel (assume 1 percent conversion of mass to energy) would be needed to achieve this?

3-24 Twin ships, one powered by oil (4×10^6 cal/lb) and the other powered by nuclear fuel (1.5×10^{26} MeV/kg), travel an equal distance. What is the ratio of the fuel used by the two ships?

3-25 Use the binomial expansion to show that the expression $\frac{1}{2}mv^2$, where m is the relativistic mass, does *not* give the relativistic kinetic energy $E - E_0$.

3-26 (a) Show that the speed of a particle, according to nonrelativistic physics, is given by dE_k/dp. (b) Show that the speed of a relativistic particle is given by dE/dp. (c) Plot $E_k^{1/2}$ as a function of v for both (a) and (b).

3-27 (a) Show that the momentum of a particle may be written as $p = (1/c)(E_k + 2E_0E_k)^{1/2}$. (b) Show that this reduces to (m_0v) in the classical limit, and to (E/c) in the extreme relativistic region.

3-28 Sketch graphs of a particle's relativistic and classical (a) momenta and (b) kinetic energies as functions of its speed over all possible values of speed.

3-29 * A 10.2 MeV electron makes a head-on elastic collision with a proton initially at rest. Show that the proton recoils with a speed approximately equal to $(2E_e/E_p)c$ and the fractional energy transferred from the electron to the proton is $(2E_e/E_p)$, where E_e is the *total* energy of the electron and E_p is the *rest* energy of the proton. *Hint*: (a) since the electron's energy is much greater than its rest energy, it may be treated as an extreme relativistic particle, and (b) since the rest energy of the proton is much greater than the *total* energy of the electron, the proton may be treated classically.)

3-30 To separate a carbon monoxide molecule, CO, into carbon and oxygen atoms requires 11.0 eV. (a) What is the fractional change in mass of a CO molecule when it is broken into the atoms C and O? (b) What is the binding energy (in eV) per molecule?

3-31 Separate masses of 1.0 kg and 4.0 kg are attached to opposite ends of a massless spring having a force constant of 1.0×10^5 N/m. The spring is then compressed 10.0 cm from its unstretched length and locked in that position. (a) If the mass of the system of coupled objects is now measured, what will be the difference in mass between the combined system and the originally separated masses? The lock is next released, and the spring expands, accelerating the two masses until they become free from the spring and move off in opposite directions. (b) By how much does the mass of each of the separate objects exceed its rest mass?

3-32   (a) Which is larger, the mass of our spinning Earth or the mass of a non-spinning Earth? (b) Calculate the difference in mass (in kg) between the spinning Earth and one that is not spinning. (c) What is the ratio of the mass difference to the total mass? The Earth's mass is 6.0×10^{24} kg and its radius is 6.4×10^6 m.

3-33 *   The Σ^+ particle is an unstable elementary particle with a rest energy of 1,190 MeV and a mean life of 0.81×10^{-10} sec in a reference frame in which the particle is at rest. Consider a Σ^+ particle that exists for one mean lifetime *in its rest frame*. What is this particle's minimum kinetic energy in a laboratory reference frame in which it is observed to travel a distance of 1.0 mm before decaying?

3-34   In inertial system S_1 a particle of rest mass m_0 is observed to be moving at constant speed $v_1 = c/2$ along the positive Y axis. (a) Use Equation 3-23 to find the particle's momentum and total energy as observed in a second inertial system S_2 that is moving along the positive X_1 axis at speed $0.80c$. (c) In what inertial system is the particle's total energy a minimum?

3-35 *   In the laboratory frame of reference an incident 2.0 GeV proton moving along the X axis collides elastically with a target proton initially at rest. After the collision each of the two protons travels at the same angle with respect to the X axis. What is this angle? (Note that for an elastic collision between particles of equal mass at *low* speeds the angle between the directions of the two outgoing particles is always 90°.)

3-36 *   In a certain inertial frame the total momentum of a system of isolated particles is Σp and the total relativistic energy is ΣE. Show that the velocity of the system's center of mass is given by $c^2 \Sigma p / \Sigma E$.

F O U R

QUANTUM EFFECTS: THE PARTICLE
ASPECTS OF ELECTROMAGNETIC
RADIATION

4-1 Quantization in classical physics   The theory of relativity and the quantum theory constitute the two great theoretical foundations of twentieth-century physics. Just as the theory of relativity leads to new insights into the nature of space and time and to profound consequences in mechanics and electromagnetism, so too the quantum theory leads to drastically new modes of thought that are the basis of an understanding of atomic and nuclear structure. Some aspects of the quantum description of nature, however, are not totally new and, indeed, are to be found in classical physics.

In the study of the physical world we find two general kinds of physical quantities; quantities that have a continuum of values and quantities that are *quantized*. The latter are quantities that are restricted to certain discrete values; they are sometimes described as having "atomicity" or "granularity."

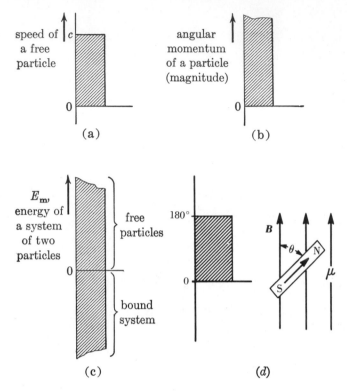

Figure 4-1. Some examples of classical physical quantities having a continuum of allowed values.

Figure 4-1 shows several examples of classical continuous, or non-quantized, physical quantities:

(a) The speed of a free particle, which can range from zero up to the speed of light.

(b) The magnitude of the angular momentum of a particle, which can take on any value from zero to infinity.

(c) The mechanical energy of a system of two particles, which can assume any negative value when the particles are bound together ($E_m < 0$) and any positive value when the particles are free ($E_m > 0$).

(d) The angle between the direction of a magnet's dipole moment and an external magnetic field, which may vary from 0° to 180°.

Figure 4-2 shows several examples of quantized physical quantities:

(a) The observed rest masses of atoms, which do not occur in a continuous range. This was first perceived in the fundamental studies of chemical combination that led to the atomic theory of Dalton.

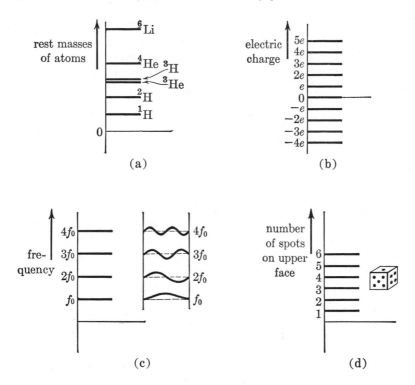

Figure 4-2. Some examples of classical physical quantities having quantized values.

The masses of atoms occurring in nature are now known with great precision, and it is interesting to note that, whereas they are *nearly* in the ratio of integers, they are *not precisely* so. One of the principal tasks of nuclear physics, as we shall see, is to explain on some fundamental basis these departures from integral ratios.

(b) Electric charge, which is quantized in that the total charge of any body is precisely an integral multiple, either positive or negative, of the fundamental electronic charge e. The quantization of charge, clearly revealed in the chemical idea of valence and in the laws of electrolysis, was most directly demonstrated in the oil-drop experiments of R. A. Millikan, in which the charge of the electron was measured directly.

(c) Standing waves and resonance, which are particularly striking manifestations of quantization in classical physics. The frequency of oscillation of a resonating vibrating string, fixed at both ends, can be only an integral multiple of the lowest, or fundamental frequency of oscillation, f_0. The fundamental frequency is determined in turn by the physical properties of the string and its length. The wave on the string is repeatedly reflected from the boundaries, or fixed ends, and constructively interferes with itself, so to speak, to produce standing waves. Resonance can be achieved only if the distance between the end points is precisely an integral multiple of half-wavelengths. It was argued in Section 1-7 that the frequency of a wave is precisely determined only when the wave has an infinite extension in space; this argument is valid even for a wave trapped between reflecting boundaries, because the wave can be imagined to be folded on itself an infinite number of times.

(d) A rolled die, which can show on its upper face only 1, 2, 3, 4, 5, or 6 spots. This is one of many everyday examples of quantized quantities; others are the face of a coin, people, and number of cents.

The quantum theory is in large measure based on the discovery that certain quantities that in classical physics had been regarded as continuous are, in fact, quantized. Historically it had its origins in the theoretical interpretation of electromagnetic radiation from a blackbody (a perfect absorber and radiator). Near the end of the nineteenth century it was found that the experimentally observed variation with wavelength of the intensity of electromagnetic radiation from a blackbody was in disagreement with the theoretical expectations of classical electromagnetism. Max Planck, formulator of the quantum theory, showed in 1900 that a revision of classical ideas, through the concept of energy quantization, led to satisfactory agreement between experiment and theory. Because a detailed analysis of blackbody radiation (Section 12-7) involves rather sophisticated arguments, we shall introduce the quantum concepts through the much simpler and in many ways more compelling considerations that arise in the phenomenon of the photoelectric effect.

4-2 The photoelectric effect   The photoelectric effect was discovered by Heinrich Hertz in 1887 during the course of experiments, the primary intent of which was confirmation of Maxwell's theoretical prediction (1864) of the existence of electromagnetic waves produced by oscillating electric currents.

The photoelectric effect is but one of several processes by which electrons may be removed from the surface of a substance (we shall refer here to metal surfaces in particular, since the effects were first observed in metals and still are most easily observed in them); these effects are the following.

Thermionic emission: heating of the metal, which gives thermal energy to the electrons and effectively boils them from the surface.

Secondary emission: transfer of the kinetic energy from particles that strike the surface to the electrons in the metal.

Field emission: extraction of electrons from the metal by a strong external electric field.

Photoelectric emission, with which we are concerned here.

The photoelectric effect occurs when electromagnetic radiation shines on a clean metal surface and electrons are released from the surface. The valence electrons in a metal are free to move about through its interior but are bound to the metal as a whole. It is such relatively free electrons with which we shall be concerned here. We can most simply describe the photoelectric effect as a light beam's supplying any electron with an amount of energy that equals or exceeds the energy with the electron is bound to the surface and so allowing that electron to escape. A more detailed description of the photoelectric effect requires a knowledge, based on experiment, of how the several variables involved in photoelectric emission are related to one another. These variables are the frequency ν of the light, the intensity I of the light beam, the photoelectric current i, the kinetic energy $\frac{1}{2}m_0v^2$ (we shall see shortly that the use of the classical kinetic-energy formula is justified), and the chemical identity of the surface from which the electrons emerge. The emergent electrons are called *photoelectrons*.

Figure 4-3 shows a schematic diagram of an experimental arrangement for studying important aspects of the photoelectric effect. Monochromatic light shines on a metal surface, the anode, enclosed in a vacuum tube (an

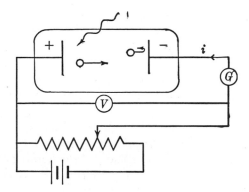

Figure 4-3. Schematic experimental arrangement for studying the photo-electric effect. V, voltmeter; G, galvanometer.

evacuated tube is used in order that collisions between photoelectrons and gas molecules are essentially eliminated). When photoelectrons are emitted, some travel toward the cathode and upon reaching it constitute the current flowing in the circuit (conventional current, as shown in the figure). Photoelectrons leave the anode with a variety of kinetic energies. The negatively charged cathode tends to repel them. When the work done on a photoelectron by the retarding electrostatic field, of potential difference V, equals the initial kinetic energy of the photoelectron, the latter is brought to rest just in front of the cathode. Thus, $eV = \frac{1}{2}m_0v^2$, where v is the speed of the photoelectron as it leaves the anode surface, and V is the potential difference that stops the photoelectron of rest mass m_0 and charge e. When the most energetic photoelectrons, of speed v_{max}, are brought to rest in front of the cathode by a sufficiently large potential difference V_0, all the other photoelectrons are, of course, stopped too, and no photocurrent exists: $i = 0$. Then

$$eV_0 = \tfrac{1}{2}m_0v_{max}^2 \qquad\qquad [4\text{-}1]$$

At still higher retarding potential differences all photoelectrons are turned *back* before reaching the cathode.

We shall first list below the results of experiment. We shall then give the results that might be expected on the basis of the classical theory of electromagnetism; it will be seen that the experimental results strongly disagree with the classical expectations. Finally, we shall see how the photoelectric effect can be understood on the basis of a quantum interpretation.

EXPERIMENTAL RESULTS OF THE PHOTOELECTRIC EFFECT   The results of experiments on the photoelectric effect are summarized in Figure 4-4. We shall take them up in the order in which they are given in the figure.

(a) When light shines on a metal surface and photoelectrons are emitted, the photocurrent begins *almost instantaneously*, even when the light beam has an intensity as small as 10^{-10} W/m² (watts per square meter), the intensity at a distance of 200 miles from a 100-watt light source. The delay in time, from the instant that the light beam first shines on the surface until photoelectrons are first emitted, is no greater than 10^{-9} sec.

(b) For any fixed frequency and retarding potential the *photocurrent i* is directly *proportional to the intensity I* of the light beam. Inasmuch as the photocurrent is a measure of the number of photoelectrons released per unit time at the anode and collected at the cathode, the relation signifies that the number of photoelectrons emerging per unit time is proportional to the light intensity (the variation in photocurrent with intensity is utilized in practical photoelectric devices).

(c) For a constant frequency ν and light intensity I *the photocurrent decreases with increasing retarding potential V and finally reaches zero when V is equal to V_0* (see Equation 4-1). With a small retarding potential the low-speed low-energy photoelectrons are brought to rest and no longer contribute to the photocurrent. When the retarding potential is equal to V_0, even the most energetic photoelectrons are brought to rest, and $i = 0$.

(d) For any particular surface the value of the *stopping potential V_0 depends on the frequency of the light but is independent of the light intensity* and therefore, from (b), independent also of the photocurrent.

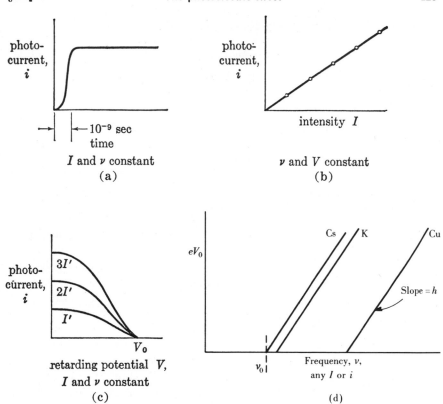

Figure 4-4. Experimental results of photoelectric emission.

Figure 4-4d shows experimental results for the three metals cesium, potassium, and copper. For each metal there is a well-defined frequency ν_0, the *threshold frequency*, which must be exceeded for photoemission to occur at all; that is, no photoelectrons are produced, however great the light intensity, unless $\nu > \nu_0$. For most metals the threshold frequency lies in the region of ultraviolet light. A typical stopping potential is several volts. The emitted photoelectrons have energies of several electron volts; therefore, we are justified in using the classical kinetic-energy formula for the photoelectrons.

With respect to any one type of metal the experimental results of Figure 4-4d may be represented by the straight-line equation

$$eV_0 = h\nu - h\nu_0$$

where h, representing the slope of the straight line, is found to be the *same* for *all* metals, and ν_0 is the threshold frequency for the particular metal.

Rearranging terms and using Equation 4-1 gives

$$h\nu = \tfrac{1}{2}m_0 v_{\max}^2 + h\nu_0 \qquad\qquad [4\text{-}2]$$

Inasmuch as $\tfrac{1}{2}m_0 v_{\max}^2$ has the dimensions of energy, the terms $h\nu$ and $h\nu_0$ must also have the dimensions of energy.

CLASSICAL INTERPRETATIONS OF THE PHOTOELECTRIC EFFECT   We now consider what effects may be expected on the basis of the classical properties of electromagnetic waves for each of the four experimental results on the photoelectric effect given in the preceding paragraphs. As before, we shall discuss them with reference to Figure 4-4 and in the same order.

(a) Because of the apparently continuous nature of light waves we expect the energy absorbed on the photoelectric surface to be proportional to the intensity of the light beam (the power per unit area), the area illuminated, and the time of illumination. All electrons that are bound to the surface of the metal with the same energy must be regarded as equivalent, and any one electron will be free to leave the surface only after the light beam has been on long enough to supply the electron's binding energy. Moreover, since any one electron is equivalent to any other electron bound with the same energy, we expect that when one electron has accumulated sufficient energy to be freed, a number of other electrons will have, too. Independent experiments show that in a typical metal the least energy with which an electron is bound to the surface is a few electron volts. A conservative calculation (see Problem 4-5) shows that in the case of an intensity as low as 10^{-10} W/m² for which delay times no longer than 10^{-9} sec have been observed, no photoemission can be expected until at least several hundred hours have elapsed! Clearly, the classical theory is unable to account for the essentially instantaneous photoelectric emission.

(b) Classical theory predicts that as the light intensity is increased, so is the energy absorbed by electrons at the surface. Hence, the number of photoelectrons emitted, or the photocurrent, is expected to increase proportionately with the light intensity. Here classical theory agrees with the experimental result.

(c) The results of these observations show that there is a distribution in the speeds, or energies, of the emitted photoelectrons; the distribution is in itself not incompatible with classical theory, because it may be attributed to the varying degrees of binding of electrons at the surface or to the varying amounts of energy extracted by electrons from the incident light beam. The fact, however, that there is a very well defined stopping potential V_0 for a given frequency, independent of the intensity, indicates that the maximum energy of released electrons is in no way dependent on the total amount of energy reaching the surface per unit time. Classical theory predicts no such effect.

(d) The existence of a threshold frequency for a given metal, a frequency below which no photoemission occurs, however great the light intensity, is completely inexplicable in classical terms. From the classical point of view the primary circumstance that determines whether or not photoemission will occur is the energy reaching the surface per unit time (or the intensity), but *not* the frequency. Further, the appearance of a single constant h that relates, through Equation 4-2, the maximum energy of photoelectrons to the frequency for any material cannot be understood in terms of any constants of classical electromagnetism.

In short, *classical electromagnetism cannot give a reasonable basis for understanding the experimental results illustrated in Figure 4-4, a, c, and d.*

QUANTUM INTERPRETATION OF THE PHOTOELECTRIC EFFECT An understanding of the photoelectric effect is to be found only through the quantum theory. Albert Einstein first applied the quantum theory to the nature of electromagnetic radiation in 1905, and this led to a satisfactory explanation of the photoelectric effect.

According to the quantum theory, the apparently continuous electromagnetic waves are quantized and consist of discrete *quanta*, called *photons*. Each photon has an energy E that depends only on the frequency (or on the wavelength) and is given by

$$E = h\nu = h(c/\lambda)$$ [4-3]

The constant h is, in fact, the very same h that appears in Equation 4-2, which summarizes the results of experiments on the photoelectric effect. This fundamental constant of the quantum theory is called *Planck's constant* because its value was first determined and its significance first appreciated by Planck in 1900 in the interpretation of blackbody radiation. The value of Planck's constant is given in joule-seconds:

$$h = 6.626 \times 10^{-34} \text{ J-sec}$$

According to the quantum theory, a beam of light of frequency ν consists of particle-like photons, each with an energy $h\nu$. A single photon can interact only with a single electron at the metal surface of a photoemitter; it cannot share its energy among several electrons. Inasmuch as photons travel with the speed of light, they must, on the basis of relativity theory, have zero rest mass and an energy that is then, entirely kinetic. When a particle with a zero rest mass ceases to move with a speed c, it ceases to exist; as long as it exists, it moves at the speed of light. Thus, when a photon strikes an electron bound in a metal and no longer moves at the unique speed c, it relinquishes its entire energy $h\nu$ to the single electron it strikes. If the energy the bound electron gains from the photon exceeds the energy binding it to the metal surface, the excess energy becomes the kinetic energy of the photoelectron.

We are now prepared to interpret on the basis of the quantum theory the experimental results of the photoelectric effect, which we now take in reverse order for convenience, referring to Figure 4-4.

(d) The terms in Equation 4-2 now give a simple meaning to the energies of the photon and photoelectron:

[4-2]
$$h\nu = \tfrac{1}{2}m_0 v_{max}^2 + h\nu_0$$

The left side of this equation gives the energy carried by a photon and supplied to a bound electron. Those electrons which are least tightly bound leave the surface with maximum kinetic energy. The right side of Equation 4-2 gives the energy gained by the electron from the photon, namely, the kinetic energy and the binding energy. The binding energy of the electrons least tightly bound to the metal surface is often represented by ϕ and called the *work function*; it represents the work that must be done to remove the least tightly bound electron. Therefore,

$$\phi = h\nu_0$$ [4-4]

and Equation 4-2 may be written in the form

$$h\nu = \tfrac{1}{2}m_0 v_{max}^2 + \phi$$ [4-5]

The value of ϕ for a particular material, determined from the photoelectric effect, agrees with the value of the work function obtained through independent experiments based on different physical principles (Section 12-9). An electron bound with an energy ϕ can be released only if a single photon supplies at least this much energy, that is, if $h\nu > \phi = h\nu_0$, or if $\nu > \nu_0$. Figure 4-4d then takes on new meaning: the ordinate may now be identified with the photon energy, as shown in Figure 4-5. (The latter figure should also be compared with the right-hand side of Figure 3-8, where for the photoelectric effect $W = h\nu$ and $E_b = \phi$.)

(c) A well-defined maximum kinetic energy of photoelectrons exists for any given frequency, because the frequency of the electromagnetic radiation determines precisely the photon energy ($E = h\nu$).

(b) The intensity of a monochromatic electromagnetic wave takes on a new meaning. It is, from the quantum point of view, the energy of each photon multiplied by the number of photons crossing a unit area per unit time. An increase in the intensity of a light beam means, therefore, a proportionate increase in the number of photons striking the

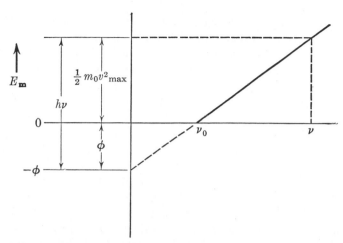

Figure 4-5. Maximum kinetic energy of photoelectrons as a function of the frequency of the incident photons for a particular material.

metal surface. It is then expected that the number of photoelectrons or the photocurrent i will be proportional to I.

(a) Photoemission occurs with no appreciable delay, because whether an electron is released depends, even at the smallest intensity, not upon its accumulating energy, but simply upon the fact of its being hit by a photon that on stopping relinquishes all of its energy to it.

Table 4-1 summarizes the results of experiment, the classical interpretation, and the quantum interpretation for each of the four effects shown in Figure 4-4.

Table 4-1

EFFECT FIGURE 4-4	EXPERIMENT	CLASSICAL ELECTROMAGNETISM	QUANTUM THEORY
(a)	Essentially instantaneous photoemission (10^{-9} sec)	Emission only after several hundred *hours* (10^6 sec) for low intensities	A single photon gives its energy to a single electron essentially instantaneously
(b)	$I \propto i$	Energy/area/time $\propto i$	$I \propto$ number of photons $\propto i$
(c)	A well-defined $\frac{1}{2}m_0v^2_{max}$, dependent only on ν	Inexplicable	A photon gives all its energy to a single electron
(d)	A threshold for photoemission, independent of I and i $h\nu = \frac{1}{2}m_0v^2_{max} + h\nu_0$	Inexplicable	Photon energy $= h\nu$; work function $= \phi = h\nu_0$

Our discussion of the photoelectric effect has thus far been in terms of the effects found when visible or ultraviolet light shines on a *metal* surface. The first detailed experiments that led historically to Einstein's quantum interpretation were performed with metal surfaces, but the effect occurs on materials other than metals and with photons of different frequencies and energies. The photoelectric effect can occur whenever a photon strikes a *bound* electron with enough energy to exceed the binding energy of the electron, for example, a photon freeing a bound electron from a single atom. The phenomenon is one of the important interactions between short-wavelength electromagnetic radiation and atoms. When a high-frequency (high-energy) photon, such as an x-ray or a gamma ray, strikes an atom, an electron bound with an energy E_b can be released, provided $h\nu > E_b$; then the photoemission results in atomic ionization. The kinetic energy of the released photoelectron must, in general, be written in the relativistic form $E - E_0$, and so the general form of Equation 4-2, the energy equation of the photoelectric effect, becomes

$$h\nu = (E - E_0) + E_b \qquad [4\text{-}6]$$

The photoelectric effect thus provides an indirect method of measuring the energy of a photon. Suppose that the photoelectron's kinetic energy $E - E_0$ is measured and the binding energy E_b is known on some other basis; then $h\nu$ may be computed from Equation 4-6. Conversely, if $h\nu$ and $E - E_0$ are measured, then E_b can be determined.

It should be remarked here that the photoelectric effect is only one of several ways in which photons can be removed from a beam of electromagnetic radiation. The photoelectric effect can occur simultaneously with, and compete with, the processes of the Compton effect and pair production, which will be discussed in detail in Sections 4-4 and 4-5.

The new and fundamental insight into the nature of electromagnetic radiation that the photoelectric effect provides is the quantization of electromagnetic waves, or the existence of photons. We may properly speak of the quantization of electromagnetic waves because the radiation may be regarded as a collection of particle-like photons, each of energy $h\nu$. When the frequency of the radiation is specified as ν, the photon can have but one energy, $h\nu$. The total energy of a beam of monochromatic electromagnetic radiation is always precisely an integral multiple of the energy $h\nu$ of a single photon; this is illustrated in Figure 4-6.

The granularity of electromagnetic radiation is not conspicuous in ordinary observations, because the energy of any one photon is very small, and because the number of photons in a light beam of moderate intensity is enormous. The situation is rather like that found in the molecular theory: the molecules are so small and their numbers so great that the molecular

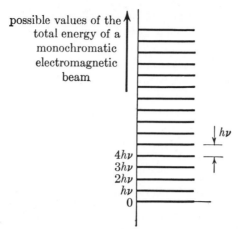

Figure 4-6. Allowed energies of a beam of monochromatic electromagnetic radiation.

structure of all matter is disclosed only in observations of considerable subtlety.

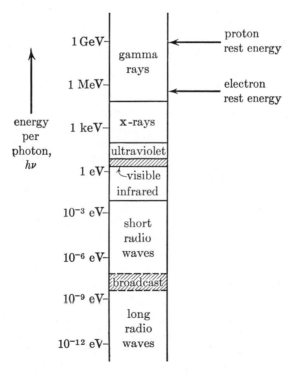

Figure 4-7. Spectrum of electromagnetic radiation on scale of photon energy.

The electromagnetic spectrum, often scaled in units of frequency, can be scaled from the point of view of the quantum theory, in units of energy per photon; see Figure 4-7.

Electromagnetic waves are commonly characterized by their wavelength. It is then useful to have a relation giving the photon energy in electron volts in terms of the corresponding wavelength in angstroms. For example, x-radiation of wavelength 1.0 angstrom (abbreviated Å) consists of photons whose energy E is

$$E = h\nu = \frac{hc}{\lambda} = \frac{(6.626 \times 10^{-34} \text{ J-sec})(2.998 \times 10^8 \text{ m/sec})}{(1.0 \text{ Å})(10^{-10} \text{ m/Å})(1.602 \times 10^{-19} \text{ J/eV})}$$

$$= 1.240 \times 10^4 \text{ eV} = 12.40 \text{ keV}$$

More generally, the photon energy E, in electron volts, in terms of the wavelength λ, in angstroms, is written

$$E = (1.240 \times 10^4 \text{ eV-Å})/\lambda = (0.01240 \text{ MeV-Å})/\lambda \qquad [4\text{-}7]$$

The energy per photon is smallest for radio-wave photons ($\approx 10^{-12}$ electron volt) and largest for gamma-ray photons (≈ 1 giga electron volt). The electromagnetic frequency spectrum corresponds exactly to the energy spectrum of a zero-rest-mass particle, or photon, whose energy can extend from zero to infinity, as shown in Figure 4-7. The rest energies of the electron and proton are also shown for comparison.

As we saw in Section 1-7, the ideas of wave and particle are apparently mutually incompatible, even contradictory. The fact that in the photoelectric effect light behaves as if it consisted of particles or photons does not mean that we can dismiss the incontrovertible experimental evidence of the wave properties of light; both descriptions must be accepted. An account of the way in which this dilemma is resolved will be postponed (Section 5-5) until after we have explored more fully the quantum attributes of light.

4-3 X-ray production and *bremsstrahlung* In the photoelectric effect a photon transfers all of its electromagnetic energy to a bound electron; the photon's energy appears as the binding energy and kinetic energy of the photoelectron. The inverse effect is that in which an electron loses kinetic energy and in so doing creates one or more photons. The process is most clearly illustrated in the production of x-rays.

First consider the fundamental process occurring when a fast-moving electron comes close to and is deflected by, the positively charged nucleus of an atom. The electron experiences a force in consequence of its near collision with the heavy atom and is diverted from its straight-line path; that is, it is accelerated. Classical electromagnetic theory predicts that any accelerated electric charge will radiate electromagnetic energy. Quantum theory requires that any radiated electromagnetic energy consist of discrete quanta, or photons. It is expected, then, that a deflected and therefore accelerated electron will radiate one or more photons and that the electron will leave the site of the collision with less kinetic energy than it had.

The radiation produced in such a collision is often referred to as *bremsstrahlung* ("braking radiation" in German). A *bremsstrahlung* collision is shown schematically in Figure 4-8, in which an electron approaches the

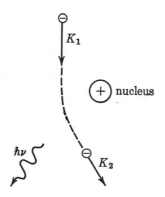

Figure 4-8. *Bremsstrahlung* collision between an electron and a positively charged nucleus with the emission of a single photon.

deflecting atom with a kinetic energy E_{k1} and recedes with a kinetic energy E_{k2} after having produced a single photon of energy $h\nu$. The conservation-of-energy law requires that

$$E_{k1} - E_{k2} = h\nu \qquad\qquad [4\text{-}8]$$

Because the atom's mass is at least two thousand times greater than the electron's, we have ignored the very small energy of the recoiling atom. Whereas classical electromagnetic theory predicts continuous radiation throughout the time that the electron is accelerated, quantum theory requires the radiation of single, discrete photons. That this occurs in the *bremsstrahlung* process is clearly illustrated in the production of x-ray photons.

X-rays were discovered and first investigated in 1895 by Wilhelm Roentgen, who assigned this name because the true nature of the radiation was at first unknown. X-rays are now known to consist of electromagnetic waves, or photons, having wavelengths of about 10^{-10} m = 1 angstrom unit. It has been experimentally confirmed that they exhibit the wave phenomena of interference, diffraction, and polarization. Because they pass readily through many materials that are opaque to visible light, and because a typical x-ray wavelength is far shorter than the wavelengths of visible light, the experiments require considerable ingenuity. We shall postpone discussion of x-ray absorption and intensity to Section 4-7 and of x-ray wavelengths to Section 5-2; our chief concern here will be with the energy characteristics of x-ray production.

The essential parts of a simple x-ray tube are shown in Figure 4-9. Electric current through the filament F heats the cathode C, and the

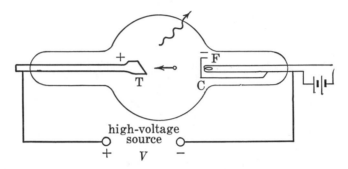

Figure 4-9. Essential parts of an x-ray tube.

electrons in the cathode are supplied with enough kinetic energy to overcome their binding to the cathode surface and be released in thermionic emission. The electrons are then accelerated through a vacuum by a large electrostatic potential difference V, typically several thousand volts, and strike the target T, which is the anode. While going from the cathode to the anode and before striking the target each electron attains a kinetic energy E_k which is given by

$$E_k = eV$$

where e is the electron charge. We have ignored the electron's kinetic energy as it left the cathode, because it is typically much less than Ve. When the electron strikes the target, it acquires an additional energy, the energy that binds it to the target surface; because the binding energy is always only a *few* electron volts whereas E_k is at least several *thousand*, we may properly ignore it, too.

Upon striking the target the electrons are decelerated and brought essentially to rest in collisions. Each electron loses its kinetic energy $E_k = eV$ because of its impact with the target. Most of this energy appears as thermal energy in the target, but there is, in addition, the production of electromagnetic radiation through the *bremsstrahlung* process. Any electron striking the target may make a number of *bremsstrahlung* collisions with atoms in the target, thereby producing a number of photons. The *most* energetic photon is produced, however, by an electron whose *entire* kinetic energy is converted into the electromagnetic energy of a *single* photon when the electron is brought to rest in a single collision. Thus $E_{k1} = eV$ and $E_{k2} = 0$, and Equation 4-8 becomes

$$eV = E_k = h\nu_{max}$$

where ν_{max} is the maximum frequency of the x-ray photons produced. More often electrons lose their energy at the target by heating it or by producing two or more photons, the sum of whose frequencies will then be less than ν_{max}. We expect, then, a distribution in photon energies with a well-defined maximal frequency ν_{max} or minimum wavelength $\lambda_{min} = c/\nu_{max}$ given by

$$\boxed{E_k = h\nu_{max} = hc/\lambda_{min} = eV} \qquad [4\text{-}9]$$

Note that this equation is equivalent to Equation 4-5 for the photoelectric effect when the binding-energy term is ignored.

Figure 4-10 shows the variation in the intensity of emitted x-rays as a function of frequency under typical operating conditions. An abrupt cutoff appears at the limit ν_{max} of the *continuous x-ray spectrum*, this limit being

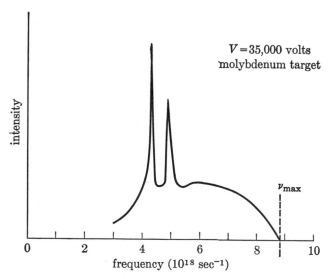

Figure 4-10. Intensity of x-rays as a function of frequency.

determined only by the accelerating potential V of the x-ray tube. The value of hc/e can be determined with considerable precision by using Equation 4-9 and simultaneous measurements of λ_{min} and V. The value obtained for Planck's constant h agrees completely with values deduced from experiments on the photoelectric effect and other experiments.

Superimposed on the continuous spectrum are sharp increases in the intensity, or peaks, whose wavelengths are characteristic of the target material; the explanation of these characteristic x-ray lines is to be found in the quantum description of the atomic structure of the target atoms. When the accelerating voltage V is changed, but the target material is not, the limit of the continuous x-ray spectrum changes, but the characteristic x-ray frequencies do not; conversely, when the target material is changed, but the accelerating voltage is not, the characteristic x-ray spectrum changes, but the limit of the continuous x-ray spectrum does not.

It is found that appreciable x-ray production occurs only if the accelerating potential V is of the order of 10,000 volts or more. Even at 10 kilovolts ($\lambda_{min} = 1.24$ Å by Equation 4-9) somewhat less than 1 percent of the total energy appears as electromagnetic radiation, the remainder appearing as thermal energy in the target.

4-4 The Compton effect   In the photoelectric effect a photon gives (nearly) all of its energy to a bound electron; it is also possible for a photon to give only part of its energy to a charged particle. This type of interaction between electromagnetic waves and a material substance is a *scattering* of the waves by the charged particles of the substance. The quantum theory of the scattering of electromagnetic waves is known as the *Compton effect*. We shall first review briefly the classical theory of the scattering of electromagnetic waves by charged particles.

When a monochromatic electromagnetic wave impinges upon a charged particle whose size is much less than the wavelength of the radiation, the charged particle will be acted upon principally by the sinusoidally varying electric field of the wave. Under the influence of this changing electric force the particle will oscillate in simple harmonic motion at the same frequency as that of the incident radiation (see Figure 4-11) and, since it is accelerated continuously, it will radiate electromagnetic radiation of the *same* frequency in all directions,† the intensity being greatest in the plane perpendicular to the direction of motion of the oscillating charge and zero along the line of oscillation. Classical theory predicts, then, that the scattered radiation will have the *same* frequency as that of the incident radiation. The charged particle plays the role of transfer agent, absorbing energy from the incident beam and reradiating this energy at the same frequency (or wavelength) but scattering it in all directions. The scattering particle neither gains nor loses energy, since it reradiates at the same rate as it absorbs. The classical scattering theory agrees with experiment for wavelengths of visible light and all other longer wavelengths of radiation. A simple example of the unchanged frequency of coherent scattered radiation

† See Sec. 41-5 in Weidner and Sells, *E. C. P.*

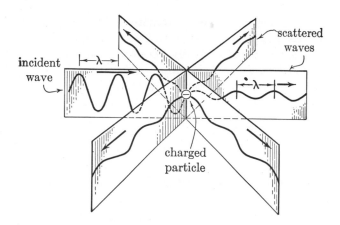

Figure 4-11. Classical scattering of electromagnetic radiation by a charged particle.

is this: light reflected from a mirror (a collection of scatterers) undergoes *no* apparent change in frequency.

The magnetic field of an incident electromagnetic wave also affects a charged particle. A charge moving in the transverse magnetic field of the electromagnetic wave is acted upon by a magnetic force *along* the direction of wave propagation.† When absorption is complete, this results in a radiation force F_r on the charged particle, given by $F_r = P/c$, where P is the power of the incident wave. Moreover, since an electromagnetic wave can exert a force on a scattering center, we attribute momentum p to the wave,

$$p = E/c$$

where E represents the electromagnetic energy of the incident wave.

Now we consider scattering from the point of view of the quantum theory. Utilizing Einstein's successful photon interpretation of the photoelectric effect, Arthur H. Compton in 1922 used the particle-like, quantum nature of electromagnetic radiation to explain the scattering of x-rays. In the quantum theory electromagnetic radiation consists of photons, each with an energy given by $E = h\nu$. Because a photon may be regarded as a zero-rest-mass particle moving at speed c, Equation 3-15 shows that the magnitude of the corresponding linear momentum p is given by E/c, in agreement with the classical result. Thus,

$$p = \frac{E}{c} = \frac{h\nu}{c} = \frac{h}{\lambda} \qquad [4\text{-}10]$$

† See Sec. 41-3 in Weidner and Sells, *E. C. P.*

Each photon in a beam of monochromatic electromagnetic radiation of wavelength λ has a momentum equal to h/λ. Equation 4-10 shows that the momentum of a photon is precisely specified when the wavelength, the frequency, or the energy of the photon is known. The direction of p is along the direction of propagation of the wave.

The distinctive feature introduced by the quantum theory is that for monochromatic waves the electromagnetic momentum occurs, not in arbitrary amounts, but only in integral multiples of the momentum h/λ carried by a single photon.

We can derive Equation 4-10 in a slightly different way, noting that the momentum of a photon must be the product of its relativistic mass and its speed:

$$p = mc = \left(\frac{E}{c^2}\right) c = \frac{E}{c} = \frac{h\nu}{c} = \frac{h}{\lambda}$$

where m is given by E/c^2. Just as a photon's energy increases with its frequency, so too its momentum increases with its frequency. Therefore, the momentum of a high-frequency and high-energy photon, such as a gamma ray, will exceed by far the momentum of a low-frequency and low-energy photon, such as a radio photon.

When we regard a monochromatic electromagnetic beam as consisting of a collection of particle-like photons, each with a precisely defined energy and momentum, the scattering of electromagnetic radiation becomes, in effect, a problem involving the collision of a photon with a charged particle. Then the problem is solved merely by applying the laws of energy and momentum conservation. Figures 4-12, a and b, show the photon and parti-

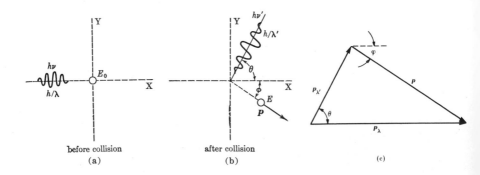

Figure 4-12. Collision of a photon and a particle initially at rest.

cle before and after collision. Of course, in applying the conservation laws we need to be concerned, not with the details of the interaction between the photon and particle during the collision, but only with the total energy and momentum going into and coming out of the collision.

Unlike the classical scattering of electromagnetic waves, in which the particle after collision is assumed to gain essentially no energy, the quantum treatment requires that it gain some, and because its kinetic energy may then be great, we must treat it relativistically.

We take the particle, of rest mass m_0 and rest energy $E_0 = m_0c^2$, to be free and initially at rest. Then we apply energy conservation to the collision of Figure 4-12 and get

$$h\nu + E_0 = h\nu' + E \qquad\qquad [4\text{-}11]$$

Here E is the energy of the recoiling *particle* after collision, and $h\nu$ and $h\nu'$ are the energies of the incident and scattered photons, respectively. Since the final energy (rest energy plus kinetic energy) of the recoil particle, $E = mc^2$, must exceed its initial energy E_0, we immediately see from Equation 4-11 that $h\nu' < h\nu$. Consequently, the scattered photon has *less* energy, a lower frequency, and a longer wavelength than the incident photon. This disagrees with the classical prediction of no frequency change upon scattering. Because the incident and scattered photons have different frequencies, the latter is *not* to be thought of as merely the incident photon moving in a different direction; rather, the incident photon is annihilated, and the scattered photon is created.

The conservation of linear momentum is implied by the vector triangle of Figure 4-12c, where $p = mv$ is the relativistic momentum of the recoiling particle, and the magnitudes of the momenta of the incident and scattered photons are, respectively, $p_\lambda = h\nu/c = h/\lambda$ and $p_{\lambda'} = h\nu'/c = h/\lambda'$. The scattering angle θ is the angle between the directions of p_λ and $p_{\lambda'}$, the directions of the incident and scattered photons.

We wish to solve for the change in wavelength $\lambda' - \lambda = \Delta\lambda$ in terms of θ. Applying the law of cosines to the triangle in Figure 4-12c, we have

$$p_\lambda^2 + p_{\lambda'}^2 - 2p_\lambda p_{\lambda'} \cos\theta = p^2 \qquad\qquad [4\text{-}12]$$

Multiplying both sides of this equation by c^2 and recalling that for a photon $pc = h\nu$, we have

$$h^2\nu^2 + h^2\nu'^2 - 2h^2\nu\nu' \cos\theta - p^2c^2 \qquad\qquad [4\text{-}13]$$

We can arrive at a similar expression by using Equation 4-11. We place $h\nu$ and $h\nu'$ on one side of Equation 4-11 and E and E_0 on the other; then squaring the equation, we get

$$h^2\nu^2 + h^2\nu'^2 - 2h^2\nu\nu' = E^2 + E_0^2 - 2EE_0 = 2E_0^2 + p^2c^2 - 2EE_0 \qquad [4\text{-}14]$$

where we have replaced E^2 with $E_0^2 + p^2c^2$, using Equation 3-14. Subtracting Equation 4-13 from Equation 4-14, we have

$$-2h^2\nu\nu'(1 - \cos\theta) = 2E_0^2 - 2EE_0$$

$$h^2\nu\nu'(1 - \cos\theta) = E_0(E - E_0) = m_0c^2(h\nu - h\nu')$$

$$\frac{h}{m_0c}(1 - \cos\theta) = c\left(\frac{\nu - \nu'}{\nu\nu'}\right) = \frac{c}{\nu'} - \frac{c}{\nu} = \lambda' - \lambda$$

The increase in wavelength $\Delta\lambda$ is, then,

$$\Delta\lambda = \lambda' - \lambda = \frac{h}{m_0c}(1 - \cos\theta) \qquad [4\text{-}15]$$

This is the basic equation of the Compton effect. It gives the increase $\Delta\lambda$ in the wavelength of the scattered photon over that of the incident photon. We see that $\Delta\lambda$ depends only on the rest mass m_0 of the recoiling particle, Planck's constant h, the speed c of light, and the angle θ of scattering. It is perhaps surprising to find that it is *independent* of the incident photon's wavelength, λ. The quantity h/m_0c, appearing on the right-hand side of Equation 4-15 and having the dimensions of length, is known as the *Compton wavelength*. Although the scattering angle θ determines the wavelength increase $\Delta\lambda$ unambiguously, we cannot predict in advance the angle at which any one photon will emerge.

If the recoiling particle is a free electron within the scattering material, then $m_0 = 9.11 \times 10^{-31}$ kg and $h/m_0c = 0.02426$ Å. When a photon emerges at, for example, $\theta = 90°$ with respect to the incident-photon direction, the wavelength change, by Equation 4-15, is 0.024 Å. When it emerges at $\theta = 180°$, traveling, in other words, in the backward direction, and the recoil electron travels in the forward direction, the collision being a precisely head-on one, then the wavelength change is a maximum and is equal to 0.049 Å. In such a collision the electron's kinetic energy is also a maximum.

For the 90° scattering, by a free electron, of incident radiation in the visible region, say of 4,000 Å, the *fractional* increase in wavelength, $\Delta\lambda/\lambda$, is only 0.006 percent. Such a shift in wavelength is completely masked in visible light by the fact that the electrons in an ordinary scattering material are not at rest but are in thermal motion. An observable shift of, say, $\Delta\lambda/\lambda = 2$ percent can be obtained by using incident radiation of wavelength $\lambda = 1$ Å; then $\Delta\lambda = 0.024$ Å. Thus, there is an easily observed shift for x-ray photons and photons of shorter wavelength. For photons of longer wavelength the fractional change in wavelength is very small, and the scattered radiation has nearly the same wavelength and frequency as the incident radiation. Classically, the wavelengths of the incident and scattered radiations are essentially equal; hence, Compton scattering agrees with classical scattering in the region of $\Delta\lambda/\lambda \ll 1$. We see here an example of the correspondence principle as applied to quantum effects, since, by Equation 4-15,

$$\underset{\substack{m_0 \to \infty \\ \text{or } h \to 0}}{\text{Limit}} (\Delta\lambda/\lambda) = \underset{\substack{m_0 \to \infty \\ \text{or } h \to 0}}{\text{Limit}} (h/m_0 c\lambda) = 0$$

That the scattering of x-rays agrees with the photon model rather than the classical model, which predicts no change in wavelength, was shown first by A. H. Compton in 1922. Figure 4-13 gives schematically the experi-

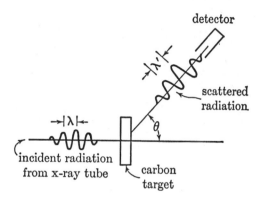

Figure 4-13. Schematic of experimental arrangement for the Compton effect.

mental arrangement for x-rays incident on a target of carbon, a substance having many free electrons (effectively free, that is). For any fixed angle θ the detector (see Sections 5-2 and 8-3) can measure the scattered radiation's intensity as a function of wavelength (compare Figure 4-13 with Figure 4-11, where $\lambda = \lambda'$ and $\Delta\lambda = 0$). Figure 4-14 shows the intensity of the scattered radiation versus the scattered wavelength for three fixed angles θ.

For any particular scattering angle θ *two* predominant wavelengths are present in the scattered radiation: one of the same wavelength λ as the incident beam, the *unmodified wave*, and a second, longer wavelength λ', the *modified wave*, given by the Compton equation, Equation 4-15. The unmodified wavelength results from the coherent scattering of the incident radiation by the inner electrons of atoms; these electrons are so tightly bound to the atoms that a photon cannot strike one of them without at the same time moving the entire atom. The mass m_0 of one of these tightly bound electrons is, then, *effectively* the mass M_0 of the atom, Therefore, in a Compton collision between a photon and a tightly bound electron the

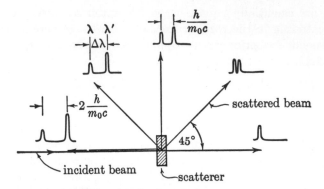

Figure 4-14. Intensity of scattered radiation versus wavelength of scattered radiation for three different angles θ.

wavelength change $\Delta\lambda$ is $(h/M_0 c)(1 - \cos\theta) \approx 0$, because M_0 is always thousands of times greater than m_0.

The Compton effect provides a simple method of determining the energy of a photon. From Equation 4-11 we have

$$E_k = E - E_0 = h\nu - h\nu'$$

Because $\nu = c/\lambda$ and $\nu' = c/\lambda' = c/(\lambda + \Delta\lambda)$, we may write this as

$$E_k = h\nu \frac{\Delta\lambda}{\lambda + \Delta\lambda} \qquad [4\text{-}16]$$

where $\Delta\lambda$ depends on the scattering angle θ and is given by Equation 4-15. The kinetic energy of the recoil electron is a maximum, $E_{k,max}$, when a head-on collision occurs, the electron recoiling in the forward direction and the scattered photon traveling in the backward direction. In such a collision $\theta = 180°$ and $\Delta\lambda = 2h/m_0 c$, and Equation 4-16 becomes

$$E_{k,max} = h\nu \left(\frac{(2h\nu/m_0 c^2)}{1 + (2h\nu/m_0 c^2)} \right) \qquad [4\text{-}17]$$

Therefore, if we measure the energy of the most energetic recoil electrons, we can compute the energy of the incident photon from Equation 4-17, and conversely.

Our treatment of the Compton collision between a photon and an electron has been based on the assumption that the scattering electron is *free* and at rest. Of course, any electron in a material is in motion and is bound to some degree to its parent atom; the outer electrons of atoms may, however, be regarded as being effectively free, because their binding energy, typically a few electron volts, is much less than the energy of a typical x-ray photon, which for $\lambda = 1$ Å is 12,400 electron volts. When electromagnetic radiation of low frequency and long wavelength, such as radio waves with $\nu = 1.0$ megacycle per second, strikes an outer electron, the energy of the incident photon, 4.1×10^{-9} eV, is much less than the binding energy of the outer electron. Therefore, the m_0 in the Compton equation is effectively the mass of the atom, and the change in wavelength is very small ($\Delta\lambda \ll \lambda$), so that the two radiations have essentially the same frequencies.

The Compton effect shows clearly the particle-like aspects of electromagnetic radiation: not only a precise energy $h\nu$ can be assigned to a photon, but also a precise momentum h/λ. Along any direction the total momentum of a monochromatic electromagnetic beam can then assume, *not* any value, but only an exactly integral multiple of the linear momentum of a single photon along that direction. In this sense the momentum, as well as the energy, of electromagnetic radiation is quantized.

Example 4-1. The photoelectric effect, that process in which a photon is annihilated and a particle is set in motion with essentially all of the energy originally carried by the photon, can take place only if the particle is originally *bound*. It is easy to show that the following process, a hypothetical photoelectric effect with a *free* particle, is forbidden: a photon collides with a free particle initially at rest; the photon is annihilated (and no second photon is created), and all of the photon's energy and momentum are transferred to the free particle. Such a collision cannot occur, because it violates the simultaneous conservations of energy and momentum.

Taking the photon energy to be $h\nu$ and the initial and final energies of the free particle to be E_0 and E, respectively, we have, from energy conservation,

$$h\nu = E - E_0$$

But momentum conservation requires that

$$h\nu/c = \sqrt{(E^2 - E_0{}^2)}/c$$

where the particle's relativistic momentum appears on the right side of the equation. Eliminating $h\nu$ from the two equations above, we see that the only possible value of E_0 is zero. Since any material particle has a nonzero rest mass, the photoelectric effect cannot take place with a *free* particle. In an actual photoelectric effect, one with *bound* electrons, the electron's mass is much less than that of the object to which it is bound. Then nearly all of the photon's energy is transferred to the electron and only a small fraction to the object to which the electron is bound. On the other hand, only a fraction of the photon's momentum is transferred to the bound electron.

Example 4-2. Using classical electromagnetic theory, we can show that the radiation pressure P_r of a completely absorbed electromagnetic beam of intensity I is given by $P_r = I/c$ for incidence along the normal to the absorbing surface.† Derive this relation by taking the radiation to consist of photons, each with a momentum $h\nu/c$.

† See Equation 41-24 in Weidner and Sells, *E. C. P.*

We assume the flux of the photon beam to be N photons per unit time, per unit area perpendicular to the beam direction. Then, with an energy $h\nu$ carried by each photon in the beam the total energy per unit time, per unit transverse area, or the intensity I, is given by

$$I = N(h\nu)$$

If the beam strikes a surface that absorbs it completely, each photon transmits a momentum $h\nu/c$ to the surface. The total momentum transmitted per unit time, per unit area, is then $N(h\nu/c)$; but the total momentum transferred per unit time is just the radiation force on the absorbing surface, and this force per unit area is the radiation pressure P_r:

$$P_r = N(h\nu/c)$$

Eliminating $Nh\nu$ from the two equations above we have

$$P_r = I/c \quad \text{for complete absorption}$$

Note that the radiation pressure is independent of the frequency. If the beam strikes a totally reflecting surface along the normal to this surface, the momentum is transferred *twice* to the surface: once when an incident photon is annihilated upon striking the surface, and again when a second photon of the same frequency is created and travels outward from the surface. Consequently, the radiation pressure for complete reflection is given by

$$P_r = 2I/c \quad \text{for complete reflection}$$

Momentum being conserved, a source emitting photons recoils in the opposite direction. Thus, one very elementary form of a "photon rocket" consists simply of a unidirectional source of electromagnetic radiation: for example, a flashlight turned on. The rocket gains momentum in the forward direction because photons are emitted to the rear. Notice that a photon carries more momentum per total energy than does a particle of nonzero rest energy; that is, from $p = (E^2 - E_0^2)^{1/2}/c$ we see that for a given energy E the momentum p is a maximum for $E_0 = 0$.

As a zero-rest-mass particle a photon always is observed to travel at the single speed c; there is no reference frame in which it has any other speed than c. Its energy $h\nu$ and momentum $h\nu/c$, on the other hand, depend on the observer's reference frame: both quantities are proportional to the photon's frequency, and the frequency depends, in turn, on the reference frame by virtue of the (relativistic) Doppler effect. Thus, if an observer travels in the same direction as that in which a photon is moving, he finds the photon's frequency, energy, and momentum all to have increased relative to their values measured in a reference frame at rest with respect to the source of photons.

4-5 Pair production and annihilation   The photoelectric effect, the *bremsstrahlung* process, and the Compton effect are all examples of the conversion of the electromagnetic energy of photons into the kinetic energy and potential energy of material particles, and vice versa. It is natural to ask whether it is possible to convert a photon's energy into *rest* mass—that is, to create pure matter from pure energy—or, on the other hand, to convert rest energy into electromagnetic energy. The answer is yes, provided such conversions do not violate the conservation laws of energy, momentum, and electric charge.

PAIR PRODUCTION   Consider first the minimum energy required to create a single material particle. Since the electron has the smallest nonzero rest mass of all known particles, it requires the least energy for its creation. A photon has zero electric charge. Thus, the law of charge conservation precludes the creation of a *single* electron from a photon. The creation of an electron pair, however, consisting of two particles with opposite electric charges, is possible and has been observed. The positively charged particle is called a *positron* and is said to be the *antiparticle* of the electron. The electron and positron are similar in all ways except in the signs of their charges, $-e$ and $+e$ (and, the effects of this difference). The minimum energy $h\nu_{\min}$ needed to create an electron-positron pair is, by the conservation of energy,

$$h\nu_{\min} = 2m_0 c^2$$

Since the rest energy $m_0 c^2$ of an electron or positron is 0.51 MeV the threshold energy $2m_0 c^2$ for pair production is 1.02 MeV. The photon's wavelength corresponding to this threshold energy is 0.012 Å; hence, electron pairs can be produced only by gamma-ray photons or by x-ray photons of very short wavelength. The process in which matter is created from electromagnetic radiation is called *pair production*, because a particle and its antiparticle must always be created together if the conservation laws are to be satisfied. The phenomenon of pair production is a most emphatic demonstration of the interconvertibility of mass and energy.

If a photon's energy exceeds the threshold energy $2m_0 c^2$, the excess appears as kinetic energy of the created pair. Applying the conservation of energy to pair production gives

$$h\nu = m^+ c^2 + m^- c^2 = (m_0 c^2 + E_k^+) + (m_0 c^2 + E_k^-)$$

$$\boxed{h\nu = 2m_0 c^2 + (E_k^+ + E_k^-)}$$ [4-18]

where ν is the frequency of the incident photon, and E_k^+ and E_k^- are the kinetic energies of the created particles. The minimum energy $h\nu_{\min}$, just enough to produce the pair, is obtained by setting the kinetic energies of the created particles equal to zero: $E_k^+ + E_k^- = 0$.

Pair production cannot occur in empty space. It is easy to prove that energy and momentum cannot simultaneously be conserved in particle-antiparticle production unless the photon is near some massive particle, such as an atomic nucleus. We can see that the presence of a heavy particle is essential by considering Figure 4-15, which is a plot of the relativistic energy E versus the relativistic momentum p, shown earlier in Figure 3-6. First assume that there is no heavy particle involved in the production of a pair and, for simplicity that, the energy of each of the created particles

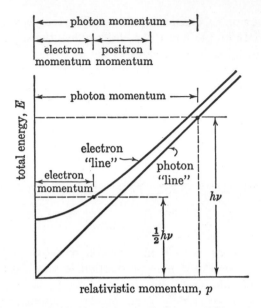

Figure 4-15. A graphical illustration of the impossibility of pair production in empty space.

is exactly half of the photon's energy. Figure 4-15 shows that the sum of the momenta of the two particles must be *less* than the momentum of the photon. Thus, the total momentum after collision will be less than the momentum of the photon, unless some particle is present that will carry away some of the photon's momentum. We can be assured, however, that any energy carried away by a recoiling heavy particle would be so small as to be excludable from Equation 4-18, because a heavy particle's mass is very large compared with that of an electron or positron.

Through another argument we can see that a photon cannot disintegrate spontaneously into an electron-positron pair when traveling through empty space. Suppose, for example, that a pair is created and that we, the observers, are at rest with respect to the center of mass of its system. Then the total momentum of the electron and positron is zero, but the photon that produced the pair would have had some nonzero momentum in this reference frame, since a photon is always found to move at the speed c, whatever the reference frame. We should then have the momentum of the photon before collision but no net momentum after. In short, a photon cannot decay spontaneously into an electron-positron pair in free space.

Figure 4-16 is a schematic drawing of pair production, and Figure 4-17 is a cloud-chamber photograph showing the creation of electron-positron pairs. Figure 4-17 shows that high-energy gamma-ray photons entered the area (top of the photograph), came close to lead nuclei, and were annihi-

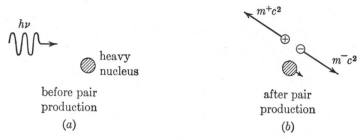

Figure 4-16. Schematic diagram of pair production.

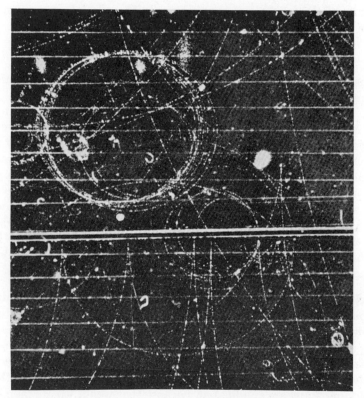

Figure 4-17. Cloud-chamber photograph showing the creation of electron-positron pairs. Photons of approximately 200 MeV, producing no tracks, appear from the top. Some photons are annihilated, and electron-positron pairs are created in the thin, horizontal lead foil; above the foil and to the right is a pair produced by the collision of a photon and a gas molecule. The external magnetic field, of flux density 1 weber per square meter, bends the paths of the electrons and positrons into opposite curvatures. (From *Cloud Chamber Photographs of the Cosmic Radiation*, C. D. Rochester and J. G. Wilson, Pergamon Press, Ltd., 1952. Courtesy of Pergamon Press, Ltd.)

lated, and that electron-positron pairs were created. The paths of the charged particles are visible because of the ionization effects they produce as they travel through the gas; the trajectories of the oppositely charged particles (with approximately equal kinetic energies†) show opposite curvatures, the particles having been deflected into oppositely directed circular arcs by a uniform magnetic field.

The energy of a photon producing an electron-positron pair can be computed by means of Equation 4-18, if the kinetic energies of the electron and positron are measured. These energies can be determined from a photograph such as Figure 4-17, if the magnetic field B and the radius r of curvature of the trajectories are measured. The relativistic momentum p of each particle is given by

[3-9] $$p = mv = QBr$$

and the total energy E or kinetic energy $E - E_0$ of the particle can then be computed by means of using Equation 3-14, $E^2 = E_0^2 + (pc)^2$.

The existence of positrons was predicted on theoretical grounds by P. A. M. Dirac in 1928. Four years later C. D. Anderson observed and identified a positron during his studies of cosmic radiation. Shortly thereafter electron-positron pairs were produced in the laboratory by means of particle accelerators operating at a few MeV of energy; they are now a commonly observed phenomenon in the interaction of high-energy photons and matter. Proton-antiproton and neutron-antineutron pairs were first created in the laboratory in 1955. Their threshold energies are several GeV (the proton and neutron masses are approximately equal to 1 GeV and therefore require accelerating machines of very high energy); see Problem 4-48.

PAIR ANNIHILATION   The annihilation of particle-antiparticle pairs and the concomitant creation of photons is the inverse of pair production. Consider the annihilation of matter and the creation of electromagnetic energy that may occur when an electron and positron are close together and essentially at rest. The total linear momentum of the two particles is initially zero; therefore, a *single* photon cannot be created when the two particles unite and are annihilated, because that would violate momentum conservation. Momentum can, however, be conserved when *two* photons, moving in opposite directions with equal momenta, are created. Such a pair of photons would have equal frequencies and energies; see Figure 4-18. (Actually, three or more photons can be created, but with a *much* smaller probability than that of two photons. Similarly, when many electron-

† To be precise, the positron has, on the average, a greater kinetic energy than the electron, because it is repelled by, and the electron is attracted by, the positively charged nucleus.

$$m_0^+ c^2$$
$$\oplus$$

$$\ominus$$
$$m_0^- c^2$$

$h\nu$

$h\nu$

before annihilation   after annihilation
(a)   (b)

Figure 4-18. Pair annihilation and the creation of two photons.

positron pairs are annihilated near a heavy nucleus, a small number of the annihilations will produce a single photon.)

Conservation of energy requires

$$m_0^+ c^2 + m_0^- c^2 = h\nu_1 + h\nu_2$$

in which the electron and positron are assumed to be at rest initially. But $m_0^+ = m_0^-$ and, by momentum conservation, $\nu_1 = \nu_2 = \nu_{\min}$; therefore,

$$2h\nu_{\min} = 2m_0 c^2$$

$$h\nu_{\min} = m_0 c^2 \qquad\qquad [4\text{-}19]$$

Since the minimum energy needed for creating a photon, $h\nu = m_0 c^2$, is 0.51 MeV, this is the minimum energy of the photon created.

Annihilation is the ultimate fate of positrons. When a high-energy positron appears, as in pair production, it loses its kinetic energy in collisions as it passes through matter, finally moving at low speed. It then combines with an electron, forming a bound system, called a positronium atom, which decays very quickly (10^{-10} sec) into two photons of equal energy. Thus, the death of a positron is signalled by the appearance of two annihilation quanta, or photons, of $\frac{1}{2}$ MeV each. The transitoriness of positrons is due, not to an intrinsic instability, but to the high risk of their collision and subsequent annihilation with electrons.

In our part of the universe there is a preponderance of electrons, protons, and neutrons; their antiparticles, when created, quickly combine with them in annihilation processes. It is conceivable, although at present purely conjectural, that there exists a part of the universe in which positrons, antiprotons, and antineutrons predominate.

Pair production and annihilation are particularly striking examples of mass-energy equivalence. They provide irrefutable confirmation of the theory of relativity.

4-6 Photon-electron interactions   Figures 4-19 summarize the important photon-electron interactions, or collisions, that we have discussed in this

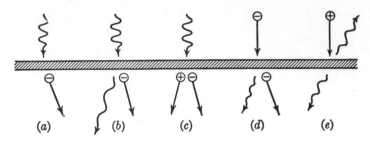

Figure 4-19. Photon-electron interactions: (a) photoelectric effect, (b) Compton effect, (c) pair production, (d) *bremsstrahlung*, and (e) pair annihilation.

chapter. In each instance a photon, electron, or positron approaches a slab of material, a collision occurs, and one or more particles emerge. We summarize briefly the salient features of each of these interactions, taking them in the order in which they appear in the figure:

The photoelectric effect: a photon strikes a bound electron and disappears, and the electron is dislodged.

The Compton effect: a photon collides with a free electron, thereby effecting the creation of a second photon of lower energy and the recoil of the electron.

Pair production: a photon is annihilated in the vicinity of a heavy particle, and an electron-positron pair is created.

Bremsstrahlung: an electron is deflected in the vicinity of a heavy particle, and a photon is created.

Pair annihilation: A positron combines with an electron, and a pair of photons is produced.

As we shall see in Section 11-1, *all* of these photon-electron interactions may be shown to be illustrations of just *one* basic interaction between the particle of the electromagnetic field (the photon) and a particle that can create an electromagnetic field (an electron or any other electrically charged particle). Even the ordinary electric, or Coulomb, force between electrically charged particles and, indeed, all other electromagnetic effects, may be shown to be basically an interchange of (virtual) photons between charged particles.

Note that the principal features of the photon-electron collisions were derived simply by applying the laws of the conservation of energy, momentum, and electric charge and by assuming the existence of photons of energy $h\nu$ and momentum h/λ. In no case did we concern ourselves with the details of the interaction. Further, we did not calculate the probability of the occurrence of any of these processes. For example, in the Compton effect, we are able to predict the wavelength of a photon deflected in any particular direction, but we are unable to predict the direction of any particular photon. The probabilities of the occurrence of a photon-electron interaction, however, can be calculated with high precision by the methods of *quantum electrodynamics.*

Highly energetic (at least 10^{19} electron volts) charged particles from the cosmic radiation enter the Earth's atmosphere. They may produce a whole succession of electron-photon interactions, as follows. A collision between a cosmic-ray particle and a nucleus may produce a high-energy gamma ray through *bremsstrahlung.* The gamma ray may be annihilated on passing near a nucleus and so produce an electron-positron pair. The created charged particles, having large kinetic energies, may collide with, and be deflected by, nuclei they encounter on their way to the Earth's surface; by virtue of their acceleration after the collisions they radiate high-energy photons by the *bremsstrahlung* process. The positron may combine with the electron, both be annihilated, and two photons be created. The secondary photons may have energies exceeding 1.02 MeV and so may produce more electron pairs. Thus, by the repeated occurrence of pair production, pair annihilation, bremsstrahlung and, to a lesser extent,

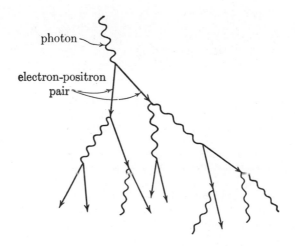

Figure 4-20. Schematic representation of a cascade shower.

Compton and photoelectric collisions a *cascade shower* of electrons, positrons, and photons is produced, the energy of the original photon having been degraded and spread among many particles. The shower is effectively extinguished when pair production becomes energetically impossible. A diagram of photon-electron interactions is shown in Figure 4-20; spectacular cloud-chamber photographs, such as Figure 4-21, have confirmed the principal features of cascade showers.

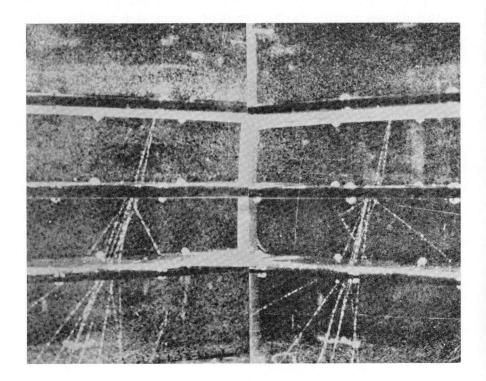

Figure 4-21. Cloud-chamber photographs of a photon-initiated cascade shower taken simultaneously with two cameras to permit three-dimensional analysis of the tracks. A 700 MeV photon (producing no track) enters from the top, and a positron-electron pair is created at the uppermost horizontal thin lead plate. Photons are created at the lower plates by *bremsstrahlung* collisions, and these photons create more pairs, leading to a shower of electrons, positrons, and photons. (Courtesy of J. C. Street, Harvard University.)

4-7 Absorption of photons Three important processes that can remove photons from a beam of electromagnetic radiation are the photoelectric effect, the Compton effect, and pair production. These are shown as the photon-electron interactions (a), (b), and (c) of Figure 4-19. In each of the processes a photon is removed from a forward-moving beam and an electron appears. Furthermore, each process occurs only when there are atoms with which the oncoming photons can collide and interact. The atoms provide bound electrons for the photoelectric effect, nearly free electrons for the Compton effect, and atomic nuclei for pair production. The intensity of the photon beam is reduced, then, only to the extent that the photons encounter and interact with atoms (there is a process, which for the moment we ignore, in which a photon is selectively absorbed by a material according to its energy, and the total internal energy of the absorbing atom is thereby increased).

An electron having kinetic energy appears as one of the outgoing particles in each of the three interactions. This fact may be utilized in devices for detecting photons. The fast-moving electrons produce ionization, which can be electrically measured; thus, the intensity of high-frequency photons to which the eye is not sensitive, such as x-rays and gamma rays, can be measured by ionization effects. Ionization measurements will be discussed in·Chapter 8; our concern here will be with the absorption of electromagnetic radiation in a material.

The intensity I of electromagnetic radiation is defined as the energy, per unit time, passing through a unit area at right angles to the direction of propagation. Put in terms of a beam of monochromatic photons, it is the energy $h\nu$ of a single photon times the number of photons, per unit time, crossing a unit area perpendicular to the direction of the beam:

$$\text{intensity of a photon beam} = \frac{\text{energy}}{\text{photon}} \times \frac{\text{number of photons}}{\text{area} \times \text{time}}$$

The *photon flux* of a beam of monochromatic electromagnetic radiation is defined as the number of photons crossing a unit area, per unit time. We represent the photon flux by N; then

$$\boxed{I = (h\nu)N} \qquad\qquad [4\text{-}20]$$

When a photon beam strikes a material, the photon flux N is reduced, because photons are removed or are deflected from the forward direction. The absorption of photons by a material is shown schematically in Figure 4-22. Clearly, the probability that a photon will be removed from the beam is greater, the greater the number of atoms the beam encounters; therefore, it is greater, the thicker the absorber. In the figure photons with a flux N are incident on a very thin absorber of thickness dx, and photons with a flux $N - dN$ emerge from the absorber in the forward direction. The number of photons removed per unit time by a unit area of the absorber is, then, dN. When the number of incident photons increases,

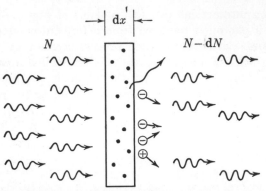

Figure 4-22. Schematic representation of the absorption of photons by a material substance.

the number of photons removed in encounters with atoms in the absorber increases proportionately; that is, dN is proportional to N. Further since the number of atoms encountered by the beam is directly proportional to the thickness of the absorber, dN is proportional also to dx. Therefore,

$$dN = -\mu N \, dx$$

where the proportionality constant is μ, called the *absorption coefficient*. The minus sign appears because N decreases as x increases. Rearranging terms and integrating x from zero thickness to a finite thickness x (Figure 4-23), and integrating the flux from N_0, the flux incident on the absorber,

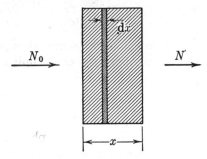

Figure 4-23. Change in photon flux through an absorber.

to N, the flux emerging from the absorber of thickness x, we have

$$\int_{N_0}^{N} \frac{dN}{N} = -\mu \int_{0}^{x} dx$$

$$ln \, (N/N_0) = -\mu x$$

$$N = N_0 e^{-\mu x} \qquad [4\text{-}21]$$

Using Equation 4-20, we can write Equation 4-21 as

$$I = I_0 e^{-\mu x}$$

[4-22]

where $I_0 = (h\nu)N_0$ is the intensity incident on the absorber, and $I = (h\nu)N$ is the intensity at a distance x from the front surface. This equation shows that the intensity of monochromatic electromagnetic radiation falls off exponentially through an absorber. The absorption increases with the thickness of the absorber (as x increases), or as the absorption coefficient μ increases. We also see from Equation 4-22 that when $\mu x = 1$, or $x = 1/\mu$, then $I = I_0/e$. Therefore, the quantity $1/\mu$ represents that absorber thickness at which the intensity I is $1/e$, or 37 percent, of the incident intensity I_0.

For a particular photon energy and for a particular absorbing material the absorption coefficient μ is a constant having the unit reciprocal length. Its value does, however, change from one material to another, and it depends as well, for a given absorbing material, on the energy (or frequency) of the radiation. Figures 4-24 show the absorption coefficients for aluminum

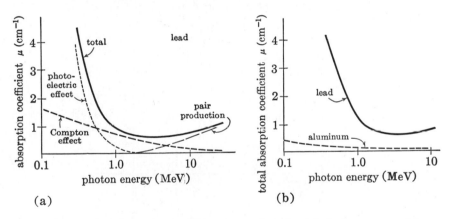

(a)   (b)

Figure 4-24. Absorption coefficients as a function of photon energy: (a) for lead with several contributions to the total absorption coefficient and (b) for lead and aluminum.

and for lead as a function of the photon energy (plotted on a logarithmic scale). The absorption coefficient μ is large for low-energy photons, whose removal occurs principally through the process of the photoelectric effect. It is smaller at intermediate energies, at which Compton collisions are the most effective in absorbing photons. It reaches a minimum in the vicinity of a few MeV and then rises again with photon energy. A little before its minimum, at 1.02 MeV (where the photons' wavelength is 0.012 Å), the threshold for pair production occurs, and at very high energies, where μ has increased somewhat, pair production predominates.

Figures 4-25 and 4-26 show how the absorption of electromagnetic radiation varies with the energy of the photons and with the identity of

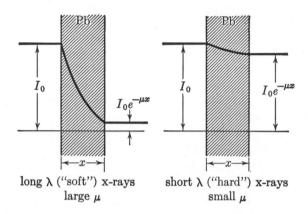

long λ ("soft") x-rays
large μ

short λ ("hard") x-rays
small μ

Figure 4-25. Exponential absorption of soft and of hard x-rays by a lead absorber.

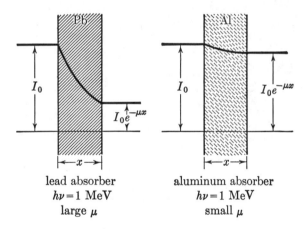

lead absorber
$h\nu = 1$ MeV
large μ

aluminum absorber
$h\nu = 1$ MeV
small μ

Figure 4-26. Exponential absorption of 1 MeV photons by lead and by aluminum.

the absorbing material. They show the intensity of the incident beam, of the beam at various depths of penetration in the absorber, and of the emergent beam. Figure 4-25 shows the absorption of long-wavelength x-rays, which are appreciably absorbed in moderate thicknesses of lead, and so are called *soft*, and the absorption of short-wavelength, or *hard*, x-rays, which are only slightly attenuated through the same thickness of lead. This illustrates that for a particular absorbing material and for photons of relatively low energy (less than 4 MeV) the coefficient decreases as the energy increases. Figure 4-26 shows the absorption of the same x-rays in lead and in aluminum of the same thickness; clearly, lead is much more effective as an x-ray absorber and therefore has much the larger absorption coefficient for a given photon energy. It is generally true that materials, such as lead, are more effective absorbers than light materials, a fact that is the basis of x-ray photography, the darkening of the photographic emulsion is a measure of the x-ray intensity, and the relative absorption properties of the variously light and dense materials are the reason for the images.

4-8 Summary   Two kinds of physical quantity can be distinguished: those with a continuous range of values and those with a discrete, or quantized, set of values. The quantum theory, formulated by Max Planck in 1900, has shown that many quantities that appear superficially to have continuous values actually have discrete values only.

Monochromatic electromagnetic radiation, when interacting with matter, must be considered to consist of photons, each photon having a discrete energy and momentum:

[4-3], [4-10] $E = h\nu$ and $p = h/\lambda$

A useful relation between the energy and the wavelength of a photon is

[4-7] $E = (0.0124 \text{ MeV-Å})/\lambda$

The following are the basic photon-particle interactions.

Photoelectric effect: the *complete* transfer of *electromagnetic energy* to a *bound electron*:

[4-6] $h\nu = E_b + (E - E_0)$

where E_b is the binding energy, or work function, of an electron.

Bremsstrahlung: The *partial* or *complete* transfer of a particle's *kinetic energy* to *electromagnetic energy*. Photons of maximum frequency (minimum wavelength) are produced when an electron is brought to rest in a single collision:

[4-9] $eV = E_k = h\nu_{max} = hc/\lambda_{min}$

Compton effect: the *partial* transfer of *electromagnetic energy* to the *kinetic energy* of a particle. When a photon of wavelength λ interacts with a (nearly) free particle essentially at rest, a photon emerges at an angle θ (scattering), and the particle recoils with kinetic energy E_k:

[4-15] $\Delta\lambda = \lambda' - \lambda = \dfrac{h}{m_0 c}(1 - \cos\theta)$

[4-16]
$$E_k = (h\nu) \frac{\Delta\lambda}{(\lambda + \Delta\lambda)}$$

where m_0 is the rest mass of the recoil particle.

Pair production and annihilation: The *complete* conversion of *electromagnetic energy* into the *rest energy* and *kinetic energy* of the created particles, and the reverse:

pair production: $h\nu = 2m_0c^2 + (E_k^+ + E_k^-)$

pair annihilation: $(m^+ + m^-)c^2 = 2h\nu$

The intensity of a monochromatic photon beam is the product of the photon energy and the photon flux N:

[4-20]
$$I = (h\nu)N$$

In materials of thickness x the absorption of monochromatic electromagnetic radiation (by the processes of the photoelectric effect, the Compton effect, and pair production) follows the relation

[4-22]
$$I = I_0 e^{-\mu x}$$

where μ is the absorption coefficient, whose value depends on the nature of the absorber and on the photon energy.

PROBLEMS

4-1   The threshold wavelength for the emission of electrons from a zinc surface is 2930 Å. (a) Calculate the binding energy, or work function, ϕ (in electron volts) of an electron at the surface of sodium. (b) What is the maximum kinetic energy (in electron volts) of a photoelectron emitted from the surface when light of 2,000 Å strikes this surface?

4-2   (a) What is the maximum speed of photoelectrons emitted from a sodium surface ($\phi = 2.3$ eV) when ultraviolet light of 2,480 Å is used? (b) Does this justify our assumption that $E_{k,\,max} = \frac{1}{2} mv_{max}^2$?

4-3   When monochromatic light of wavelength 4,046 Å shines on a certain metal surface, the most energetic photoelectrons are stopped by a retarding potential of 1.60 V: when the wavelength is 5769 Å, the stopping potential is 0.45 V. Assuming h and e unknown, what are (a) the work function (in volts) of this photoemitter and (b) the value of h/e computed from these data?

4-4   *   A 1,240 Å photon strikes a tungsten target normally and releases a photoelectron from the surface, the photoelectron moving in the direction opposite to that of the incident photon. The work function for tungsten is 4.5 eV. Assume that essentially all the photon's energy is given to the electron. (a) Calculate the maximum speed of the released electron. (b) Using the conservation-of-momentum law, find the momentum imparted to the target. (c) The target has a mass of 100 g; calculate the fraction of the photon's energy given to the target. This justifies our original assumption that in the photoelectric effect practically all the energy of the photon is transferred to the electron.

4-5 * Light of intensity 1.0×10^{-10} W/m² falls normally upon a silver surface, where there is one free electron per atom. The atoms are approximately 2.6 Å apart. Treat the incident radiation classically (as waves), and assume the energy to be uniformly distributed over the surface and all the light to be absorbed by the surface electrons. (a) How much energy does each free electron gain per second? (b) The binding energy of an electron at a surface is 4.8 eV; how long must one wait, after the beam is switched on, before any one electron gains enough energy to overcome its binding energy and be released as a photoelectron? Compare this with the experimental results.

4-6 * A photon enters a so-called lead "radiator" (which radiates photoelectrons) and interacts with an inner electron bound to a lead atom with a binding energy of 89.1 keV. The photoelectron released then enters a uniform magnetic field, and Br (where r is the radius of curvature of the electron in the magnetic field B) is found to be 2.0×10^{-3} Wb/m. (a) What is the momentum of the photoelectron (in MeV/c)? (b) What is the kinetic energy of the photoelectron? (c) What is the energy of the incident photon?

4-7 The photoelectric effect cannot take place with a free electron. Knowing this, show that the following process cannot take place; a charged particle initially in motion spontaneously slows down and emits a photon corresponding to its loss of kinetic energy. In other words, show that a photon cannot be emitted by a single particle having no internal structure and being free of the influence of any other near-by object. *Hint*: imagine the hypothetical photoelectric effect with a free electron to run backward in time.

4-8 * A 1.24 Å photon strikes a hydrogen atom at rest, thereby releasing the bound electron (binding energy, 13.6 eV). Suppose that the electron moves in the same direction as that of the incident photon. What are the electron's (a) kinetic energy and (b) momentum? What are the recoiling ion's (c) momentum and (d) kinetic energy?

4-9 (a) Planck's constant h has units of energy multiplied by time: show that h has the units of angular momentum. (b) A circularly polarized electromagnetic wave of energy E has an angular momentum $L = E/\omega$, where ω is the angular frequency of the wave:† show that from the point of view of the quantum theory such a beam consists of photons each with an angular momentum of $h/2\pi$. An alternative formulization to $E = h\nu$ of the basic quantum condition is this: every photon, quite apart from its frequency, has the same angular momentum of magnitude $h/2\pi$.

4-10 For any ideal gas under standard temperature and pressure the average number density of molecules is 2.7×10^{20} cm⁻³, and the molecular translational kinetic energy per cubic centimeter is 9.5×10^{-18} eV/cm³. What is the average number density of photons in a monochromatic, unidirectional electromagnetic beam having the same energy density as an ideal gas under STP?

† See Sec. 47-6 in Weidner and Sells, *E. C. P.*

4-11   A well-accommodated human eye is capable of detecting single photons of visible light. At what distance from an eye having a pupil 4 mm in diameter would an isotropic point source radiating 5,000 Å light equally in all directions at a rate of 1 W have to be placed so that the number of photons reaching the eye's retina is one per second on the average?

4-12   A uniform beam of red light (7,000 Å wavelength) has intensity of 4.0×10^{-8} W/m². (a) Find the energy of one photon of this wavelength. (b) How many photons cross a 1 cm² surface normal to the beam in one second? (c) How many wavecrests pass this surface in one second?

4-13   The average kinetic energy per gas molecule at room temperature is 1/25 eV. What is the wavelength of a photon having the same energy?

4-14   A unidirectional monochromatic beam of photons has an intensity I and frequency ν. Show that the average density of photons in the beam is given by $I/h\nu c$.

4-15   A monochromatic point source of light radiates continuously. How does the density of photons vary with the distance r from the source in any one direction?

4-16   One way of defining the focal point of a lens is to say that it is that point at which all rays from a point source intersect. How would the focal point be defined in terms of the density of photons?

4-17 *   A 200 keV electron is deflected by a copper atom (mass, 64) initially at rest. A single x-ray photon is created in the collision, and the photon and deflected electron are observed to travel in opposite directions, both perpendicular to that of the original incident electron. (a) What is the recoil kinetic energy of the copper atom? (b) What is the energy of the x-ray photon? (c) What is the kinetic energy of the deflected electron?

4-18   Electron 1 is accelerated from rest through a potential difference V. Electron 2, also accelerated from rest through the same potential difference, collides with a target, comes to rest, and thereby creates a single photon. Which has the larger momentum, electron 1 or the photon produced by electron 2?

4-19   What is the wavelength of a photon having the same (a) energy and (b) momentum as a 10 eV electron?

4-20   (a) Across what minimum potential difference must electrons be accelerated from rest so that upon striking a target they produce photons with a momentum of 1.0 keV/c? (b) Across what potential difference must electrons be accelerated from rest to acquire a momentum of 1.0 keV/c?

4-21   (a) Compute the energy of a photon having the same momentum as a 4.0 eV electron. (b) Where does this radiation lie in the electromagnetic spectrum?

4-22   A laser may produce a highly monochromatic pulse of visible electromagnetic radiation with a power as great as 2.0 MW. The duration of the pulse is about 1.0 msec. Take the wavelength of the emitted radiation to be 6,000 Å. (ρ) What is the total momentum of the emitted light pulse? (b) How many photons are produced?

4-23   A radar transmitter produces pulses of microwave radiation: the power of each pulse is 10 MW and the duration 1.0 μsec. Take the wavelength of the emitted radiation to be 1.0 cm. (a) What is the total momentum of the emitted radar pulse? (b) How many photons are emitted per pulse?

4-24 * Consider a photon rocket an isotropic point source of radiation (possibly polychromatic) of 1,000 MW, located at the focus of a parabolic reflector (Figure 4-27). Show that the radiation force imparted to the rocket by the emitted radiation lies between 1.6 and 3.4 N.

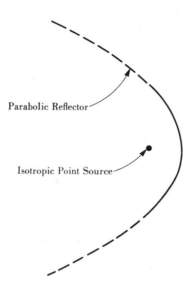

Parabolic Reflector

Isotropic Point Source

Figure 4-27.

4-25 A unidirectional electromagnetic beam with an intensity of 100 W/m² shines on a perfectly reflecting mirror: the angle between the direction of beam propagation and the normal to the mirror is 60°. What is the magnitude of the radiation pressure on the mirror?

4-26 A 1.0 kW isotropic point source of electromagnetic radiation is at the center of a perfectly absorbing spherical shell. For what radius is the radiation pressure on the inner wall of the sphere equal to that of standard atmospheric pressure (1.0×10^5 N/m²)?

4-27 * The intensity of solar radiation at the Earth's surface is 1,400 W/m². (a) What is the pressure of this radiation at the Earth's surface? (b) Compute the total force on the Earth due to this radiation from the Sun (Earth's radius, 4.0×10^3 mi), assuming complete absorption.

4-28   (a) A beam of monochromatic photons of wavelength 0.124 Å strikes a metal target. If one observes the scattered radiation at an angle of 90° relative to the incident beam, what *two* predominant wavelengths will be detected? (b) What wavelengths are observed at a scattering angle of 60°?

4-29   Photons of wavelength 0.0124 Å are scattered by free electrons. What are the wavelengths of those scattered photons whose angle of scattering is (a) 90° and (b) 180°? What are the energies transferred to the free electrons (c) in part (a) and (d) in part (b)?

4-30 *   An incident photon is scattered by a free electron initially at rest. The *scattered* photon may later produce an electron-positron pair. Show that if the angle between the scattered photon and the incident photon is greater than 60°, the scattered photon cannot create an electron-positron pair, no matter how large the energy of the incident photon.

4-31   A 124 keV electron strikes a copper target, is brought to rest, and produces a single x-ray photon. This photon then enters a carbon target and is scattered by a free electron. What is the maximum kinetic energy of the recoil Compton electron?

4-32 *   A monochromatic photon beam is allowed to strike a sheet of copper, and Compton collisions result. It is found that the recoil electrons have a maximum kinetic energy of 0.68 MeV. What is the energy of the photons?

4-33   Sketch a graph showing how the kinetic energy E_k of the recoil electron in the Compton effect varies with the angle θ between the scattered and incident photons, for an incident 0.51 MeV photon.

4-34 *   A beam of photons strikes a target, and Compton electrons with a maximum kinetic energy of 10 keV are observed emerging in the forward direction. (a) What is the wavelength of the incident radiation? (b) What is the energy of a Compton electron emerging at 30° to the beam direction?

4-35   A free *proton* originally at rest is struck by a photon in a Compton collision, and the proton thereby acquires a kinetic energy of 5.7 MeV. What is the minimum photon energy?

4-36   Derive the relation for the Compton wavelength shift, assuming (strictly, improperly) that the kinetic energy and momentum of the electron are given by the *classical* relations. You should find exactly the same relation as that derived from the relativistic expressions for the electron momentum and kinetic energy. Why should this result be expected? (*Hint*: The shift in wavelength is independent of the wavelength of the incident photon.)

4-37 *   A light source emits photons of frequency ν, as measured by an observer at rest with respect to the light source. The observer now travels away from the light source at a speed $v = \frac{1}{2}c$ relative to the light source. By what factors are the following photon properties changed, all relative to their respective values when measured by an observer at rest relative to the source; (a) frequency, (b) wavelength, (c) speed, (d) energy and (e) momentum? (*Hint*: See Problem 2-15, which gives the relativistic Doppler relation.)

4-38 *   Two identical flashlights are pointed in opposite directions and fastened together. Both flashlights are turned on, and we first view the flashlights and their emitted beams as an observer at rest with respect to them;

beams of equal intensities and momenta are emitted in opposite directions, and the net radiation force on the flashlight pair is zero. Suppose now that we view the same situation as an observer traveling along the direction of one of the emitted beams. Because of the Doppler effect the frequencies of the beams in the two directions are different. Consequently, a photon traveling in one direction has a different momentum from that of a photon traveling in the opposite direction. (a) Is there now a net radiation force on the pair of flashlights? (b) Are the densities of photons in the two beams the same? (c) Resolve the (apparent) paradox.

4-39 * A monochromatic beam of photons strikes a block of metal, and a detector registers the photons emerging from the block at 90° with respect to the incident beam: see Figure 4-28a. Figure 4-28b shows the energy spectrum

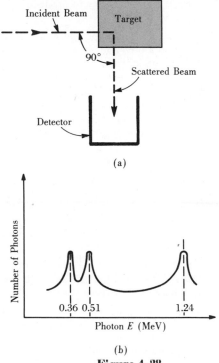

Figure 4-28.

of the photons observed at 90°. There are three distinct peaks; at 0.36, 0.51, and 1.24 MeV. (a) What is energy per photon in the incident beam? (b) Give the physical basis of each of the three peaks.

4-40 A 0.0124 Å photon passing near a gold nucleus (atomic weight, 197) is annihilated, and an electron-positron pair is created. (a) Calculate the energy of the photon (in MeV), and compare this with the total rest energy of the created pair. (b) If the electron and positron are at rest after being created (the photon having just the threshold frequency), a small part of the photon's energy must be transferred to the gold nucleus, because the nucleus must carry away the original photon momentum: calculate the momentum imparted to the gold nucleus. (c) Find the energy imparted to the nucleus, and compare this with the original photon energy.

4-41 * A 2.04 MeV photon produces an electron-positron pair, and both the created particles travel in the forward direction with equal energies. What are the direction and magnitude of the momentum imparted to a near-by heavy nucleus?

4-42 A hypothetical x-ray tube accelerates electrons, which strike the x-ray target and thus produce radiation. Some of these x-ray photons then enter a lead plate and create electron-positron pairs. (a) Describe the type of energy conversion in each of the processes; electron acceleration, x-ray production, and pair production. (b) What is the minimum potential difference of the x-ray tube necessary to produce photons that can in turn produce electron-positron pairs?

4-43 * If the radii of curvature of both the electron and positron created when a photon interacts with a heavy nucleus are 4.0 cm when the particles are bent in a uniform magnetic field of 0.10 Wb/m², what is the wavelength of the incident photon?

4-44 * A monochromatic beam of very-high-energy photons strikes a sheet, and the electron-positron pairs produced move at right angles to a uniform magnetic field. The electron and positron in each pair do not necessarily have the same energy. Show that, even if the electron and positron energies differ, the energy of the photon producing a pair is directly proportional to the sum of the radii of curvature of the electron and positron.

4-45 * An electron and positron are moving together as a system (positronium) at a velocity of $c/2$. If these two particles are annihilated, and two photons are created, (a) what are the energy and momentum of each photon, and (b) what is the angle between the direction of motion of these two photons? (An experiment involving positronium atoms moving at $\frac{1}{2}c$ was performed by D. Sadeh in 1963; the angle between the annihilation quanta was found, as expected, to be less than 180°.)

4-46 A cascade shower is initiated by a photon with an energy of 350 MeV. What is greatest number of positrons it can produce?

4-47 A particle of mass m moving at nonrelativistic speed is to strike another particle of mass m, initially at rest, in a completely inelastic collision and thereby dissipate energy E. Show that the minimum kinetic energy of the particle initially in motion is $2E$, not E. *Note:* both energy *and momentum* must be conserved in every collision.

4-48 * Antiprotons were produced and first identified in the laboratory in 1955 (by Chamberlain, Segre, Wiegand, and Ypsilantis, using the Bevatron accelerator at the University of California Radiation Laboratory). The reaction was $p^+ + p^+ \rightarrow p^+ + p^+ + (p^+ + p^-)$; that is, an incident proton struck a proton at rest, and an additional proton and antiproton were created in the collision. Show that the minimum kinetic energy of the incident proton needed for this reaction is 5.6 GeV or *six* times the proton rest energy. (*Hint:* First see Problem 4-47. Superficially, one might imagine that only *two* times the proton rest energy would be required to create an additional proton and antiproton. However, since both energy *and momentum* must be conserved in every collision, the four particles emerging from the collision must have a total momentum equal to that of the incident proton. Consequently, the particles must emerge from the collision with some kinetic energy, and only a fraction of the incident proton's kinetic energy is available to create the additional two particles. Moreover, the computation requires relativistic dynamics.)

To solve for the threshold energy we might use the following argument. Viewing from a reference frame at rest with the respect to the system's center of mass, we see the incident proton and target proton approach in opposite directions with equal energies and equal momentum magnitudes, collide and, for the threshold energy, create four particles at rest. Thus, as seen from the laboratory reference frame, the four particles after the collision have the *same* momentum, and this momentum is, by momentum conservation, just one fourth that of the incident proton. On this basis it can be shown that the incident particle must have a momentum of $4(3^{1/2})Mc$, where M is the proton rest mass. The corresponding kinetic energy of the incident proton is $6Mc^2$.

4-49 The intensity of a beam of 0.20 MeV photons is reduced by a factor 10 when the beam passes through 17 cm of water. What is the absorption coefficient of water for this photon energy?

4-50 Gamma rays with energies of 0.10, 1.0, and 10 MeV but with equal intensities are incident on a lead absorber. The absorption coefficients in lead for these three energies are 59.9, 0.77, and 0.61 cm^{-1}, respectively. (a) Calculate the thickness of lead necessary to reduce the intensity of each monoenergetic beam to one tenth its original intensity. (b) What is the ratio of the total intensity (of all three photon energies), at any depth x, to the total incident intensity?

4-51 Show that the thickness of absorbing material necessary to reduce the intensity of a beam of radiation to one half its original intensity is $ln_e \, 2/\mu$, where $ln_e \, 2$ is the logarithm of 2 to the base e.

4-52 A shield of lead absorbing material is to be designed for polychromatic electromagnetic radiation. Explain which frequencies, low or high, determine the choice of the absorber thickness, assuming that there are no photons in the radiation having an energy (a) greater than 4.0 MeV, (b) less than 4.0 MeV.

F I V E

QUANTUM EFFECTS: THE WAVE ASPECTS
OF MATERIAL PARTICLES

5-1 De Broglie waves We have seen that electromagnetic radiation has two aspects: a wave aspect and a particle aspect. Experiments that show the interference and diffraction of electromagnetic radiation can be explained only if the radiation is assumed to consist of waves. The distinctively quantum effects of electromagnetic radiation, such as the photoelectric and Compton effects, can be explained only if light is assumed to consist of particle-like photons, each photon having an energy E and momentum p, which are specified precisely by the frequency ν and wavelength λ of the radiation as follows:

$$\nu = E/h \qquad\qquad [5\text{-}1]$$

$$\lambda = h/p \qquad\qquad [5\text{-}2]$$

Note that in these equations two quantities that have clear meanings only when a wave is being described appear on the left, and on the right appear two quantities usually associated with a particle. Thus, the wave-particle duality of electromagnetic radiation is implied in these fundamental relations, and it is the fundamental constant of the quantum theory, Planck's constant h, that relates the wave characteristics to the particle characteristics. We may say that electromagnetic waves under some circumstances will behave as particles and that photons (zero-rest-mass particles) under some circumstances will behave as waves.

It is natural to wonder whether the two equations, which ascribe both a wave and a particle nature to electromagnetic radiation, have an even greater generality—whether they apply to *all* particles, that is, to *finite-rest-mass* as well as to zero-rest-mass particles. This question was first posed by Louis de Broglie in 1924. De Broglie conjectured that because of the symmetry of nature a material particle might well exhibit wave properties. He assumed further that the equations, which give the particle characteristics of electromagnetic waves, give also the wave characteristics of material particles, such as electrons. Experiments have emphatically confirmed the correctness of de Broglie's hypothesis, and the wave character of material particles is now well established. Because the wavelength can be measured from interference or diffraction effects, we shall concentrate our attention on the second of the relations, Equation 5-2 (the significance of the de Broglie wavespeed $\nu\lambda$ and its relation to the particle speed v is discussed in Section 5-8).

The wavelength λ of a material particle having a momentum $p = mv$, where m is the relativistic mass of the particle and v is its velocity, is given by the *de Broglie relation*

$$\lambda = h/p = h/mv \qquad [5\text{-}3]$$

where h is Planck's constant.

One might well ask, "If an electron is, at least under some circumstances, to be regarded as a wave, what is it that is waving?" In this connection it is useful to recall that the same sort of question was raised concerning the fundamental nature of light. It was not until the electromagnetic theory of Maxwell and the experiments of Hertz that physicists could assert that the wave properties of light corresponded to oscillations of the electric and magnetic fields, but the ignorance of light's electromagnetic nature did not prevent physicists long before Maxwell and Hertz from discovering the wave-like properties of light and interpreting interference and diffraction on this basis. Therefore, to establish whether a material particle has a wave nature it is *not* necessary to know first what the nature of the wave phenomenon is. To test the de Broglie hypothesis is to determine on the basis of experiment whether material particles show interference and diffraction effects. Of course, the question of the physical nature of a material particle's wave aspect is a crucial one; we shall, however, postpone it until after we have discussed the experiments that confirm that a material particle has a wavelength $\lambda = h/mv$.

The electron was discovered in 1897 by J. J. Thomson. He showed that electrons follow well-defined paths, have a well-defined charge-to-mass ratio (for $v \ll c$), and have mass, momentum, and energy that can be localized in space: that is, electrons show the attributes of a particle. The wave nature of electrons was not discovered until 1927, when the electron diffraction experiments of C. Davisson and L. H. Germer confirmed the de Broglie relation. Why were the wave characteristics of electrons discovered only many years after their particle nature had been established? We might suspect that the origin of the difficulties of observing the wave properties of electrons is similar to that of observing the wave nature of light, namely a very small wavelength. As Equation 5-3 shows, a 1.0 kg particle moving at 1.0 m/sec has a wavelength of only 6.6×10^{-34} m $= 6.6 \times 10^{-24}$ Å. Clearly, we should not expect, in throwing baseballs through an open window, to find a discernible diffraction pattern of hits on a distant wall any more than we should expect to see one when visible light passes through such a wide "slit." The wavelength of an ordinary material particle is very small compared with the dimensions of ordinary objects, so that interference and diffraction effects are subtle. Therefore, if an object's wavelength is to be large enough to produce observable wave effects, its mass and velocity, as we see from Equation 5-3, must be small (clearly, for a large wavelength and low speed nonrelativistic relations may be used).

The diffraction grating having the smallest distance between "lines" is a crystal, a solid in which the atoms are located in a three-dimensional geometrical array. A typical distance between adjacent atoms is of the order of 10^{-10} m, or 1 Å. The most favorable conditions for observing the diffraction of particles are those in which the particle has a wavelength of comparable size. Since the wavelength varies inversely with the particle's mass and velocity, to have the longest wavelength we must choose a particle having the smallest possible mass, namely the electron.

Let us compute the kinetic energy of an electron with a wavelength λ of 1.00 Å. An electron with electric charge e, accelerated from rest by an electrostatic potential difference V, acquires a final kinetic energy $\frac{1}{2}mv^2$ when

$$eV = \tfrac{1}{2}mv^2 = \frac{1}{2m}p^2 = \frac{1}{2m}\left(\frac{h}{\lambda}\right)^2$$

$$V = \frac{h^2}{2me\lambda^2} = \frac{(6.62 \times 10^{-34} \text{ J-sec})^2}{2(9.11 \times 10^{-31} \text{ kg})(1.60 \times 10^{-19} \text{ C})(1.00 \times 10^{-10} \text{ m})^2}$$

$$V = 150 \text{ V}$$

An electron of 150 electron volts has a wavelength of 1 angstrom. Since this wavelength is comparable to that of a typical x-ray photon, we may expect that both electrons and x-rays will show similar diffraction effects when passing through a crystal.

5-2 The Bragg law Max von Laue was the first to suggest in 1912 that crystalline solids, in which the arrangement of atoms follows a regular pattern, and in which the distance between atoms is approximately one angstrom, might be used as diffraction gratings for measuring x-ray wavelengths.

Consider a crystal of sodium chloride, which has a particularly simple structure, and which is used as a standard material for x-ray diffraction. Examination of the external geometrical features of a rock-salt crystal suggests that the sodium and chlorine atoms (strictly, Na$^+$ and Cl$^-$ ions) are arranged in a simple cubic lattice, as shown in Figure 5-1. The sodium

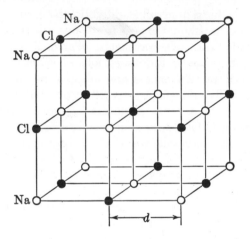

Figure 5-1. Crystal structure of rock salt (NaCl).

and chlorine atoms are located at alternate corners of identical elementary cubes, each with a distance d along an edge.

It is easy to compute the *lattice spacing d* from the density of the sodium chloride crystal and the atomic weights of sodium and chlorine. If d is the distance in centimeters from a sodium atom to a nearest chlorine atom, then there are $1/d$ atoms (half Na, half Cl) along an edge of a cube 1 cm long. Further, in a cube of sodium chloride crystal 1 cm along an edge there are altogether $1/d^3$ atoms. Therefore, the total number of atoms per unit volume is $1/d^3$. The atomic weight of Na is 23.00, and that of Cl is 35.45, so the molecular weight of NaCl is 58.45. Because Avogadro's number, 6.022×10^{23}, gives the number of atoms in one gram-mole, it follows that there are 6.022×10^{23} Na atoms in 23.00 g of Na, 6.022×10^{23} Cl atoms in 35.45 g of Cl, and therefore $2 \times 6.025 \times 10^{23}$ atoms (half Na, half Cl) in 58.45 g of NaCl. The measured density of sodium chloride in the crystalline form of rock salt is 2.163 g/cm^3. Therefore, we can write

$$\frac{\text{atoms}}{\text{volume}} = \frac{2 \times 6.022 \times 10^{23} \text{ atoms/mole} \times 2.163 \text{ g/cm}^3}{58.45 \text{ g/mole}} = \frac{1}{d^3}$$

$$d = 2.820 \text{ Å}$$

which is the lattice spacing of sodium and chlorine atoms in a crystal of rock salt. This distance, which is typical of the interatomic spacing of atoms in any solid, is, of course, comparable to the wavelength of x-rays or of electrons of 150 eV. We shall see how it is possible to determine x-ray and electron wavelengths from the lattice spacing and the geometrical character of the atomic arrangement.

When a wave impinges upon a collection of scattering centers, such as the atoms in a crystalline solid, each scattering center generates waves, which radiate outward from it in all directions. The resultant wave from all scattering centers, measured in any one direction, depends, of course, on the interference between all of the separate centers. It is a remarkable fact, proved in detail in Section 5-4, that the atoms lying on any one plane within the crystal act with respect to the incident wave as a partially silvered mirror with respect to visible light; that is, they reflect a portion of the wave while allowing the remainder to pass through; see Figure 5-2.

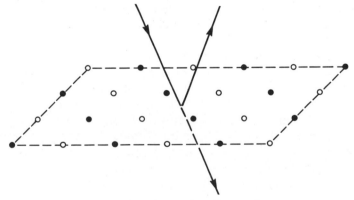

Figure 5-2. Atoms in a Bragg plane.

These *Bragg planes* and *Bragg reflections* are named after W. H. Bragg, who with his son, W. L. Bragg, developed the fundamental theory of x-ray diffraction by crystals in 1913. Given this fact, we can deal, not with the interference between the waves generated by all of the scattering centers individually but, more simply, with the interference between the waves reflected from parallel Bragg planes.

Consider the reflection of waves from two adjacent and parallel Bragg planes as shown in Figure 5-3. The directions of the incident and reflected waves, both denoted by θ, are specified by the angle between the direction

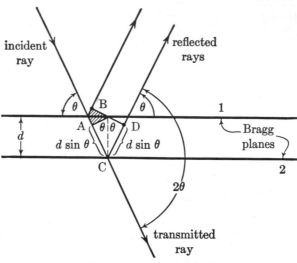

Figure 5-3. Reflection of waves from two adjacent, parallel Bragg planes.

of propagation of the waves and the Bragg plane (*not* the normal to the reflecting planes). At each plane we regard the incident wave as partially transmitted undeviated and partially reflected.

The incident ray is partially reflected at the first Bragg plane, the reflected ray AB making an angle θ with plane 1. That part, AC, of the incident ray which is transmitted through the first plane is partially reflected from the second plane, also in the direction θ. We concentrate on the wave front BD perpendicular to the two reflected rays. The reflected rays will constructively interfere at some distant point only if they have the same phase at the points B and D. The points B and D are in phase when the path difference ACD $-$ AB $= 2d$ sin θ is an integral multiple n of the wavelength λ. The condition, then, for constructive interference of waves reflected from adjacent parallel Bragg planes is

$$n\lambda = 2d \sin \theta \qquad [5\text{-}4]$$

where n, the *order of the reflection*, can have the values 1, 2, 3, ... This equation,† known as *Bragg's law*, is the basis of all coherent x-ray and electron diffraction effects in crystals. Rays reflected at any angles except those satisfying the equation destructively interfere, and the incident beam is completely transmitted. The Bragg law is the means of measuring wavelengths comparable to interatomic distances, for clearly, if n, d, and θ

† Equation 5-4, Bragg's law, bears a resemblance to the equation that applies to an ordinary ruled diffraction grating. The two equations, however, are *not* the same.

are known, λ can be computed. We note that in Figure 5-3 the angle between the transmitted and the reflected rays is 2θ and that the Bragg planes bisect this angle.

5-3 X-ray and electron diffraction   The essential elements of an *x-ray spectrometer*, a device for measuring x-ray wavelengths, are shown in Figure 5-4. A source of monochromatic x-rays shines on a crystal whose structure

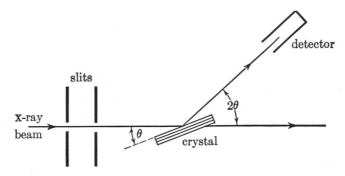

Figure 5-4. Schematic diagram of an x-ray crystal spectrometer.

and interatomic dimensions are known. A detector, such as a chamber that is sensitive to x-ray ionization effects, measures the intensity of x-rays entering it. Both the crystal and the detector are rotatable, but the detector is always set at an angle 2θ from the forward beam, θ being the angle between the incident rays and the Bragg planes from which reflection is to be observed. The x-ray intensity in the detector will indicate a strong maximum when the conditions of Equation 5-4 for Bragg reflection are satisfied. Thus, since d is known from the crystalline structure, and θ is measured, the wavelength λ can be computed. For a given set of Bragg planes, grating space d, wavelength λ, and order n there is a *single direction* 2θ away from the direction of the incident beam in which the diffracted beam is strong.

Consider a thin metallic foil through which a monochromatic x-ray beam is sent. The foil consists of a very large number of simple, perfect crystals, randomly oriented with respect to one another within the foil. Only those particular microcrystals which are so oriented that the Bragg condition is fulfilled will produce a strongly diffracted beam; the other microcrystals will not diffract the incident beam coherently. Therefore, the emerging beam will consist of two parts: an intense, central, undeviated beam and a beam scattered in a conical shape that makes an angle 2θ with respect to the incident beam; see Figure 5-5. The angle θ is uniquely determined, for a given order, by the Bragg relation.

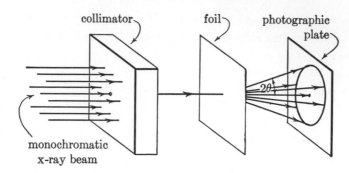

Figure 5-5. Scattering of monochromatic x-rays by a thin metallic foil from one set of Bragg planes.

When the scattered beam strikes a flat photographic plate, a pattern of intensities appears, consisting of a strong central spot surrounded by a circle. The radius of the circle is easily measured, and the distance from the scattering foil to the photographic plate is known, and so the angle 2θ can be found; finally, the wavelength of the x-rays can be computed from the Bragg relation.

Thus far we have taken any given crystal to have only one set of parallel Bragg planes, but in actuality there are many sets of planes in any single crystal. To see how this affects x-ray and electron diffraction, let us consider again the arrangement of atoms in the sodium chloride crystal. A Bragg plane is any plane that contains atoms, and there are many such planes in a cubic crystal, as shown by Figure 5-6. It is clear that the various planes, of which only a very few are shown in the figure, will differ in the

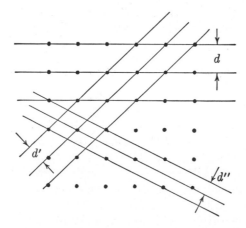

Figure 5-6. Three sets of parallel Bragg planes with different grating spacings.

value of the grating space d; consequently, there will be a number of Bragg angles θ, each satisfying the Bragg relation for a particular set of Bragg planes. The x-ray diffraction pattern will therefore be somewhat more complicated than that indicated in Figure 5-5; it will commonly show, not a single circle, but a number of concentric circles, each one corresponding to diffraction from a particular set of Bragg planes. The intensities of the reflected beams from the different planes will, however, not be the same, inasmuch as the number of atoms per unit area in one plane, which determines the intensity of a reflected beam, may differ from that in another plane. Figure 5-7 is an x-ray diffraction pattern of a sample of polycrystalline aluminum.

Our discussion of diffraction from crystals has concerned the use of x-rays. As we have seen, electrons with a kinetic energy of 150 eV have

Figure 5-7. X-ray diffraction pattern of polycrystalline aluminum. The center is dark because a hole was cut in the photographic plate to allow the strong central beam to pass through it. (Courtesy of Mrs. M. H. Read, Bell Telephone Laboratories, Murray Hill, New Jersey.)

the same wavelength as x-rays, 1 angstrom, and a monoenergetic† electron beam should and does show essentially the same diffraction effects as do x-rays. Figure 5-8 is an electron diffraction pattern from a metallic foil; the pattern is in complete accord with the Bragg and de Broglie relations. In short, *electron diffraction experiments confirm the relation* $\lambda = h/mv$.

Electron and x-ray diffraction patterns can be used for measuring the wavelengths of electrons and x-rays when the crystalline structure is known; conversely, when the wavelengths of the x-rays and electrons are known, the diffraction patterns can be used to deduce the geometry of the crystalline structure and the interatomic spacings of the solids. We mention briefly two applications of the principles of x-ray diffraction:

(a) The Compton effect, in which scattered photons appear with an unmodified and a modified wavelength, can be verified by using an x-ray spectrometer to measure the wavelengths of the radiation scattered by a target.

(b) When a beam of x-rays having a continuous range of wavelengths is incident on a crystal, there is constructive interference leading to a beam deviated by an angle 2θ only if the Bragg law is satisfied. For a given angle θ, order n, and interatomic spacing d the value of the wavelength is uniquely specified by the Bragg law, Equation 5-4, and only a single wavelength will be strongly reflected at the angle 2θ. A crystal in this arrangement acts as a *monochromater*, in that it selects from the continuous range of wavelengths incident on the crystal a single monochromatic beam emerging at the angle 2θ.

Let us now consider briefly the experiment of Davisson and Germer, in which the wave properties of electrons were first confirmed. A beam of electrons of energy 54 electron volts is incident on a single crystal of nickel. Electrons leave the nickel surface for two reasons: secondary emission, in which the incident electrons impart their kinetic energy to electrons in the metal, which are then released, and electron diffraction, in which the incident electrons are diffracted by reflection from the Bragg planes within the nickel crystal. Davisson and Germer found that in addition to the smooth variation in electron intensity arising from secondary emission there was a pronounced peak at $\phi = 50°$, which could be attributed to electron diffraction: the computed direction for strong reflection of electrons of 54 eV in nickel is 50°. Thus the de Broglie relation was confirmed. The analysis of the experiment was complicated, however, by the fact that the wavelength of electrons within a crystal is *not* the same as the wavelength in free space. The difference arises from a change in the speed of

† A monoenergetic beam of particles not only has a single energy but also has, of course, a single wavelength and is therefore usually spoken of, with reference to its wave aspect, as "monochromatic."

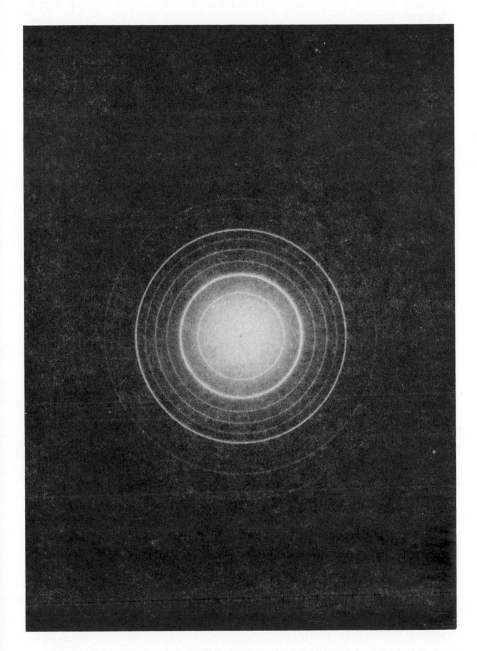

Figure 5-8. Electron diffraction pattern of polycrystalline tellurium chloride. (Courtesy of RCA Laboratories, Princeton, New Jersey.)

electrons as they enter or leave the nickel surface; they move faster as they pass into the interior of the material because of work done on them by an electric field at the surface (the work function of the particular material). Because of the change in speed the electrons are refracted at the surface; see Figures 5-9.

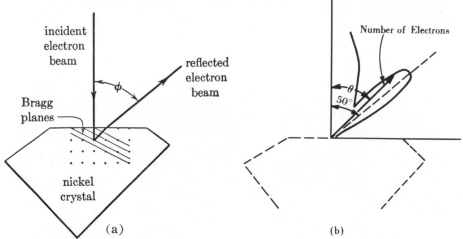

Figure 5-9. (a) Reflection of electron waves by one set of Bragg planes in a crystal of nickel; (b) number of electrons reflected from a nickel crystal as a function of angle ϕ is shown by a polar plot.

Shortly after Davisson and Germer's confirmation of the de Broglie relation for electrons G. P. Thomson observed diffraction rings due to the transmission of electrons through a thin metallic foil, similar to Figure 5-8. It is interesting to note that Thomson, whose experiments showed the wave properties of electrons (1927), was the son of J. J. Thomson, whose cathode ray experiments showed the particle properties of electrons (1897).

The fact that an object of mass m and velocity v has a wavelength h/mv has been established by experiments not only on electrons but also on atoms, molecules, and the uncharged nuclear particle, the neutron. When a neutron passes through a material it makes collisions with the atoms of the material. At first the neutron loses kinetic energy at each collision, the struck atoms gaining the energy it loses. This continues until its energy is comparable to the thermal energy of the atoms in the material. Then, having reached thermal equilibrium with the material, the neutron has equal probabilities of gaining and losing kinetic energy in a collision. Its behavior is like that of a molecule in a gas, and a temperature can be attributed to it. The relationship between average translational kinetic energy per particle and the absolute temperature is

$$E_\mathrm{k} = \tfrac{1}{2}mv^2 = \tfrac{3}{2}kT$$

When the temperature T of the material is room temperature, 300°K, a neutron with this average kinetic energy is said to be a *thermal neutron*. The wavelength of a thermal neutron whose mass is 1.67×10^{-27} kg is, then,

$$\tfrac{1}{2}mv^2 = \frac{p^2}{2m} = \frac{1}{2m}\left(\frac{h}{\lambda}\right)^2 = \tfrac{3}{2}kT$$

$$\lambda = \frac{h}{\sqrt{3mkT}} = 1.4 \text{ Å}$$

This wavelength is comparable to the distance between atoms in a crystalline solid, and *neutron diffraction* of thermal neutrons is observed.

The de Broglie relation attributes a wavelength to *any* particle that has momentum. Since neutrons, which are uncharged particles, can be diffracted, their wave properties are not dependent on their having an electric charge. Furthermore, atoms and molecules, which have internal structure, show diffraction effects: therefore, the de Broglie relation applies even to systems of particles.

5-4 A proof of Bragg reflection In deriving the Bragg relation, Equation 5-4, an important assumption was made: x-ray or electron waves incident upon a Bragg plane, a plane containing atoms as scattering centers, are reflected as if the Bragg plane were a partially reflecting mirror. The detailed proof is given here.

We recognize that an electromagnetic wave incident upon the atoms in a crystal sets each of the charged particles in oscillation and that each atom re-emits radiation of the same frequency but in all directions. A de Broglie wave (that is, the wave of a material particle) is similarly scattered. Whether the waves scattered from two or more atoms interfere constructively or destructively depends on the path difference alone.

Consider radiation incident upon two atoms A and B in the direction given by angle θ and scattered at the angle θ', Figure 5-10. The distance between A and B is b. From the geometry of the figure we see that

$$BD = b \cos \theta$$

$$AE = b \cos \theta'$$

The path difference between the two rays is $BD - AE$, and the scattered waves from atoms A and B will interfere constructively if this path difference is an integral multiple of the wavelength λ:

$$\text{path difference} = BD - AE = b \cos \theta - b \cos \theta'$$

$$b(\cos \theta - \cos \theta') = k\lambda \qquad [5\text{-}5]$$

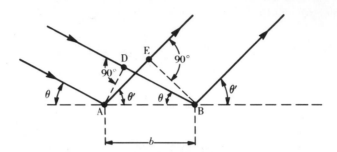

Figure 5-10. Radiation incident upon atoms A and B separated by b.

where k is an integer (including zero). Now consider the constructive inter-ference from another pair of atoms, B and C, as shown in Figure 5-11. Line BC of this figure is perpendicular to the line AB of Figure 5-10. Scattering centers B and C are separated by a distance a; the angles of the incident and scattered rays are again given by θ and θ'. From the geometry of Figure 5-11 we have

$$CF = a \sin \theta$$
$$CG = a \sin \theta'$$

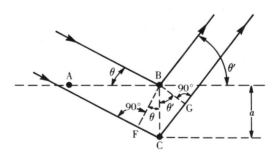

Figure 5-11. Radiation incident upon atoms B and C separated by a.

As before, constructive interference occurs when the path difference is an integral multiple of the wavelength:

$$\text{path difference} = CF + CG = a \sin \theta + a \sin \theta'$$
$$a(\sin \theta + \sin \theta') = l\lambda \qquad [5\text{-}6]$$

where l is an integer. Atoms A, B, and C are just three atoms of a large array in a lattice, in which neighboring atoms are separated by distance b horizontally and a vertically, as shown in Figure 5-12. Consequently, if both Equations 5-5 and 5-6 are satisfied, then the waves scattered from *all* of the atoms in the geometrical array will interfere constructively to give strong diffraction maxima.

Suppose that a plane MN (a line in our two-dimensional figure) is drawn through the point C in such an orientation that the incident rays and scattered rays make *equal* angles ϕ with respect to it, as shown in Figure 5-12. Then, as the figure shows,

$$\phi = \theta + \alpha$$
$$\phi = \theta' - \alpha$$

[5-7]

where α is the angle between MN and AB. Equation 5-5 may then be written

$$b[\cos(\phi - \alpha) - \cos(\phi + \alpha)] = k\lambda$$

which simplifies to

$$2b \sin \phi \sin \alpha = k\lambda$$

[5-8]

Similarly, Equation 5-6 may be written, by means of Equation 5-7, as

$$a[\sin(\phi - \alpha) + \sin(\phi + \alpha)] = l\lambda$$
$$2a \sin \phi \cos \alpha = l\lambda$$

[5-9]

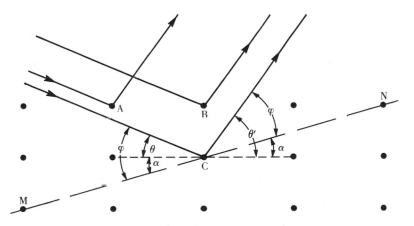

Figure 5-12. Radiation incident upon atoms A, B, and C (as shown in Figures 5-10 and 5-11). Line MN is so drawn that the incident and reflected rays make equal angles ϕ with it.

Dividing Equation 5-8 by Equation 5-9, we have

$$\tan \alpha = ka/lb \qquad [5\text{-}10]$$

Thus, the angle α between the plane MN and the crystal surface (the line containing atoms A and B) is given by Equation 5-10 in terms of the integers k and l and the lattice spacings a and b but *not* in terms of the angles θ and θ' or the wavelength λ. Moreover, the plane MN contains, through the construction chosen, one atom at the point C. Indeed, this plane contains an array of regularly spaced atoms. Recall now that the plane MN, with an array of atoms in it, was so chosen that the incident and scattered rays made equal angles with respect to it. We have proved that a Bragg plane may be thought of as reflecting waves incident upon it when the condition for constructive interference is satisfied.†

5-5   The principle of complementarity   We have seen that it is necessary to attribute both wave characteristics and particle characteristics to electromagnetic radiation and to material particles. Of course, this wave-particle duality makes us uneasy at first sight. Here we shall examine the origin of our uneasiness and what is implied when it is stated that both electromagnetic radiation and a material particle behave as both waves and particles and we shall see how this dilemma is resolved by the principle of complementarity.

The concepts of particle and of wave are basic in physics, because they represent the only two possible modes of the transport of energy; when energy is transported, we can always describe its propagation by waves or by particles. In describing any ordinary large-scale phenomenon of energy transport in classical physics we are always successful in applying one of the descriptions. For example, a disturbance that travels on the surface of a pond of water is certainly a wave phenomenon, and a thrown baseball illustrates the transport of energy by a "particle." There is never any doubt about which description we should apply in such instances, in which we can see directly the moving disturbances.

Now let us turn to somewhat less direct illustrations of wave and particle behavior. The propagation of sound through an elastic medium can be understood as a wave disturbance. We do not see the waves, as we did the water waves; nevertheless, we apply the wave description to the propagation of sound with confidence, because the phenomenon is altogether similar, insofar as the interpretation of diffraction and interference is concerned, to that of water waves. Therefore, when we say that the propagation of sound shows wave aspects, what we are implying is that the propagation of sound can be explained by a *wave model*, because a wave model agrees with *all* experimental observations of sound. Next let us consider particle

† The analysis given here is based on that given by L. R. B. Elton and D. F. Jackson, *American Journal of Physics*, Vol. 34, p. 1036, November 1966.

behavior as it appears in the kinetic theory of gases. We never see the molecules of a gas directly, but we are quite sure that their behavior is rather like that of very small, hard spheres, because a variety of experiments shows it to be so. Again what we are saying is that a *particle model* is the only appropriate means of describing its behavior. Thus, when we describe phenomena that are somewhat remote from our ordinary experience, whose details we do not "see" directly, we still apply one or the other of the two modes of description, because one of them is always successful in accounting for the experimental facts.

The wave and particle descriptions are mutually incompatible and contradictory. Recall (Section 1-7) that if a wave is to have its frequency or its wavelength given with infinite precision, then it must have an infinite extension in space. Conversely, if it is confined to some limited region of space, so that its energy is confined at any one time to a limited region, then it *resembles* a particle by virtue of its localizability, but it cannot be characterized by a single frequency and wavelength; instead, a large number of ideal sinusoidal waves, each with a specific frequency and wavelength, must be superimposed to give the confined-wave disturbance (see Section 1-7). Therefore, an ideal wave, one whose frequency and wavelength are known with certainty, is altogether incompatible with an ideal particle, which has a zero extension in space and to which, therefore, such terms as frequency and wavelength are irrelevant.

Any energy-transport phenomenon, whether or not remote from our direct observation or experience, must be described in terms of waves or of particles. If the phenomenon is to be *visualized* at all, if we are to have some sort of *picture* of what goes on in interactions that are inaccessible to direct and immediate observation, it must be in terms of a wave behavior or a particle behavior. There is no alternative; because of the mutually contradictory characteristics of a particle and of a wave, we cannot *simultaneously* apply a particle description and a wave description. We can and must use one or the other, never both at the same time.

Now, what is disturbing about the descriptions of electromagnetic radiation and of material particles is the fact that we apply *both* the wave and particle models; yet, if we review our interpretation of the experiments discussed thus far, we find that we have *never* applied the descriptions *simultaneously*, which is, as we have seen, logically impossible.

Consider first electromagnetic radiation. The wave model is used to describe the experiments in interference and diffraction. We say that light consists of waves because in interference and diffraction we are confronted with alternate light and dark bands (that is, alternating regions of great and small light intensity) that are predicted and accounted for by wave theory. We never apply the particle description to interference and diffraction. Of course, our confidence in the wave model of the *propagation* of light is strengthened by the fact that Maxwell's classical theory of electromagnetic waves predicts all the *wave* phenomena observed for light, but it would be rash, in view of the open-ended, tentative, and incomplete nature of all physical theory, to conclude that Maxwell's equations are the final equations or the last word on electromagnetic theory. In fact, we have seen that classical electromagnetism is incomplete in that it cannot account for certain quantum effects. In summary, we use the wave model to describe the *propagation* of light; we do not, need not, and cannot apply the particle model to interference and diffraction effects.

Now let us turn to those phenomena which call for a particle model of electromagnetic radiation. They are the photoelectric effect, the Compton effect, pair production, and pair annihilation. All of them show electromagnetic radiation in *interaction* with material particles. We assume that the radiation consists of photons and ascribe to each photon a specific energy and momentum. To ascribe energy and momentum to an electromagnetic *wave* is perfectly possible and indeed necessary (see Section 1-4), but to ascribe them to an electromagnetic *particle* is to imply that they are localized at a particular point in space, namely at the position of the particle, the photon. Interactions between radiation and matter require the particle description, inasmuch as the interactions are best described as collisions. We can make sense of the experiments only when electromagnetic radiation is assumed to consist of particles making collisions. In short, if we are to visualize the photon-electron interactions by means of a model, it must be the *particle model*; we cannot, and need not, apply the wave model.

Electromagnetic radiation shows both wave and particle aspects but *not* in the same experiments. An experiment showing interference or diffraction requires a wave interpretation, and it is impossible to apply simultaneously a particle interpretation; an experiment showing distinctively radiation-electron interactions requires a particle interpretation, and it is impossible to apply simultaneously a wave interpretation. Both the wave and the particle aspects are essential features of electromagnetic radiation, and we must accept both. According to the *principle of complementarity*, enunciated by Niels Bohr in 1928, *the wave and particle aspects* of electromagnetic radiation *are complementary*. To interpret the behavior of electromagnetic radiation in any one experiment in terms of a meaningful visual picture we must choose either the particle or the wave description. The wave and particle aspects are *complementary* in that our knowledge of the properties of electromagnetic radiation is partial unless both the wave and particle aspects are known; but the choice of one description, which is imposed by the nature of the experiment, precludes the simultaneous choice of the other. We are confronted with a true dilemma, in which we must make one of two possible choices. Electromagnetic radiation is a more complicated entity than can be comprehended in the simple and extreme notions of wave and particle, notions that are borrowed from our direct, ordinary experience with large-scale phenomena. Just as the theory of relativity reveals that the common-sense ideas of space, time, and mass are inapplicable to high-speed phenomena, so too the quantum theory, through the wave-particle duality, shows that simple common-sense concepts are inadequate to describe submicroscopic phenomena.

We have seen how Bohr's principle of complementarity elucidates the dual wave-particle aspects of electromagnetic radiation. Let us now examine the wave-particle duality of particles, such as electrons, to see how the complementarity principle applies. Many experiments illustrate the particle-like nature of electrons; consider J. J. Thomson's cathode-ray experiments, which first showed electrons to be particles. The electrons in a cathode-ray tube follow well-defined paths and indicate their collisions with a fluorescent screen by very small, bright flashes. They also are deflected by electric and magnetic fields. It is inferred that electrons are particles (or, more properly, that a particle model can be used to describe their behavior in cathode-ray experiments), because all the effects observed in cathode-ray experiments make sense if the energy, momentum, and electric charge of the electron are assigned at any one time to a small region of space. When they interact with other objects, electrons behave *as if* they were particles. We see the particle nature of electrons revealed in the cathode-ray experiments and, therefore, by the principle of complementarity, the wave nature of electrons *must* be suppressed.

The wave nature of electrons appears in the experiments showing electron diffraction, where it is assumed that electrons are propagated as waves having a precisely defined wavelength; the waves have an indefinite extension in space, and it is, of course, impossible to specify the location of the electron or to follow its motion. In short, the electron diffraction experiments show the wave nature of electrons and, by the principle of complementarity, the particle nature is suppressed in these experiments. The wave and particle aspects of electrons complement each other; to understand fully electron properties we must accept both. Again, the electron or any other material particle is a more complicated entity than can be fully comprehended in the simple and extreme notions of particle and wave; we may use one or the other to visualize the results of any particular experiment, but not both simultaneously.

5-6 The probability interpretation of de Broglie waves The wave nature of electromagnetic radiation is illustrated by oscillating electric and magnetic fields in space; therefore, the *wave associated with a photon is the electromagnetic field*. We wish to inquire more closely into the nature of waves associated with a material particle, and to answer the question "What is it that is waving when we say that an electron or any other material particle shows wave properties?''

First consider a screen illuminated by a monochromatic beam of electromagnetic radiation falling perpendicularly on the surface. When the intensity of the light is fairly great, it appears to the eye to be uniformly illuminated over the entire area; equivalently, a photographic plate placed at the screen will, after being exposed and developed, show a uniform darkening over its entire area. When the intensity of the light beam is great, then the number of photons arriving at the screen is so great that the essentially granular and discrete nature of the electromagnetic radiation is obscured by the great number of photons, and the distinct and randomly arranged bright flashes merge into a seemingly continuous and constant illumination. The intensity I of the illumination, the energy per unit area per unit time, is given by

$$I = \epsilon_0 \mathcal{E}^2 c$$

where ϵ_0 is the electric permittivity of free space and $\mathcal{E}$ is the magnitude of the instantaneous electric field at any point on the screen (Section 1-4).†

Suppose that the intensity of the beam is made extremely weak: instead of a uniformly illuminated area what is seen is a collection of distinct, bright flashes randomly arranged over the plate, each bright flash corresponding to the arrival of a single photon.‡ Neither the position nor the time at which a single photon will strike the screen can be predicted, the distribution of photons being completely random, but the *average* number of photons arriving per unit area per unit time can be predicted; this number is the photon flux N. The intensity of a monochromatic beam is given in terms of the photon flux as follows:

[4-20] $$I = (h\nu)N$$

where $h\nu$ is the energy per photon.

Suppose that instead of increasing the intensity to get the appearance of a uniformly illuminated screen we use a very weak beam, record on the screen the position of each flash as it comes along; then we shall find that, after a long time has elapsed, the screen is again uniformly covered.

The situation we have been discussing is rather like that encountered in the kinetic theory of gases, in which one attributes the apparently continuous pressure of a gas on the walls of its container to the combined effects of individual molecular impacts on the walls. The arrivals of the

---

† We could, of course, express the intensity equally well in terms of the magnetic field, rather than the electric field: $I = B^2 c/\mu_0$.
‡ Actually, sophisticated instruments, rather than the eye or a photographic plate, can record the arrival of photons one by one.

molecules are essentially random and discrete, but because of their enormous number the net effect of their impacts is one of continuous pressure.

Consider a beam of monochromatic light of very low intensity, 1.00×10^{-13} watts per square meter (approximately one hundred millionth the intensity of starlight at the Earth's surface), and suppose that it consists of visible-light photons, each with an energy of 5.00 eV $= 8.00 \times 10^{-19}$ J. Then the photon flux is

$$N = \frac{I}{h\nu} = \frac{1.00 \times 10^{-13} \text{ W/m}^2}{8.00 \times 10^{-19} \text{ J/photon}}$$

$$= 1.25 \times 10^5 \text{ photon/m}^2\text{-sec}$$

$$= 12.5 \text{ photon/cm}^2\text{-sec}$$

This means that 12.5 bright flashes will be observed over an area of 1 cm^2 during a period of 1 sec. It is, of course, impossible to observe a fraction of a photon, so we shall never see 12.5 photons; but in one interval 11 flashes might be seen, in another 13, and so on, and the average will be 12.5. Furthermore, the spatial distribution of photons over the 1 cm^2 area will *not* be the same for all 1 sec intervals: the flashes will be distributed randomly and will approach a uniform distribution only over a long period of time. *The photon flux does not give precisely the time and location of any one photon but gives only the probability of observing a photon:*

$$N \propto \text{ probability of observing a photon}$$

We can define the intensity of monochromatic electromagnetic radiation by either the wave description, $I = \epsilon_0 \mathcal{E}^2 c$, or the particle description, $I = h\nu N$. This is highly significant, for in the intensity we have a quantity that has a precise meaning in both descriptions. The intensity bridges the gap between the two disparate models.

Let us see what new meaning can be assigned to the square of the electric field strength, $\mathcal{E}^2$, in view of the photon description of light. If we equate the two expressions for the intensity, we have

$$I = h\nu N = \epsilon_0 \mathcal{E}^2 c$$

Therefore,
$$N \propto \mathcal{E}^2$$

and
$$\boxed{\mathcal{E}^2 \propto \text{ probability of observing a photon}}$$

The probability of observing a photon at any point in space is proportional to the square of the electric field strength at that point.

Thus, the electric field is, from the point of view of the quantum theory, not only a quantity that gives the electric force per unit electric charge;

it is also that quantity, or function, whose square gives the probability of observing a photon at any given place. Classical electromagnetic theory is capable of yielding, through computed values of $\mathcal{E}^2$, the probability of observing photons, although it is incapable of yielding the strictly quantum features of electromagnetic radiation.

We are able to give meaning to the wave nature of a material particle, such as an electron, in the following way. We assume the relation between the probability of observing a particle and the square of the amplitude of its wave is exactly analogous to the relation between the probability of observing a zero-rest-mass photon and the square of the amplitude of its wave (electric field). The amplitude of the wave associated with a particle is represented by ψ, called simply the *wave function*.

The wave function ψ is that quantity whose square ψ^2, is proportional to the probability of observing a material particle.

Thus, if ψ represents the wave function at the location x, the probability of observing the particle's being between x and $x + dx$ is given by $\psi(x)^2\,dx$:

> probability of observing a particle in the interval $dx \propto \psi^2\,dx$

The wave function of a particle, then, is analogous to the electric field of a photon, and just as the latter will, in general, be a function of both position and time, so too, in general, will the wave function.

It is impossible to specify with complete certainty the particular position of a photon at a particular time but it is possible to specify by $\mathcal{E}^2$ the probability of observing it; similarly it is impossible to specify with complete certainty the particular position of a particle at a particular time, but it is possible to specify by ψ^2 the probability of observing it. Thus, a particle's wave function gives rise, in essence, to a *probability interpretation* of the position of a particle.

The interpretation of the wave nature of material particles in terms of probabilities was first given in 1926 by Max Born. That branch of quantum physics which deals with the problem of finding the values of ψ is known as *wave mechanics*, or *quantum mechanics*. The two principal originators of the wave mechanics of particles were Erwin Schrödinger (1926) and Werner Heisenberg (1925), who independently formulated quantum mechanics in different but equivalent mathematical forms.

Just as the electromagnetic theory of Maxwell is summarized in the Maxwell equations, which are the basis for computing values of $\mathcal{E}$, the wave mechanics of matter is governed by the *Schrödinger equation*, which is the basis for computing values of ψ in any problem in quantum physics. Here the parallel stops, however. Whereas the electric field, which has its origin in electric charges, gives not only the probability of observing a photon but also the electric force on a unit positive electric charge, the wave function of the Schrödinger equation has a physical meaning *only* in terms of the probability interpretation: it does *not* indicate any sort of force. The wave function is not directly measurable or observable; it does, however, give the most information one can extract concerning any system of objects, and *all* measurable quantities, such as the energy and momentum, as well as the probability of location, can be found from it. The Schrödinger equation is derived and applied to a number of simple situations in Section 5-10.

Interference experiments have been performed with a Michelson interferometer and very weak sources of light, so weak, in fact, that on the average only a *single photon* was to be found between the light source and the observation screen at any one time. In the Michelson instrument the interference pattern arises from the interference between *two* light beams. The light follows two paths going at right angles to one another from a partially silvered mirror.† We might imagine that, when a single photon passes through the instrument, it travels along only one of the two possible paths; yet the experimental results, from data collected over a long time, show the customary interference pattern of alternating light and dark bands, implying that the single photon has traveled both routes simultaneously and has interfered with itself. The complementarity principle resolves the apparent paradox. If we speak of the photon as traveling along one of two possible routes, we are localizing it, regarding it as a particle, and precluding consideration of its wave aspects; on the other hand, if we speak of its interference pattern, we are regarding it as a wave. And to regard it both ways at once is meaningless.

A similar situation arises in the passage of waves through two parallel slits. When either one of the two slits is closed, the pattern is the typical single-slit diffraction pattern: a broad, central maximum flanked by weaker, secondary maxima, as in Figure 1-8a. When both slits are open, the pattern is as shown in Figure 5-13: interference fine structure within a diffraction envelope. The pattern is not merely two single-slit diffraction patterns superposed; the interference between waves traveling through *both* of the slits is responsible for the rapid variations in intensity. In short, in a case in which waves can take two or more routes from a source to an observation point we solve the problem by first superposing the wave functions (or electric fields) from the two separate routes to find the resultant wave function (or electric field) and then squaring to find the probability (or intensity). That is to say, if ψ_1 and ψ_2 represent the wave functions for passage through slits 1 and 2 separately, then $(\psi_1 + \psi_2)^2$, not $\psi_1 + \psi_2^2$, gives the probability of observing a particle on the screen. If, then, a single electron or photon is directed toward a pair of slits, we cannot

† See Sec. 45-8 in Weidner and Sells, *E. C. P.*

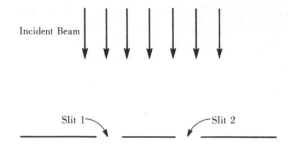

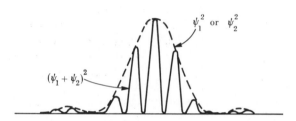

Figure 5-13. Double-slit diffraction of particles. The wave functions ψ_1 and ψ_2 give the diffraction pattern when either slit 1 or slit 2 is open; the superposed wave function, $\psi_1 + \psi_2$, gives the pattern when both slits are open. (The distance between the slits is grossly exaggerated in the figure.)

say which of the two slits it will pass through; we must speak in the language of waves and say, in effect, that it passes through *both* slits.

5-7 The uncertainty principle   The principle of complementarity shows that it is impossible to apply simultaneously the wave and particle descriptions to a material particle or to a photon. If we choose one description, we preclude the other. If we describe, for example, electromagnetic radiation in the language of particles and locate a photon at any instant with complete precision, then the *uncertainties* in position and time are both zero, $\Delta x = 0$ and $\Delta t = 0$; on the other hand, the uncertainties in the photon's wave attributes, wavelength λ and frequency ν, are then infinitely great, $\Delta \lambda = \infty$ and $\Delta \nu = \infty$.

Now consider a less extreme situation, one in which we are content to locate a photon in position and time, not with complete certainty, but with finite uncertainties Δx and Δt.

Our earlier analysis in Section 1-7 showed that, if the frequency ν of a wave is measured for only a *finite* time interval Δt, then the frequency is uncertain by an amount $\Delta \nu$:

[1-16] $\Delta \nu \, \Delta t \geq 1$ [5-11]

Similarly, if the wavelength λ is measured over a *finite* distance Δx along the direction of wave propagation, the wavelength is uncertain by an amount $\Delta \lambda$:

[1-19] $\Delta x \, \Delta \lambda \geq \lambda^2$ [5-12]

It is to be noted that these relations were derived on the basis of strictly classical considerations, without there being (at least explicitly) any quantum connotations. Their important implications for quantum physics arise from the fact that we must associate a frequency $\nu = E/h$ and wavelength $\lambda = h/p$ with an object having energy E and momentum p.

An uncertainty in frequency $\Delta \nu$ implies, then, an uncertainty ΔE in energy, which is given by

$$\Delta E = h \Delta \nu \qquad \text{[5-13]}$$

Eliminating $\Delta \nu$ from Equations 5-11 and 5-13, we have

$$\boxed{\Delta E \, \Delta t \geq h} \qquad \text{[5-14]}$$

Thus, the product of the uncertainties in energy and in time is at least as large as Planck's constant h.† The meaning, in words, of Equation 5-14 is as follows. If an object—a photon, an electron, or even a system of particles—is known to exist in a state of energy E over a period of time Δt, then this energy is uncertain by at least an amount $h/\Delta t$; therefore, the energy of an object is given with infinite precision ($\Delta E = 0$) only if the object exists for an infinite time ($\Delta t = \infty$). Equation 5-14 is one form of the celebrated *uncertainty principle*, or *principle of indeterminacy*, first introduced by Werner Heisenberg in 1927. We shall explore its fuller meaning after we have given it another formulation.

The uncertainty in wavelength $\Delta \lambda$ of an object of wavelength $\lambda = h/p_x$ (along the X direction) is related to the uncertainty in the magnitude of the momentum Δp_x by

$$\Delta \lambda = \frac{h}{p_x{}^2} \Delta p_x$$

† The value of the constant on the right side of Equation 5-14 depends on the precise definitions of the uncertainties ΔE and Δt. For the rather conservative convention used in Section 1-7 the constant is h, but if ΔE and Δt represent the root-mean-square values of a number of distinct measurements, then the constant becomes $h/4\pi$.

Substituting this equation in Equation 5-12 gives

$$\Delta\lambda\,\Delta x = (h\,\Delta p_x/p_x{}^2)(\Delta x) \geq \lambda^2$$

$$\Delta p_x\,\Delta x \geq (\lambda p_x)^2/h$$

$$\boxed{\Delta p_x\,\Delta x \geq h} \qquad\qquad [5\text{-}15]$$

which is the other formulation of the Heisenberg uncertainty principle. The wavelength was assumed to be measured over the finite distance Δx along the direction of wave propagation; with reference to the wave-particle duality the quantity Δx may be interpreted as the uncertainty in the position of the particle. Thus, the formulation of the uncertainty relation given in Equation 5-15 says that the product of the uncertainties in position and momentum equals or exceeds Planck's constant. Note that the momentum and position referred to in the equation are both measured along the *same* direction: according to the uncertainty relation, it is impossible to specify simultaneously and with infinite precision the linear momentum and the *corresponding* position of a particle or photon. Although $\Delta p_x\,\Delta x$ is equal to or greater than h, the product $\Delta p_y\,\Delta x$ can be equal to zero: there is no restriction on the simultaneous measurements of mutually perpendicular momentum and displacement.

The fundamental limitation on the certainty of measurements of energy and time or of position and momentum is in harmony with the principle of complementarity. If the particle nature of, say, an electron is to be perfectly displayed, then both Δx and Δt must be zero. Therefore, when the particle aspect is chosen, the wave aspect is necessarily suppressed. All of the quantities ν, E, λ, and p are then completely uncertain, which follows either from the uncertainty principle or from the principle of complementarity. On the other hand, if the wave characteristics of a material particle or of electromagnetic radiation are to be defined, perfectly, that is, if $\Delta\nu = 0$ and $\Delta\lambda = 0$ (also $\Delta E = 0$ and $\Delta p = 0$), then by the principle of complementarity or by the uncertainty principle we are prevented from giving simultaneously the distinctively particle characteristics of precise location in space and in time, and x and t are completely uncertain.

Suppose that we wish to represent an electron by its wave properties and yet localize it in space to some degree. We cannot use a single, sinusoidal wave: such a wave extends to infinity and is certainly not localized. We can, however, superpose a number of sinusoidal waves differing in frequency over a range of frequencies $\Delta\nu$ and so have a *wave packet*, as described in Section 1-7. The component waves constructively interfere over a limited region of space Δx, identified as the somewhat uncertain location of the "particle," and so yield a resultant wave function ψ of the sort shown in Figure 5-14. Because there is a range in frequency and a range

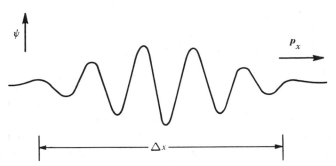

Figure 5-14. The wave function of a wave packet.

in wavelength, $\Delta\nu$ and $\Delta\lambda$, the associated momentum and energy are necessarily uncertain, and it is impossible to predict precisely where or when the wave packet will reach another point and what the momentum and energy will then be.

Since the uncertainty relation implies an uncertainty in energy, of magnitude $h/\Delta t$ over a time interval Δt, it also implies that the law of energy conservation may actually be violated—by that amount, $\Delta E = h/\Delta t$, but only for the time interval Δt. The greater the amount of energy borrowed or discarded, the shorter the time interval over which the nonconservation of energy may take place. Similarly, the uncertainty in a particle's momentum, $h/\Delta x$, implies that the law of momentum conservation may be violated, but only by that amount, $\Delta p = h/\Delta x$, over a region of space of Δx.

To derive the uncertainty principle in a different way, we consider the diffracting of waves by a single, parallel-edged slit. A monochromatic plane wave is incident on a slit of width w, and the diffraction pattern is formed on a distant screen, as shown in Figure 5-15. The location of the

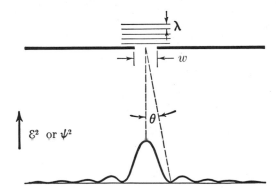

Figure 5-15. Diffraction pattern of a monochromatic plane wave incident on a slit of width w.

points of zero intensity is given by the equation†

$$\sin \theta = n\lambda/w \qquad [5\text{-}16]$$

where λ is the wavelength and n is 1, 2, 3, ... The total intensity within the central maximum is much greater than that within any of the secondary humps, since the area under it far exceeds that under any of the others. In fact, the area under the central hump is approximately three times the area under all the others; therefore, roughly three fourths of the energy passing through the slit falls within this central region. The limits of the central region are given by the following equation for $n = 1$:

$$\sin \theta = \pm \lambda/w \qquad [5\text{-}17]$$

We have not yet specified what sort of wave is diffracted by the slit. If the wave consists of electromagnetic radiation, then the intensity of the diffraction pattern is proportional to $\mathcal{E}^2$, the square of the electric field at the screen. If, on the other hand, the wave consists of a beam of electrons, the intensity of the diffraction pattern is proportional to ψ^2, which is the square of the wave function at the screen and gives the probability of finding an electron at any point along the screen. Whether the waves are of electromagnetic radiation or of a material particle, the diffraction effects are pronounced only when their wavelength is comparable to the slit width (see Figure 1-8); if it is much less than the slit width, the intensity pattern on the screen corresponds to a geometrical shadow cast by the edges of the slit.

Suppose now that we reduce drastically the amount of radiation or the number of electrons, as the case may be. Then, when we observe the screen, we no longer see smooth variations along it but, instead, photons or electrons arriving one by one. The intensity of the diffraction pattern is given by $\mathcal{E}^2$ for photons and by ψ^2 for electrons; thus, in Figure 5-15 the intensity represents the *probability* that a particle will strike a certain spot on the screen. There is a 75 percent probability that it will fall within the central region in the diffraction pattern, a smaller probability that it will fall in any other, and *zero* probability that it will fall at the zeros in the pattern. At very low illumination, bright flashes appear over a large area of the screen. As time passes, more and more particles accumulate on the screen, and the distinct bright flashes merge and form the smoothly varying intensity pattern predicted by wave theory.

There is *no* way of predicting in advance where any one electron or photon will fall on the screen. All that wave mechanics permits us to know is the probability of a particle's striking any one point. Before the particles pass through the slit, their momentum is known with complete precision both in magnitude (monochromatic waves) and in direction (vertically

† See Sec. 46-3, Weidner and Sells, *E. C. P.*

down in this case). When they pass through the slit, their position along a line in the X direction, completely uncertain before they reached the slit, is now known with an uncertainty $\Delta x = w$, the slit width. What is not known, however, is precisely where any one particle will strike the screen. Any particle has approximately a three-to-one chance of falling anywhere within the central region, whose boundaries are given by Equation 5-17. There will be an uncertainty in the X component of the momentum p that is *at least* as great as $p \sin \theta$, as may easily be seen in Figure 5-16.

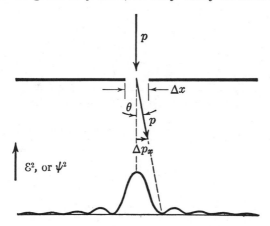

Figure 5-16. An illustration of the uncertainty in the momentum of a particle that has passed through a single slit.

Therefore we write

$$\Delta p_x \geq p \sin \theta$$

Using Equation 5-17, we have

$$\Delta p_x \geq p\lambda/\Delta x$$

and since $p = h/\lambda$, we have

$$\Delta p_x \, \Delta x \geq h$$

the *Heisenberg uncertainty relation*.

Now suppose that Δx in our example is very large; that is, the slit is very wide. Then the uncertainty in position is increased, and we cannot be certain as to where an electron is located along X. But the uncertainty in the momentum is reduced correspondingly, which is shown by the fact that the diffraction effect becomes less pronounced and essentially all electrons fall within the geometrical shadow (see Figure 1-8). Conversely, as the slit is reduced in width and Δx becomes very small, the diffraction pattern is expanded along the screen, and for the increase in our certainty of the electron's position we must pay by a correspondingly greater uncertainty in the electron's momentum.

We see that when the slit width is much greater than the wavelength, particles pass through the slit undeviated to fall within the geometrical shadow. This is in agreement with classical mechanics, where the wave aspect of material particles is ignored. Thus, there is a close parallel in the relationship of wave optics to ray optics, and of wave mechanics to classical mechanics. Ray optics is a good approximation of wave optics whenever the wavelength is much less than the dimensions of obstacles or apertures that the light encounters; similarly, classical mechanics is a good approximation of wave mechanics whenever a particle's wavelength is much less than the dimensions of obstacles or apertures encountered by material particles. Symbolically, we can write

$$\lim_{\lambda/w \to 0} (\text{wave optics}) = (\text{ray optics})$$

$$\lim_{\lambda/w \to 0} (\text{wave mechanics}) = (\text{classical mechanics})$$

No ingenious subtlety in the design of the diffraction experiment will remove the basic uncertainty. We do *not* have here, as in the large-scale phenomena encountered in classical physics, a situation in which the disturbances on the measured object can be made indefinitely small by ingenuity and care. The limitation here is rooted in the fundamental quantum nature of electrons and photons; it is intrinsic in their complementary wave and particle aspects.

Example 5-1.   As an illustration of the uncertainty principle, we compute the uncertainty in the momentum of a 1,000 eV electron whose position is uncertain by no more than 1 Å = 1.0×10^{-10} m, the approximate size of atoms. From $\Delta p_x \geq h/\Delta x$ it follows that $\Delta p_x = 6.6 \times 10^{-24}$ kg-m/sec. Now let us compare this uncertainty in the momentum with the momentum itself, $p_x = (2mE_k)^{1/2} = 17 \times 10^{-24}$ kg-m/sec. Therefore, the fractional uncertainty in the momentum is $\Delta p_x/p_x = 6.6/17$, about 40 percent! Because of the uncertainty principle, it is impossible to specify the momentum of an electron confined to atomic dimensions with even moderate precision.

Consider now the uncertainty involved when a 10.0 g body moves at a speed of 10.0 cm/sec; that is, an ordinary-sized object is moving at an ordinary speed. Let us further assume that the position of the object is uncertain by no more than 1.0×10^{-3} mm. We wish to find the uncertainty in the momentum and, more especially, the fractional uncertainty in the momentum. We find $\Delta p_x = 6.6 \times 10^{-28}$ kg-m/sec and $p_x = 1.0 \times 10^{-3}$ kg-m/sec; therefore, $\Delta p_x/p_x = 6.6 \times 10^{-25}$! The fractional uncertainty in the momentum arising in this example of a macroscopic body is so extraordinarily small as to be negligible compared with all possible experimental limitations. The uncertainty principle imposes a fundamental limitation on the certainty of measurements only in the microscopic domain, where the wave-particle duality is important. In the macroscopic domain the uncertainties are, in effect, trivial (see Figure 1-1).

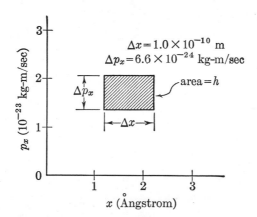

Figure 5-17. Uncertainties in the simultaneous measurements of position and momentum of an electron.

Figure 5-17 shows the momentum p_x of the electron in our example above, plotted against its position x. The uncertainty principle requires that the shaded area in this figure, which gives the product of the uncertainties in the momentum and the position, be equal in magnitude to Planck's constant h. If the position is known with high precision, the momentum is rendered highly uncertain; if the momentum is specified with high certainty, the position must necessarily be highly indefinite. It is therefore impossible to predict and follow in detail the future path of an electron confined to essentially atomic dimensions. Newton's laws of motion, which are completely satisfactory for giving the paths of large-scale particles, cannot be applied here; to predict the future course of any particle it is necessary to know not only the forces that act on the particle but also its initial position and momentum. Because *both* position and momentum cannot be known simultaneously without uncertainty, it is not possible to predict the future path of the particle in detail. Instead, *wave mechanics* must be used to find the probability of locating the particle at any future time.

Consider again the 10.0 g body moving at 10.0 cm/sec. Figure 5-18 shows its momentum and position. The area h, representing the product of the uncertainties in momentum and position, is so extraordinarily tiny in such macroscopic circumstances that it appears as an infinitesimal point on the figure. In this case the classical laws of mechanics may be applied without entailing appreciable uncertainty.

Here we have seen still another example of the correspondence principle as it applies to relations between classical physics and quantum physics. The *finite size* of Planck's constant is responsible for quantum effects. Quantum effects are subtle because Planck's constant is very small—but not zero. Recall that the relativity effects are subtle because the speed of light is very large—but not infinite. If somehow Planck's constant were zero, the quantum effects would disappear. Thus classical physics is the correspondence limit of quantum physics as h is imagined to approach zero. Symbolically,

$$\underset{h \to 0}{\text{Limit}} \; (\text{quantum physics}) = (\text{classical physics})$$

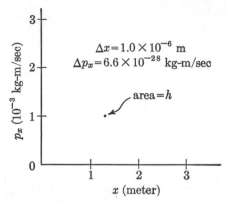

Figure 5-18. Uncertainties in the simultaneous measurements of position and momentum of a 10 g body. (On the scale of this drawing the uncertainty, area h, has been exaggerated by a factor of 10^{26}.)

5-8 Wave packets and the de Broglie wavespeed The speed of a wave of frequency $\nu = E/h$ and wavelength $\lambda = h/p$ is given by

$$v_{\mathrm{ph}} = \nu\lambda = (E/h)(h/p) = E/p \qquad [5\text{-}18]$$

where the subscript denotes that the speed is the *phase* speed, the rate at which a point of constant phase travels through space. Using the angular frequency $\omega = 2\pi\nu$ and the wavenumber $k = 2\pi/\lambda$, we may write

$$E = \hbar\omega, \qquad p = \hbar k$$

$$v_{\mathrm{ph}} = \omega/k \qquad [5\text{-}19]$$

where $\hbar$ equals $h/2\pi$. The energy E and momentum p of a particle of relativistic mass m traveling at the speed v are given by

$$E = mc^2, \qquad p = mv \qquad [5\text{-}20]$$

In assigning a speed v to a particle we imply that its energy and momentum are to some degree localized and are transported at this speed. We can compare the speed v with the phase speed v_{ph} of the associated wave by substituting Equations 5-20 in Equation 5-18:

$$v_{\mathrm{ph}} = E/p = mc^2/mv = c^2/v \qquad [5\text{-}21]$$

Suppose that the particle is a photon, with a zero rest mass. Then its speed is $v = c$, and from Equation 5-21 we have

$$v_{\mathrm{ph}} = c \quad \text{for} \quad m_0 = 0$$

A photon travels at the *same* speed c as does the associated electromagnetic wave. Now suppose that the particle's rest mass is finite; then its speed v must always be less than c. With $v < c$ in Equation 5-21 we have

$$v_{\mathrm{ph}} > c \quad \text{for} \quad m_0 > 0$$

The phase speed of the associated wave *exceeds* the speed of light. Consequently, a monochromatic wave associated with a material particle is unobservable—a circumstance that is not disturbing from the point of view of wave mechanics, since observations are those of the probability of finding a particle, not of the speed with which the phase advances.

Of course, if we are to think of some object bearing energy and momentum as a particle, its energy and momentum confined to a small region of space, then the amplitude of the associated wave function must be concentrated in a relatively small region of space, as shown in Figure 5-14. The figure does not depict a wave of a single frequency, for such a wave would be strictly sinusoidal and have infinite extension; it shows a wave packet, composed of waves of different frequencies. The component waves interfere constructively at the location of the particle, in the region where the resultant wave function is large, and they interfere destructively in all other regions, as shown in Figure 1-14. Since the particle's location is that for which the wave function and the probability are large, the speed v at which the particle moves is the speed at which the region of constructive interference advances through space.

Recall now some general results given in Section 1-8 concerning phase and group velocities. When a group, or packet, of individual sinusoidal waves differing in frequency *and in phase speed* combine to produce a region of strong constructive interference, the speed at which that region advances, the *group speed* v_{gr}, is related to the angular frequency ω and wavenumber k of the component waves by the relation

[1-32] $v_{gr} = d\omega/dk$ [5-22]

As the arguments above have suggested, the speed v_{gr} of the *group* of waves in the packet should equal the particle speed v. Let us prove it.

Since $\omega = E/\hbar$ and $k = p/\hbar$, then Equation 5-22 may be written

$$v_{gr} = d\omega/dk = dE/dp$$ [5-23]

The particle's total energy E is related to its relativistic momentum p by

[3-14] $E = \sqrt{E_0^2 + (pc)^2}$

Taking the derivative, we have

$$\frac{dE}{dp} = \frac{pc^2}{\sqrt{E_0^2 + (pc)^2}} = \frac{pc^2}{E} = \frac{mvc^2}{mc^2}$$

so that Equation 5-23 becomes

$$v_{gr} = v$$ [5-24]

The particle's speed *is* just the group speed of the particle's wave packet.

5-9 The quantum description of a confined particle A particle that is completely free from any external influence will, by Newton's first law, move in a straight line with a constant momentum. In the language of wave mechanics, such a particle, having a constant, well-defined momentum, must be represented by a monochromatic sinusoidal wave with a well-defined wavelength. If the wavelength is to be precisely defined, the wave must have an infinite extension in space. In accordance with the uncertainty principle, when the wavelength and, therefore, the momentum of the particle are specified precisely, the position of the particle is altogether uncertain and indeterminate.

In Figure 4-2c we saw an example from classical physics of waves that had perfectly defined wavelengths and yet confined to a limited region of space: the example was resonant standing waves on a string fixed at both ends. The wave on the string is repeatedly reflected from the boundaries, the fixed ends, and it constructively interferes with itself. Resonance is achieved only when the length of the string is some integral multiple of the half-wavelengths; the standing-wave pattern therefore fits between the boundaries.

Consider an elementary wave-mechanical problem that is analogous to that of standing waves on a string. Let us have the wave associated with a particle confined in the same way that a transverse wave on a string is confined. We assume that the particle moves freely back and forth along the X axis but that it encounters an infinitely hard wall at $x = 0$ and another at $x = L$; it is, then, confined between these boundaries. The infinitely hard walls correspond to an infinite potential energy V for all values of x less than zero and greater than L. Because the particle is free between zero and L, its potential energy V in this region is constant. The situation we have described is that of a *particle in a one-dimensional box*, or a particle in an infinitely deep potential well. Because the walls are infinitely hard, the particle imparts none of its kinetic energy to them, its total energy remains constant, and it continues to bounce back and forth between the walls unabated.

From the point of view of wave mechanics we may say that, if the particle is confined within the limits stated, and its potential energy between zero and L is taken as zero for convenience, then the probability of finding it outside these limits is zero. Therefore, the wave function ψ, whose square represents this probability, must be zero for $x \leq 0$ and $x \geq L$.

We may summarize mathematically the conditions of our problem as follows:

$$V = \infty \quad \text{for} \quad x < 0, \quad x > L$$
$$V = 0 \quad \text{for} \quad 0 < x < L$$
$$\psi = 0 \quad \text{for} \quad x \leq 0, \quad x \geq L$$

Only those wave functions which satisfy the conditions are allowed. Since the particle is free and the magnitude of its momentum is constant in the entire region between the walls, we know that it is represented by a sinusoidal wave. To satisfy the conditions at the boundaries, only those wavelengths are allowed which will permit an integral number of half-wavelengths to be fitted between $x = 0$ and $x = L$. The condition for the existence of *stationary*, or standing, waves is, then,

$$L = n(\lambda/2) \qquad\qquad [5\text{-}25]$$

where λ is the wavelength and n is the *quantum number* having the possible values 1, 2, 3, etc.

Figure 5-19 shows the wave function ψ and the probability ψ^2 plotted against x, for the first three possible *stationary states* of the particle in the

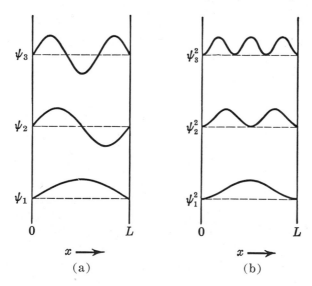

(a)   (b)

Figure 5-19. The first three stationary states of a particle in a one-dimensional box: (a) wave functions and (b) probability distributions.

box. Note that, whereas ψ can be negative as well as positive, ψ^2 is always positive.

The probability distribution is such that ψ^2 is always zero at the boundaries. For the first state, $n = 1$, the most probable location of the particle is the point midway between the two walls, at $x = L/2$; for the second state, $n = 2$, however, the least probable location is this point, where, in fact, $\psi^2 = 0$, which is to say that it is impossible for the particle to be located there!

The imposition of the boundary conditions on ψ, that is, the fitting of the waves between the walls, has restricted the wavelength of the particle to the values given by Equation 5-25. Now, if only certain wavelengths are permitted, the magnitude of the momentum also is restricted to certain values, since $p = h/\lambda$. Therefore, the permitted momenta are given by

$$p = h/\lambda = hn/2L \qquad [5\text{-}26]$$

Finally, the kinetic energy E_k (and, therefore, the total energy E of the particle, since the potential energy is zero) is given by

$$E_k = E = \tfrac{1}{2}mv^2 = p^2/2m = (hn/2L)^2/2m$$

$$\boxed{E_n = n^2 \frac{h^2}{8mL^2}} \qquad [5\text{-}27]$$

where m is the particle's mass (this equation holds only for nonrelativistic speeds). The subscript n signifies that the possible values of the energy depend only on the quantum number n for fixed values of m and L. By this equation we see that the *energy* of the particle in the one-dimensional box is *quantized*. The particle cannot assume any energy or speed but only those particular energies and speeds which satisfy the boundary conditions placed upon the wave function. The quantization of the energy is analogous to the classical quantization of the frequencies of waves on a string fixed at both ends.

Let us compute the possible values of the energy by assuming that an electron with $m = 9.1 \times 10^{-31}$ kg is constrained to move back and forth within a distance of $L = 4$ Å, or 4×10^{-10} m. Setting these values in Equation 5-27 gives for the energy of the first state, $n = 1$, the value $E_1 = 2.3$ eV. Because $E_n = n^2(h^2/8mL^2) = n^2E_1$, the next possible energies of the particle are $4E_1$, $9E_1$, $16E_1$, ... The permitted energies of the electron in a 4-angstrom box are shown in Figure 5-20, which is called an *energy-level diagram*. It is significant, in relation to atomic structure, that, when an electron is confined to a distance approximately the diameter of an atom, its possible energies are in the range of a few electron volts, comparable to the binding energy of electrons in atoms.

Now consider the allowed energies of a relatively large object confined in a relatively large box; assume that $m = 9.1$ mg $= 9.1 \times 10^{-6}$ kg and that $L = 4$ cm $= 4 \times 10^{-2}$ m. Equation 5-27 shows that for these values $E_1 = 2.3 \times 10^{-41}$ eV, a fantastically small amount of energy! Figure 5-21 shows the energy-level diagram for these circumstances; there the energy is plotted to the *same* scale as in Figure 5-20. The spacing between adjacent energies in a diagram for such macroscopic conditions is so very small that energy is effectively continuous. That is why we never see any obvious

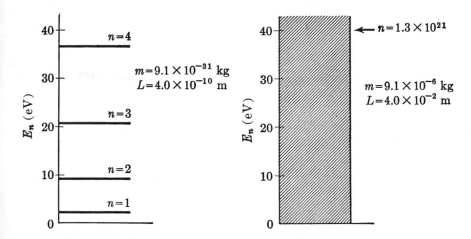

Figure 5-20. Allowed energies of an electron confined to a one-dimensional box of atomic dimensions.

Figure 5-21. Allowed energies of a 9.1 mg particle confined to a 4 cm one-dimensional box.

manifestation of the quantization of the energy of a macroscopic particle; the quantization is there, but it is too fine to be discerned. This result agrees, of course, with the correspondence principle, which requires that the discrete energies of a bound system appear continuous in large-scale phenomena.

Note that the lowest possible energy of a particle in an infinitely deep box is not zero, but E_1. This is in accord with the uncertainty principle. If the particle's energy were zero, the particle being at rest somewhere within the box ($\Delta x = L$), both the momentum, p, and the uncertainty in the momentum, Δp_x, would be zero. This would violate the uncertainty relation, since the product $\Delta p_x \Delta x$ would be $(0)(L) = 0$, not h. For $x = L$ the uncertainty in momentum is given by $\Delta p_x = h/\Delta x = h/L$. The particle's momentum p_x in one direction must then be at least as great as the uncertainty Δp_x. Moreover, we cannot know whether the particle travels to the left or to the right, so that, all told, $\Delta p_x = 2p_x$. Under these circumstances the particle's energy is $E = p_x^2/2m = (\Delta p_x/2)^2/2m$. With $\Delta p_x = h/L$ we have $E = h^2/8mL$, exactly the energy of the first allowed state, given by Equation 5-27.

For an electron confined within atomic dimensions the energy in the state of lowest energy, or the *ground state*, is a few electron volts. The electron is never at rest but bounces back and forth between the confining walls with its lowest possible energy, the so-called *zero-point energy*. This is, of course, true of any confined particle. Let us compute the minimum speed of the 9.1 mg particle restricted to 4 cm. Since $E_1 = 2.3 \times 10^{-41}$ eV $= \frac{1}{2}mv^2$, we find that $v = 9.0 \times 10^{-28}$ m/sec, or a mere 10^{-7} angstrom per millennium. The particle is effectively at rest.

The problem of the particle in the box is a somewhat artificial one, since there is no such thing as an infinitely great potential energy, and a particle cannot be made completely free from all external influences while inside a box. Nevertheless, the problem is an important one, because it reveals the quantization of the energy. Energy quantization occurs, basically, because only certain discrete values of the wavelength can be fitted between the boundaries.

5-10 The Schrödinger equation Starting with the general wave equation, we can arrive at the time-independent Schrödinger equation, whose solution yields the permitted wave functions and the quantized energies of bound systems.

Any wave propagated along the X direction obeys the general wave equation,

$$\frac{\partial^2 F}{\partial x^2} = \frac{1}{w^2} \cdot \frac{\partial^2 F}{\partial t^2} \qquad [5\text{-}28]$$

where F is the wave function, depending on both the coordinate x and the time t, and w is the wavespeed. When transverse waves are propagated along a taut string, the function F is the transverse displacement of the string from equilibrium, and w is the speed of the wave along the string; when electromagnetic waves are propagated through a vacuum, F is the electric or magnetic field, and w is the speed of light; when sound waves are propagated through a gas, F is the pressure difference, and w is the speed of sound. In the wave-mechanical behavior of particles the wave function is that quantity whose square gives the probability of locating a particle at any point in space; we shall now find it convenient to call it Ψ.

We consider only systems whose total energy E is constant and whose particles move along the X axis and are bound. Then the frequency $\nu = E/h$ associated with the bound particle is also constant, and we can take the wave function $\Psi(x, t)$ to be separable into the spatial-dependent term $\psi(x)$ and a time-dependent term $f(t)$:

$$\Psi(x, t) = \psi(x)\, f(t)$$

Since the frequency is assumed to be precisely defined, the time-dependent term $f(t)$ must vary sinusoidally with time, and we can take it to be given by

$$f(t) = \cos 2\pi\nu t$$

The second partial derivatives required in Equation 5-28 are

$$\frac{\partial^2 \Psi}{\partial x^2} = f(t) \frac{d^2\psi}{dx^2}$$

$$\frac{\partial^2 \Psi}{\partial t^2} = \psi(x) \frac{d^2 f}{dt^2} = -4\pi^2\nu^2 f(t)\psi(x)$$

Setting these results in Equation 5-28 yields

$$f(t) \frac{d^2\psi}{dx^2} = -\frac{4\pi^2\nu^2}{w^2} f(t)\psi(x)$$

$$\frac{d^2\psi}{dx^2} = -\left(\frac{2\pi}{\lambda}\right)^2 \psi = -\left(\frac{p}{\hbar}\right)^2 \psi \qquad [5\text{-}29]$$

where the wavelength is $\lambda = w/\nu$, and the momentum of the particle is $p = h/\lambda$.

We take the particle of mass m to be interacting with its surroundings (of infinite mass) through a potential-energy function $V = V(x)$. The total energy E of the system is then given by

$$E = E_k + V = (p^2/2m) + V$$

where E_k is the particle's kinetic energy. Then we have

$$p^2 = 2m(E - V).$$

and Equation 5-29 becomes

$$\frac{\hbar^2}{2m} \cdot \frac{d^2\psi}{dx^2} + (E - V)\psi = 0 \qquad [5\text{-}30]$$

This equation is the one-dimensional, time-independent, non-relativistic Schrödinger equation.† To obtain the Schrödinger equation applicable to

---

† Although the correct form of the time-independent Schrödinger equation (Equation 5-30) can be arrived at from the general wave equation (Equation 5-28), the latter is not appropriate for probability wave functions. For one thing, the correct Schrödinger time-dependent wave equation contains only the first derivative with respect to time, not the second. Furthermore, the total wave function $\Psi(x, t)$ must in general be complex; as a consequence, the probability of finding a particle is given by $\Psi^*\Psi$, where Ψ^* is the complex conjugate of Ψ.

particles in three dimensions we merely replace $d^2\psi/dx^2$ in this equation with $(\partial^2\psi/\partial x^2 + \partial^2\psi/\partial y^2 + \partial^2\psi/\partial z^2)$.

In deriving the Schrödinger equation it was assumed that the "particle" propagates as a wave (we used a *wave* equation) but that it interacts with its surroundings as a particle (the potential energy V is given as a function of *points* in space). The complementarity principle is built into the Schrödinger equation.

If we know the force acting on a bound particle—that is, if we know the potential energy as a function $V(x)$ of the particle's position—we can find the allowed wave functions and allowed energies of the system. An acceptable solution $\psi(x)$ must be finite, continuous, and single-valued and, most especially, it must be consistent with the boundary conditions imposed by the character of the potential energy V. Indeed, it is the imposition of boundary conditions upon the wave function that leads to the quantization of the energy of a bound system. To put it in nonanalytical terms: we must regard the particle as a wave reflected back and forth within the confines of a bound system, forming standing waves; it is the fitting of stationary waves to boundary conditions that leads to the quantized values of a system's permitted energies. If the potential energy is dependent upon position, but the system's total energy E is constant, then the particle's kinetic energy, momentum, and wavelength all must depend upon position. For example, the wavelength is given by

$$\lambda = \frac{h}{p} = \frac{h}{\sqrt{2m(E - V)}} \qquad [5\text{-}31]$$

PARTICLE IN A ONE-DIMENSIONAL POTENTIAL WELL OF INFINITE HEIGHT The simplest problem to solve with the Schrödinger equation is that of a single particle confined to a one-dimensional box of width L; that is, the particle is imagined to be in an infinitely deep potential well, as shown in Figure 5-22. The potential energy $V(x)$ is constant within the box (and taken to be zero for convenience), and V rises to infinity at the boundaries, $x = 0$ and $x = L$. For the interval $0 < x < L$ the Schrödinger equation, Equation 5-30, then becomes, with $V = 0$,

$$\frac{\hbar^2}{2m} \cdot \frac{d^2\psi}{dx^2} + E\psi = 0$$

or

$$\frac{d^2\psi}{dx^2} = -B^2\psi \qquad [5\text{-}32]$$

where

$$B^2 \equiv 2mE/\hbar^2$$

The walls being infinitely high, the particle cannot be found outside the box. This implies that $\psi(x)$ must be zero for all points at and beyond the box's boundaries. Thus, the allowed solutions must be consistent with the boundary conditions, which are $\psi(0) = 0$ and $\psi(L) = 0$. A suitable solution is

$$\psi(x) = A \sin Bx$$

as may be verified by substitution in Equation 5-32. The first boundary condition, $\psi(0) = 0$, is satisfied for the sine function (it would *not* be satisfied for a cosine function, so the cosine is discarded). The second boundary condition, $\psi(L) = 0$, is satisfied only if $BL = n\pi$, where n is an integer (since $\sin n\pi = 0$). Substituting for B, we then have

$$n\pi = BL = \sqrt{2mE}(L/\hbar) \qquad\qquad [5\text{-}33]$$

The energies and wave functions of a free particle confined to a box of infinitely high walls are, therefore,

[5-27]

energies: $E_n = n^2\pi^2\hbar^2/2mL^2$

wave functions: $\psi_n(x) = A_n \sin(n\pi x/L)$

These results agree with those obtained in Section 5-9. The sinusoidal wave functions and the quantized energies, varying as the square of the quantum number, are shown in Figures 5-19a and 5-20.

PARTICLE IN A ONE-DIMENSIONAL POTENTIAL WELL OF FINITE HEIGHT
Suppose now that the walls of the one-dimensional box are not infinitely high but have a finite height V_d, as shown in Figure 5-23. We again choose

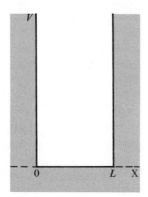

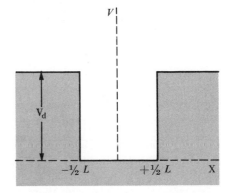

Figure 5-22. Potential energy of an infinitely deep well of width L.

Figure 5-23. Potential energy of a well of finite depth V_d and width L.

the bottom of the well as the zero of the potential energy. The zero of x is now taken to be at the center of the well. We know that in classical physics the particle must remain inside the square well if its kinetic energy is less than the magnitude of V_d; that is, if the particle is bound, with a total energy E less than V_d, it cannot possibly be found anywhere but in the region $-L/2 < x < L/2$. In wave mechanics the condition is less stringent: the particle *may* be found outside the limits defined by classical physics. What appears superficially to be a violation of energy conservation is permitted through the uncertainty relation. Thus, the wave function may actually be nonzero outside the well, that is, at $x < -L/2$ and $x > L/2$. In the interior of the well, where the potential energy is constant, the wave functions are sinusoidal, as before, but they now do not necessarily drop to zero at the boundaries, $x = -L/2$ and $x = +L/2$.

For $x < L/2$ or $x > L/2$ we may write the Schrödinger equation, Equation 5-30, as follows:

$$\frac{d^2\psi}{dx^2} = \frac{2m(V_d - E)}{\hbar^2}\psi$$

The potential energy of a bound particle exceeds the total energy E, so that $V_d - E$, appearing on the right-hand side of the equation, is *positive*. If we use $C^2 \equiv 2m(V_d - E)/\hbar^2$, this equation becomes

$$\frac{d^2\psi}{dx^2} = C^2\psi$$

where C^2 is a positive quantity for the regions outside the potential well.

The possible solutions of this equation are $\psi = A_+e^{+Cx}$ and $\psi = A_-e^{-Cx}$, as may be verified by substitution. First we concentrate on the exterior region on the right, where $x > L/2$. If x is positive, we can rule out $\psi = A_+e^{+Cx}$ on the following grounds: although an acceptable wave function may be nonzero beyond the walls of the one-dimensional box, it cannot be infinite and, if $\psi = A_+e^{+Cx}$ were a solution, we should find it to be infinite at infinite distances from the box along the positive of the X axis, implying an infinite probability of finding the particle at the greatest distances from the box. Clearly, this is untenable, and we are left, then, with the solution $\psi = A_-e^{-Cx}$, which means that the wave function decays exponentially in a direction away from the box on the positive of the X axis and becomes zero at infinitely great distances. The wave function also decays exponentially along the negative of the X axis: since x is negative to the left of the box, the appropriate form there for ψ is A_+e^{+Cx}.

To sum up, the wave function is a sinusoid inside the box and a decaying exponential outside it. The inside and outside wave functions must, however, join smoothly at the points $x = +L/2$ and $x = -L/2$. At both these points

$$\psi_{inside} = \psi_{outside}$$

$$\frac{d\psi_{inside}}{dx} = \frac{d\psi_{outside}}{dx}$$

The complete wave functions of the first two allowed states are shown in Figure 5-24. The energies are lower than those in a box with infinitely high

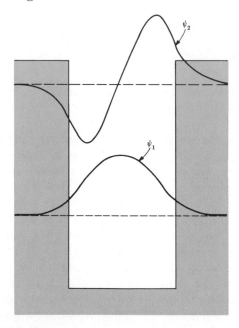

Figure 5-24. Wave functions for the first two states of a particle in a potential-energy well of finite depth.

walls. This results from a greater wavelength (hence a lesser momentum and lesser kinetic and total energies), which arises in turn from the fact that the wave functions do not drop to zero at the walls.

THE TUNNEL EFFECT   Since a particle can, wave-mechanically, spill over its classical confines, we have a curious possibility when it strikes a potential wall of finite width and height, as in Figure 5-25. In classical physics a particle whose kinetic energy is less than the height of the wall would never get through to the other side either by climbing or passing through; it simply could not, because of the conservation of energy. In wave mechanics this *is* a possibility. As we have seen, the wave function is nonzero and decays exponentially when the potential energy exceeds the

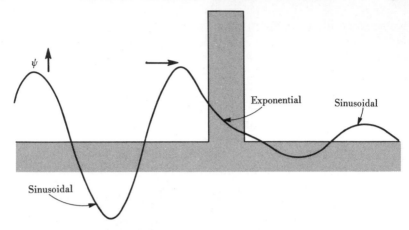

Figure 5-25. Wave function of a particle incident from the left upon a barrier of finite height and width.

total energy. Thus, the wave function of a particle approaching the wall from the left is sinusoidal to the left of the wall, exponential through the wall, and sinusoidal, but of much smaller amplitude, to the right of the wall. Since the amplitude of a wave function gives a measure of the probability of locating a particle, there is a small but finite probability that the particle that has approached from the left will be on the *right*. In other words, the particle has a high probability of being found on the left, a smaller probability of being found within the wall, and a still smaller probability of being found on the right. The particle or, more properly, the wave can penetrate, or tunnel through, the classically insurmountable barrier. The probability of this *tunnel effect* is vanishingly small except at the atomic and nuclear level. The effect is observed, however, in the behavior of certain semiconducting devices (the so-called tunnel diodes) and in the emission of alpha particles from unstable, heavy nuclei.

OTHER EXAMPLES OF BOUND PARTICLES   We have discussed bound particles in a one-dimensional potential well, and two others may be mentioned; Figures 5-26 show the energies and wave functions of all three for comparison. In a one-dimensional simple harmonic oscillator (Section 12-2) a particle is bound to the potential energy $V(x) = \frac{1}{2}kx^2$. A particle subject to an inverse-square attractive force, with $V(r) = -ke^2/r$, is the problem of the hydrogen atom; the figure shows a graph of the wave functions for the spherically symmetrical solutions (the s states) for this potential. The mathematical solutions of the simple harmonic oscillator and hydrogen atom are too involved to be given here, but Problem 5-46 and Section 6-7, respectively, concern their wave functions and energies.

The following are some general features of wave-mechanical solutions, which may be seen in the examples given in Figure 5-26.

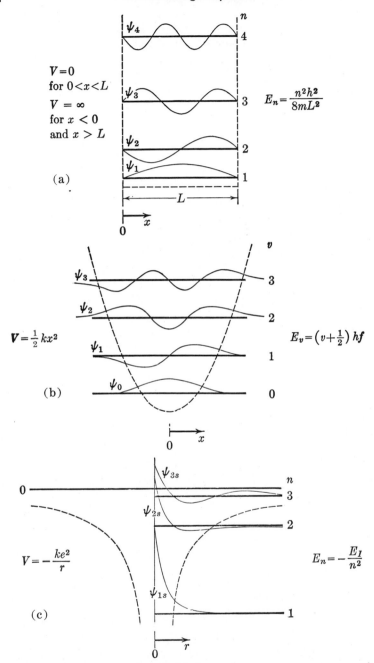

$V=0$
for $0<x<L$
$V = \infty$
for $x < 0$
and $x > L$

(a)

$E_n = \dfrac{n^2 h^2}{8mL^2}$

$V = \dfrac{1}{2} kx^2$

(b)

$E_v = \left(v+\dfrac{1}{2}\right) hf$

$V = -\dfrac{ke^2}{r}$

(c)

$E_n = -\dfrac{E_1}{n^2}$

Figure 5-26. Potential-energy functions, wave functions, and allowed energies of three simple potential energies: (a) an infinitely deep well, (b) a simple harmonic oscillator, and (c) a particle (hydrogen atom) subject to an inverse-square attractive force.

(a) The wave function of a particle in a box of infinite height is exactly zero at the boundaries and at all exterior points. Those of the other two potentials, however, are finite at, and extend beyond, the classical boundaries.

(b) Integral multiples of half-wavelengths, $1(\lambda/2)$, $2(\lambda/2)$, $3(\lambda/2)$, . . ., successively are fitted between the boundaries at states of progressively higher energies.

(c) The wavelength is constant (is independent of x) and the wave function consequently sinusoidal at a constant potential energy, as that inside the infinitely deep well, but the wavelength is not constant (is dependent on x) and the wave function consequently not sinusoidal for a potential energy that varies with x, as those of the simple harmonic oscillator and of the hydrogen atom. From Equation 5-31, $\lambda = h/[2m(E - V)]^{1/2}$, it follows that the wavelength depends on the potential-energy function $V(x)$ and therefore on x. For this reason it is small wherever the kinetic energy $E - V$ is large, and conversely.

(d) The lowest energy is *not* zero.

(e) For a particle in the infinitely high well the energy levels are crowded at the bottom, for the simple harmonic oscillator they are equally spaced, and for the hydrogen atom they are crowded at the top. This behavior is related to the shape of the curve of the potential energy: in Figure 5-26a the potential energy is bent toward the vertical with respect to that of the simple harmonic oscillator, Figure 5-26b, whereas in Figure 5-26c it is bent toward the horizontal.

Example 5-2. Sketch the wave function of an excited state of a particle moving in the potential shown in Figure 5-27. This is nothing more than the wave-

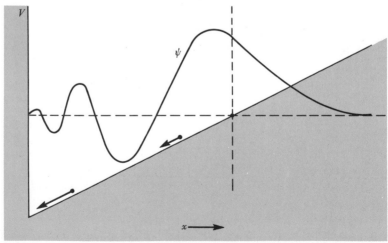

Figure 5-27. The wave-mechanical inclined plane: potential-energy function and wave function of the fifth allowed state.

mechanical version of a standard example in elementary mechanics: a particle sliding on a frictionless inclined plane (here with an infinitely high wall at the bottom of the incline). Solving the problem in complete analytical detail would involve finding solutions to the Schrödinger equation for a potential energy that rises to infinity at $x = 0$ and increases steadily with x, according to $V = ax$, for $x > 0$, but we can show, even without detailed analysis, the general features of the wave-mechanical solution.

Since the potential rises to infinity at $x = 0$, the wave function must be zero there. At the other extreme, where the particle may be found outside the classical upper limit, the wave function must decay to zero. In between the particle has some nonzero kinetic energy, and so the wave function is undulatory there. Further, in the case of a relatively highly excited state the features of the wave-mechanical solution must, through the correspondence principle, approach the classical features of a particle sliding on an inclined plane and colliding with a hard wall at the bottom. Since the particle moves at high speed at the base of the incline and at less speed at the top, the wavelength of the wave function must be smallest near the base and increasingly large toward the top. Moreover, the classical high speed at the base and low speed at the top imply that the particle is more likely to be found at the top than at the bottom. Thus, the amplitude of the wave function must be greatest at the top and least at the bottom. Given all these features, we know that the wave-mechanical solution of an excited state is as shown in Figure 5-27.

In the next energy state up we should find one additional half-wavelength fitted between the left and right extremes, and in the next energy state down we should find one less half-wavelength; in the lowest state, we should find a single hump in ψ between the zeroes in ψ at the left and right extremes.

5-11 Summary Every particle, whether of finite or zero rest mass, has associated with it a frequency and wavelength given by

[5-1], [5-2] $$\nu = E/h \quad \text{and} \quad \lambda = h/p$$

The wavelengths of electrons of 150 eV, thermal neutrons (1/25 eV) to typical x-rays and the interatomic spacings of a solid are all of the order of 1 angstrom.

When a wave is incident upon a set of parallel Bragg planes separated by a distance d, constructive interference occurs, according to the Bragg relation, when

[5-4] $$n\lambda = 2d \sin \theta$$

X-rays and electrons can be diffracted by crystalline solids. The x-ray and electron diffraction effects may be used for measuring x-ray and electron wavelengths and interatomic spacings and for producing monochromatic beams.

According to Bohr's principle of complementarity, the wave and particle aspects of electromagnetic radiation and of material particles are complementary, but the use of one description precludes the use of the other in a given circumstance.

The wave-mechanical description of material particles parallels that of electromagnetic radiation as follows:

Electromagnetic radiation (photons)	Material particles
Wave function: electric field $\mathcal{E}$ (or magnetic field)	*The* wave function ψ
Probability of observing particle in interval dx $\mathcal{E}^2 \, dx$	$\psi^2 \, dx$

The Heisenberg uncertainty principle imposes a limit on the certainty of simultaneous measurements of energy E and time t and of momentum p_x and position x:

[5-14]
$$\Delta E \, \Delta t \geq h$$

[5-15]
$$\Delta p_x \, \Delta x \geq h$$

A particle may be represented by a packet of waves; the group velocity of the wave packet is the velocity of the particle.

A free particle confined to a one-dimensional box (L) of infinitely high walls is restricted to those states in which an integral multiple of the particle's wavelength is fitted between the boundaries. The particle's energy is thereby quantized and given by

[5-27]
$$E_n = n^2 h^2 / 8mL^2$$

where n is the quantum number $n = 1, 2, 3, \ldots$.

By the correspondence principle,

$$\underset{h \to 0}{\text{Limit}} \text{ (quantum physics)} = \text{(classical physics)}$$

The wave functions ψ and allowed energies E of the stationary states of a particle of mass m confined by a potential-energy function V are determined by the time-independent Schrödinger equation, which for one dimension has the form

[5-30]
$$\frac{\hbar^2}{2m} \cdot \frac{d^2\psi}{dx^2} + (E - V)\psi = 0$$

The wave function is single-valued and continuous and chosen to be consistent with the boundary conditions imposed by the nature of the potential-energy function $V(x)$.

BIBLIOGRAPHY

The World of the Atom, ed. H. A. Boorse and L. Motz. New York: Basic Books, Inc., 1966. This two-volume book contains many original papers on fundamental discoveries in atomic and nuclear physics together with biographical sketches of the scientists. Chapters 51, 52, and 68: x-ray and electron diffraction: Chapters 63, 64, 65, 66, and 71: de Broglie waves, probability interpretation of particle waves, the uncertainty relation, complementarity.

Albert Einstein: Philosopher-Scientist, ed. P.A. Schilpp. Evanston, Illinois: The Library of Living Philosophers, Inc., 1949. Chapter 7, "Discussion with Einstein on Epistemological Problems in Atomic Physics," written by Niels Bohr, contains a penetrating discussion of the implications of the uncertainty principle and some hypothetical machines devised in an attempt to violate this principle. It emerges that all these attempts fail.

Heisenberg, W., *The Physical Principles of the Quantum Theory*. Chicago, Illinois: The University of Chicago Press, 1930. The first four chapters concentrate on the uncertainty principle, its meaning, and its consequences.

Heitler, W., *Elementary Wave Mechanics*: Oxford: The Clarendon Press, 1946. The first hundred pages give a mathematically simple development of the wave mechanics and the Schrödinger equation.

Sherwin, C. W., *Introduction to Quantum Mechanics*. New York: Henry Holt and Company, 1959. Chapter 3 shows through an elementary argument how the imposition of boundary conditions on the wave functions results in the quantization of energy.

PROBLEMS

5-1 What are the wavelengths of (a) a 1.00 MeV photon, (b) a 1.00 MeV (kinetic energy) electron, and (c) a 1.00 MeV (kinetic energy) proton?

5-2 A proton and electron are both accelerated from rest by an electric potential difference of 100 kV. What is the ratio of the proton's wavelength to the electron's wavelength?

5-3 Two low-speed particles with mass m_1 and m_2 have the same kinetic energy. What is the ratio of their wavelengths?

5-4 According to Equation 4-7, the wavelength of a photon of energy E is given by $\lambda = (0.0124 \text{ MeV-Å})/E$. Show that the same relation gives the wavelength of a particle of nonzero rest mass when the particle's total energy E greatly exceeds its rest energy E_0.

5-5 (a) At the Stanford Linear Accelerator Center electrons are accelerated to a kinetic energy of 20 GeV; what is their wavelength at that energy? (b) In the high-energy accelerator soon to be constructed at Weston, Illinois, protons will have energies of 200 GeV; what will be their wavelength at that energy?

5-6 For a gas of molecular hydrogen at 300 °K the root-mean-square molecular speed is 1.84 km/sec; what is the wavelength of such a hydrogen molecule?

5-7 (a) What is the kinetic energy of a hydrogen atom whose wavelength is comparable to its diameter (≈ 1 Å)? (b) What is the kinetic energy of a proton whose wavelength is comparable to its diameter ($\approx 2 \times 10^{-15}$ m)?

5-8 Show that the wavelength of a particle of rest energy E_0 and kinetic energy E_k is given (a) by hc/E_k when $E_k \gg E_0$ and (b) by $hc/(2E_0E_k)^{1/2}$ when $E_k \ll E_0$.

5-9   Show that the wavelength of a particle of rest energy E_0 and kinetic energy E_k is given by $hc/E_k^{1/2}(2E_0 + E_k)^{1/2}$.

5-10 *   Particles of mass m and charge Q pass undeflected through a region of space with an electric field ε transverse to the beam direction and a magnetic field B also transverse to the beam direction but perpendicular to the direction of the electric field. What is the wavelength of the emerging particles?

5-11 *   What is the wavelength of particles, of rest energy E_0 and charge Q, that move in a circular path of radius r in a magnetic field B?

5-12 *   The single-slit diffraction pattern shown in Figure 5-15 is observed only when the conditions for Fraunhofer diffraction are met. If Fraunhofer, rather than Fresnel, diffraction is to be observed, the plane on which the pattern will be seen must be at a great enough distance D from the slit for the path difference between rays drawn from the center of the slit and the edge of the slit to the observation plane to be small compared with the wavelength λ. (a) Show that for a slit of width w Fraunhofer diffraction is observed when $D \geq w^2/8\lambda$. (b) If particles of 1 kg mass and 1 m/sec speed pass through a slit 1 m wide, at what approximate minimum distance (in light years) from the slit must the observation plane be located if the Fraunhofer diffraction pattern is to be observed?

5-13   Compute the lattice spacing of atoms in a single crystal of KCl, which has a simple cubic structure like that of NaCl. The atomic masses of potassium and chlorine are 39.1 and 35.5, respectively, and the density of KCl is 1.98 g/cm³.

5-14   Monochromatic x-rays consisting of photons with an energy of 6.2 MeV are incident upon a NaCl single crystal, whose lattice spacing is 2.82 Å. At what angle with respect to the incident beam would one observe first-order Bragg reflection?

5-15   A narrow beam of thermal neutrons is incident upon a single crystal whose lattice spacing is 1.80 Å. (a) At what angle with respect to the incident beam must the Bragg planes be oriented so as to produce strong first-order diffraction for those neutrons with a kinetic energy of 0.040 eV? (b) What is then the angle between the incident and the diffracted beams?

5-16   A narrow beam of x-rays of 0.248 Å is incident upon KCl powder consisting of randomly oriented microcrystals. The lattice spacing of KCl is 3.14 Å. A flat photographic plate is 10.0 cm behind the powder target and is perpendicular to the incident beam; see Figure 5-5. (a) What is the radius of the circle, on the photographic plate, arising from the first-order diffraction from Bragg planes separated by 3.14 Å? (b) What is the radius of the circle arising from second-order diffraction from the same Bragg planes?

5-17 *   In treating x-ray diffraction we have assumed that the scattered x-rays have the same wavelength as the incident x-rays. Strictly, of course, the wavelength of the scattered photon is, through the Compton effect, greater than that of the incident photon. Show that this correction is negligible by computing the maximum fractional change in the wavelength of 0.10 Å x-rays scattered from an atom of atomic mass 40.

5-18   Two parallel wire-mesh screens are separated by 0.25 m. A monochromatic beam of radio waves is incident upon the screens, and strong first-order Bragg diffraction occurs when the angle between the incident and diffracted beams is 60°. What is the frequency of the radio waves?

5-19 *   A monoenergetic beam of 54 eV electrons is incident, as in the Davisson-Germer experiment, upon a single crystal of nickel; see Figure 5-28. (a) What is the wavelength of these electrons? (b) Show that, if the diffracted beam is observed at angle θ with respect to the normal to the crystal surface, and the spacing between atoms on the surface is d, the first maximum in the beam diffracted from the surface only should appear at the angle specified by $d \sin \theta = \lambda$. (c) If the atomic spacing d of nickel is 2.15 Å, what is the angle θ for the first maximum? (Davisson and Germer observed a maximum at $\theta = 50°$.)

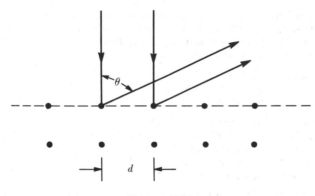

Figure 5-28.

5-20 *   The attractive potential energy between a certain solid substance and electrons entering at its surface is 10 V. Suppose that 50 eV electrons enter the surface at an angle of incidence (with respect to the normal to the surface) of 60°. (a) What is the angle of refraction of the electrons within the material? (b) What is the electron's wavelength inside?

5-21   Show that the phase speed of the wave associated with a particle of rest mass m_0 and wavelength λ is given by $c[1 + (m_0 c \lambda / h)^2]^{1/2}$.

5-22   An electron has a kinetic energy of 5.1 eV. What are (a) the phase speed and (b) the group speed of the waves associated with this electron? (c) If the waves comprise a packet confined to 100 Å, what is the uncertainty in the electron's momentum? (d) What is the fractional uncertainty in the electron's momentum?

5-23   A free particle of mass m and velocity v is represented at one instant by a wave packet of "width" Δx. (a) What is the uncertainty in the magnitude of the particle's momentum? (b) What is the width of the associated wave packet at some later time Δt?

5-24   The intensity of a monochromatic beam of electromagnetic radiation is 10 W/m². What is the density of the photons, or their average number per cubic centimeter, if the beam consists of (a) 100 kHz radio waves, (b) 5,000 Å visible light, and (c) 12.4 MeV gamma rays?

5-25   A partially localized particle is represented by a wave packet extending, at one instant, over a region of space Δx in size. The component waves in the packet do not travel at the same phase speed, because the waves associated with particles show dispersion, that is, because the phase speed depends on the wavelength (see Problem 5-21). Does the wave packet extend over a larger or a smaller region of space at some later time?

5-26   A 1 μg particle moves along the X axis; its speed is uncertain by 6.6×10^{-6} m/sec. What are the uncertainties in its position along (a) the X axis and (b) the Y axis? An electron with the same uncertainty in speed moves along the X axis: what are the uncertainties in its position along (c) the X axis and (d) the Y axis?

5-27   A virus is the smallest object that can be "seen" in an electron microscope. Suppose that a small virus, with a size of 10 Å, and a density equal to that of water (1 g/cm^3) is localized in a region of space equal to its size. What is the minimum speed of the virus?

5-28   The momentum component along the direction of motion of a 10.2 MeV electron is uncertain by 1 part in 10^3. Over what minimum region of space does the electron extend?

5-29   A camera with a fast shutter takes a photograph during an exposure of 1.0×10^{-5} sec. (a) What is the uncertainty in the energy of any one photon passing through the shutter? What is the corresponding fractional uncertainty in the wavelength of (b) a 10 eV photon of visible light and (c) a 10 GeV gamma-ray photon?

5-30   What is the minimum kinetic energy of (a) an electron and (b) a proton confined to a region of space the size of a nucleus, about 10^{-14} m? (c) It is known that particles within the atomic nucleus have energies of the order of a few mega electron volts and that the attractive potential energy between a pair of nuclear particles is of the same order; which particles, electrons or protons, might be found within an atomic nucleus?

5-31   The wavelength of a photon is measured to an accuracy of 1 part in 10^8 ($\Delta\lambda/\lambda = 10^{-8}$). What is the uncertainty Δx in the simultaneous localization of (a) a photon of visible light of 6,000 Å wavelength, (b) a radio photon of 100 kHz frequency, (c) an x-ray photon of 1.0 Å wavelength, and (d) a gamma-ray photon of 12.4 GeV energy?

5-32   A particle is confined to a region having the dimensions of an atomic nucleus (about 2×10^{-15} m). (a) Use the uncertainty relation to compute its approximate momentum. (b) If the particle's kinetic energy is a few mega electron volts, what is its rest energy? (c) What ordinary particle meets the requirements of parts (a) and (b)?

5-33 *   The uncertainty relation can be written in terms of linear momentum and position ($\Delta p_x \, \Delta x \geq h$) or of energy and time ($\Delta E \, \Delta t \geq h$). Still another formulation of the uncertainty relation is in terms of angular momentum L and angle θ, $\Delta L \, \Delta \theta \geq h$, where ΔL is the uncertainty in a particle's angular momentum relative to some chosen point and $\Delta \theta$ is the uncertainty in its angular position relative to the same point. See Figure 5-29, where

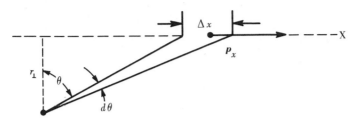

Figure 5-29.

a free particle is in motion along a straight line and its angular momentum $L = r_\perp p_x$ and angular position θ are measured relative to point P. (a) Derive the uncertainty relation for L and θ from the uncertainty relation in p_x and x. (b) According to a simple atomic model, the electron in the hydrogen atom circles the nucleus, and the angular momentum of the orbiting electron relative to the nucleus is $h/2\pi$; what does the uncertainty relation imply about the localization of the electron in the circular orbit?

5-34 The uncertainty relation $\Delta E\, \Delta t \geq h$ can be derived from the uncertainty relation $\Delta p_x\, \Delta x \geq h$ through the following considerations. The position of a particle traveling along the X axis is uncertain by Δx. Therefore, the uncertainty in the time at which the particle will arrive at some one more distant point along the X axis is $\Delta t = \Delta x/v$, where v represents the average speed of the particle. (a) Find the uncertainty in the particle's kinetic energy in terms of the particle's average speed v. (b) Find the uncertainty in its momentum $\Delta p_x = m\, \Delta v_x$, where Δv_x is the uncertainty in the particle's speed. (c) From the results above show that $\Delta E\, \Delta t = \Delta p_x\, \Delta x \geq h$.

5-35 * A π meson is an elementary particle with a rest mass of 140 MeV. Suppose that a proton spontaneously creates such a particle, $p \rightarrow p + \pi$, the energy required for doing so being allowed by the uncertainty principle. (a) For what maximum period of time can a π meson remain in existence or, in other words, for how long can 140 MeV be borrowed according to the uncertainty relation? (b) Assuming (for simplicity) a π meson to travel at or near the speed of light, what is the maximum distance it can travel before going out of existence by, for example, amalgamating spontaneously with a second proton? The attractive force between nuclear particles, protons and neutrons, may be attributed to the exchange of π mesons between them; the nuclear force drops to zero when particles are separated by more than about 2×10^{-15} m.

5-36 In an electron microscope a beam of electrons replaces a light beam, and electric and magnetic focusing fields replace refracting lenses. The smallest distance that can be resolved by any microscope under optimum conditions (its resolving power) is approximately equal to the wavelength used in the microscope. (a) A typical electron microscope might use 50 keV electrons; compute the minimum distance that can be resolved in such a microscope. (b) By what factor does the actual resolving power of about 20 Å, attained in well-designed electron microscopes, exceed the ultimate resolving power (minimum separation between two point objects distinguishable as two distinct objects), which is limited by the wave properties of electrons?

5-37 The ultimate resolving power (see Problem 5-36) of any microscope depends solely on the wavelength. Suppose that we wish to study an object having dimensions of 0.20 Å; what are the minimum energy and momentum if we use (a) electrons and (b) photons? (c) Why is an electron microscope preferable to a gamma-ray microscope?

5-38 When a monochromatic beam of electrons passes through a single slit and produces a diffraction pattern on a distant screen, any one electron may be deflected from its initial course. Then it acquires a momentum component at right angles to the direction of the slit and, by momentum conservation, the slit itself must acquire a compensating momentum. Show that for a beam of many particles the net momentum imparted to the slit is zero.

5-39 A particle of mass m is confined to a three-dimensional box of dimensions a, b, and c. Show by imposing boundary conditions on the wave functions in each of the three dimensions that the particle's allowed energies are given by $E = (\pi^2 h^2/2m)[(n_1/a)^2 + (n_2/b)^2 + (n_3/c)^2]$, where the quantum numbers n_1, n_2, and n_3 can take the integral values 1, 2, 3, ...

5-40 A small bead of mass m slides freely along a circular ring of radius R. (a) What are the allowed energies of the bead? (b) What are the allowed angular momenta?

5-41 A billiard ball of mass m is confined to a two-dimensional box (a billiard table) of dimensions L and W. (a) What are the billiard ball's permitted energies? (b) What is a billiard ball's minimum kinetic energy (a ball of mass 0.14 kg on a table 3.7 m by 1.9 m)?

5-42 Figure 5-30 shows three potential-energy wells. Using the facts that the wavelength is small where the kinetic energy is relatively high (and the potential energy relatively low), the wave functions drop to zero for infinite distances, and the wave functions must, in the correspondence limit of high quantum numbers, yield the corresponding classical results, sketch the approximate wave functions of the fifth lowest energy level.

5-43 Show that in the classical limit of very large quantum numbers the probability of a particle's being in any small but finite interval Δx in a one-dimensional box is independent of its position within the box. This result is in agreement with the classical expectation that the probability of finding a particle that moves at constant speed within a one-dimensional box is the same at all points.

5-44 The wave functions of a particle in a one-dimensional box of width L and and infinitely high walls are given by $\psi_n = A_n \sin(\pi n x/L)$. Impose the requirement that the total probability of the particle's being somewhere between $x = 0$ and $x = L$ is 100 percent, $\int_0^L \psi_n^2\, dx = 1$, to show that $A_n = (2/L)^{1/2}$.

5-45 Show that the fractional difference in energy between two adjoining energy levels of a particle in a one-dimensional box is given by $\Delta E/E = (2n + 1)/n^2$. Take the limit for large quantum number n to verify that the discrete energy levels in quantum physics approach the continuous distribution of energies in classical physics.

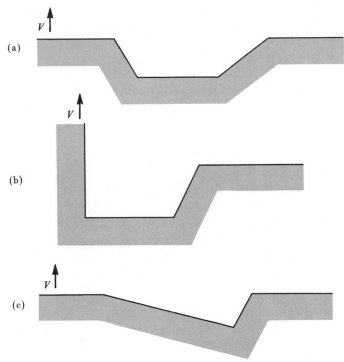

Figure 5-30.

5-46 * Consider the Schrödinger equation for a mass m in simple harmonic motion, with a potential energy $V = \frac{1}{2}kx^2$. (a) Show that the wave function $\psi = e^{-ax^2}$ is a solution. (b) Show that the energy corresponding to this wave function is $\frac{1}{2}\hbar\omega$, where ω is the corresponding classical angular frequency of oscillation, $\omega = (k/m)^{1/2}$.

5-47 * The Schrödinger equation takes on a particular simple form when length and energy are measured in the so-called atomic units. The atomic unit of length is $h^2/4\pi^2kme^2$, where k is the Coulomb-force constant ($F = kQ_1Q_2/r^2$), m is the electron's rest mass, and e is the electron's charge. The atomic unit of energy is $2\pi^2k^2me^4/h^2$. (As we shall see in Section 6-4, the atomic units of length and energy are, respectively, the radius of the first Bohr orbit of the hydrogen atom and the magnitude of the energy of a hydrogen atom in its lowest quantized state.) Show that, when length and energy are measured in atomic units, the time-independent one-dimensional Schrödinger equation becomes $d^2\psi/dx^2 + (E - V)\psi = 0$.

S I X

THE STRUCTURE OF THE HYDROGEN ATOM

6-1 Alpha-particle scattering Our modern concept of the structure of an atom posits these essential features: a *nucleus* occupying a very small region of space, in which all of the positive charge and practically all of the atom's mass are concentrated, and negatively charged electrons, which surround the nucleus. Let us examine the evidence for this concept of atomic structure, first proposed by Ernest Rutherford in 1911.

At the end of the nineteenth century it was known that the negative electric charge of the atom is carried by electrons, whose mass is but a small fraction of the total mass of the atom. Because atoms as a whole are ordinarily electrically neutral, it follows that, if we were to remove all of an atom's electrons, then what would remain would contain all of the positive electric charge and essentially all of the mass. The question is, then, "How are the mass and positive charge distributed over the volume of the atom?" Atoms are known, from a variety of experiments, to have a "size" (diameter) of the order of one angstrom unit, and because the positive charge and mass are confined to at least this small a region, it is impossible by any direct measurement to see and observe any details of the atomic structure. An indirect measurement must be resorted to. One of the most powerful methods of studying the distribution of matter or of electric charge is the method of *scattering*, and it was by the alpha-particle scattering experiments, suggested by Rutherford, that the existence of atomic nuclei was established.

We can best grasp the strategy of the scattering method by considering first a simple example of a scattering experiment. Suppose that we are confronted with a large black box, the mass of whose contents is known. We are not allowed to look inside to examine its internal structure, but we are asked to determine how the mass is distributed throughout the interior of the box. The box might, for instance, be filled completely with some material of relatively low density, such as wood, or it might be only partly filled with one of high density. How can we find out whether one of these two possibilities represents the actual distribution of material within the box? We can use a very simple expedient: shoot bullets into the box and see what happens to them. If we find all of the bullets emerging in the forward direction with reduced speeds, then we might infer that the box is filled with some such material as wood which deflects the bullets only slightly as they pass through. On the other hand, if we find a few bullets greatly deflected from their original paths, then we might assume that they had collided with small, hard, and massive objects dispersed throughout the box. It is possible, then, by studying the distribution of the scattered bullets to learn much concerning the arrangement of material within the box. Note that it is *not* necessary to aim the bullets; the shots may be fired randomly over the front of the box. This is the essence of the particle-scattering experiments in atomic and nuclear physics.

Rutherford suggested that the mass and positive charge of an atom are essentially a point charge and point mass, called the *nucleus*. He further suggested that his hypothesis could be tested by shooting high-speed, positively charged particles (the bullets) through a thin metallic foil (the black box), and then examining the distribution of the scattered particles. At the time of Rutherford's suggestion the only available and suitable charged particles were alpha particles, with energies of several million electron volts, from radioactive materials. Rutherford had shown earlier that an alpha particle is a doubly ionized helium atom; therefore, it has a positive electric charge twice the magnitude of the electron charge and a mass several thousand times greater than the mass of an electron but considerably smaller than the mass of such a heavy atom as gold. To confirm Rutherford's nuclear hypothesis H. Geiger and E. Marsden in 1913 scattered alpha particles from thin gold foils.

The essentials of the scattering apparatus are shown in Figure 6-1. A collimated beam of particles strikes a thin foil of scattering material, and a detector counts the number of particles scattered at some scattering angle θ from the incident direction within an angle $d\theta$. The experiment consists

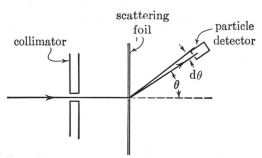

Figure 6-1. Arrangement for a simple scattering experiment: collimator, scattering material, and detector.

of measuring the relative number of scattered particles at various scattering angles θ. In one of their experiments Geiger and Marsden used alpha particles having a kinetic energy of 7.68 MeV from a radioactive source (polonium); the particles struck a gold foil, whose thickness was 6.00×10^{-5} cm. The rotatable detector consisted of a zinc sulfide screen, which was viewed through a microscope; the particles striking the screen produced bright flashes, or scintillations, which could be observed and counted for any angle θ.

Consider the behavior of the α-particles as they traverse the interior of the scattering foil. We may dismiss as inconsequential any encounters an α-particle may have with electrons within the material, because, since the mass of the particle is very much greater than that of an electron, the particle is essentially undeflected in such collisions, and a negligible fraction of its energy is transferred to any one electron. Thus, the α-particles are appreciably deflected and scattered only by close encounters with the nuclei. The nucleus of a gold atom has a mass that is considerably greater than (fifty times) that of the α-particle; therefore, in the collision it does not recoil appreciably and may be assumed to remain at rest. Since the α-particles and the nuclei are both positively charged, they repel each other. Rutherford assumed, not only that the nuclei were point charges, but also that the *only* force acting between a nucleus and an α-particle was the Coulomb electrostatic force. As we know, that force varies inversely with the square of the distance between the charges; therefore, although it is never zero (except for at infinite separation between the charges) the α-particle is acted upon by a *strong* repulsive force only when it comes quite close to a nucleus†.

† Since from the standpoint of quantum theory a beam of monoenergetic particles is in effect a beam of monochromatic waves (Section 5-2), the scattering process consists of the diffraction of incident waves by scattering centers. It is a remarkable fact that a thoroughgoing wave-mechanical treatment of scattering by an inverse-square force yields precisely the same result as that yielded by the strictly classical particle analysis, discussed here. In cases of other types of force, however, the classical and wave-mechanical results differ.

In Figure 6-2 are shown a number of paths of α-particles as they move

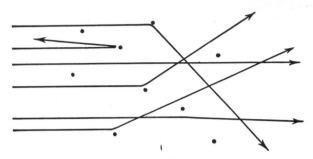

Figure 6-2. Scattering of alpha particles by the nuclei of a material (the number scattered through sizable angles is greatly exaggerated).

through the interior of a scattering foil. Most of the particles pass through the material with only a slight deviation from their original course; the chances of a close encounter with a nucleus, or scattering center, are fairly remote. On the other hand, those few α-particles which barely miss head-on collisions are deflected at sizable angles, and those extremely rare ones which make head-on collisions are deflected through 180°, that is, are brought to rest momentarily and then returned along their paths of incidence.

Now let us consider in somewhat greater detail the collision of a positively charged particle (e.g., an α-particle) with a heavy nucleus (e.g., gold). The incident particle is scattered by an angle θ, as shown in Figure 6-3. It moves in a nearly straight line, until it comes fairly close to the scattering center, which is the dot in the figure (the shading signifies a circular area about the nucleus, seen almost on edge); it is deflected and continues in a nearly straight line, its path being that of a hyperbola. It

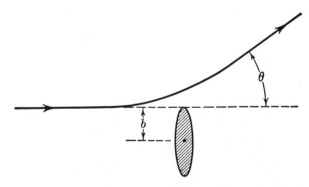

Figure 6-3. Scattering of an alpha particle that approaches a heavy nucleus with an impact parameter b.

would have passed the nucleus at a distance b if there had been no force between them. This distance is called the *impact parameter*.

We see from Figure 6-3 that all incident particles headed in such a direction to strike at the circumference, or rim, of a circle drawn about the nucleus and having a radius b, will be deflected by an angle θ. Furthermore, any particles so headed as to strike anywhere within the shaded area πb^2 will be deflected by an angle greater than θ. A particle that makes a head-on collision ($b = 0$) is, of course, deflected 180°. The target area πb^2 is called the *cross section σ*:

$$\sigma = \pi b^2 \qquad\qquad [6\text{-}1]$$

Thus, associated with every scattering center is an area σ such that an incident particle heading for it will be scattered an angle θ or greater. When a particle is deflected an appreciable angle, the cross section is extraordinarily small; that is, in large-angle scattering each nucleus presents a very small target to an incident particle.

Let us now calculate the total target area presented by *all* of the scattering centers within a foil of area A and thickness t. We assume the foil to be so thin that the cross-sectional area presented by any one nucleus does not overlap that of any other nucleus; see Figure 6-4, the total area of

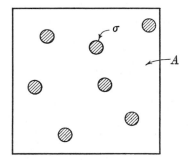

Figure 6-4. Target areas presented by the scattering centers of a thin foil resulting in the scattering of incident particles through an angle θ or greater.

which represents the area of the foil. If the total shaded area is very small compared with the area of the foil, there is a very low probability that an incident particle will be perceptibly deflected by more than one nucleus; that is, if the foil is sufficiently thin and the cross section σ is small, "*single scattering*" rather than "multiple scattering" will occur. The total number of scattering centers per unit volume is n. The value of n may be computed from Avogadro's number N_A, the density ρ, and the atomic mass M_a of the scattering foil from $n = N_A \rho / M_a$ (see a similar computation in Section

5-2). If there are n nuclei per unit volume, then in a foil having a volume At there are altogether nAt nuclei. The target area for scattering by at least as much as θ, is, then, $\sigma(nAt)$.

We wish to calculate what fraction of the incident particles will be scattered an angle θ or more. The incident beam cannot be aimed to strike any one nucleus in the foil, because the beam is spread over an area very large compared with that of σ. Therefore, the probability that any one incident particle will be deflected an angle greater than θ is simply the ratio of the shaded target area σnAt to the total area A of the foil. Of a large number of incident particles the fraction scattered is, then, given by $\sigma nAt/A$, or

$$\boxed{\frac{N_s}{N_i} = \sigma nt}$$ [6-2]

where N_i is the number of particles incident on the foil, and N_s is the number of these incident particles scattered an angle θ or more. The particle detector actually measures the number dN_s of scattered particles within the angle $d\theta$ subtended by the detector at a scattering angle θ. The corresponding target area that will scatter particles into angles from θ to $\theta + d\theta$ is the differential cross section $d\sigma$, which by Equation 6-1 is

$$d\sigma = 2\pi b \, db$$ [6-3]

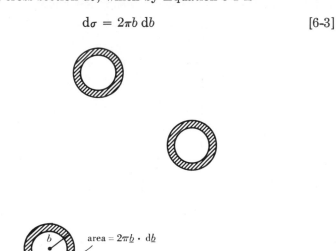

Figure 6-5. Nuclear target area for the differential cross section.

This follows as well from Figure 6-5, where we see the differential cross section of each nucleus as a ring of radius b, circumference $2\pi b$, and width db. An incident particle heading toward the shaded area now is scattered between θ and $\theta + d\theta$.

The number dN_s of particles scattered between the angles θ and $\theta + d\theta$ is, then, by Equations 6-2 and 6-3,

$$dN_s/N_i = nt\, d\sigma = 2\pi b\, nt\, db \qquad [6\text{-}4]$$

This equation is the basis of all scattering experiments with thin foils. The numbers of incident and scattered particles N_i and dN_s may be directly measured by experiment, and their ratio may be compared with that computed from this equation. To compute dN_s/N_i one must know how the impact parameter b is related to the angle of scattering, θ.

The relation between b and θ in the scattering of particles of charge Q_1 and kinetic energy E_k by an infinitely massive point charge Q_2 is given by†

$$b = \frac{k}{2} \cdot \frac{Q_1 Q_2}{E_k} \cot \frac{\theta}{2} \qquad [6\text{-}5]$$

where $k = 1/4\pi\epsilon_0$, the constant in Coulomb's law, and where $Q_1 = +2e$ and $Q_2 = +Ze$, the quantity Z being the charge of the nucleus in multiples of the electron charge e. This equation is derived from the laws of the conservation of energy, linear momentum, and angular momentum and by assuming the Coulomb force to be a conservative, central, inverse-square force.

Example 6-1.   Let us apply the theory of the scattering of alpha particles to the conditions of the Geiger and Marsden experiment, in which 7.68 MeV alpha particles were scattered by a 6.00×10^{-5} cm gold foil. We use the following known values, choosing θ to be 90°:

$\theta = 90°$ $k = 8.99 \times 10^9$ N-m²/C²

$t = 6.00 \times 10^{-7}$ m $\rho = 1.93 \times 10^4$ kg/m³

$E_k = 7.68$ MeV $w = 197.2$

$Z = 79$ $N_A = 6.02 \times 10^{26}$ atoms/kg-mole

$e = 1.60 \times 10^{-19}$ C

Equations 6-5, 6-1, and 6-2 then yield, respectively,

$$b = 1.48 \times 10^{-14}\,\text{m}$$
$$\sigma = 6.88 \times 10^{-28}\,\text{m}^2$$
$$N_s/N_i = 2.43 \times 10^{-5}$$

Under the conditions of this experiment any incident particle that originally moves so as to miss a head-on collision with a nucleus by no more than 1.48×10^{-14} m will be deflected by at least 90°. Notice that this impact parameter is much less than the di tance between gold nuclei, approximately 3×10^{-10} m, which is also the size of a gold atom. The cross section, or target area, for the scattering of

† See Sec. 25-6, Weidner and Sells, *E. C. P.*

α-particles through an angle greater than 90° is 6.88 × 10⁻²⁸ m², a very small area. Finally, we see that N_s/N_i is 2.43 × 10⁻⁵: according to theory, in the stated conditions, slightly more than two out of every hundred thousand incident α-particles will be deflected 90° or more. The assumption that the shaded area of Figure 5-4 is much less than the total area of the foil is amply justified, and therefore only single scattering is important in the case of such a large scattering angle. If the computation is repeated for $\theta = 1°$, one finds $N_s/N_i = 0.320$; that is 32.0 percent of the incident particles are expected to be scattered 1° or more.

From Equation 6-5 we have

$$db = \frac{-kQ_1Q_2}{4E_k} \csc^2 \frac{\theta}{2} \, d\theta$$

The minus sign implies that the scattering angle θ increases as the impact parameter b *decreases*; we shall not, however, use it hereinafter. Putting the relations for b and db into Equation 6-4, we have

$$\frac{dN_s}{N_i} = \frac{\pi n t}{4} \left(\frac{kQ_1Q_2}{E_k}\right)^2 \cot \frac{\theta}{2} \csc^2 \frac{\theta}{2} \, d\theta = \frac{\pi n t}{4} \left(\frac{kQ_1Q_2}{E_k}\right)^2 \frac{\cos(\theta/2) \, d\theta}{\sin^3(\theta/2)}$$

By using the trigonometric identity $\sin \theta = 2 \sin(\theta/2) \cos(\theta/2)$ we may rewrite this relation:

$$\frac{dN_s}{N_i} = \frac{n t}{16} \left(\frac{kQ_1Q_2}{E_k}\right)^2 \frac{(2\pi \sin \theta \, d\theta)}{\sin^4(\theta/2)} \qquad [6\text{-}6]$$

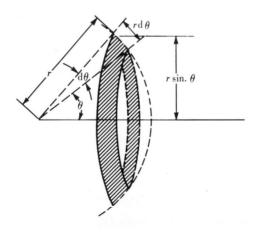

Figure 6-6. The solid angle $d\Omega$ subtended at the scattering angle θ by the incremental angle $d\theta$. By definition, $d\Omega/4\pi$ is the shaded area divided by the entire area of spherical surface, the shaded area being equal to $2\pi(r \sin \theta)(r \, d\theta)$. Then $d\Omega/4\pi = (2\pi r^2 \sin \theta \, d\theta)/4\pi r^2$; therefore $d\Omega = 2\pi \sin \theta \, d\theta$.

Now, the quantity $2\pi \sin\theta\, d\theta$ gives, as Figure 6-6 shows, the entire solid angle $d\Omega$ subtended by the incremental scattering angle $d\theta$. The scattering detector, rotated at a fixed distance about the scattering foil, always subtends a solid angle proportional to $d\Omega$; that is, the factor $d\Omega = 2\pi \sin\theta\, d\theta$ does not change as the detector is rotated, to count particles scattered at various scattering angles θ. From Equation 6-6 it follows, then, that

$$\frac{dN_s}{N_i} \propto \left(\frac{Q_1 Q_2}{E_k}\right)^2 \frac{nt}{\sin^4(\theta/2)} \qquad\qquad [6\text{-}7]$$

For α-particle scattering, $Q_1 = 2e$ and $Q_2 = Ze$, and this equation becomes

$$\frac{dN_s}{N_i} \propto \frac{Z^2 e^4 nt}{E_k^2 \sin^4(\theta/2)}$$

Since the number of scattered particles varies inversely as $\sin^4(\theta/2)$, the number dN_s falls off drastically as θ increases. For example, for every million particles observed at $\theta = 10°$ there are only 232 deflected at $\theta = 90°$ and a mere 58 deflected at $\theta = 180°$.

On the assumption of nuclear point charges most of the incident particles should be deflected only slightly and a small but significant number be deflected at large angles. If we had chosen an entirely different model, one in which the positive charge of the atom was assumed to be uniformly spread over a substantial region of the atom's volume, the probability of scattering through large angles with a thin foil would have been zero. Such a model was proposed by J. J. Thomson, but scattering experiments showed it to be incorrect. The nuclear hypothesis of Rutherford was confirmed by the experiments of Geiger and Marsden in that the measured distribution of the scattered α-particles was in agreement with the distribution predicted on the assumption of scattering under a Coulomb force by point charges, i.e. a scattering that is proportional to $1/[\sin^4(\theta/2)]$. They confirmed the Rutherford theory for a variety of α-particle energies, foil materials, and foil thicknesses.

Scattering experiments show, however, that Coulomb's law does *not* hold when the charged particles, the nucleus and the α-particle, are separated by distances somewhat less than 10^{-14} m. Discrepancies between Coulomb-scattering theory and experiment are found when one compares the observed and predicted numbers of high-energy α-particles that are scattered at very large angles: the α-particles may come closer than 10^{-14} m from the nucleus. Thus, for distances of this order or smaller the force between the nucleus and an α-particle is not given merely by Coulomb's law, and a distinctive, additional force, called the *nuclear force*, must be assumed to act between the particles. These deviations from the Coulomb force are crucial in our considerations of nuclear physics; at the moment we shall be content to note that the mass and the positive electric charge in any atom are located within a region no larger than 10^{-14} m. It is certainly proper to assume that in a typical atom, having a size of approximately 10^{-10} m, the electrons are subject to a strictly electrostatic Coulomb force of attraction originating from a point charge, the nucleus.

6-2 The classical planetary model That the nucleus is the center of positive charge and mass in the atom and that the force between charged particles at atomic dimensions is the Coulomb electrostatic force may be used as the basis of a very simple, classical model of atomic structure. Let us consider the structure of hydrogen, the simplest of all atoms, in terms of this classical model. Ordinary hydrogen consists of a nucleus having a single positive charge (a proton) and one electron. The proton, which is 1,836 times more massive than the electron, attracts the electron with a Coulomb electrostatic force that varies inversely as the square of the distance between them (the gravitational force between the particles is 10^{39} times smaller than the electric force and may therefore be neglected). The situation is similar to that of our solar system: the Sun's mass greatly exceeds that of a planet, and the planet and Sun attract one another by an inverse-square gravitational force. For the planet to be bound to the Sun it must move in an elliptical or circular path about it. The atomic planetary model assumes that an atom is like a miniature solar system, in which the nucleus replaces the Sun, an electron replaces a planet, and the Coulomb force replaces the gravitational force. The model is strictly classical; no wave aspects are ascribed to the electron, and all quantum effects are excluded. It is assumed, for simplicity, that the electron moves in a circular orbit about the hydrogen nucleus, the nucleus remaining at rest.

We shall compute the energy of the hydrogen atom and the frequency of the orbital motion. The total mechanical energy E of the system (excluding the rest energies of the electron and proton) is the sum of the electron's kinetic energy E_k and the electric potential energy E_p between the electron and proton. An electron with mass m is assumed to move at a speed v (nonrelativistic) in a circle of radius r; the electron and proton each carry an electric charge of magnitude e. Therefore,

$$E = E_k + E_p$$
$$= \tfrac{1}{2} mv^2 + (-ke^2/r) \qquad [6\text{-}8]$$

where $k = 1/4\pi\epsilon_0 = 8.99 \times 10^9$ N-m²/C². The inward radial force maintaining the electron in its circular orbit is supplied by the electric force due to the nucleus. Thus,

$$F = ma$$
$$ke^2/r^2 = mv^2/r$$
$$mv^2 = ke^2/r \qquad [6\text{-}9]$$

We see from Equations 6-8 and 6-9 that, when an orbit is circular, the *kinetic energy is one half the magnitude of the potential energy*. Putting Equation 6-9 in Equation 6-8 gives

$$E = \tfrac{1}{2}(ke^2/r) - (ke^2/r)$$

$$\boxed{E = -(ke^2/2r)} \qquad [6\text{-}10]$$

This equation shows that the total energy of the system is negative. As the radius of the electron orbit increases, E approaches zero; this means that the electron is most tightly bound to the nucleus when it moves in a small, circular orbit and that the electron is free of the binding to the nucleus only when it is separated from it by an infinite distance. When E is negative, the electron and proton form a bound system.

It is known that a hydrogen atom has a diameter of approximately one angstrom and that the electron in hydrogen is bound to the nucleus with an energy of 13.6 eV. Putting $E = -13.6$ eV in Equation 6-10 gives $r = 0.53$ Å; thus far the hydrogen planetary model shows agreement with experimental facts.

Let us now consider electromagnetic radiation from a classical planetary hydrogen atom. Classically, electromagnetic waves are produced by an accelerated electric charge, and the frequency of the waves is precisely the frequency of oscillation of this charge.† The electron in a planetary hydrogen atom is continuously accelerated in that it moves in a circular path; therefore, the atom radiates continuously. The frequency of the radiation, moreover, is expected to be equal to the frequency f of the electron's orbital motion. The orbital frequency is given by

$$f = \omega/2\pi = v/2\pi r \qquad [6\text{-}11]$$

where ω is the orbital angular speed of the electron. Equation 6-9 may be written in the form

$$v/r = \sqrt{ke^2/mr^3} \qquad [6\text{-}12]$$

Putting this in Equation 6-11 gives

$$f = (1/2\pi)\sqrt{ke^2/mr^3} \qquad [6\text{-}13]$$

If one puts $r = 0.5$ Å in this equation, the orbital frequency f is found to be 7×10^{15} sec^{-1}; at this radius the frequency of radiation should lie in the ultraviolet region of the electromagnetic spectrum. Now, if the atom radiates, its total energy E must decrease and become even more negative. We see from Equation 6-10 that, if the total energy E decreases, the orbital radius r must also decrease and, from Equation 6-13, that f increases as r decreases. In short, when energy is radiated, E decreases, r decreases, the

---

† See Sec. 41-5, Weidner and Sells, *E. C. P.*

orbital frequency f increases and, hence, the radiated frequency continuously increases.

The classical planetary theory, then, predicts that the electron, starting from some initial orbit, will spiral inward toward the nucleus, the atom will radiate a *continuous* spectrum, and the frequency will increase as the electron's radius decreases; see Figure 6-7. Calculations show that the electron

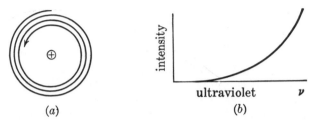

(a)   (b)

Figure 6-7. Classical collapse of an atom due to continuous radiation by the orbiting electron: (left) radius decreases; (right) classical intensity distribution of electromagnetic radiation as a function of frequency.

in this classical model reaches the nucleus and combines with it in less than 10^{-8} sec. The atom collapses! The classical planetary atomic model is clearly untenable on two important counts: it predicts that atoms are unstable, and it predicts a continuous radiation spectrum. This is completely in disagreement with the experimental facts: atoms *are* stable, and atoms radiate *discrete* spectra of frequencies, as we shall see in the next section.

6-3 The hydrogen spectrum We have seen that the strictly classical planetary model leads to the expectation that a continuous range of electromagnetic radiation will be emitted from hydrogen atoms and that the atom will collapse. Because the observed radiation from hydrogen is not continuous, and because hydrogen atoms are stable, the model is fundamentally defective; a correct model must be able to account in detail for the observed spectra and the stability. Before we discuss the model that adequately describes the structure of hydrogen atoms, the natural starting point for any theoretical description of atomic structure, let us set down the known facts concerning the hydrogen spectrum.

In order to observe the spectrum of isolated hydrogen atoms it is necessary to use gaseous atomic hydrogen, because in it the atoms are so far apart that each one behaves as an isolated system (molecular hydrogen, H_2, and solid hydrogen radiate spectra that reflect some aspects of hydrogen atoms bound together).

The visible spectrum emitted by hydrogen may be studied with a spectrometer of the type shown schematically in Figure 6-8, which is a prism spectrometer; a diffraction grating may be used instead of a prism for

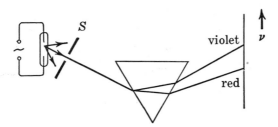

Figure 6-8. Schematic diagram of a prism spectrometer.

dispersing the radiation. The hydrogen gas is excited by an electrical discharge or by extreme heating and emits radiation. Some of this radiation passes through a narrow slit S and is dispersed by a prism or grating. The radiation, now separated into its various frequency components, falls on a screen or photographic plate, making it possible to measure the frequencies and intensities of the *emission spectrum*.

Any instrument that disperses and measures the various wavelengths of a beam of electromagnetic radiation is called a *spectrometer*. An instrument that disperses the light and photographs the spectrum is known as a *spectrograph*; one that makes the spectrum visible directly to the eye is called a *spectroscope*. Spectrometers are designed for the study of each of the several regions of the electromagnetic spectrum, such as radiofrequency, x-rays, and gamma rays. That branch of physics which deals with the study of electromagnetic radiation emitted or absorbed by substances is called *spectroscopy*. Spectroscopy is a very powerful method of inquiry into atomic, molecular, and nuclear structure; it is characterized by very great precision (frequencies or wavelengths are easily measured to one part in ten million) and very high sensitivity (emission or absorption from samples as small as fractions of a microgram can be observed).

The spectrum from atomic hydrogen given by a prism or diffraction-grating spectrometer consists of a number of sharp, discrete, bright lines on a black background, the lines being images of the slit. In fact, the spectra of all chemical elements in monoatomic gaseous form are composed of such bright lines, each spectrum being characteristic of the particular element. The spectrum is known as a *line spectrum*. The *emission spectrum* from atomic hydrogen, then, is a bright line spectrum characteristic of hydrogen. Since each chemical element has its own characteristic line spectrum, spectroscopy is a particularly sensitive method of identifying the elements.

The line spectrum from atomic hydrogen in the visible region is shown in Figure 6.9. The lines are labeled H_α, H_β, etc., in the order of increasing frequency and decreasing wavelength. Ordinarily the H_α line is much more intense than the H_β, which is in turn more intense than the H_γ, and soon. The spacings between adjacent lines become smaller as the frequency in-

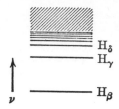

Figure 6-9. Frequency distribution of radiation from atomic hydrogen in the visible region. This particular group of spectral lines is the Balmer series.

creases and the discrete lines approach a *series limit*, above which there appears a weak continuous spectrum. This group of hydrogen lines, which appears in the visible region of the electromagnetic spectrum, is known as the *Balmer series*, because in 1885 J. J. Balmer arrived at a simple empirical formula, called the Balmer formula, from which all of the observed wavelengths in the group could be computed. This formula, giving the wavelength λ for all spectral lines in this series, may be written

$$\frac{1}{\lambda} = R\left(\frac{1}{2^2} - \frac{1}{n^2}\right) \qquad [6\text{-}14]$$

where

$$R = 1.0967758 \times 10^7 \, \text{m}^{-1} \approx 1.0968 \times 10^{-3} \, \text{Å}^{-1}$$

and n is an integer having the values 3, 4, 5, ...

Putting $n = 3$ in this formula gives $\lambda = 6{,}564.7$ Å, the H_α line; similarly, putting $n = 4$ gives $\lambda = 4{,}862.7$ Å, the H_β line. The wavelength of the series limit is given by the Balmer formula when $n = \infty$. The constant R is known as the *Rydberg constant*; its value is chosen by trial to give the best fit for the measured wavelengths. In atomic spectroscopy spectral lines typically are specified by their wavelengths rather than their frequencies, because it is the wavelength that is measured.

Besides the Balmer series in the visible region hydrogen radiates a series of lines in the ultraviolet region and several series of lines in the infrared.

Each series may be represented by a formula similar to the Balmer equation. In fact, one general formula may be written, from which *all* of the spectral lines of hydrogen can be computed. It is known as the *Rydberg equation* and is written

$$\frac{1}{\lambda} = R\left(\frac{1}{n_l^2} - \frac{1}{n_u^2}\right)$$

[6-15]

where:

$n_l = 1$ and $n_u = 2, 3, 4, \ldots$, *Lyman* series, ultraviolet region

$n_l = 2$ and $n_u = 3, 4, 5, \ldots$, *Balmer* series, visible region

$n_l = 3$ and $n_u = 4, 5, 6, \ldots$, *Paschen* series, infrared region

and so on, to further series lying in the far infrared. The value of the Rydberg constant in this equation is *precisely* the same as its value in Equation 6-14; in fact, Equation 6-15 becomes Equation 6-14 when n_l is set equal to 2. The choice of u ("upper") and l ("lower") as subscripts for the integers in the Rydberg formula will become obvious in Section 6-4. The several series of hydrogen lines are named after their discoverers. Although the Rydberg formula is remarkably successful in summarizing the wavelengths radiated by atomic hydrogen, it must be recognized that it is merely an empirical relation, which in itself supplies no information about the structure of hydrogen. On the other hand, a truly successful theory of the hydrogen atom must be capable of predicting the spectral lines; that is, it must be able to yield the Rydberg formula as a result.

We have been concerned with the spectrum given by hydrogen when it is excited by an electrical discharge or by extreme heating. Atomic hydrogen at room temperature does *not*, by itself, emit appreciable electromagnetic radiation, but at room temperature it can selectively absorb electromagnetic radiation, giving an *absorption spectrum*. The absorption spectrum of atomic hydrogen is observed when a beam of white light (all frequencies present) is passed through atomic hydrogen gas and the spectrum of the transmitted light is examined in a spectrometer. What is found is a series of dark lines superimposed on the spectrum of white light; this is known as a *dark-line spectrum*. The gas is transparent to waves of all frequencies except those corresponding to the dark lines, for which it is opaque; that is, the atoms absorb only waves of certain discrete, sharp frequencies from the continuum of waves passing through the gas. The absorbed energy is very quickly radiated by the excited atoms, but in *all directions*, not just in the incident direction. The dark lines in the absorption spectrum of hydrogen occur at precisely the same frequencies as do the bright lines in the emission spectrum, as shown schematically in Figure 6-10, where the

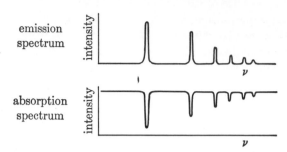

Figure 6-10. Variation of intensity with frequency in emission and absorption spectra of hydrogen.

intensity is plotted as a function of frequency. Hydrogen is a radiator of electromagnetic radiation only at the specific frequencies or wavelengths given by the Rydberg formula; it is an absorber of radiation only at the same frequencies.

What we have discussed concerning the emission and absorption spectra of atomic hydrogen holds equally well for the line spectra of all elements. A characteristic set of frequencies is emitted when the atoms radiate energy; the same set of frequencies is absorbed by the atoms when a continuous frequency band of electromagnetic radiation is sent through the gas.

6-4 The Bohr theory of atomic structure The planetary model of the hydrogen atom developed in Section 6-2 is a classical one in that it treats the electron strictly as a particle and the electromagnetic radiation strictly as continuous waves. It fails in that it does not include the quantum effects, the wave properties of the electron and the particle properties of the radiation. Any successful model must take these quantum effects into account.

The first quantum theory of the hydrogen atom was developed in 1913 by Niels Bohr, a student of Rutherford. The photon nature of electromagnetic radiation had been established, but the wave aspects of material particles were not to be recognized until 1924. Nevertheless, in our treatment of the Bohr atom we shall take advantage of the now well-established wave nature of particles. We shall see shortly that doing so is equivalent to Bohr's original procedure, although that did not explicitly involve the electron's wave nature.

The Bohr model of the atom was the first step toward a thoroughgoing wave-mechanical treatment of atomic structure; it should be realized at the start, however, that the Bohr theory has limited applicability. Even so, it retains enough classical features for the atomic structure to be readily visualized in terms of a particle model, and it introduces enough quantum features to give a fairly accurate description of the atomic spectrum of hydrogen. Bohr's theory is, therefore, transitional between classical mechanics and the wave mechanics developed during the nineteen-twenties. A strictly wave-mechanical treatment of the hydrogen atom, in which the Schrödinger equation is used, is given in Section 6-7.

Bohr's theory of the hydrogen atom is based on three basic postulates that contain the essential quantum aspects. Rather than list the postulates now we shall show that the Bohr theory may be developed in a quite natural way from the fundamental quantum effects discussed in Chapters 4 and 5.

The postulates will then appear as necessary consequences of the wave nature of particles and the photon nature of radiation. At the end of this section we shall list them explicitly.

Like the strictly classical model of the hydrogen atom, the Bohr theory assumes the proton to be at rest and the electron to move in a circular orbit about it. The force maintaining the electron in its orbit is the attractive electrostatic Coulomb force between the electron and the proton. Thus, Equation 6-9, $mv^2 = ke^2/r$, applies, and the total energy of the atom is again given by Equation 6-10, $E = -ke^2/2r$. So far, nothing new.

We can see how the wave aspect of the electron may be incorporated into the theory by first recalling an analogous situation involving transverse waves on a wire. If the wire is fixed at both ends, only certain wavelengths will lead to resonant oscillations, those at which the length of the wire is an integral multiple of one half-wavelength; in such allowed states standing waves exist. The wire, when in an allowed state, can in principle oscillate with a constant energy for an indefinite period of time. Now let us imagine that the wire is bent into a closed, circular loop. If transverse waves are to be propagated around the loop, then the wave will destructively interfere with itself, unless it joins *smoothly* onto itself. Therefore, in a closed, circular loop standing, resonant waves exist only if an *integral* number of *whole* wavelengths can be fitted around the circumference.

Let us apply similar conditions to the electron orbits in hydrogen. We have seen that a wave nature must be attributed to a material particle, the wavelength being given by $\lambda = h/mv$ (Equation 5-3). Thus, we may regard the electron *as a wave* that is propagated in a circular orbit; stationary waves in the orbit can exist only when the circumference, $2\pi r$, is an integral multiple of the electron's wavelength; see Figure 6-11. In the *stationary states* the energy of the atom is taken as constant, despite classical radiation theory. Thus, *the atom does not radiate electromagnetic waves while in any stationary state* The "stationary orbits," those for which there is no radiation, satisfy the relation

$$n\lambda = 2\pi r \qquad [6\text{-}16]$$

where n is equal to 1, 2, 3, . . . and is called the *principal quantum number*. Of course, if the orbital radius is restricted to certain permitted values, then

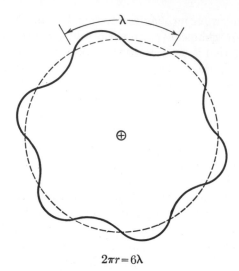

$$2\pi r = 6\lambda$$

Figure 6-11. Stationary waves in an electron orbit; in this example the circumference of the orbit is six wavelengths.

the energy E of the atom is also restricted to certain discrete values by this equation. Simply by taking into account the wave properties of the electron we have been able to bring stability to an atomic model.

When we replace the wavelength λ with h/mv in Equation.6-16, we have

$$nh/mv = 2\pi r$$

$$mvr = n\left(\frac{h}{2\pi}\right) = n\hbar \qquad [6\text{-}17]$$

The symbol $\hbar$, Planck's constant divided by 2π, is introduced for convenience. The left-hand side of this equation is just the angular momentum mvr of the electron in its orbital motion relative to the nucleus. The description of stationary states may, then, be put in a different way: stationary states, or stationary orbits, of an atom are those for which the orbital angular momentum of the atom is $\hbar$, $2\hbar$, $3\hbar$, ...

The atom has a constant, precisely defined energy in any one of the permitted stationary states. Let us calculate the allowed energies E_n, the allowed orbital radii r_n, and the speeds v_n . . .; these quantities are identified by the subscript n because the respective values will depend on the quantum number n. Equations 6-9 and 6-17 can be solved simultaneously for r and v. Solving Equation 6-17 for the tangential speed of the electron, we have

$$v_n = n\hbar/mr_n \qquad [6\text{-}18]$$

and using this in Equation 6-9, we have

$$m(n\hbar/mr_n)^2 = ke^2/r_n$$

$$r_n = n^2\hbar^2/kme^2 \qquad [6\text{-}19]$$

where again $n = 1, 2, 3, \ldots$. The smallest allowed radius, the so-called radius of the first Bohr orbit, is given by

$$\boxed{\begin{aligned} r_1 &= \hbar^2/kme^2 \\ r_1 &= 0.528 \text{ Å} \end{aligned}} \qquad [6\text{-}20]$$

in which the values of the known atomic constants have been used. The Bohr model predicts, then, that the size of the hydrogen atom with the smallest stationary orbit is of the order of 1 angstrom, in good agreement with experimental determinations. We may express all of the allowed radii in a simpler form by putting Equation 6-20 in Equation 6-19:

$$\boxed{r_n = n^2 r_1} \qquad [6\text{-}21]$$

The radii of the stationary orbits are, therefore, r_1, $4r_1$, $9r_1$, $\ldots$.

The orbital speed of the electron in the stationary states can be found immediately from Equation 6-18 where we now replace r_n with $n^2 r_1$:

$$v_n = n\hbar/m(n^2 r_1)$$

$$= (1/n)(\hbar/mr_1) = (1/n)(ke^2/\hbar) \qquad [6\text{-}22]$$

This equation may be written

$$\boxed{v_n = v_1/n} \qquad [6\text{-}23]$$

where $v_1 = \hbar/mr_1 = ke^2/\hbar$. The permitted orbital speeds are v_1, $v_1/2$, $v_1/3$, $\ldots$, the electron having a maximum speed v_1 in the first Bohr orbit. The ratio of this speed to the speed of light, v_1/c, is represented by the symbol α. From Equation 6-22 we have

$$\alpha = v_1/c = ke^2/\hbar c \qquad [6\text{-}24]$$

Inserting the known values of the constants in the right-hand side of this equation shows that $\alpha = 1/137.0388$. Thus, the electron in the first Bohr orbit moves at $1/137$ the speed of light. The quantity α, which appears frequently in the theory of atomic structure, is known as the *fine-structure constant*.† To treat the Bohr hydrogen atom as a nonrelativistic problem is not unreasonable, but because of the very high precision of wavelength

---

† The fine-structure constant plays a crucial role in quantum electrodynamics, because it gives a relationship involving the fundamental constants of electromagnetism (k and e), of the quantum theory ($\hbar$), and of relativity (c).

measurements in spectroscopy relativistic effects can be observed and so must be included in a more complete theory.

The allowed values of the total energy (excluding the rest energies of the proton and electron) of the hydrogen atom can now be determined easily from Equations 6-10 and 6-21:

$$E_n = -ke^2/2r_n = -(1/n^2)(ke^2/2r_1) \qquad [6\text{-}25]$$

If we represent the quantity $ke^2/2r_1$ by E_I, then this equation becomes

$$\boxed{E_n = -\frac{E_\mathrm{I}}{n^2}} \qquad [6\text{-}26]$$

Thus, the only possible energies of the bound electron-proton system constituting the hydrogen atom are $-E_\mathrm{I}$, $-E_\mathrm{I}/4$, $-E_\mathrm{I}/9$, ... The permitted energies are discrete, and therefore *the energy is quantized*. The lowest energy (that is, the most negative energy) belongs to the state in which the principal quantum number n equals 1, called the *ground state*. In the ground state the energy is $E_1 = -E_\mathrm{I}$, and its value computed from Equations 6-25 and 6-20, is

$$E_n = -(k^2e^4m)/(2n^2\hbar^2) \qquad [6\text{-}27]$$

$$E_1 = -E_\mathrm{I} = -13.58 \text{ eV} \qquad [6\text{-}28]$$

Figure 6-12 shows an energy-level diagram of a hydrogen atom. We note

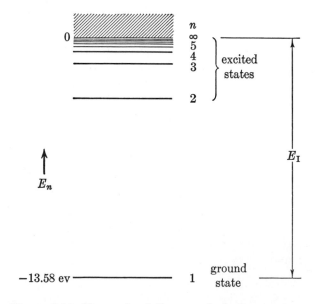

Figure 6-12. Energy-level diagram of a hydrogen atom.

from Equation 6-26 that for bound states E is less than zero, and only discrete energies are allowed. As n approaches infinity, the energy difference between adjacent energy levels approaches zero. When n equals infinity, E_n equals zero, and the hydrogen atom may be dissociated into an electron and proton, separated by an infinite distance and both at rest. In this condition the atom is said to be ionized, and the energy that must be added to it when it is in its lowest, or ground, state ($n = 1$) to bring its energy up to $E_n = 0$ is just E_I, the so-called *ionization energy*. The value predicted by the Bohr theory, $E_I = 13.58$ eV, is in complete agreement with the value obtained by experiment. When the total energy is positive, and the electron and proton are unbound, no longer constituting an atom, the electron does not move in a closed orbit. The electron's wavelength, then, is not restricted to the fitting of an integral number of waves around the path; hence the total energy is not restricted. *All* possible positive energies are allowed, and there is a continuum of energy levels for $E > 0$.

It is interesting to compare Figure 6-12, the energy-level diagram of a two-particle system according to the quantum theory, with Figure 4-1c, the energy-level diagram of a two-particle system according to the classical theory. Whereas there is a continuum of energies for both the bound and unbound systems in the classical theory, the quantum theory requires quantized states (e.g., energy, angular momentum) for a bound system.

Each of the permitted, or quantized, energies of Figure 6-12 corresponds to a stationary state in which the atom can exist without radiating. All the stationary states above the ground state, $n = 2, 3, 4, \ldots$, are called *excited states*, because an atom in one of them tends to make a transition to some lower stationary state. In the downward transition the electron may be imagined to jump suddenly from one orbit to a smaller orbit. When an atom is in some excited state and has an energy E_n, the amount by which this energy exceeds that of the ground state is called the *excitation energy*. We use the term *binding energy* to denote the energy that must be added to an atom in any state to free the bound particles and thereby make $E_n = 0$.

Consider an atom, initially in an *upper*, excited, state and having an energy E_u, which makes a transition to a *lower* state E_l. When the transition occurs, the atom loses an amount of energy $E_u - E_l$. Bohr assumed that in such a transition a single photon having an energy $h\nu$ is created and emitted by the atom. By the conservation of energy:

$$\boxed{h\nu = E_u - E_l} \qquad \text{[6-29]}$$

We see here that the Bohr theory incorporates the particle nature of electromagnetic radiation by assuming that a single photon is created whenever the atom makes a transition to a lower energy. It gives no details of the electron's quantum jump or of the photon's creation. The situation is like that we encountered in photon-electron interactions (photoelectric effect, Compton effect, etc.) in that we did not concern ourselves with the details of the interactions but merely applied the conservation laws to the states before and after the interaction.

Let us compute the frequencies and wavelengths of the photons that can, according to the Bohr model, be radiated by a hydrogen atom. Using Equations 6-29 and 6-26, we have

$$\nu = \frac{E_u - E_l}{h} = \left(\frac{-E_I}{n_u^2 h}\right) - \left(\frac{-E_I}{n_l^2 h}\right)$$

$$= \frac{E_I}{h}\left(\frac{1}{n_l^2} - \frac{1}{n_u^2}\right) \qquad [6\text{-}30]$$

where n_u and n_l are the quantum numbers for the upper and lower energy states, respectively. The wavelengths $\lambda = c/\nu$ of emitted photons may then be expressed as

$$\frac{1}{\lambda} = \frac{E_I}{hc}\left(\frac{1}{n_l^2} - \frac{1}{n_u^2}\right) \qquad [6\text{-}31]$$

This equation is of precisely the same mathematical form as the empirically derived Rydberg formula:

[6-15] $$\frac{1}{\lambda} = R\left(\frac{1}{n_l^2} - \frac{1}{n_u^2}\right)$$

By comparing these two equations for $1/\lambda$ we can evaluate the Rydberg constant R from known atomic constants and compare it with the experimentally determined value 1.0968×10^{-3} Å^{-1} for hydrogen.

$$\boxed{R = \frac{E_I}{hc} = \frac{k^2 e^4 m}{4\pi\hbar^3 c}} \qquad [6\text{-}32]$$

To arrive at the last term of this equation we have used $E_I = ke^2/2r_1$ (Equation 6-25) and $r_1 = \hbar^2/kme^2$ (Equation 6-20). Setting the known values of the physical constants in this equation, we compute the value of R and find it to be 1.0974×10^{-3} Å^{-1}, in close agreement with the experimental spectroscopic value. Thus, the Rydberg formula, which summarizes the emission and absorption spectrum of hydrogen, follows as a *necessary consequence* of the Bohr atomic model.

Finite Nuclear Masses and Hydrogenic Atoms   It has been assumed up to this point that the nuclear mass is effectively infinite and that the nuclear charge has the magnitude e. It is a simple matter to extend the Bohr theory to include (a) *finite* nuclear masses and (b) *hydrogenic* atoms, or atoms in which a single electron moves about a nucleus of charge $+Ze$.

(a) In an isolated atom both the electron of mass m and nucleus of mass M are in motion with respect to the atom's center of mass, which remains at rest. To take into account the motion of the nucleus we may merely replace the electron's mass m, wherever it appears in a relation, with the so-called *reduced mass*, $\mu = m/(1 + m/M)$; see Problem 6-37. Thus, the Rydberg constant for an atom with nuclear mass M becomes, from Equation 6-32, $R_M = R_\infty /[1 + m/M]$, where R_∞ represents the Rydberg constant in Equation 6-32. For example, for hydrogen ^{1}H, with a single proton as nucleus and with a nuclear mass of $\mu = 1.00728$ u it is $R_M = 1.09678 \times 10^{-3}$ Å^{-1}, with corresponding changes in the wavelengths in the emitted and absorbed radiation. On the other hand, for deuterium, ^{2}H, or heavy hydrogen, whose nucleus of mass $\mu = 2.01355$ u consists of a proton and neutron bound together, the Rydberg constant is $R_M = 1.09707 \times 10^{-3}$ Å^{-1}. Although small, the differences in wavelength can be measured. For example, for ^{1}H the H$_\alpha$ line is 6,562.80 Å; for ^{2}H it is 6,561.01 Å. Indeed, deuterium was first discovered, in 1932, through the observation of closely spaced pairs of hydrogen spectral lines.

(b) A hydrogenic atom has a single electron bound to a nucleus whose charge is $+Ze$. Here Z represents the atomic number, or the number of protons in the nucleus. For example, doubly ionized lithium, Li^{++}, with $Z = 3$, is a hydrogenic atom. To find the energies, frequencies, and emitted wavelengths of hydrogenic atoms one merely replaces the quantity e^2, wherever it appears in a relation given by the Bohr theory, with Ze^2.

The observed spectral lines of hydrogen may now be understood in terms of the energy-level diagram Figure 6-13. The vertical lines represent transitions between stationary states; the lengths of these lines are proportional to the respective photon energies and, therefore, to the frequencies. The

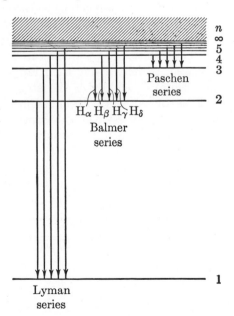

Figure 6-13. Some possible energy transitions in atomic hydrogen.

lines of the Lyman series correspond to those photons produced when hydrogen atoms in any of the excited states in which $n_u = 2, 3, 4, 5, \ldots$ undergo transitions to the ground state, in which $n_l = 1$. Transitions from the unbound states ($E > 0$) to the ground state account for the observed continuous spectrum lying beyond the series limit. We account in a similar way for the Balmer series, which is produced by transitions from the excited states in which $n_u = 3, 4, 5, \ldots$ to the first excited state, in which $n_l = 2$. Still further emission series involve downward transitions to $n_l = 3$, $n_l = 4$, etc., these series falling progressively toward longer wavelengths.

We have examined the emission from a single hydrogen atom. The atom can exist in only *one* of its quantized energy states at any one time, and when it makes a transition from one state to a lower state, it emits a *single* photon. When the entire emission spectrum from an excited hydrogen gas, a collection of a very large number of hydrogen atoms, is observed in a spectroscope, we see the simultaneous emission of many photons produced by downward transitions from each of the excited states. Therefore, to observe the entire emission spectrum we must have a very large number of hydrogen atoms in each of the excited states, making downward transitions to all lower states.

Now we also have a basis for understanding the characteristics of absorption spectra. As shown in Figure 6-10, an absorption spectrum shows dark lines on a white background with the same wavelengths as the bright lines on the black background of the corresponding emission spectrum. When white light, consisting of photons having all possible frequencies, or energies, passes through a gas, those particular photons having energies equal to the energy difference between stationary states can be removed from the beam. They are annihilated, thereby giving their radiant electromagnetic energy to the internal excitation energy of the atoms. The same set of quantized energy levels participates in both emission and absorption; for this reason the frequencies of the emission and absorption lines are identical. (Because atoms remain in an excited state for only a very short time, the Lyman series is the only one observed in absorption.)

We have used the fundamental postulates of the Bohr theory implicitly in developing a model of the hydrogen atom. It is useful, however, to isolate them, since they are retained in their essential forms in more complete wave-mechanical treatments of atomic structure:

> (1) *A bound atomic system can exist without radiating only in certain discrete stationary states.*
> (2) *The stationary states are those in which the orbital angular momentum, mvr, of the atom is an integral multiple of ℏ, Planck's constant divided by 2π. (This quantization of angular momentum is a natural consequence of the wave properties of the electron confined to a semiclassical circular orbit.)*

(3) *When an atom undergoes a transition from an upper energy state E_u to a lower energy state E_l, a photon of energy $h\nu$ is emitted, the conservation of energy requiring that $h\nu$ be equal to $E_u - E_l$; if a photon is absorbed, the atom will make a transition from the lower to the higher energy state, according to the same relation.*

6-5   The hydrogen atom and the correspondence principle   According to the quantum theory, the frequency of the photon emitted or absorbed in a transition is determined solely by the difference in energy between the two participating stationary states,

$$\nu = \frac{E_u - E_l}{h}$$

[6-30]
$$\nu = \frac{E_\mathrm{I}}{h}\left(\frac{1}{n_l^2} - \frac{1}{n_u^2}\right) = cR\left(\frac{1}{n_l^2} - \frac{1}{n_u^2}\right)$$
[6-33]

We recall that in the classical planetary model of the hydrogen atom it was assumed, following classical electromagnetism, that the frequency of the electromagnetic waves generated by the accelerated electric charge is precisely the frequency of motion of the electron about the nucleus:

[6-13]
$$f = (1/2\pi)\sqrt{ke^2/mr^3}$$
[6-34]

Equations 6-33 and 6-34 were derived from different assumptions, and we see clearly that the two predicted frequencies are quite dissimilar. The quantum theory is, of course, the correct theory; it not only explains short-wavelength visible radiation from atomic systems but also describes correctly long-wavelength radiation, such as radio waves. The classical electromagnetic theory fails to explain atomic spectra; on the other hand, it agrees with experiments performed with long-wavelength radio waves, in which it is found that the frequency of the radiation is, in fact, equal to the frequency of the oscillation of the electric charges.

The general correspondence principle (Section 1-5) requires that the quantum theory, the more general theory, yield the *same* results as the more restricted, classical theory in those circumstances in which the classical theory suffices. Therefore, for atomic radiation the frequencies ν of the emitted photons must approach the orbital frequencies f when, and only when, the hydrogen atom can be regarded as approximating the conditions in which the classical theory applies. We wish to show, then, that $\nu = f$ in the correspondence limit.

It is easy to show that the Bohr atom approaches classical conditions as the principal quantum number n becomes a very large integer and small quantum jumps are involved. As n becomes large, the discrete energy levels crowd more closely together, approaching the continuum characteristic of the classical bound system (see Figure 6-12). When n is large, the photons emitted in transitions between adjacent energy levels are of very long wavelength. Furthermore, as n increases, the radii of the stationary orbits become large, and the hydrogen atom approaches a macroscopic system, for which classical physics is adequate.

Let us compute the frequency of a photon emitted in the transition between the adjacent states $n_u = n$ and $n_l = n - 1$, when $n \gg 1$. Rewriting Equation 6-33, we have

$$\nu = cR \left(\frac{n_u^2 - n_l^2}{n_u^2 n_l^2} \right)$$

$$= cR \frac{(n_u - n_l)(n_u + n_l)}{n_u^2 n_l^2} \qquad [6\text{-}35]$$

But $n_u - n_l = 1$, $n_u + n_l \approx 2n$, and $n_u^2 n_l^2 \approx n^4$. Therefore this equation becomes, for large n,

$$\nu = \frac{2cR}{n^3} \qquad [6\text{-}36]$$

We wish to show that this quantum frequency ν equals the classical orbital frequency f. Using Equation 6-20, the electron radius r, in Equation 6-34 gives

$$f = (1/2\pi)\sqrt{ke^2/mr^3} = (1/2\pi)\sqrt{(ke^2/m)(ke^2m/n^2\hbar^2)^3}$$

$$= (2c/n^3)(k^2e^4m/4\pi\hbar^3c) \qquad [6\text{-}37]$$

The second quantity in parentheses is simply the Rydberg constant R of Equation 6-32. Therefore, the equation reduces to

$$f = \frac{2cR}{n^3} \qquad [6\text{-}38]$$

Comparing Equations 6-36 and 6-38, we see that

$$\nu = f$$

as the correspondence principle requires.

Actually, it was by applying the correspondence principle that Bohr first arrived at the quantization of orbital angular momentum, the second postulate of his atomic theory. In his original paper on the quantum theory of the hydrogen atom Bohr stated:†

> "... we only assume (1) that the radiation is sent out in quanta $h\nu$, and (2) that the frequency of the radiation emitted during the passing of the system between successive stationary states will coincide with the frequency of revolution of the electron in the region of slow vibrations."

Bohr showed that the quantization of orbital angular momentum is a

† *Philosophical Magazine*, Vol. 26, p. 1 (1913), "On the constitution of atoms and molecules."

necessary consequence of these two postulates. In our treatment of the Bohr atom we have reversed the procedure; that is, we assumed the electron's wave properties and found them to be equivalent to the quantization of orbital angular momentum; the identity of the photon and orbital frequencies in the correspondence limit was a result.

6-6 The successes and failures of the Bohr theory The following features of the Bohr atomic theory are general ones that apply to *any* comprehensive theory of atomic structure: (a) the existence of nonradiating, stationary states, (b) the quantization of the energy of a bound system of particles, (c) the quantization of angular momentum, and (d) the emission or absorption of photons in transitions between stationary states.

More specifically, the Bohr theory explains (a) the stability of atoms, (b) the wavelengths of the emission and absorption spectra of hydrogenic atoms, and (c) the measured ionization energies of one-electron atoms.

The Bohr atomic theory has, however, certain serious shortcomings: (a) it is nonrelativistic, (b) it gives no method of calculating the intensities of the spectral lines, (c) it is incapable of explaining the spectra of atoms having more than one electron, (d) it does not explain the binding of atoms in molecules, liquids, and solids, (e) even for hydrogen it fails to account for the fine details of the spectrum (high-resolution spectrographs show that each "line" predicted by the Bohr theory consists of two or more very closely spaced lines, or fine-structure), and it gives for orbital angular momentum — while taking into account its quantization — a rule that is less complicated than that which it actually follows.

All these defects are corrected in a relativistic wave-mechanical treatment, which because of its mathematical sophistication lies beyond the intent of this book. A fundamental reason that the Bohr theory is defective is that it overemphasizes the classical particle nature of the electron: the electron is considered to move in a well-defined circular path, the radii, speeds, and orbital frequencies being precisely defined. In the wave-mechanical treatment the electron, regarded as a three-dimensional wave, must be allowed to extend and move throughout the whole region of space surrounding the nucleus. The problem, which is that of fitting, through the solutions of the Schrödinger equation, three-dimensional electron waves to find the quantized stationary states, is taken up in a description of some simple and special cases in the next section.

6-7 The hydrogen atom and its wave functions from the Schrödinger equation
The problem is that of finding allowed wave functions of the time-independent (non-relativistic) Schrödinger equation,

(5-30)
$$\frac{\partial^2 \psi}{\partial x^2} + \frac{\partial^2 \psi}{\partial y^2} + \frac{\partial^2 \psi}{\partial z^2} + \frac{2m}{\hbar^2}(E - V)\psi = 0$$
[6-39]

for a particle of mass m (the electron) under the influence of an inverse-square attractive force (the Coulomb force of the nucleus).

We wish to find solutions to the Schrödinger equation for the Coulomb electric potential energy,

$$V = -ke^2/r$$

between two point charges, each of magnitude e, separated by r. The positive point charge remains fixed at the origin. To arrive at the most general solutions of the Schrödinger equation we might transform the rectangular coordinates of Equation 6-39 into spherical coordinates (r, θ, ϕ), thereby anticipating that the solutions will take on their simplest mathematical form when the symmetry of the potential energy (involving the coordinate r only) is matched by that of the coordinate system. We shall, however, follow a still simpler course.

Since the potential energy depends only on the radial distance r, there must be a class of wave functions satisfying Equation 6-39 that are spherically symmetrical, that is, depend only on the coordinate r:

$$\psi = F(r)$$

As written in Equation 6-39, the Schrödinger equation contains partial derivatives involving the rectangular coordinates x, y, and z. Since we seek solutions depending only on r, we must first transform this equation into one involving derivatives of r only. Clearly,

$$r = \sqrt{x^2 + y^2 + z^2}$$

Thus,

$$\frac{\partial r}{\partial x} = \frac{1}{2} \left(\frac{2x}{(x^2 + y^2 + z^2)^{1/2}} \right) = \frac{x}{r}$$

Now consider $\partial^2 \psi / \partial x^2$. Remembering that ψ is to depend only on r, we have

$$\frac{\partial \psi}{\partial x} = \frac{d\psi}{dr} \left(\frac{\partial r}{\partial x} \right) = \frac{x}{r} \left(\frac{d\psi}{dr} \right)$$

The second derivative is then

$$\frac{\partial^2 \psi}{\partial x^2} = \frac{\partial}{\partial x} \left(\frac{\partial \psi}{\partial x} \right) = \frac{\partial}{\partial x} \left(\frac{x}{r} \frac{d\psi}{dr} \right) = \frac{1}{r} \left(\frac{d\psi}{dr} \right) - \frac{x^2}{r^3} \left(\frac{d\psi}{dr} \right) + \frac{x^2}{r^2} \left(\frac{d^2\psi}{dr^2} \right) \qquad [6\text{-}40]$$

The derivatives for $\partial^2 \psi / \partial y^2$ and $\partial^2 \psi / \partial z^2$ are just as given here except that y and z replace x. Adding the three equations, we have

$$\frac{\partial^2 \psi}{\partial x^2} + \frac{\partial^2 \psi}{\partial y^2} + \frac{\partial^2 \psi}{\partial z^2} = \frac{3}{r} \left(\frac{d\psi}{dr} \right) - \frac{x^2 + y^2 + z^2}{r^3} \left(\frac{d\psi}{dr} \right) + \frac{x^2 + y^2 + z^2}{r^2} \left(\frac{d^2\psi}{dr^2} \right)$$

$$\frac{\partial^2 \psi}{\partial x^2} + \frac{\partial^2 \psi}{\partial y^2} + \frac{\partial^2 \psi}{\partial z^2} = \frac{2}{r} \left(\frac{d\psi}{dr} \right) + \frac{d^2\psi}{dr^2}$$

Equation 6-39 then becomes

$$\frac{d^2\psi}{dr^2} + \frac{2}{r}\left(\frac{d\psi}{dr}\right) + \frac{2m}{\hbar^2}\left(E + \frac{ke^2}{r}\right)\psi = 0 \qquad [6\text{-}41]$$

Rather than attempt to solve this analytically in detail, we shall choose what appears to be a reasonable form of the wave function for the ground state and then test whether it is, in fact, a solution. We know that the electron is more likely to be found near the nucleus rather than very far from it and the probability of finding the electron at infinity is zero. This implies that the wave function ψ is relatively large for small r and is zero for $r = \infty$. A wave function satisfying these requirements is

$$\psi = e^{-ra} \qquad [6\text{-}42]$$

where the size of a determines the exponential decay outward along r; see Figure 6-14. Now we test whether this trial wave function satisfies the Schrödinger equation.

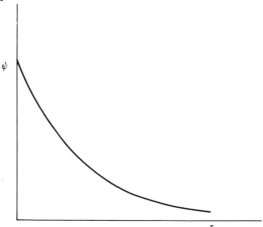

Figure 6-14. The wave function $\psi = e^{-ra}$ for the ground state of hydrogen.

From Equation 6-42 we have

$$d\psi/dr = -ae^{-ra} = -a\psi$$

$$d^2\psi/dr^2 = a^2e^{-ra} = a^2\psi$$

Setting ψ, $d\psi/dr$, and $d^2\psi/dr^2$ in Equation 6-41 we have

$$\left[a^2 - \frac{2}{r}a + \frac{2m}{\hbar^2}\left(E + \frac{ke^2}{r}\right)\right]\psi = 0 \qquad [6\text{-}43]$$

One possible solution is $\psi = 0$ everywhere, but this is unacceptable. Therefore, regrouping the terms in Equation 6-43, we have

$$\left(a^2 + \frac{2m}{\hbar^2}E\right) + \frac{1}{r}\left(\frac{2mke^2}{\hbar^2} - 2a\right) = 0 \qquad [6\text{-}44]$$

This equation must hold for all values of r from zero to infinity. When we put $r = 0$, and $1/r = \infty$, we see that the two terms on the left side can add to yield zero only if the term in the second parentheses is zero. Therefore,

$$a = \frac{mke^2}{\hbar^2}$$

[6-20]
$$\frac{1}{a} = \frac{\hbar^2}{mke^2} = r_1 = 0.53 \text{ Å} \qquad [6\text{-}45]$$

Here we recognize $1/a$ to be nothing more than the reciprocal of r_1, the radius of the first Bohr orbit.

Now suppose that we let r assume any finite value in Equation 6-44. Since the second term is zero, the first term must also be zero, if that equation is to be satisfied, and

$$E = -\frac{a^2\hbar^2}{2m} = -\left(\frac{mke^2}{\hbar^2}\right)^2 \frac{\hbar^2}{2m}$$

[6-27]
$$E = -\frac{mk^2e^4}{2\hbar^2} = -13.6 \text{ eV}$$

The energy of the atom is $E = -13.6$ eV, just the energy of the hydrogen ground state, according to the Bohr theory. The wave function assumed in Equation 6-42 is, in fact, the one corresponding to the ground state in the Bohr theory.

Recall that $\psi^2 \, dv$ is the probability of finding a particle in the volume element dv. For a hydrogen atom in the ground state the probability of the electron's being within a small volume element dv is proportional to

$$\psi^2 \, dv = e^{-2ra} \, dv$$

For this state we are more likely to find the electron in a volume element dv at the nucleus $(r = 0)$ than in the same volume element anywhere else. We now ask what the probability is of the electron's being *between* r and $r + dr$, that is, within a spherical shell of radius r, thickness dr, and volume $4\pi r^2 \, dr$. Although $\psi^2 \, dv$ is a maximum at the origin, the volume of a spherical shell there is very small, whereas at very large distances from the origin the volume is large and the probability density very small.

There must be a maximum in the probability of finding the electron in the spherical shell between the two extremes, $r = 0$ and $r = \infty$. In a shell of radius r and thickness dr, $dv = 4\pi r^2\, dr$; the corresponding probability is proportional to $r^2 e^{-2ra}$. This is shown plotted in Figure 6-15. The curve

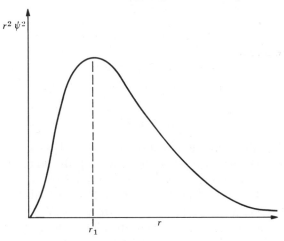

Figure 6-15. The probability of finding an electron in the hydrogen ground state between r and $r + dr$ (proportional to $r^2\psi^2$) as a function of distance r from the nucleus.

rises initially (because of r^2), reaches a maximum, and then goes to zero for large r (because of e^{-2ra}). At what distance r from the nucleus, within the range dr, is the electron most likely to be located? This value of r is, of course, the value corresponding to the maximum in Figure 6-15. The peak of $r^2 e^{-2ra}$ occurs at the following location:

$$\frac{d}{dr}\,(r^2 e^{-2ra}) = 0$$

$$2r e^{-2ra} - 2ar^2 e^{-2ra} = 0$$

$$r_{\max} = \frac{1}{a} = r_1$$

The maximum is exactly at the radius of the first Bohr orbit. Although the electron may be found anywhere, the electron is more likely to be a distance r_1 from the nucleus in the ground state than any other distance from it.

Still other spherically symmetrical wave functions exist. It is easy to show by substitution in Equation 6-41 that the wave function $\psi_2 = e^{-ra/2}(2 - ra)$ also is a solution. The corresponding energy is found to be $E_2 = -13.6$ eV$/4 = -3.4$ eV, the energy of the first excited state of hydrogen. Indeed, the energies E_n of the hydrogen atom for all spherically symmetrical wave functions are given by

[6-27]
$$E_n = -\left(\frac{mk^2e^4}{2\hbar^2}\right)\frac{1}{n^2} = -\frac{E_I}{n^2}$$
[6-46]

with $n = 1, 2, 3, \ldots$, again in agreement with the Bohr theory.

Since the potential energy $V = -ke^2/r$ is spherically symmetrical, there are spherically symmetrical wave functions, as we have seen. But there are also nonspherically symmetrical wave functions. The simplest of these is

$$\psi = x\,F(r)$$
[6-47]

where $F(r)$ is again a function of r only. That this is a solution is tested by computing the derivatives $d\psi/dr$ and $d^2\psi/dr^2$ and setting them in Equation 6-41. The corresponding energy with $F(r) = e^{-ar/2}$ is found to be $E_2 = -13.6\,\text{eV}/4 = -3.4\,\text{eV}$, that of the first excited state of hydrogen.

If $\psi = x\,F(r)$ is a solution, then so are $\psi = y\,F(r)$ and $\psi = z\,F(r)$, where $F(r)$ is the same for all three states. The energy is the *same* for all three states. Nonspherically symmetrical wave functions of the type

$$\psi = x\,F(r), \quad \psi = y\,F(r), \quad \text{and} \quad \psi = z\,F(r)$$

are called p states (the spherically symmetrical solutions are called s states). Figure 6-16 shows probability distributions for a p state (or a p orbital) in a polar diagram.

All spherically symmetrical states have in common the fact that the atom's orbital angular momentum is zero. For nonspherically symmetrical states, such as the p states of Figure 6-16, it is *not* zero; indeed, it can be shown that the orbital angular momentum (along any one direction in space) is always an integral multiple of $\hbar$.

6-8 Atomic excitation by collision: the Franck-Hertz experiment Atomic systems, such as the hydrogen atom, are quantized. The allowed energies are discrete and, as a consequence, a photon can be absorbed only if its energy $h\nu$ matches the energy difference $E_u - E_l$ between two allowed states. For example, only photons with an energy of 10.2 eV will cause hydrogen atoms in the ground state to change to the first excited state. We might well ask whether the energy of a quantized system may change, not only through collisions with photons, but also through collisions with particles of nonzero rest mass, such as an electron. The experiment of J. Franck and G. Hertz in 1914 first demonstrated that the excitation of atoms by particle bombardment is possible and that the process is also governed by the quantization of energy.

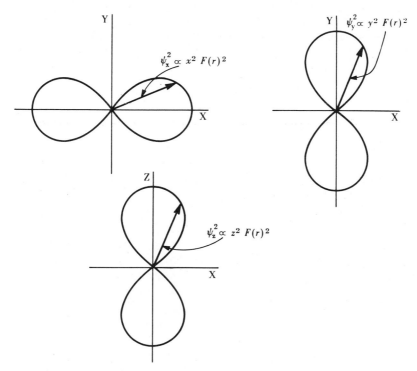

Figure 6-16. Polar plot of a variation of ψ^2 with angle for p states.

First consider atomic hydrogen. Suppose that hydrogen atoms in the ground state are bombarded by a monoenergetic beam of electrons whose kinetic energy is less than 10.2 eV, the excitation energy of the first excited state of hydrogen. Because a hydrogen atom in the ground state cannot increase its energy by any amount less than that, the electrons hit the hydrogen atoms in *perfectly elastic* collisions, the total kinetic energy of the particles emerging from a collision being precisely the total kinetic energy going into it. On the other hand, monoenergetic electrons with a kinetic energy of exactly 10.2 eV strike hydrogen atoms in the ground state, the collisions can be inelastic, and the electron's initial kinetic energy is transformed into internal energy in the hydrogen atom as the latter makes an upward transition from the ground state to the first excited state.† Since some atoms are in this way promoted to an excited state, they can subsequently decay to the ground state with the emission of a photon of 10.2 eV.

† Because momentum must be conserved in every collision, the struck atom's momentum after the collision is equal to that of the electron before, but its kinetic energy is negligible compared with the change in its internal energy, since its mass far exceeds that of the electron.

When bombarding electrons have a kinetic energy greater than 10.2 eV, the collisions are again inelastic; only 10.2 eV is transformed into internal atomic excitation energy. The remaining kinetic energy cannot be absorbed by the hydrogen atom, and it necessarily appears as the kinetic energy of the electron emerging from the collision (and, to a lesser extent, as kinetic energy of the struck atom). With a further increase in the bombarding particles' energy, atoms may be promoted to the second excited state and to still higher ones. In each such inelastic collision the atom absorbs only that energy which will produce a transition from one quantized energy level to a higher one; see Figures 6-17. In short, if an atom's excitation energy is denoted by E_e and the light bombarding particle's kinetic energy by E_k, then inelastic collisions with atomic excitation occur only if

$$E_k \geq E_e \qquad\qquad [6\text{-}48]$$

In the original Franck-Hertz experiment electrons were made to collide with mercury atoms in a vapor. The wavelength of radiation corresponding to a transition between the ground state and the first excited state of mercury is 2,536 Å; the equivalent photon energy, equal to the excitation energy, is 4.88 eV. Franck and Hertz found that electrons of at least that kinetic energy were required to produce an excitation of mercury atoms. This was inferred from the fact that the collisions were perfectly elastic when the electrons' energy was less than 4.88 eV but some inelastic collisions occurred when it was more. At the same time it was found that mercury atoms emit radiation of 2,536 Å if, and only if, electrons having at least the excitation energy of 4.88 eV collide with them.

The historical significance of the Franck-Hertz experiment is this: it showed that atomic systems are quantized, as exhibited not only in photon absorption and emission but also in particle bombardment. In practice the inelastic collisions of electrons are observed through a measurement of the electric current arising from electrons in motion through a gas of molecules. If the electrons' speeds are reduced drastically by inelastic collisions resulting in atomic excitation, then the current registered drops sharply when their kinetic energy corresponds to the excitation energy. Indeed, if the electrons are sufficiently energetic, any one of them may make a number of inelastic collisions in passing through the gas, losing an energy E_e in each. Thus, the current observed as a function of the electric accelerating potential (which determines the total electron kinetic energy in the absence of inelastic collisions) shows a number of sharp drops, each drop corresponding to an integral multiple of E_e. At the same time photons of energy E_e are observed to be emitted when the inelastic electron collisions first produce atomic excitations.

Ionization also can result from collisions. If the bombarding particles are electrons, the atoms are ionized by those having a kinetic energy equal to the atom's ionization energy.

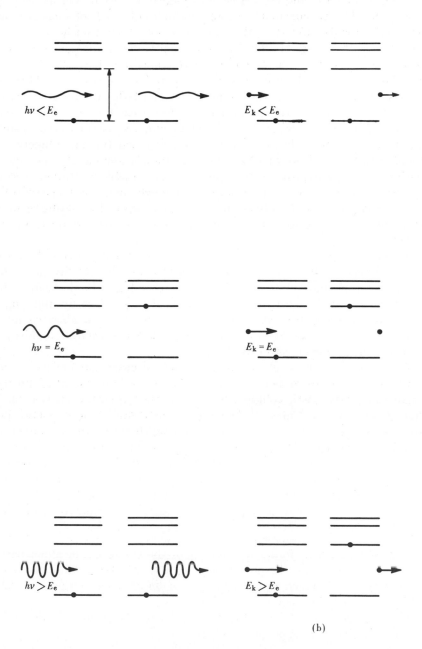

(b)

Figure 6-17. Excitation of a quantum transition: (a) by photon bombardment, where E_e is the atomic excitation energy; (b) by particle bombardment, where E_k is the particle kinetic energy.

At room temperature essentially all of the atoms of a hydrogen gas are in the ground state, and noticeable emission cannot occur. Let us see why this is true. The average kinetic energy per molecule, $\frac{3}{2}kT$, of a gas at room temperature is 0.04 eV; thus, there are very few atoms that have a translational kinetic energy of 10.2 eV, the minimum energy necessary to raise a hydrogen atom from the ground state, in which $n = 1$ and $E_1 = -13.6$ eV to the first excited state in which $n = 2$ and $E_2 = -3.4$ eV. Thermal excitation of atoms occurs when some of the translational kinetic energy of two colliding atoms is transformed into *internal* excitation energy of one or both of the atoms; *translational* kinetic energy is *not* conserved in such a collision, and thus the collision is *inelastic*. When the gas temperature is raised to the point at which the average translational kinetic energy of the atom, $\frac{3}{2}kT$, is approximately equal to some possible excitation energy, appreciable numbers of atoms can absorb enough energy in inelastic collisions to raise them to this higher state. To excite atoms by heating requires very high temperatures; for instance $\frac{3}{2}kT$ is 10 eV for a temperature of 75,000 °K.

A simpler and commoner method of exciting atoms, suggested by the Franck-Hertz experiment, involves the use of an electric discharge, by which electrons and ions are accelerated to very high kinetic energies by an external electric field; this is accomplished in practice by applying a potential difference between two electrodes placed in a glass chamber containing the gas. Thermal excitation and electrical excitation thus are means of producing emission spectra.

We can now see why, in the kinetic theory of gases, gas molecules and atoms may be regarded as inert particles having no internal structure and making perfectly elastic collisions with each other when the gas is at moderate temperatures. Unless the average translational kinetic energy per atom is comparable to the difference in energy between the ground state and the first excited state, the internal structure of the atom cannot change, the total translational kinetic energy in a collision is conserved, and the collision is perfectly elastic. If the gas temperature is sufficiently high, inelastic collisions occur. Some atoms are thereby excited, and they can no longer be considered inert particles, incapable of undergoing internal change.

6-9 Summary   Rutherford's experiments in the scattering of alpha particles showed that all of the positive charge and essentially all of the mass of an atom are confined to a very small region of space (no greater than 10^{-14} m), called the nucleus.

The fraction of incident particles scattered by a thin foil of thickness t containing n scatterers per unit volume is

[6-2] $$N_s/N_i = \sigma n t$$

where σ is the cross section associated with each scattering center.

The classical planetary model predicts that atoms are unstable and that they emit a continuous spectrum.

Hydrogen atoms are observed to emit and absorb discrete spectral lines, whose wavelengths λ are given by

[6-15] $$1/\lambda = R(1/n_l^2 - 1/n_u^2)$$

where R is the Rydberg constant and n_l and n_u are integers.

The Bohr quantum atomic theory assumes (a) stationary states, (b) orbital angular momentum $n\hbar$, and (c) $h\nu = E_u - E_l$ in transitions.

The energies and radii predicted by the Bohr atomic theory for hydrogen are given by

[6-26] $\quad E_o = -E_I/n^2,$ $\quad$ where $\quad E_I = k^2e^4m/2\hbar^2 = 13.58$ eV

[6-21] $\quad r_n = n^2 r_o,$ $\quad$ where $\quad r_1 = \hbar^2/kme^2 = 0.530$ Å

Wave-mechanical solutions of the Schrödinger equation for hydrogen yield the same energies; the radius r_1 of the first Bohr orbit gives that distance from the nucleus at which the electron in the ground state is most likely to be found.

The Franck-Hertz experiment confirmed that the excitation and ionization of atoms by particles in inelastic collisions follows the quantum condition.

BIBLIOGRAPHY

Boorse, H. A., and L. Motz, Eds., *The World of the Atom.* New York: Basic Books, Inc., 1966. These two volumes contain many original papers on fundamental discoveries in atomic and nuclear physics together with biographical sketches of the scientists. Chapters 43 and 44 deal with the Rutherford scattering experiments, Chapter 45 with Bohr's theory of hydrogen, and Chapter 46 with the Franck-Hertz experiment.

Feynman, R. P., R. L. Leighton, and M. Sands, *The Feynman Lectures on Physics.* (Vol. 3, Quantum Mechanics). Reading, Mass.; Addison-Wesley Publishing Company, Inc., 1965. Chapter 19 deals with the wave-mechanical solution of Schrödinger's equation for hydrogen. The book as a whole is an imaginative course in elementary quantum mechanics.

Friedman, F. L., and L. Sartori, *Origins of Quantum Physics* (Vol. I, The Classical Atom). Reading, Mass.: Addison-Wesley Publishing Company, Inc., 1965. Chapter 3, on atomic constituents and atomic models, describes in some detail the development of the Thomson and Rutherford atomic models.

Heitler, W., *Elementary Wave Mechanics.* Oxford: The Clarendon Press, 1946. A simple wave-mechanical treatment of the hydrogen atom, on which the material in Section 6-7 is based, is to be found in Chapters 2 and 3 of this small book.

PROBLEMS

6-1   Twenty thousand small hard spheres, each 2.0 mm in diameter, are dispersed randomly throughout the interior of a cubical box 1.0 m along an edge. (a) If one million particles, each very small compared with the spheres within the box, are shot randomly over a broad face of the box, how many can be expected to be scattered from the forward direction by collisions with the spheres? (b) If one million spheres, each 2.0 mm in diameter, are fired at the spheres within the box, how many of them will be scattered?

6-2   What are (a) the momentum and (b) the wavelength of an 8.0 MeV α-particle?

6-3   Alpha particles are scattered from a thin foil of a material with atomic number Z_1, density ρ_1, and atomic weight w_1 and are observed at some fixed angle θ. The first foil is replaced with a second one (Z_2, ρ_2, and w_2) having the same total area and mass. What is the ratio of the number of particles observed at θ for the first and second foils?

6-4   Alpha particles scattered from a thin foil are observed at some fixed scattering angle θ. By what factor is the number of scattered particles per time, observed at θ, changed when (a) the speed of the incident particles is doubled with no change in the number of particles striking the foil per unit time, and (b) the speed of the incident particles is doubled and the electric current of the incident beam is also doubled?

6-5   An α-particle makes a head-on collision with, in turn, (a) a gold nucleus, (b) an α-particle, and (c) an electron, each initially at rest. What fraction of the α-particle's initial kinetic energy is transferred to the struck particle in each instance?

6-6   An 8.0 MeV α-particle makes a head-on collision with an electron initially at rest. What are the kinetic energies after the collision of (a) the electron and (b) the α-particle? (c) How many such head-on collisions with electrons initially at rest are required to reduce the α-particle's initial kinetic energy by 10 percent?

6-7   Suppose that 7.68 MeV α-particles, incident upon a gold foil 6.00×10^{-5} cm thick, are scattered *twice* within the foil, each time by an angle of 1.0° (for simplicity we assume that the foil has the same thickness in both scatterings). For what fraction of the incident particles will this double scattering occur?

6-8   A 5.0 MeV α-particle approaches an iron nucleus ($Z = 26$, atomic weight 56). (a) Calculate its kinetic energy when it is at a distance of 3.2×10^{-14} m from the nucleus. (b) Show that, if this is the smallest distance separating the α-particle and the iron nucleus during this non-head-on collision, the impact parameter must be 2.3×10^{-14} m. (*Hint:* Use angular-momentum conservation.)

6-9   Show that a positively charged particle approaches a heavy nucleus more closely in a head-on collision than in a non-head-on one. (*Hint*: Use energy conservation.)

6-10 * Alpha particles with an energy of several MeV are incident on a target of helium atoms in a gas at room temperature. The target particles are effectively α-particles at rest, since the average thermal energy per helium molecule is only 0.04 eV. Because the target particles are not much more massive than the incident particles, the scattering relations derived on this assumption do not apply in this instance. Show that *no* α-particles, incident or target, can be observed at a scattering angle greater than 90°.

6-11   Since the number of particles scattered by Coulomb collisions with target particles is proportional to $1/[\sin^4 (\theta/2)]$, the number of scattered particles observed at any particular scattering angle θ is very sensitively dependent upon θ. Moreover, in the derivation of this relation it was assumed that the incident beam makes an angle of 90° with the plane of the thin scattering foil. Suppose that the foil is slightly misaligned; will the small misalignment from 90° have a drastic effect upon the number of particles observed at any fixed point?

6-12   A 6.0 MeV α-particle is scattered 45° by a gold nucleus. (a) What is the corresponding impact parameter? (b) If the gold foil is 3.00×10^{-7} m thick, what fraction of the incident 6.0 MeV α-particles is expected to be scattered by more than 45°?

6-13 *   A 5.0 MeV α-particle travels 3.5 cm through air before coming to rest. An α-particle loses energy, approximately 5 eV per collision, through excitation and ionization as it collides with molecules in air. Compute an approximate cross section for the excitation and ionization of air molecules by α-particles, and compare this area with atomic dimensions (air density ≈ 1 kg/m³, molecule weight ≈ 30).

6-14   (a) Compute the electric current for an electron imagined to move in the first Bohr orbit. (b) At the site of the proton what is the magnitude of the magnetic field arising from the orbiting electron? (c) Is this magnetic field aligned with or against the vector representing the electron's orbital angular momentum?

6-15   A hydrogen atom is in an excited state, for which the *binding* energy of the electron to the proton is 1.51 eV. The atom makes a transition to a state for which the *excitation* energy is 10.18 eV. What is the energy of the photon emitted?

6-16   Show that the quantized energies of the hydrogen atom may be written in the form $E_n = -\frac{1}{2}\alpha^2 (mc^2)/n^2$, where α is the fine-structure constant and mc^2 is the electron rest energy.

6-17   (a) Show that the product of the radius of the first Bohr orbit and the fine-structure constant is equal to the electron's Compton wavelength divided by 2π. (b) Show that the radius of the first Bohr orbit equals $\alpha/4\pi R_\infty$.

6-18   Consider the Earth-Sun system to be a giant-sized hydrogen atom, the objects interacting, however, by the gravitational force. (a) What is the quantum number, according to the Bohr theory, for the Earth's orbit about the Sun? The Earth's mass is 6.0×10^{24} kg, the mean Earth-Sun distance is 1.5×10^{11} m, and G is 6.7×10^{-11} N-m²/kg². (b) Suppose that the Earth were to make a transition to the next lowest quantum state. By what amount would its distance from the Sun increase?

6-19   Assume that 6,000 hydrogen atoms are initially in the $n = 4$ state. The atoms then proceed to make transitions to lower energy states. (a) How many distinct spectral lines will be emitted? (b) Assuming for simplicity that for any given excited state all possible downward transitions are equally probable, what is the total number of photons emitted?

6-20 * The muon is an elementary particle with the same electric charge as the electron but with a mass 207 times greater. A muon can be captured by a proton (and also by other nuclei), so that a "muonic" atom is formed. (a) Calculate the radius of the first Bohr orbit for such an atom. (b) What is the ionization energy of a muon-proton atom? (c) Compare the speed of the muon in the first orbit with that of the electron in the first orbit.

Because the muonic hydrogen atom is far smaller than an ordinary hydrogen atom, a pair of muonic atoms can come so close together, even at moderate temperatures, that the two nuclei can *attract* one another by the nuclear force between them, and a nuclear reaction can take place. To produce a nuclear reaction between the atoms of a gas of ordinary hydrogen atoms requires temperatures of millions of degrees (see Section 10-9). Thus, muonic hydrogen atoms can be used in a process known as "cold fusion."

6-21 The Sun, like the Earth, is approximately a sphere rotating about an axis. It does not, however, rotate as a rigid body: the nearer the Equator, the faster the rotation. When the absorption spectrum of the H_α radiation coming from opposite sides of the Sun's equator are compared, a wavelength difference of 0.0914 Å is found. Attributing this difference to the Doppler effect (see Problem 6-23), find the period of rotation at the Sun's equator. The diameter of the Sun is 1.4×10^9 m.

6-22 A galaxy, Galaxy 273, has been observed receding from us at the fantastically high speed of $0.81c$. (a) Compute the wavelength of the H_α line emitted by hydrogen atoms in that galaxy when observed on Earth. (b) In what region of the electromagnetic spectrum would this line be found?

6-23 The Doppler effect for light occurs when the frequency ν' measured by an observer differs from that of the frequency ν emitted by the source. In the special case in which the observer and source move away or toward one another along the line between them with a relative velocity v, where $v \ll c$, the *apparent* frequency ν' is given by $\nu' = \nu(1 \pm v/c)$, the minus sign signifying recession and the positive sign approach. Thus, the fractional change in frequency or wavelength is $\Delta\nu/\nu = \Delta\lambda/\lambda = v/c$. The Doppler effect is one reason that spectral lines are not infinitely sharp. The various radiating atoms have different velocity components along the direction of propagation of the light that enters the spectrometer. Assuming that an excited hydrogen gas is at a temperature of 6,000 °K and taking the maximum velocities of recession and approach to be given approximately by $\frac{1}{2}mv^2 = \frac{3}{2}kT$, calculate the width (in angstroms) of the H_α line due to Doppler broadening.

6-24 The quantization of the energy of an atomic system such as the hydrogen atom implies, through the mass-energy equivalence of relativity theory, that the mass of the bound system is quantized. Sketch the possible values of the total mass of a hydrogen atom.

6-25 A hydrogen atom in the first excited state makes a transition to the ground state. By what fraction is the rest mass of the atom reduced?

6-26 * When an atom in an excited state and initially at rest emits a photon, momentum conservation requires that it recoil. Thus, the energy difference between the two stationary states of the atom is, strictly, the energy of the emitted photon plus that of the recoiling atom. (a) Show that when the atomic recoil energy is taken into account, the frequency of the emitted photon is reduced by a fraction $h\nu/2Mc^2$, where ν is the photon frequency (computed approximately) and M is the atomic mass. (b) What is the fractional correction made to the frequency Lyman alpha of the photons emitted by hydrogen when this effect is taken into account?

6-27 What are the (a) energy, (b) momentum, and (c) wavelength of the photon emitted when a hydrogen atom undergoes the Lyman alpha transition? (d) Assuming the hydrogen atom to be initially at rest, with what energy does it recoil when such a photon is emitted?

6-28 (a) What is the frequency of the photon emitted by a hydrogen atom undergoing a transition from the $n = 11$ to the $n = 10$ state? (b) What is the frequency of the equivalent classically orbiting electron in the $n = 10$ state?

6-29 An atom remains in a certain excited state for an average time of 10^{-8} sec before making a transition to some lower energy state. (a) What is the uncertainty in the energy (in electron volts) of the atom for this excited state? (b) If the subsequent downward transition results in the emission of a photon of 5,000 Å, what is the fractional uncertainty in the frequency, or wavelength, of the emitted radiation? (c) Suppose now that a downward transition results in the emission of a photon of frequency 10 MHz, again with a lifetime of 10^{-8} sec in the upper state. What is then the fractional uncertainty in the frequency of the emitted radiation?

6-30 A hydrogen atom's total energy in any quantized state is very sharply defined. Yet the position of the electron is, according to wave mechanics, uncertain (see Figure 6-15), as is also, then, the electron momentum and kinetic energy. How must the uncertainty in the electron's kinetic energy compare with the uncertainty in the potential energy of the electron-proton system?

6-31 If the wave function of the ground state of the hydrogen atom is Ae^{-ra}, as given in Equation 6-42, the coefficient A can be so chosen that the total probability that the electron will be somewhere is 100 percent. Find A on this basis.

6-32 * (a) Show that the wave function of the hydrogen atom, $\psi = e^{-ra/2}(2 - ra)$, is a solution of the Schrödinger equation. (b) Show that the corresponding energy of the hydrogen atom is $-13.6/4$ eV, the energy of its first excited state.

6-33 In the ground state of hydrogen how much more probable is it to find the electron at the Bohr radius from the proton than at ten times this distance?

6-34 * The energy of a hydrogen atom may be computed approximately by using the uncertainty relation. For a hydrogen atom in the ground state the uncertainty in the distance of the electron from the proton is approximately one Bohr radius (see Figure 6-15); consequently, the electron's momentum in the ground state is uncertain by at least h/r_1. The absolute value of the electron's momentum must be at least as great as the uncertainty in its momentum. Compute the uncertainty in the electron's kinetic energy on this basis, and compare it with the energy of hydrogen in the ground state.

6-35 What is the third ionization potential of lithium? That is, after the first two of the three electrons are removed, how much energy is required to remove the third electron?

6-36 (a) Sketch the energy-level diagrams of atomic hydrogen, singly ionized helium, and doubly ionized lithium, with a common zero of energy. (b) Which states up to $n = 3$ of these three atomic systems are identical in energy (ignoring the differences in the nuclear mass)? (c) Which photon frequencies up to states with $n = 3$ would be alike in absorption or emission?

6-37 * Derive the relation for the reduced mass as follows. Two particles interact with one another through a central force, as shown in Figure 6-18. (a) The location and mass of particle 1 are r_1 and m_1, and the force on this particle, from particle 2, is $F_1(r/r)$, where $r = r_1 - r_2$ is the displacement of particle 1 relative to particle 2; write Newton's second law in vector form as it applies to the motion of particle 1 in terms of m_1, r_1, and $F_1(r/r)$. (b) The

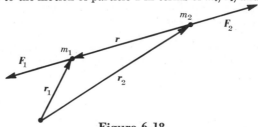

Figure 6-18.

location and mass of particle 2 are r_2 and m_2; write Newton's second law as it applies to this particle in terms of r_2, m_2, and $F_1(r/r)$. (c) Combine the two equations to arrive at the relation $d^2r/dt^2 = (1/m_1 + 1/m_2)F_1(r/r)$; note that only the displacement r of one particle relative to the other enters. (d) Show that a single equivalent particle with a *reduced mass* μ, given by $1/\mu = 1/m_1 + 1/m_2$, can be thought to move under the influence of a force dependent only on the distance between the two actual interacting particles.

6-38 Show that failing to take into account the fact that an atom's nucleus has a *finite* mass M results in the theoretical prediction of spectral lines whose energy is too large and whose wavelength is too small, both by a fraction m/M, where m is the electron mass.

6-39 Given that the Rydberg constant for an infinitely massive nucleus is 1.097373×10^{-3} Å^{-1}, show that for ordinary hydrogen (of atomic mass 1) it is 1.09678×10^{-3} Å^{-1} (the proton mass is 1,836.10 times that of the electron).

6-40 Compute the Rydberg constants for ordinary hydrogen, ^{1}H with a nuclear mass of 1.007276 u, and heavy hydrogen, ^{2}H with a nuclear mass of 2.001355 u, and from these the wavelengths of their respective H$_\alpha$ lines (the observed difference in wavelengths is 1.79 Å).

6-41   What is the minimum kinetic energy of electrons for producing (a) emission of the H_α line when they strike hydrogen atoms in the ground state and (b) emission of *all* lines in the hydrogen spectrum?

6-42   What is the minimum kinetic energy of electrons which can make inelastic collisions with singly ionized helium atoms in the ground state?

6-43 * (a) Two hydrogen atoms in the ground state make a head-on collision at equal speeds: what is the minimum kinetic energy of either atom (in terms of the hydrogen atom's ionization energy E_I) needed to raise one atom to the first excited state? (b) A hydrogen atom in the ground state collides with a second hydrogen atom also in the ground state but initially at rest; what is the minimum kinetic energy required to raise one of the atoms to the first excited state?

6-44   Atomic hydrogen in the ground state is bombarded, and spectral lines with wavelengths as short as the third line in the Lyman series are emitted. What are the minimum kinetic energies of bombarding (a) mono-energetic electrons producing this emission, (b) photons producing this emission, and (c) hydrogen atoms in the ground state producing this emission?

6-45   What is the approximate minimum temperature of a gas of atomic hydrogen that will produce such ionization of the atoms that they are broken up into protons and electrons (a plasma)?

6-46 * The phenomena of the aurora borealis (Northern Lights) and the aurora australis (Southern Lights), the luminous displays in the sky near the Earth's poles, are produced when charged particles thrown out by the Sun collide with oxygen and nitrogen 100 km or more above the Earth's atmosphere, thereby exciting and ionizing these atoms. (a) The charged particles are known to travel the 1.5×10^{11} m from the Sun to the Earth in about 24 hr; assuming that they are protons, what is their average kinetic energy? (b) Why do they produce appreciable ionization of oxygen and nitrogen only in the vicinity of the Earth's poles?

6-47   Spectroscopic observation shows that radiation with a wavelength of 5,893 Å is emitted when sodium vapor is bombarded with electrons that have been accelerated from rest through a potential difference of 2.11 V (the so-called sodium D lines thereby emitted arise from transitions between the ground and the first excited state). Compute the value of h/e from these data.

SEVEN

MANY-ELECTRON ATOMS

Although the Bohr atomic theory is incapable of describing the structure and spectra of atoms in detail, some of its essential quantum features are found to hold for many-electron atomic systems. These unchanged features include the existence of stationary states, the quantization of energy, and the quantization of angular momentum. A correct treatment of the many-electron atom is strictly wave-mechanical; it is mathematically difficult and does not lend itself to a simple visualization of the atomic structure. In wave mechanics an atomic electron must be regarded as a three-dimensional wave surrounding the nucleus; therefore, it is incorrect, indeed impossible, to assign a well-defined path to the electron's motion. Instead, wave mechanics yields through the wave function only the probability of an electron's being at a particular location. Nevertheless, with these limitations in mind we can gain certain insights into the results of wave mechanics by using results applicable to a completely classical particle model. First we discuss the classical problem of a particle moving under an inverse-square attractive force. Next we give, without proof, a few important results of wave mechanics. It will then be possible to interpret these results by analogy with the corresponding classical model.

7-1   Constants of the motion in a classical system   When a particle moves under the influence of a central, attractive, inverse-square force, as does a planet about the Sun or an electron about a positive massive particle, the isolated, bound system is characterized by several *constants of the motion*. The constants of the motion are physical quantities that do not change with time and include the system's total energy and angular momentum. It is useful to review the constants of the motion of a classical planetary system as a prelude to discussing the wave-mechanical aspects of atomic systems, because each one corresponds in wave mechanics not merely to a quantity that is constant in time but one that also is *quantized*.

We know that the path traced out by a bound particle moving under the influence of a central inverse-square force from a fixed point is an ellipse whose force center is at one focus. The first constant of the motion, the total energy, or kinetic energy plus potential energy, of a classical planetary system, such as a hydrogen atom of enormous size, is given by $E = -ke^2/2a$, where a is the semimajor axis of the ellipse, as shown in Figure 7-1. For a

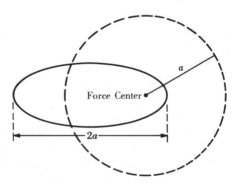

Figure 7-1. For an inverse-square attractive force a system's total energy depends only on the semimajor axis a.

given pair of interacting particles the energy E depends only on a. Thus, the system's total energy is the same for each of the two orbits shown in Figure 7-1, one a fairly eccentric ellipse and the other a circle with the force center at its center (and having a radius a). Although all orbits with the same value of a have the same energy, they differ in the magnitude of the second constant of the motion: the system's total orbital angular momentum.

The angular momentum of an orbiting particle, measured relative to a point at the fixed force center, is given by $L = r \times mv$; see Figure 7-2. So long as the force on the moving particle is central (along the line connecting it with the force center), the system's orbital angular momentum

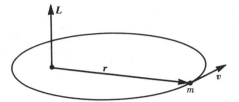

Figure 7-2. The angular momentum $L = r \times mv$ of an orbiting particle.

L is constant both in magnitude and direction. The direction of L is at right angles to the plane of the orbit, and it is related to the sense of rotation of the particle by the right-hand rule.

Now consider a number of elliptical orbits, all with the same semimajor axis a and therefore the same total energy, but differing in eccentricity. The least eccentric orbit is that in which the particle moves in a circular path, always at the same distance a from the force center; the most eccentric is that of an ellipse so collapsed as to be a straight line with a focus near a turning point. The circular orbit represents the state of maximum orbital angular momentum, and the collapsed orbit represents the state of zero orbital angular momentum. The magnitude of L ranges continuously between these extremes, as shown in Figure 7-3; so for a given total energy there is a variety of orbital angular momenta ranging continuously from zero to a maximum.

Since the isolated system's orbital angular momentum L is constant both in direction and in magnitude, its component L_z along some axis Z in space is also constant; this is the third constant of the motion. From Figure 7-4a we see that $L_z = L \cos \theta$, where θ is the angle between L and the positive Z axis. In classical physics there is no restriction on the choice of the Z direction, so L_z may range continuously from $+L$ to $-L$, as shown

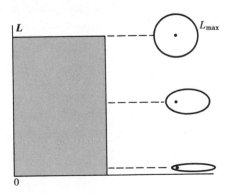

Figure 7-3. Classical allowed values of the orbital angular momentum of elliptical orbits of the same major axis, or energy.

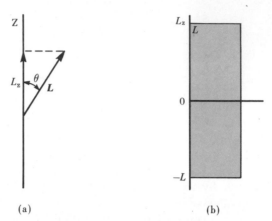

(a)   (b)

Figure 7-4. Component of the orbital angular momentum in some arbitrary Z direction: (a) orientation with respect to L; (b) classically allowed values for a given value of L.

in Figure 7-4b. In other words, depending on the choice of Z direction, the angle θ can take on any value from 0° to 180°. In short, there is no classical restriction on possible directions of the orbital angular momentum vector L. This seemingly trivial consideration has important consequences in the wave-mechanical analogue.

If an orbiting object has some finite extension in space and is spinning about an internal axis of rotation, then in addition to the system's orbital angular momentum there is a *spin angular momentum*. The spin angular momentum of an orbiting object (the daily rotation of the Earth about its center of mass, for example) is computed by finding the contribution of each of the particles in the spinning object. We use the vector relation $L = r \times mv$ (or its scalar equivalent, $L = r_{\perp} mv$, along the direction of L). The remarkable property of spin angular momentum is that its magnitude and direction along the spin axis are constant and *independent of the choice of the axis for computing angular momentum*, provided only that the spinning object is symmetrical and rotates about an axis of symmetry.

The proof is straightforward. Consider the two particles, each of mass m, moving in opposite directions at the same speed v in Figure 7-5. They are symmetrically situated relative to the spin axis and each a distance r from the center of the circle in which they travel. We compute the total angular momentum of this pair of particles relative to the arbitrarily chosen point P. Taking into account the fact that the angular momentum of one particle is positive while the other is negative, we have for the total angular momentum of the pair

$$L_{\text{pair}} = mv(r_{\perp} + 2r) - mvr_{\perp} = 2mvr$$

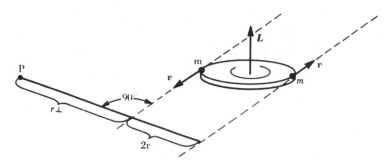

Figure 7-5. The total spin angular momentum L, with respect to an arbitrary point P, of two particles symmetrically located with respect to the spin axis.

The angular momentum $2mvr$ of this symmetrically located pair of particles is *independent* of the location of P (independent of $r_\perp$). Since the spinning object is taken to be symmetrical about the rotation axis, we can imagine it to be composed of such pairs of particles, each contributing an angular momentum independent of the choice of axis. Thus, the object's total spin angular momentum is independent of axis. It is customary to locate the spin angular momentum vector along the spin axis, as shown in Figure 7-5; in view of the proof given above it could be located *anywhere*. It is not hard to show that spin angular momentum is independent of the inertial frame, too. The angular momentum of a spinning symmetrical object is, then, an intrinsic property of the object; it is sometimes referred to as *intrinsic angular momentum*.

The total angular momentum of a system of objects consists of the vector sum of the orbital and spin angular momenta; when the system is isolated, its total angular momentum is constant. We shall see that such particles as electrons must be assigned intrinsic angular momenta in addition to their orbital angular momenta.

7-2 The quantization of orbital angular momentum The Bohr theory of a one-electron atom introduces the principal quantum number n, whose integral value determines the total energy of the atom according to the relation $E_n = -E_I/n^2$, where E_I is the ionization energy. The quantum number n also specifies the magnitude of the angular momentum L due to the electron's orbiting the nucleus in a circular path, according to $L = n\hbar$, where $\hbar$ is Planck's constant divided by 2π. It is, however, not proper from the point of view of wave mechanics to visualize the electron as moving in a well-defined path, circular or otherwise, and the Bohr rule for the quantization of the magnitude of the orbital angular momentum is *not* correct.

Wave mechanics, in contrast with classical theory, shows that the magnitude of the orbital angular momentum L of an atomic system is quantized, the possible values being given by

$$L = \sqrt{l(l + 1)}\hbar \qquad [7\text{-}1]$$

where l is an integer called the *orbital angular-momentum quantum number*. The possible values of l for a given value of the principal quantum number n go from zero to $n - 1$ by integers:

$$l = 0, 1, 2, 3, \ldots, n - 1$$

Thus, for $n = 1$ the only possible value of l is 0, and from Equation 7-1 the value of L is 0. For $n = 2$ the value of l is restricted to 0 or 1, and the corresponding values of L are 0 and $\sqrt{2}\hbar$, respectively. In general, for a given n there are n possible values of l and, therefore, n possible values of the orbital angular momentum. The integral values of the quantum number l are often represented by letter symbols (for reasons that are of historical origin), as follows:

$$l = 0, 1, 2, 3, 4, 5, \ldots$$
$$\text{symbol} = S, P, D, F, G, H, \ldots$$

Whereas in the Bohr theory the state of an atom is specified by the quantum number n (hence, the radius of the circular orbit, or the total energy), in wave mechanics the state of an atom is specified by the values of *all* the appropriate quantum numbers. To every state there corresponds a distinctive wave function ψ, differing from the others in the way in which it depends on the spatial coordinates. Those states for which, say, n is 3 and l is 0, 1, and 2 are called $3S$, $3P$, and $3D$ states, respectively. The corresponding values of the orbital angular momentum in these states are 0, $\sqrt{2}\hbar$, $\sqrt{6}\hbar$; see Figure 7-6. Since the $3S$, $3P$, and $3D$ states have a

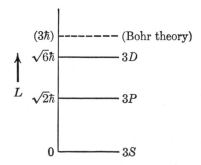

Figure 7-6. Allowed values of the magnitude of the orbital angular momentum for $n = 3$.

common value, 3, of the principal quantum number n, then for a single electron under the influence of a Coulomb force from a nucleus assumed to be a point charge the three states have identical energies but differ in angular momentum and in the spatial dependence of the wave function. Such states, which are identical in total energy but differ in some other respect, are said to be *degenerate*.

Recall that in the classical planetary model a bound system's total energy depends only on the magnitude of the major axis of the ellipse and not on the eccentricity of the orbits or on the orbital angular momentum. A similar situation obtains in the quantum theory: for a given value of n, which specifies the energy of the atom, there are n possible values of l, each l specifying a different possible value of the orbital angular momentum. An important difference is·that whereas the classical theory places no restriction on the possible values of orbital angular momentum, the quantum theory limits them to discrete, quantized values.

In the classical theory the orbits corresponding to the small values of angular momentum are those of high eccentricity, the circular orbit having the largest angular momentum for a given major axis, or energy. One may paraphrase this by saying that for a given major axis, or energy, an orbit of small angular momentum is one in which the orbiting particle spends an appreciable amount of time in each cycle close to the force center, whereas an orbit of large angular momentum is one in which the circulating particle is always far from the force center. The corresponding wave-mechanical situation is analogous: by examining wave functions derived from the Schrödinger equation we find that for a given value of n, or total energy, the probability that an electron will be at or close to the nucleus is greater for a state of low angular momentum (small l) than for a state of high angular momentum (large l).

Consider the hydrogen atom's wave function ψ plotted as a function of the distance r of the electron from the nucleus for the states in which n is 1, 2, and 3, respectively (see Fig. 7-7; and see Sec. 6-7 for the solution of the Schrödinger equation leading to ψ for the $n = 1$ state). We see that ψ is a maximum at $r = 0$ for an S state ($l = 0$) at *any* value of n; on the other hand, it is zero at $r = 0$ for states of $l > 0$ and nonzero angular momentum. The probability that the electron will be within any small volume element dv of *fixed* size is proportional to ψ^2. It follows that when the angular momentum is zero, the electron is more likely to be within a given dv near the nucleus than away from it. On the other hand, for states of higher angular momentum the electron is more likely to be within the same dv away from the nucleus than near it.

Now consider a related but different probability: that of the electron's being between r and $r + dr$, or within a spherical shell of radius r, thickness dr, and volume d$v = 4\pi r^2$dr. The probability of its being within the volume

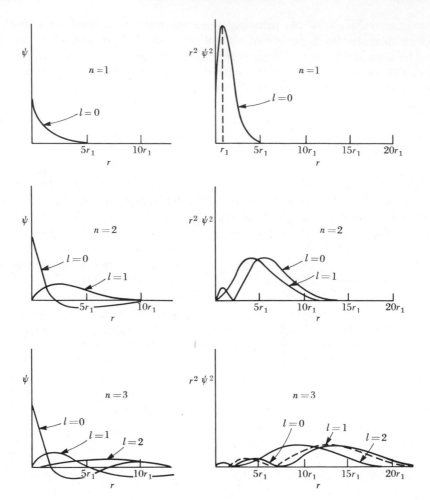

Figure 7-7. Wave functions ψ (left-hand graphs) and probabilities of particles being between r and $r + dr$ (proportional to $r^2\psi^2$) (right-hand graphs) for $n = 1$, 2, and 3.

element dv, *not* fixed in size, is proportional to $\psi^2 dv = \psi^2(4\pi r^2)\ dr$, so that the probability of its being within a spherical shell of *fixed thickness* dr is proportional to $r^2\psi^2$. The graphs on the right in Figure 7-7 show $r^2\psi^2$ as a function of r for the several wave functions plotted on the left. We see that the peaks shift to progressively larger values of r as the quantum number n, and the total energy, increases. This corresponds to the classical increase in orbit size with energy.

Figure 7-7 shows hydrogen wave functions as a function of the radial distance r only. A complete knowledge of the wave function in three dimensions involves, of course, its dependence on two other spatial coordinates.

For the S states, with $l = 0$, the wave function is spherically symmetrical and depends *only* on the radial distance r. From the right-hand graphs of the figure we see that, roughly speaking, an electron in an S state may be thought of as a ball of electric charge around the nucleus for the $n = 1$ state, as a ball of charge surrounded by a shell of charge for the $n = 2$ state (because $r^2 \psi^2$ has a zero between the two peaks), and as a ball of charge surrounded by shells of successively larger sizes for higher and higher values of n. Wave functions for $l = 1$ states are not spherically symmetrical. For example, the P wave functions have the general form $x \, F(r)$, $y \, F(r)$, $z \, F(r)$, or linear combinations thereof, where $F(r)$ is a function of r only. The D wave functions, also not spherically symmetrical, have the general form of $x^2 \, F(r)$, $y^2 \, F(r)$, $xy \, F(r)$, . . ., involving the coordinates x, y, z to the second power, where again $F(r)$ is a function of r only. Figure 6-16 shows the probability distribution in space for a P wave function with $n = 1$.

Consider again an energy-level diagram of hydrogen, Figure 7-8, in which the states are identified according to orbital angular-momentum quantum number l and the principal quantum number n. The n-fold degeneracy for each energy is shown. The diagonal lines connecting states represent possible transitions between stationary states leading to the emission of photons; such transitions are only those in which l changes by one unit. Wave mechanics selects from all the combinations of stationary states only those that make for appreciable radiation (emission, or absorption). Transitions for which l changes by 1, that is, for which the change Δl is $+1$ or -1, are called *allowed transitions*. The *selection rule* for allowed transitions is, then,

$$\boxed{\Delta l = \pm 1} \qquad \qquad \text{[7-2]}$$

All other transitions are called *forbidden transitions*. They are not absolutely prohibited, but have a probability of occurrence which is at least a million times smaller than the allowed transitions. No selection rule restricts the possible changes in the quantum number n.

The selection rule for l requires, in effect, that the atom's orbital angular momentum change when a photon is emitted or absorbed. By the law of angular-momentum conservation the total angular momentum of an atom in an excited state before emission must equal the total angular momentum of the atom-plus-photon after emission. Since only the angular momentum of the atom alone changes in the emission or absorption of a photon, *the photon itself must carry angular momentum*. Thus, a photon carries energy, linear momentum, and angular momentum. There is a classical analogue to the angular momentum of the photon in the angular momentum ascribed to circularly polarized electromagnetic waves.†

† See Sec. 47-6, Weidner and Sells, *E. C. P.*

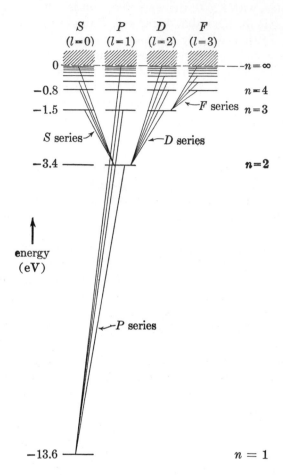

Figure 7-8. Energy-level diagram of hydrogen showing the S, P, D, and F series.

The photon energies in the hydrogen spectrum shown in Figure 7-8 are precisely those given by the simple Bohr theory (Figure 6-13). Wave mechanics gives the same allowed energies: $E_n = -E_I/n^2$. The transitions are, however, arranged in groups, or series, which are labeled according to the l value of the *originating* state in a downward transition. Thus, the P series shown consists of the transitions $2P \rightarrow 1S$, $3P \rightarrow 1S$, $4P \rightarrow 1S$, etc. (other P series, such as $3P \rightarrow 2S$, $4P \rightarrow 2S$, $5P \rightarrow 2S$, etc., occur but ordinarily with less intensity than these). Note that in hydrogen or in any one-electron atom many of the indicated allowed transitions give rise to photons having the same energy, or wavelength: for example, the H_α line arises from the transitions $3S \rightarrow 2P$, $3P \rightarrow 2S$, and $3D \rightarrow 2P$. We shall see that the distinction between these transitions, although insignificant with respect to hydrogen, is significant with respect to many-electron atoms.

7-3 Hydrogen-like atoms A number of many-electron atoms resemble a hydrogen atom. One group consists of the elements listed in the first column of the periodic table, called the *alkali metals*; another group consists of the singly ionized elements in the second column of the periodic table, called the *alkaline earths*. Table 7-1 shows these elements, together with the rare gases, which precede the respective alkali metals in the periodic table. The *atomic number*, which gives the number of electrons in a neutral atom and therefore also the positive charge of the nucleus in multiples of the electron charge, is given as a presubscript to the chemical symbol.

Table 7-1

Rare gases	Alkali metals	Singly ionized alkaline earths
	$_1$H	$_2$He$^+$
$_2$He	$_3$Li	$_4$Be$^+$
$_{10}$Ne	$_{11}$Na	$_{12}$Mg$^+$
$_{18}$Ar	$_{19}$K	$_{20}$Ca$^+$
$_{36}$Kr	$_{37}$Rb	$_{38}$Sr$^+$
$_{54}$Xe	$_{55}$Cs	$_{56}$Ba$^+$

Recall some properties of these elements. All the elements in each column are chemically similar. The rare gases are chemically inert and can be ionized only by energies that considerably exceed those needed for ionizing other elements; the alkali metals show a valence of $+1$ and are extremely active chemically; the alkaline earths typically show a valence of $+2$. It is reasonable to suppose that in, for example, the rare gas neon, the ten electrons are somehow arranged so as to form a relatively inert configuration around the nucleus. When the atom is in its lowest energy state, any one electron can be extracted from this stable arrangement only through a great expenditure of energy. The electrons in a rare-gas atom may be imagined to form a tightly bound shell of negative charge around the nucleus.

An atom of sodium has eleven electrons when neutral. Because its valence is $+1$ and it is very active chemically, it may be regarded as a neon atom whose nuclear charge has increased by 1 and whose electrons also have increased by 1. The last electron is very loosely bound to the atom, and the atom readily loses it to form a positively charged ion. It is then useful to imagine the first ten electrons as forming a relatively inert, closed shell, about which the eleventh electron moves. Similarly, the neutral atom of magnesium with atomic number 12 and valence $+2$ may be regarded as consisting of an inner shell of ten inactive electrons surrounded by two chemically active electrons. When magnesium is singly ionized, only one valence electron remains outside the closed shell. An atom of sodium or of singly ionized magnesium thus bears a resemblance to that of hydrogen in that the chemical properties are due chiefly to a single electron held to an inert core.

If the valence electron were to stay completely outside the inner core of nucleus and electrons, it would "see" an electric charge of $+Ze$ from the nucleus, a charge of $-(Z - 1)e$ from the inner electrons, and therefore a net electric charge of $+Ze - (Z - 1)e = +1e$, just the electric charge of the nucleus of the hydrogen atom. Of course, the electron's "position" is given by its wave function, which extends over space. We recall some general features of the hydrogen wave function and the inferences concerning probability, illustrated in Figure 7-7:

     (a) For a given value of n, the electron is most likely to be at or near the nucleus for a small value of l.
     (b) As n increases, the electron is most likely to be at increasingly greater distances from the nucleus.

Applying these results to a hydrogen-like atom, we see that those states in which the valence electron is far from the nucleus (and inner electron core) may be expected to be like those of hydrogen. Thus, the energy of states with large n values should be the same as for hydrogen. Moreover, for any given n value the state of the largest possible l value should be most nearly hydrogen-like. For example, of the possible states $3S$, $3P$, and $3D$, the last should have an energy closer to that of hydrogen than the first two. In the $3S$ state, on the other hand, the valence electron has a high probability of being *at* the nucleus, *inside* the core of inner electrons. If it is inside the core, however, the nuclear charge is less well shielded by electrons in the closed shell. The valence electron will then experience a force arising from an effective charge *greater* than $+1e$. A more strongly attractive force implies a more tightly bound system, one whose energy is more negative and whose energy level is displaced downward. This follows also from the relation $E_n = -Z^2 E_I/n^2$, which gives the energy of a single-electron atom with a nucleus of electric charge Ze: when Z is greater than 1, as it is when a valence electron penetrates the core, then the atom's energy E_n becomes more negative.

We see these effects in the energy-level diagram of the hydrogen-like

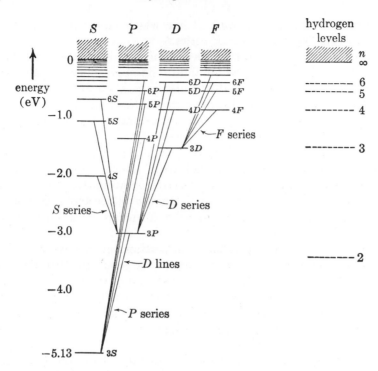

Figure 7-9. Energy-level diagram of sodium. For comparison, the hydrogen energy levels are shown on the right.

atom sodium, shown in Figure 7-9. The hydrogen levels are shown for comparison. First note that energy levels corresponding to $n = 2$ and $n = 1$ are *not* found; the reasons that the valence electron is excluded from those states will be explored in Section 7-8. Each of the $n = 3$ states ($3S$, $3P$, and $3D$) has less energy than the corresponding state in hydrogen. Furthermore, the $3S$ state is lower than the $3P$, which is in turn lower than the $3D$. These three states in sodium all have different energies and are, therefore, *not* degenerate, despite the fact that the valence electron has the same quantum number n. The energy of the sodium atom is *not* independent of the value of the orbital angular momentum, but is, instead, lowest for the smallest orbital angular momentum. At higher values of n the energy levels more closely approach those of hydrogen.

The allowed transitions, according to the selection rule $\Delta l = \pm 1$, are classified as S, P, D, and F series, as in Figure 7-8 for hydrogen, but the corresponding emitted photons are of different frequencies and do *not* correspond. For example, the $4S \rightarrow 3P$ and $4P \rightarrow 3S$ transitions in sodium yield two *different* spectral lines. The most prominent line in the spectrum of sodium is the so-called sodium D line which arises from the $3P \rightarrow 3S$ transition, the first line of the P series.†

The emission and absorption spectra of the other alkali metals (see Table 7-1) are similar to those of sodium. The singly ionized alkaline earths (Table 7-1) are *isoelectronic* with the alkali metals, two adjacent elements having the same number of electrons; they differ principally in the size of the nuclear charge. In the $_{12}Mg^+$ atom, for example, there are ten electrons in a closed shell like that of $_{10}Ne$, a single valence electron, just as in $_{11}Na$; when the valence electron is outside the inert core, it sees a net positive charge of $+2e$. Thus, the "nonpenetrating" energy states of $_{12}Mg^+$ will correspond closely to those of the one-electron atom $_2He^+$, whose nuclear electric charge also is $+2e$. States with small n values and, especially, with small l values will, however, be displaced downward with respect to those of $_2He^+$.

We have seen that it is possible to understand qualitatively the energy levels and spectra of hydrogen-like atoms by assuming that the excited states are due to the last, the valence, electron of the atom. We shall see that the inertness of the closed shells arise in a natural way from fundamental principles. The energy levels and spectra of atoms containing more than one active valence electron are much more complex.

7-4 Space quantization
In a classical planetary model the total energy, the magnitude of the orbital angular momentum, and the component of the orbital angular momentum along any direction in space are constants of the motion. In wave mechanics the energy of a one-electron atom is quantized and identified by the principal quantum number n, and its orbital angular momentum is quantized, the possible values depending on the value of the orbital angular-momentum quantum number l; the third classical constant of the motion, the component of the orbital angular

---

† The labels S, P, D, and F were assigned to these and similar series early in the history of spectroscopy for the following reasons: the lines of the S series were relatively "sharp," the lines of the P series were the "principal" lines in the emission or absorption spectra in that they were found even for relatively small excitation of the source (the P lines result from transitions from the *first* and higher excited P states to the *ground* state), the lines of the D series were rather "diffuse," and the lines of the F series, lying in the infrared, had frequencies the lowest of any of the series, corresponding to the "fundamental."

The label D for the strong yellow lines of sodium has no connection with the symbol D designating $l = 2$. Fraunhofer discovered in 1809 that the spectrum from the Sun contains a number of dark absorption lines (*Fraunhofer lines*) which arise from the absorption of radiation from the interior of the Sun by elements in the Sun's atmosphere. These lines were labeled A, B, C, D, etc. The D Fraunhofer line corresponds to absorption by sodium vapor in the $3P \rightarrow 3S$ transition. Close observation shows that this transition actually consists of two closely spaced yellow lines having wavelengths of 5,890 and 5,896 angstroms. Other lines in the sodium spectrum show a similar fine structure, whose origin will be treated in Section 7-6. Also appearing in the Sun's absorption spectrum were lines identified with the element helium and named for the sun (*helios*); helium was later isolated and identified on Earth.

momentum along a fixed direction in space, also is quantized and specified by a quantum number, called m_l. This additional quantization, which can be derived formally in wave mechanics, is closely related to magnetic effects in atoms.

Consider the magnetic effects associated with a classical, orbiting, charged particle. The orbital angular momentum L of a particle moving in closed orbit is represented by a vector oriented at right angles to the plane of the orbit. A circulating negative electric charge constitutes an electric-current loop and has associated with it a magnetic field, as shown in Figure 7-10. The magnetic field at any point is proportional to the magni-

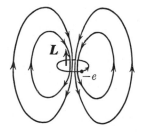

Figure 7-10. Magnetic field of a magnetic dipole consisting of a circulating negative electric charge.

tude of the current. The magnetic-field configuration is like that of a small permanent magnet, and we may associate a *magnetic dipole moment* μ with the circulating electron. The direction of μ is perpendicular to the plane of the electron's loop and related to the sense of a rotating *positive* charge through the right-hand screw rule. Thus, for a negatively charged particle the angular momentum L and magnetic moment μ point in opposite directions, as shown in Figure 7-11. We wish to find the proportionality constant between the magnitudes of L and μ.

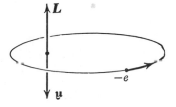

Figure 7-11. Orbital angular momentum L and magnetic moment μ of an orbiting electron.

A magnetic moment $\mathbf{\mu}$ in a magnetic field $\mathbf{B}$ may be defined by the relations[†]

$$\tau = \mathbf{\mu} \times \mathbf{B}$$

$$\Delta E_m = -\mathbf{\mu} \cdot \mathbf{B}$$

where τ is the magnetic torque tending to align $\mathbf{\mu}$ with $\mathbf{B}$ and ΔE_m is the magnetic potential energy change of the dipole in the external field. Denoting the direction of $\mathbf{\mu}$ relative to that of $\mathbf{B}$ by the angle θ, as shown in Figure 7-12a, we may write the last equation in the form

$$\Delta E_m = -\mu B \cos \theta \qquad\qquad [7\text{-}3]$$

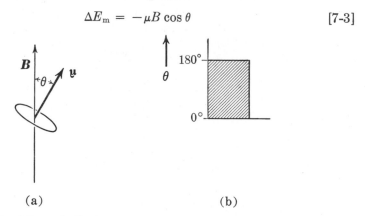

(a)   (b)

Figure 7-12. Magnetic dipole in a magnetic field: (a) relative directions of $\mathbf{B}$ and $\mathbf{\mu}$; (b) orientations permitted in classical physics.

When the dipole is aligned with the external field and θ is zero, then ΔE_m equals $-\mu B$, a minimum. When work is done on the dipole to turn it so that it is aligned in a direction opposite to that of $\mathbf{B}$ and θ is 180°, then ΔE_m equals $+\mu B$, a maximum. We know that in classical physics all orientations of the dipole between 0° and 180° and, therefore, all energies between $-\mu B$ and $+\mu B$ are allowed, as shown in Figure 7-12b.

The magnitude of the magnetic moment of an electric current i enclosing a loop in a plane of area A is given by[‡]

$$\mu = iA$$

When a particle of charge e completes one loop in the time T, the current is $i = e/T$; then the equation above may be written

$$\mu = eA/T \qquad\qquad [7\text{-}4]$$

The orbital angular momentum L relative to the force center for a particle of mass m moving under the influence of a central force, such as the Cou-

[†] See Sec. 32-8, Weidner and Sells, *E. C. P.*
[‡] See Equation 32-19, Weidner and Sells, *E. C. P.*

lomb force between particles, remains constant and may be written, in general, as

$$L = 2m \, (dA/dt)$$

where dA/dt represents the rate, at which a radius vector from the force center to the moving particle sweeps out area, and m is the mass of the electron (this is merely Kepler's second law of planetary motion†).Over the time T of one complete cycle the area swept out is A; then $dA/dt = A/T$. Substituting this result in the last equation, we have

$$L = 2mA/T \qquad\qquad [7\text{-}5]$$

Finally, combining Equations 7-4 and 7-5, we have

$$\boxed{\mathbf{\mu} = -\frac{e}{2m}\mathbf{L}} \qquad\qquad [7\text{-}6]$$

The minus sign has been introduced because the magnetic-moment and angular-momentum vectors point in opposite directions. We see that $\mathbf{\mu}$ is directly proportional to $\mathbf{L}$. The proportionality constant $-e/2m$, is the constant we set out to find; it is customarily called the *magnetogyric ratio*.

Wave mechanics gives precisely the same relation for the magnetogyric ratio of an electron in an atom with an orbital angular momentum $L = [l(l+1)]^{1/2}\hbar$ that classical physics gives, despite the fact that it is impossible to visualize the connection between the magnetic effects and the angular momentum in terms of a well-defined electron orbit. Since L depends on the orbital angular-momentum quantum number l, so too must the magnetic moment μ. Using Equation 7-1 in Equation 7-6, we have

$$\mu_l = \frac{e}{2m}\sqrt{l(l+1)}\hbar \qquad\qquad [7\text{-}7]$$

where the subscript denotes the magnetic moment associated with l.

Consider now the change in the energy ΔE_m of an atom that occurs when the atom with magnetic moment μ_l is placed in an external magnetic field of flux density $\mathbf{B}$. Combining Equations 7-3 and 7-7 and now taking θ to be the angle between $\mathbf{L}$ and $\mathbf{B}$ rather than that between $\mathbf{\mu}$ and $\mathbf{B}$, we have

$$\Delta E_m = \frac{e\hbar}{2m}\sqrt{l(l+1)}B\cos\theta \qquad\qquad [7\text{-}8]$$

Thus, when the atom is immersed in an external magnetic field, its energy depends on the angle θ between the orbital angular-momentum vector and the external field. If there were no restriction on the angle θ, the com-

† See Sec. 15-3, Weidner and Sells, *E. C. P.*

ponent of the orbital angular momentum in the direction of the magnetic field could assume any value between positive and negative $[l(l + 1)]^{1/2}\hbar$ and, similarly, ΔE_m could assume any value between positive and negative $(e\hbar/2m)B[l(l + 1)]^{1/2}$, according to Equation 7-8. In short, if there were no rule restricting, i.e. quantizing, the values of L in the field direction, there would exist a *continuum* of possible energies, quite unlike the situation that has heretofore been found to hold in bound atomic systems. Then the emission lines from atoms with magnetic moments and in magnetic fields would be continuously broadened and not split into discrete lines.

The emission lines from atoms placed in a strong external magnetic field were studied in 1896 by P. Zeeman. At first he found that upon application of the field the lines broadened, but with a higher instrumental resolution he discovered that they actually had become split and consisted of two or more closely spaced, sharp lines. Such splitting of a spectral line into discrete components by a magnetic field is known as the *Zeeman effect*. A proper understanding of it lies in the wave-mechanical phenomenon called *space quantization*.

According to wave mechanics, an orbital angular-momentum vector L *cannot* assume *any* direction with respect to an external magnetic field; rather, it is restricted to those particular orientations for which its *component in the direction of the magnetic field is an integral multiple of* $\hbar$. We take the direction of the external magnetic field to be the Z direction. The possible values of the Z component of L (see Figure 7-13) are given by the rule

$$L_z = m_l \hbar \qquad\qquad [7\text{-}9]$$

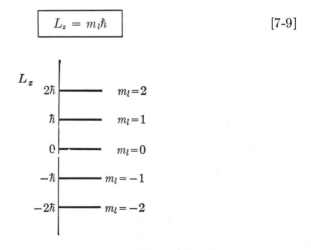

Figure 7-13. Permitted quantum values of the component of the orbital angular momentum along the direction of a magnetic field for a D state.

where m_l, the *orbital magnetic quantum number*, can assume for a given value of l the integral values

$$m_l = l, l-1, l-2, \ldots, 0, \ldots, -l \qquad [7\text{-}10]$$

For example, in a D state with $l = 2$ the possible values of m_l are $+2$, $+1, 0, -1$, and -2. In this state, then, the component L_z can assume only the values $2\hbar, 1\hbar, 0, -1\hbar, -2\hbar$, while the magnitude of L is $\sqrt{6}\hbar$. Figure 7-14 shows the possible orientations of the orbital angular-momentum

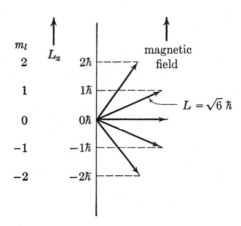

Figure 7-14. Space quantization of the orbital angular-momentum vector L for a D state.

vector with respect to an external magnetic field (compare with Figure 7-4). Because the angular-momentum vector is restricted to certain discrete orientations in space, it is said to be *space-quantized*. Further, since L_z is $L \cos \theta$, the rule governing the orientation of the L vector, that is, the rule for space quantization, is

$$\cos \theta = \frac{m_l}{\sqrt{l(l+1)}} \qquad [7\text{-}11]$$

Note that L's maximum component in the direction of space quantization, $L_z = l\hbar$, is always *less* than its magnitude, $L = [l(l+1)]^{1/2}\hbar$. The orbital angular-momentum vector can never be perfectly aligned in the direction of an external magnetic field or in the opposite direction. Wave mechanics permits the magnitude of L and its Z component to be precisely specified but, paradoxically, does not allow its X and Y components to be. It is customary to regard the L vector as *precessing* around the Z axis at a constant angle θ, thereby tracing out a cone, for any particular allowed value of m_l; this is how its magnitude and Z component are known but its X and Y components unknown.†

7-5 The normal Zeeman effect

If the orientation of the angular momentum vector is quantized, so are the possible orientations of the associated magnetic dipole moment $\mathbf{\mu}_l$, and so too is the magnetic potential energy ΔE_m of the state. Using Equation 7-11, the rule for space quantization, in Equation 7-8, the equation for the change in energy of a state with quantum numbers l and m_l, we have

$$\Delta E_m = m_l \left(\frac{e\hbar}{2m}\right) B \qquad \text{[7-12]}$$

Figure 7-15 shows the *changes* in the energies of S, P, D, and F states having respectively 1, 3, 5, and 7 *magnetic sublevels*; in general, the num-

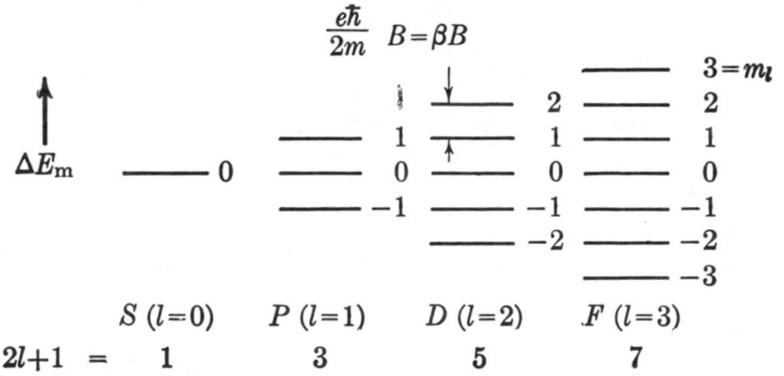

Figure 7-15. Energy splitting of S, P, D, and F states of an atom in a magnetic field.

ber of Zeeman components for a given l is equal to $2l + 1$. The difference in energy between adjacent magnetic sublevels is equal to $(e\hbar/2m)B$ and is independent of the value of l. The quantity $e\hbar/2m$ has the units of magnetic moment; it is known as the *Bohr magneton*, β, because β is the magnetic moment of a classical electron orbiting about the hydrogen nucleus at the radius of the first Bohr orbit:

$$\text{Bohr magneton } \beta = e\hbar/2m = 0.9273 \times 10^{-23} \text{ J/(Wb/m}^2)$$

Consider the spectrum of lines emitted from excited atoms in transitions between a D state and a P state in the presence of a magnetic field; see Figure 7-16. When B is zero, the energy of the D state is E_D (for all five m_l values), the energy of the P state is E_P (for all three m_l values), and

† The indefiniteness of the X and Y components can be shown to be a necessary consequence of the uncertainty principle. See Problem 5-33.

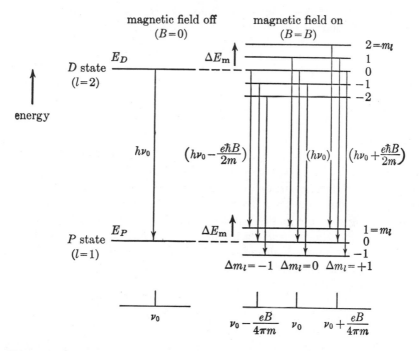

Figure 7-16. Energy levels and spectra of a $D \to P$ transition: (left) zero magnetic field; (right) nonzero magnetic field, normal Zeeman effect.

photons having the single frequency ν_0 are emitted according to $h\nu_0 = E_D - E_P$. When the field is turned on, the D state splits into five equally spaced magnetic sublevels, and the P state splits into three equally spaced magnetic sublevels, the difference in energy between any two adjacent magnetic sublevels being $(e\hbar/2m)B$. The transitions between the D state ($l = 2$) and the P state ($l = 1$) obey the selection rule $\Delta l = \pm 1$; the selection rule for transitions between magnetic sublevels is

$$\boxed{\Delta m_l = 0 \quad \text{or} \quad \pm 1} \qquad \text{[7-13]}$$

That is, only those transitions are allowed in which the magnetic quantum number m_l is unchanged or in which it changes by one unit. The permitted transitions and the spectrum of the emitted lines are shown in Figure 7-16. It may be seen that the differences $h\nu$ for allowed transitions take one of three possible values:

$$\left. \begin{array}{lll} \Delta m_l = -1: & h\nu = h\nu_0 - (e\hbar/2m)B \\ \Delta m_l = \ \ 0: & h\nu = h\nu_0 \\ \Delta m_l = +1: & h\nu = h\nu_0 + (e\hbar/2m)B \end{array} \right\} \qquad \text{[7-14]}$$

Dividing both sides of these equations by h gives the frequencies of the emitted radiation:

$$\left.\begin{array}{l} \nu = \nu_0 - (e/4\pi m)B \\ \nu = \nu_0 \\ \nu = \nu_0 + (e/4\pi m)B \end{array}\right\} \qquad [7\text{-}15]$$

Thus, a single line in the spectrum is split by an external magnetic field into three equally spaced components: the original line of frequency ν_0 and two equally spaced satellite lines, whose separation $(e/4\pi m)B$ from ν_0 is proportional to the magnetic field B. Using Equation 7-14, we see that for a relatively strong magnetic field, say $B = 1.0$ Wb/m^2 (10,000 gauss), the difference in energy between adjacent Zeeman levels is only 9.3×10^{-23} joule, or 5.8×10^{-4} eV. Since the typical difference between levels giving rise to emission in the visible region of the spectrum is a few electron volts, the energy, frequency, or wavelength is changed by less than one part in a thousand when a strong magnetic field is applied. For this reason observation of the Zeeman effect requires spectrometers of moderately high resolution.

Figure 7-16 shows the energy levels and allowed transitions between a D and a P state. The value of ΔE_m and the selection rules governing m_l are both independent of l; therefore:

All transitions for which Δl is ± 1 will give rise to the same Zeeman effect, three equally spaced Zeeman component lines.

This is called the *normal Zeeman effect*, and the observed splittings of some lines from *some* elements, such as calcium and mercury, are in complete agreement with the spectrum shown in the figure. On the other hand, the spectra of most elements do *not* show a normal Zeeman effect, in that the magnitude of the splittings and the number of Zeeman components is *not* in accord with the theory presented here. Such Zeeman spectra are said to be *anomalous*, inasmuch as the emitted radiation cannot be accounted for simply in terms of the space quantization of the *orbital* angular momentum vector and the associated magnetic effects.

Note that the frequency difference $(e/4\pi m)B$ in Equation 7-15 does not involve the quantum constant h. This suggests that it may not be a distinctly quantum effect. Indeed, as Problem 7-11 shows, the so-called normal Zeeman effect can be derived on the basis of a strictly classical computation.

The space-quantization rule, which limits the value of the component of the orbital angular momentum in any direction in space to integral multiples of $\hbar$, holds whether or not a magnetic field is applied. When a magnetic field is applied, its direction specifies the direction of space quantization, and the energies of the several states differ according to the value of m_l. When the magnetic field is turned off, the space quantization persists; now, however, the energies of the states corresponding to the several possible values of m_l are all identical. Therefore, in the absence of a magnetic field any state with orbital angular-momentum quantum number l has $2l + 1$ substates, which are identical both in their energy, $\Delta E_m = 0$, *and* in the magnitude of the orbital angular momentum, $[l(l + 1)]^{1/2}\hbar$, but which differ in the component of the angular-momentum vector, $m_l\hbar$, in a direction in space. Thus, in the absence of a magnetic field there is a $(2l + 1)$-fold degeneracy in the energy of the states for any particular value of l.

7-6 Electron spin   We have seen that three classical constants of the motion of a particle subject to an inverse-square force of attraction—the energy, the magnitude of the orbital angular momentum, and the component of the orbital angular momentum in a fixed direction in space—are quantized in the quantum theory. In classical mechanics the energy of a particle in an elliptical orbit is determined by the *size* of the orbit, that is, by the major axis of the ellipse; the magnitude of the orbital angular momentum is determined for a given major axis by the *shape* of the elliptical orbit, that is, by the eccentricity of the elliptical path; the component of the orbital angular momentum along a direction in space is determined by the *orientation* of the elliptical orbit. To these constants of the motion there correspond in quantum mechanics the quantum numbers n, l, and m_l. In this section we introduce the fourth and final quantum number s, which is associated with the concept of electron spin.

We have remarked that the strongest emission from sodium comes from the $3P \rightarrow 3S$ transition. When this radiation is examined with a spectrometer of moderately high resolution, it is seen that the transition corresponds to *two* closely spaced yellow lines (at 5,890 and 5,896 Å), called the sodium D lines (see Section 7-3). In fact, each of the spectral lines of sodium exhibits such *fine structure*: for each transition shown in Figure 7-9 there are actually two or three distinct lines separated from one another by no more than a very few angstroms of wavelength. The fine structure is *anomalous* in that it occurs without the application of an external magnetic field and so cannot be accounted for as a *normal* Zeeman effect (see Section 7-5). Fine structure in emission and absorption spectra is a common feature of all atomic line spectra. Apparently, a distinctive, additional feature of atomic structure is manifest in fine structure, one that cannot be accounted for in terms of the quantum numbers n, l, and m_l.

It is suggestive to attribute fine structure to an *internal* Zeeman effect, within the atom. Such an effect would require the presence of an internal atomic magnetic field and a new source of magnetic moment and angular momentum within the atom. The orbital angular momentum of the atom has already been taken into account; what other contribution to the angular momentum can be imagined?

S. A. Goudsmit and G. E. Uhlenbeck suggested in 1925, that an intrinsic angular momentum quite apart from orbital motion was associated with an electron. It is named *electron spin*, for it may be visualized as analogous to the intrinsic angular momentum that any extended object has by virtue of rotation, or spin, about its center of mass. (Recall that a symmetrical spinning object has spin angular momentum, which is independent of the choice of axis in computations of angular momentum; in other words, the angular momentum of a spinning object is an intrinsic property of the object.) Now it is, of course, not proper in wave mechanics to regard an electron as a simple sphere of electric charge; but for the sake of identifying the electron-spin angular momentum with some sort of model that can be visualized it is useful to imagine it as having an extension in space and as continuously spinning around an axis of rotation. The electron spin, then, is the intrinsic angular momentum L_s arising from the rotation of the charge cloud about a rotation axis fixed with respect to the electron. Furthermore, because negative electric charge is imagined to be rotating, a magnetic field will be produced by the spinning electron, and a magnetic moment $\mathbf{\mu}_s$, opposite in direction to that of the spin angular momentum L_s, may be attributed to the electron spin; see Figure 7-17.

If an electron, with its permanent spin magnetic moment, were in a magnetic field, we should expect its spin to be space-quantized. The spin axis, magnetic moment, and spin angular momentum would then be restricted to certain quantized orientations, and the energy of the atom would differ according to the particular orientation.

The internal atomic magnetic field that can act on an electron with a spin angular momentum L_s and a spin magnetic moment $\mathbf{\mu}_s$ may be thought of as originating the following way. If a spinning electron orbits a nucleus, then an observer fixed with respect to the electron sees the nucleus orbiting it. The orbiting positive charge produces at the site of the electron a magnetic field, whose magnitude and direction depend on the magnitude and

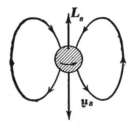

Figure 7-17. Electron-spin angular momentum L_s and magnetic moment $\mathbf{\mu}_s$ with associated magnetic field.

direction of the electron's *orbital* angular momentum. The field acts on the spin magnetic moment $\boldsymbol{\mu}_s$. The interaction between electron spin and orbital angular momentum is aptly called *spin-orbit interaction*. The interaction exists in all orbital states save S states (with $l = 0$).

We now turn to spectroscopic evidence to find the allowed values of the spin angular momentum L_s and the spin magnetic moment μ_s. A study of the spectral lines from an atom with a single valence electron, such as sodium, in the *absence* of an *external* magnetic field indicates that each of the orbital energy levels (except the S state) is split into two components (a doublet), the S state remaining unsplit (a singlet). It is for this reason that the $3P \rightarrow 3S$ transition in sodium consists of the two closely spaced D lines: the $3S$ state is a singlet, the $3P$ state a doublet. How can the doubling of all states (except the S states) be interpreted in terms of an internal magnetic field space-quantizing the electron-spin angular momentum? In the normal Zeeman effect any state having an orbital quantum number l is split, under the influence of an external magnetic field, into $2l + 1$ sublevels. We assume that, similarly, a state having a *spin angular-momentum quantum number* s is split into $2s + 1$ components under the influence of an internal magnetic field. Because the number of components of all fine-structure states with a nonzero orbital angular momentum is always 2, the quantity $2s + 1$ must equal 2 and the spin quantum number s have the *single value* $\frac{1}{2}$:

$$2s + 1 = 2, \quad \text{or} \quad s = \tfrac{1}{2}$$

Since the spin is an intrinsic characteristic of the electron, every electron has a spin quantum number with the unique value $\frac{1}{2}$. The spin, or intrinsic, angular momentum of such a particle as an electron is as basic a characteristic as its charge and mass. The magnitude of the spin angular momentum L_s is given by a relation analogous to that for orbital angular momentum (Equation 7-1):

$$\boxed{L_s = \sqrt{s(s + 1)}\hbar = \tfrac{1}{2}\sqrt{3}\hbar} \qquad [7\text{-}16]$$

It is easy to see why the S state of sodium is a singlet. The internal magnetic field due to orbital motion is zero ($l = 0$); hence, the two spin states are unsplit, and therefore *degenerate*. The degeneracy can, however, be removed by an external magnetic field.

In the presence of a magnetic field the electron spin is space-quantized, such that the component $L_{s,z}$ of the spin angular momentum in the direction of the magnetic field is

$$\boxed{L_{s,z} = m_s\hbar} \qquad [7\text{-}17]$$

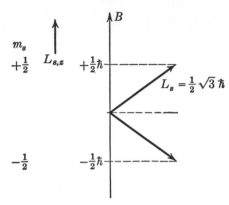

Figure 7-18. Space quantization of electron-spin angular momentum.

where the *spin magnetic quantum number* m_s has two possible values, $+\frac{1}{2}$ and $-\frac{1}{2}$. The space quantization of the electron-spin angular momentum due to a magnetic field, as shown in Figure 7-18, restricts the orientation of the electron-spin vector $\boldsymbol{L}_s$ to those two possible states in which its component along Z is $+\frac{1}{2}\hbar$ or $-\frac{1}{2}\hbar$. For $m_s = +\frac{1}{2}$ the spin angular momentum vector points more nearly in the direction of the magnetic field than away from it, and the magnetic moment $\boldsymbol{\mu}_s$ is aligned more nearly against the field than with it. Thus, the magnetic potential energy arising from the orientation of the electron-spin magnetic moment is higher for the state with $m_s = +\frac{1}{2}$ than for the state with $m_s = -\frac{1}{2}$.

As in the case of orbital motion, in spin motion the magnetic moment lies along the same line as the angular-momentum vector but points in the opposite direction. A detailed study of the Zeeman effect for atoms having fine structure and theoretical analysis shows that the magnetogyric ratio associated with the electron spin is given by

$$\mu_s/L_s = 2(1.001159615)(e/2m) \qquad [7\text{-}18]$$

where e and m are the electron charge and mass, respectively. The magnetogyric ratio of the electron spin is very closely two times that of the electron orbital motion; that is, for a given angular momentum a spinning electron is twice as effective in magnetic effects as an orbiting one.

The magnetic potential energy change ΔE_s of an electron-spin magnetic moment in a magnetic field B is given by

$$\boxed{\Delta E_s = m_s[2(e\hbar/2m)]B} \qquad [7\text{-}19]$$

which is much like Equation 7-12.

It is interesting to calculate the approximate magnitude of the magnetic field that splits the P state in sodium. Figure 7-19 shows the $3S$ and $3P$ states of sodium. The two transitions giving rise to the sodium D lines

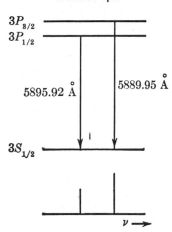

Figure 7-19. Energy levels and spectrum of the sodium D lines (not to scale).

differ by $\Delta\lambda = 6$ Å; therefore, the energy difference ΔE between the two P states is given by

$$\Delta E = \frac{hc\,\Delta\lambda}{\lambda^2} = 2\mu_{s,z}B$$

Then $B = 20 \text{ Wb/m}^2 = 200{,}000 \text{ gauss}$

which is a very strong field. The fine-structure splitting of energy levels, arising from spin-orbit interaction, is in complete agreement with the experimental observations of fine structure in spectral lines. For quantitative details the sophisticated methods of quantum mechanics are required. The internal magnetic fields are extraordinarily strong, and the fine-structure splitting, typically of 10^{-3} eV, or a few angstroms in wavelength in visible lines, is in accord with theoretical predictions.

In an atom there are, then, two contributions to the total angular momentum of the atom: the orbital angular momentum and the electron spin angular momentum.† The quantum theory correctly predicts that the *total angular momentum* L_j of an atom with a single valence electron is characterized by the *total angular-momentum* quantum number j and has a magnitude given by

$$L_j = \sqrt{j(j+1)}\hbar \tag{7-20}$$

† The nucleus of an atom, too, may have spin, or intrinsic angular momentum, called *nuclear spin*, which is added to the angular momentum of the electrons. *Hyperfine structure*, consisting of very closely spaced spectral lines (typically less than 10^{-3} angstrom), has its origin in the interaction of the spin and magnetic moment of nuclei with those of the electrons. The magnetic moments associated with nuclei are always smaller than the Bohr magneton by a factor of approximately 10^3, and the hyperfine splitting is correspondingly less than the fine splitting. In terms of a classical planetary model the nuclear spin is analogous to the spin angular momentum of the Sun.

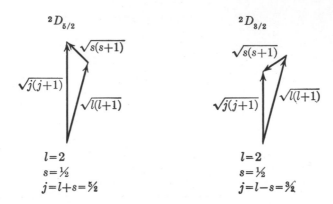

Figure 7-20. Vector relations between the orbital, spin, and total angular momentum vectors for the $^2D_{5/2}$ and the $^2D_{3/2}$ states.

The number j can assume either of the two values $l + s$ and $l - s$, where l and s are the orbital and spin quantum numbers. Figure 7-20 shows the vector relations between the orbital, spin, and total angular momentum vectors. It can be seen that the orbital and spin vectors are never completely aligned or antialigned with the total vector. A useful means of illustrating the coupling between the orbital and spin angular momenta is the so-called *vector model*. In this model the spin and orbital angular-momentum vectors are imagined to precess about the L_j vector at a constant rate.

All the electrons within a closed shell of an atom with a single valence electron are so arranged that (as we shall see in Section 7-8) the total angular momentum and total magnetic moment of the closed shell are zero. For an illustration of the combination of the orbital and spin quantum numbers consider the $3P$ states of sodium. We have $l = 1$ and $s = \frac{1}{2}$; therefore, the total angular-momentum quantum number j has the two possible values $1 + \frac{1}{2} = \frac{3}{2}$ and $1 - \frac{1}{2} = \frac{1}{2}$. These two states are represented in the conventional spectroscopic notation as $3^2P_{3/2}$ and $3^2P_{1/2}$ (read as "three doublet P three halves" and "three doublet P one half"); the presuperscript gives the value of $2s + 1$, and the postsubscript gives the value of j. Similarly, we have the states $3^2D_{5/2}$ and $3^2D_{3/2}$ of sodium. Figure 7-21 shows the splitting of several states of sodium.

In an external field (less than 10^2 Wb/m^2) the total angular momentum L_j of magnitude $[j(j + 1)]^{1/2}\hbar$ is space-quantized in the field direction, which is again chosen to be along the Z axis. The permitted $2j + 1$ components of L_j are

$$L_{j,z} = m_j\hbar$$

where m_j is equal to $j, j - 1, \ldots, -j$. This is the basis of the *anomalous Zeeman effect*, which occurs whenever there is spin-orbit interaction.

The computation of anomalous Zeeman splitting requires a knowledge of the magnetic moment $\mathbf{\mu}_j$ associated with the *total* angular momentum L_j, and the computation of $\mathbf{\mu}_j$ is somewhat involved (see Problem 7-27). Further, an analysis of the structure of atoms is increasingly complex as the number of valence electrons increases, because one must combine the spin and orbital angular-momentum vectors of two or more electrons. Here we shall describe merely the normal Zeeman effect in an atom of two valence electrons.

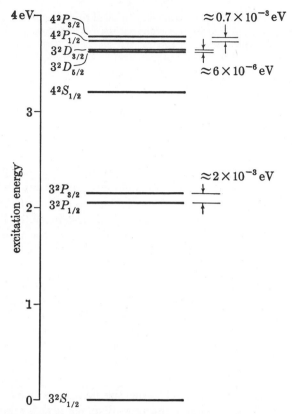

Figure 7-21. Splitting of several states of sodium, due to spin-orbit interaction (the splittings are grossly exaggerated).

The two electron-spin angular-momentum quantum numbers $s_1 = \frac{1}{2}$ and $s_2 = \frac{1}{2}$ usually combine to form the total spin quantum number S of the atom, where $S = s_1 + s_2 = 1$ (parallel spins) or $S = s_1 - s_2 = 0$ (antiparallel spins). Similarly, the two orbital angular-momentum quantum numbers, usually l_1 and l_2, form a total orbital angular-momentum quantum number L. The resultant spin and orbital quantum numbers S and L then combine to form a total angular-momentum quantum number J of the atom. Consider a state for which $S = 0$; such a state is a singlet state, inasmuch as $2S + 1 = 1$ (when $S = 1$ and $2S + 1 = 3$, the state is a triplet). Then $J = L$, and the total angular momentum is due only to orbital motion. In a magnetic field the transitions between *singlet* states exhibit the *normal* Zeeman effect. In general, the occurrence of the *normal* Zeeman effect requires that the *total spin* angular momentum of the atom be *zero*, which is to say that the atom have an *even* number of electrons grouped in pairs of antialigned spins.

In a nonrelativistic wave-mechanical analysis of atomic structure the three quantum numbers n, l, and m_l emerge in a natural way by the fitting of three-dimensional waves, representing the electrons, into the region surrounding the nucleus. The electron spin, which has no classical analogue (except for the fictitious model of a spinning sphere of charge), is *not* a consequence of nonrelativistic wave mechanics. The first relativistic wave-mechanical treatment incorporating the three space and one time coordinates was successfully made by P. A. M. Dirac in 1928. In his relativistic quantum theory the electron spin, having an angular momentum of $[s(s + 1)]^{1/2}\hbar$ and a magnetogyric ratio of $2(e/2m)$, emerges in a natural way with the three quantum numbers n, l, and m_l. Another consequence of the Dirac wave mechanics was the first prediction of the electron's antiparticle, the positron. The positron has a spin angular-momentum quantum number s of $\frac{1}{2}$ and a magnetogyric ratio of $2(e/2m)$, just like those of the electron, but its spin angular-momentum and magnetic moment vectors point in the same direction, by virtue of the positive electric charge.

7-7 The Stern-Gerlach experiment   The space-quantization phenomenon, which limits the orientations of the angular-momentum and magnetic-moment vectors in a magnetic field, is demonstrated *directly* in the experiment of O. Stern and W. Gerlach, performed first in 1921. They showed that atoms of silver, in which the only contribution to the angular momentum of the atom is that made by the spin of a single electron, are space-quantized in a magnetic field.

To see the basis of the direct experimental confirmation of space quantization let us consider a magnetic dipole. A magnetic dipole moment $\mathbf{\mu}$ in a uniform magnetic field $\boldsymbol{B}$ (one in which the magnetic lines of force are uniformly spaced and parallel) is subject to a torque,[†]

$$\boldsymbol{\tau} = \mathbf{\mu} \times \boldsymbol{B}$$

which tends to orient the magnet along the field lines. The dipole is *not*, however, subject to a *net* force tending to displace it as a whole. Consider now the behavior of a magnetic dipole in an *inhomogeneous* magnetic field, one showing a divergence of the magnetic field lines. Figure 7-22 illustrates that a *net* force pulls the magnet into the region of strong field when the

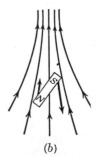

(a)   (b)

Figure 7-22. Force on a magnetic dipole in an inhomogeneous magnetic field for two orientations.

[†] See Equation 32-20, Weidner and Sells, *E. C. P.*

magnet and the field are more nearly aligned than not and that it pushes it out when they are more nearly antialigned.

Let us compute the force on a magnetic moment in an inhomogeneous magnetic field. The magnetic potential energy of the electron spin is given by

[7-19] $$\Delta E_s = m_s[2(e\hbar/2m)]B$$

Inasmuch as a force is just the negative space derivative of the corresponding energy,‡ the magnetic force acting on the dipole is given by

$$F_z = -(d/dz)(\Delta E_s) = -m_s(e\hbar/m)(dB/dz) \qquad [7\text{-}21]$$

where the Z direction is the symmetry direction of the inhomogeneous magnetic field of gradient dB/dz as well as the direction of space quantization of the electron spin.

Consider now the arrangement of the original Stern-Gerlach experiment, shown in Figure 7-23. Silver atoms leave an oven at relatively high speeds, are collimated by slits, pass through an inhomogeneous magnetic field,

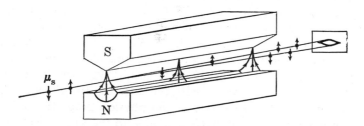

Figure 7-23. Schematic representation of the Stern-Gerlach experiment.

and fall upon a photographic plate, where their final location is recorded. The electron spins are space-quantized in the magnetic field into such orientations that the component of the electron-spin angular momentum is $+\frac{1}{2}\hbar$ or $-\frac{1}{2}\hbar$ for an m_s or $+\frac{1}{2}$ or $-\frac{1}{2}$, respectively. For $m_s = +\frac{1}{2}$ the atoms are deflected downward; for $m_s = -\frac{1}{2}$ they are deflected upward. On the photographic plate there is, then, *not* a continuous spread in the positions of the arriving atoms, as would be expected if space quantization had not occurred; rather, two distinct lines, corresponding to the silver atoms in the two allowed spin orientations, are observed. In general, for an atom's total angular-momentum quantum number J the number of lines appearing on the plate is $2J + 1$; thus atomic beams may be used for evaluating angular-momentum quantum numbers.

‡ See Equation 12-15, Weidner and Sells, *E. C. P.*

7-8　The Pauli exclusion principle and the periodic table　To specify the state of an electron in an atom is, in the quantum theory, to specify the values of each of the four quantum numbers n, l, m_l, and m_s (the number s need not be indicated, for there is no other possible value than $\frac{1}{2}$). By the procedures of the quantum mechanics it is possible to compute an atom's energy in the absence or presence of an external magnetic field, its angular momentum, its magnetic moment, and other of its measurable characteristics. Indeed, it is possible, at least *in principle*, to predict *all* properties of the chemical elements. In practice such a program cannot easily be carried out, because formidable mathematical difficulties arise with systems having many component particles. In fact, only the problem of the simplest atom, hydrogen, has been solved completely by relativistic quantum theory. Work on this atom has shown essentially perfect agreement between experiment and theory.

Even though solutions for the other atomic elements are not known exactly, the quantum theory does provide a wealth of information concerning their chemical and physical properties. One of its greatest achievements is a basis for understanding the ordering of the chemical elements as they appear in the periodic table (it should be recalled that the periodic table was first constructed merely by listing elements in the order of their atomic weights, and it was found that remarkable periodicities in the properties of the elements were thereby revealed). We shall discuss the means by which this ordering may be understood in terms of the quantum theory. The key is a principle proposed by W. Pauli in 1924, the Pauli exclusion principle. This principle together with the quantum theory can be used to predict many of the known chemical and physical properties of atoms.

Consider again the energy levels available to the single electron in the hydrogen atom. These energy levels are shown schematically (but *not* to scale) in Figure 7-24. Each horizontal line corresponds to a particular possible set of values for the quantum numbers n, l, and m_l. For each line there are two possible values of the electron-spin quantum number, $m_s = \pm\frac{1}{2}$. The occupancy of an available state by an electron is indicated by an arrow, whose direction indicates the electron-spin orientation, up for $m_s = +\frac{1}{2}$ and down for $m_s = -\frac{1}{2}$. For brevity only the energy levels with principal quantum numbers 1, 2, and 3 are shown. For a given value of n the S states are lowest, the P states next lowest, etc. For a given value of the orbital angular-momentum quantum number l the possible values of the orbital magnetic quantum number m_l are shown horizontally arranged. Every one of the states (two for each dash) is available to the electron in the hydrogen atom. Some of the states are degenerate, having the same total energy; they are, nevertheless, distinguishable when a strong magnetic field or other external influence is applied to the atom.

Let us review the rules governing the possible values of the quantum numbers:

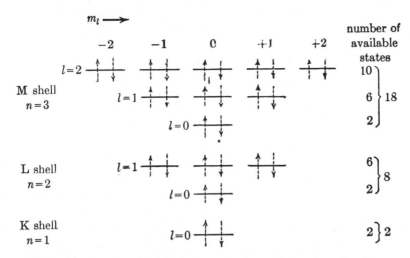

Figure 7-24. Representation of the energy states available to the electron in the hydrogen atom (not to scale). There are two states for each horizontal line, corresponding to the two electron-spin orientations.

For a given n:	$l = 0, 1, 2, \ldots, n - 1$ (n possibilities)
For a given l:	$m_l = l, l - 1, \ldots, 0, \ldots, -(l - 1), -l$
	($2l + 1$ possibilities)
For a given m_l:	$m_s = +\frac{1}{2}, -\frac{1}{2}$ (2 possibilities)

[7-22]

When the hydrogen atom is in its lowest, or ground, state, the single electron is in the state in which $n = 1$, $l = 0$, $m_l = 0$, and $m_s = -\frac{1}{2}$. The ground state of the hydrogen atom is thus $1^2S_{1/2}$, where, as before, the first numeral is the value of n, the presuperscript gives $2s + 1 = 2$ with $s = \frac{1}{2}$, the symbol S denotes the atom's orbital quantum number ($L = 0$), and the postsubscript gives the atom's total angular-momentum quantum number $J = \frac{1}{2}$. Excitation of the hydrogen atom may promote the electron to any of the higher-lying available states, from which the atom can then decay to the ground state by downward transitions with the emission of one or more photons. Figure 7-25 depicts a hydrogen atom in its ground state and in an excited $3D$ state.

Consider next the element helium, $_2$He. This atom has two electrons to be arranged among the levels shown in Figure 7-24. The separation between the levels is, however, *not* the same as in hydrogen, because the nuclear charge, $+2e$, is different, and also because there are three interacting particles rather than two. Nevertheless, the order of the states is the same. When the helium atom is in its ground state, both electrons are in the $1S$ state, with $n = 1$, $l = 0$, and $m_l = 0$. Then for each electron two values of m_s are possible, $\frac{1}{2}$ and $-\frac{1}{2}$.

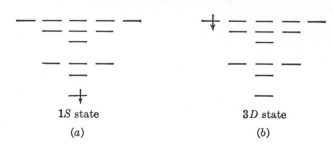

Figure 7-25. Hydrogen atom in its ground state (1*s*) and in a 3*D* state.

The possible values of m_s for each of the two electrons in helium are found in a study of its spectrum. When the various states of the helium atom are inferred from its spectrum, it is found that there is *no* 1^3S_1 state, although there is a 1^1S_0 state. A 1^3S_1 state would represent that situation in which both electron spins had the same m_s value, yielding the atomic total spin quantum number $S = 1$ (for which $2S + 1 = 3$, a triplet); the postsubscript, giving the total angular-momentum quantum number J, is 1, inasmuch as the orbital angular momentum is zero. But only the 1^1S_0 state is found in helium, a state in which the total spin quantum number S is zero and the two electrons have *different* m_s values. Therefore, in the ground state the two electrons, which have identical values of n, l, and m_l, must have spin magnetic quantum numbers $m_s = \frac{1}{2}$ and $m_s = -\frac{1}{2}$, respectively. We can interpret the nonoccurrence of the 1^3S_1 state in helium in the following way: two electrons in a helium atom cannot have the same set of four quantum numbers; that is, the two electrons cannot exist in the same state.

Spectroscopic evidence from all elements is similar; it shows that atoms simply never occur in Nature with two electrons occupying the same state. The Pauli exclusion principle formalizes this experimental fact:

> *No two electrons in an atom can have the same set of quantum numbers n, l, m_l, and m_s; or, no two electrons in an atom can exist in the same state.*

Exceptions to the exclusion principle, which applies also to other systems than atoms and to other particles than electrons, have never been found. The Pauli principle is analogous, but not equivalent, to the classical assertion that no two particles can be in the same place at the same time (the particles being regarded as impenetrable).

Thus, the two electrons in helium in the normal state occupy the two lowest available states indicated in Figure 7-24. No more electrons can be added to the $n = 1$, or K shell,; in helium the K shell is filled, or closed. The electron spins being oppositely aligned in the 1^1S_0 state, the helium atom has no magnetic moment and no angular momentum, either orbital or spin. Furthermore, the two electrons are tightly bound to the nucleus, and a considerable amount of energy is required to excite one of them to a higher energy state. It is primarily for these reasons that helium is chemically inactive.

When the values of the quantum numbers of each and every electron in an atom are known, the *electron configuration* of the atom is given. A simple convention is used for specifying an electron configuration, which we illustrate with an example. When a helium atom is in its ground state, the two electrons each have $n = 1$ and $l = 0$, and their configuration is represented by $1s^2$. The leading number specifies the n value, the lower-case letter s designates the orbital quantum number l of *individual* electrons, and the postsuperscript gives the number of electrons having the particular values of n and l. An energy-level diagram of neutral helium is shown in Figure 7-26. The energy levels are segregated according to whether they are singlets or triplets, that is, whether the two electron spins are anti-aligned or aligned, respectively. Note that the 1^3S state does *not* exist. When the atom is in an excited state, one of the electrons may remain a $1s$ electron in the K shell and the second electron occupy any of the higher excited levels. For example, the electron configuration of the first excited state in helium is $1s^1 2s^1$. Typically, transitions occur only between singlet states or only between triplet states.

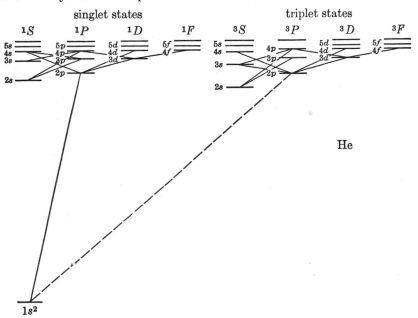

Figure 7-26. Energy-level diagram of helium, showing some possible transitions. Note that the 1^3S_1 state does *not* exist.

The element with the next lowest atomic number, $Z = 3$, is lithium, $_3$Li. Of the three electrons in this atom the first two occupy the two available $n = 1$ states. Therefore, as the exclusion principle requires, when lithium is in its ground state, the third electron goes to the lowest of the remaining available levels. The next lowest available level after the K shell is $n = 2$ and $l = 0$. Then the ground-state configuration of the electrons in lithium is $1s^2 2s^1$, indicating two electrons in the closed K shell and one electron in the incomplete $l = 0$ subshell of the L shell; see Figure 7-27.

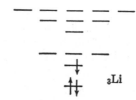

Figure 7-27. Electron configuration of lithium in the ground state.

Proceeding in this fashion—adding one electron as the nuclear charge or atomic number is increased by one unit, but always with the restriction that no *two* electrons within the atom can have the same set of quantum numbers—we can find the ground-state electron configurations of other atoms. We see from Figure 7-24 that two electrons can be accommodated in the s subshell of the L shell and six electrons in the p subshell, after which the L shell is completely occupied, holding its full quota of eight electrons. Table 7-2 gives the electron configurations of the elements from beryllium to sodium.

Table 7-2

ELEMENT	ELECTRON CONFIGURATION FOR THE GROUND STATE			
$_4$Be	$1s^2$	$2s^2$		
$_5$B	$1s^2$	$2s^2$	$2p^1$	
$_6$C	$1s^2$	$2s^2$	$2p^2$	
$_7$N	$1s^2$	$2s^2$	$2p^3$	
$_8$O	$1s^2$	$2s^2$	$2p^4$	
$_9$F	$1s^2$	$2s^2$	$2p^5$	
$_{10}$Ne	$1s^2$	$2s^2$	$2p^6$	
$_{11}$Na	$1s^2$	$2s^2$	$2p^6$	$3s^1$

We shall shortly note the chemical properties of a number of the elements listed in Table 7-2 with respect to their electron configurations and the occurrence of closed shells and subshells, but first we shall note some of the properties of sodium that are directly related to its electron configuration, $1s^2 2s^2 2p^6 3s^1$. A single valence electron is outside the closed L shell, and the lowest state available to this valence electron being the $3s$ state. In the inner, closed subshells the electrons' total angular momentum and magnetic moment is zero, since both their orbital angular momenta and spin angular momenta are paired off. These closed shells, $1s^2$, $2s^2$, and $2p^6$, are chemically inert and correspond to the electron configuration of the inert gas neon. The reason that sodium behaves approximately as a hydrogen atom is clear: a single valence electron moves about inner, inert, closed electron shells. The optical spectrum of sodium originates from the change in the state of the valence electron, while the ten electrons in the inner closed shells remain in their same states.

As the atomic number increases, there is a continuous filling of the sublevels in the expected order $1s$, $2s$, $2p$, $3s$, and $3p$, the last element with three energy levels n being argon, $_{18}$Ar, whose complete electron configuration in the ground state is $1s^2 2s^2 2p^6 3s^2 3p^6$, or $3p^6$ for short. After the completion of the $3p$ subshell with argon we might expect that the succeeding elements would fill, in sequence, the ten available states of the $3d$ sublevel. Spectroscopic and chemical evidence indicates, however, that the $4s$ subshell is filled first, because its two electrons have a lower energy and are more tightly bound to the atom than $3d$ electrons. We can understand this apparent anomaly in the following way. The wave function of a $4s$ electron at the site of the nucleus is greater than that of a $3d$ electron. Consequently, a $4s$ electron is more strongly attracted to the nucleus, and the atom's energy is lowered more by the addition of a $4s$ electron than by the addition of a $3d$ electron. For example, the electron configuration of the element potassium, $_{19}$K, is $1s^2 2s^2 2p^6 3s^2 3p^6 4s^1$. Note that the last electron is a $4s$, not a $3d$. Whereas in hydrogen the $3d$ state lies *below* the $4s$ state, in potassium, with nineteen electrons, the reverse is true. According to experimental evidence, the general order in which the electron subshells are filled as the atomic number increases is as follows:

$$1s, \; 2s, \; 2p, \; 3s, \; 3p, \; 4s, \; 3d, \; 4p, \; 5s, \; 4d, \; 5p, \; 6s, \; 4f, \; 5d, \; 6p, \; 7s, \; 6d$$

The periodic table of chemical elements is shown in Table 7-3. The electron configuration of the outer electrons in the free atom is given with the atomic number and chemical symbol of each element. The arrangement is such that any column typically contains elements with a common orbital state and also with the same number of electrons in this orbital state. For example, carbon, $_6$C, which has an outer electron configuration of $2p^2$, is found above silicon, $_{14}$Si, which has an outer electron configuration of $3p^2$; both have two electrons in an incomplete p subshell. The groups of elements corresponding to the filling of the $3d$, $4d$, $4f$, and $5d$ subshells are listed separately. It is clear why the main body of the periodic table has a

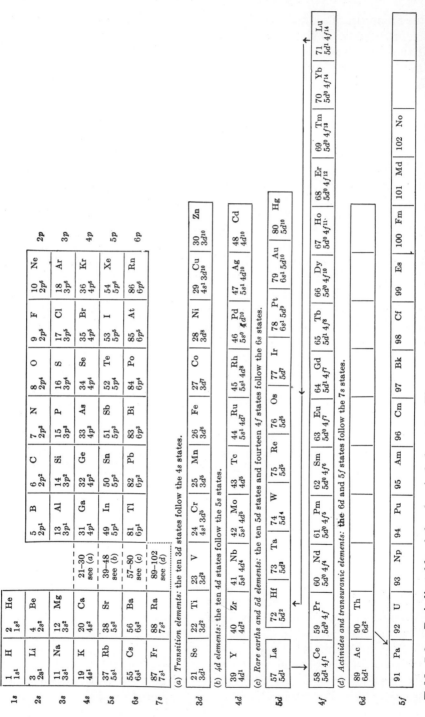

Table 7-3. Periodic table of the chemical elements. The ground-state configuration for the outermost electron shell is given, except when an inner shell is incomplete, in which case both shell configurations are given. For example, the element $_{42}$Mo has the complete electron configuration of $1s^2\, 2s^2\, 2p^6\, 3s^2\, 3p^6\, 3d^{10}\, 4s^2\, 4p^6\, 5s^1\, 4d^5$.

periodicity of 8: the total number of electrons completing an s subshell (two) and a p subshell (six) is eight.

The basis of the chemical properties of elements is the electron configurations of the atoms. Atoms with similar electron configurations show remarkably similar chemical behavior; the periodicity of chemical properties reflects the periodicity of the electron configurations. Let us consider some of these properties.

THE RARE GASES   The inert, or noble, rare gases are $_2$He, $_{10}$Ne, $_{18}$Ar, $_{36}$Kr, $_{54}$Xe, and $_{86}$Rn. We see from Table 7-3 that all these elements, except helium, have configurations in which the outermost electrons complete a p subshell. All rare gases have a ground state of $^1S_0$. The total angular momentum of the atom, from orbital motion and from electron spin, is zero; therefore, the total magnetic moment of the atom is zero. The atoms are chemically inert, or almost so, because there is no excess of electrons beyond a closed subshell and no deficiency of electrons in a subshell. Electrons within closed subshells are very strongly bound; thus, the ionization energies of elements in this group are particularly high. The atoms ordinarily fail to form chemical compounds, or nonmonatomic molecules. Furthermore, the rare gases have very low electrical conductivities and liquefaction (boiling) points.

THE ALKALI METALS   The alkali metals, in the first column of the periodic table, are $_3$Li, $_{11}$Na, $_{19}$K, $_{37}$Rb, $_{55}$Cs, and $_{87}$Fr. In every atom of an alkali metal there is a single electron outside a closed rare-gas subshell; in the ground state this electron is in an s subshell. The chemical activity of the elements may be attributed to this single electron, whose binding energy is relatively low, and which can be removed easily from the neutral atom to form a singly charged, positive ion. Alkali metals, then, have a valence of $+1$. Clearly, they may be regarded as hydrogen-like, their spectra resembling the spectrum of hydrogen.

THE ALKALINE EARTHS   The alkaline earths, in the second column of the periodic table, are $_4$Be, $_{12}$Mg, $_{20}$Ca, $_{38}$Sr, $_{56}$Ba, and $_{88}$Ra. All have two s electrons outside a closed p subshell when in the normal state. The two electrons have a relatively small binding energy and are responsible for the valence of $+2$. When the elements are singly ionized, they become hydrogen-like, their spectra being are similar to those of the alkali metals.

THE HALOGENS   The halogen group consists of the elements in the seventh column of the periodic table: $_9$F, $_{17}$Cl, $_{35}$Br, $_{53}$I, and $_{85}$At. The atoms lack one electron for completing a closed p subshell; therefore, they have a valence of -1. The halogen elements are highly active chemically and form stable compounds when combined with elements of the alkali-metal group; an example is the compound NaCl. When two respective atoms of these groups are in close proximity, the halogen atom, lacking one electron of a closed subshell, wants an additional electron to complete its p subshell, and the alkali-metal atom, having one electron outside a closed subshell, is ready to relinquish its last valence electron. When halogen and alkali-metal elements unite to form compounds, each atom increases the stability of its electron configuration. Formation of the molecule by such combination of ions is called ionic binding (Section 12-1).

THE TRANSITION GROUP   The so-called transition group, in which the $3d$ subshell progressively is filled, contains $_{21}$Sc, $_{22}$Ti, $_{23}$V, $_{24}$Cr, $_{25}$Mn, $_{26}$Fe, $_{27}$Co, $_{28}$Ni, $_{29}$Cu, and $_{30}$Zn. The electrons in the incomplete $3d$ subshell are responsible for some important properties of these elements. Many of these substances are either paramagnetic (weakly magnetic) or ferromagnetic (strongly magnetic) as elements or in compounds. Their magnetism has its origin in the incomplete $3d$ subshell, whose total magnetic moment is *not* zero. On the other hand, their chemical activity is primarily a result of the outer, the $4s$, electrons.

THE RARE EARTHS   The atoms of the fourteen rare earths $_{58}$Ce to $_{71}$Lu, have incomplete $4f$ subshells. The $4f$ electrons are well shielded from the $6s$ valence electrons. Thus, the chemical properties of the rare earths result primarily from the $6s$ electrons, and for this reason the elements are nearly chemically indistinguishable.

7-9 Characteristic x-ray spectra   When atoms are bombarded by electrons having only a few electron volts of kinetic energy, the resulting excitation or ionization involves a change in the state of one or more of the weakly bound, outer electrons. The optical emission spectrum is induced by such collisions, while the more tightly bound electrons in the inner closed shells remain in their initial states. An inner electron, however, also can be excited or removed, provided sufficiently great energy is added to the atom. In this section we shall discuss the spectrum produced when an inner electron is displaced: the *characteristic x-ray spectrum*.

Consider the schematic diagram Figure 7-28, which indicates the electron configuration and energy levels of copper, $_{29}$Cu, in the ground state. Fine structure splittings are ignored. The K, L, and M shells are completely filled with their respective quotas of electrons (2, 8, and 18), specified by the exclusion principle. There is a single electron, the valence electron, in the N shell. Near the top of the diagram are the unfilled shells, or "optical" levels; transitions of the outer electron to these states give rise to the optical spectrum. The difference in energy between any of the unfilled levels and the onset of the continuum, $E = 0$, is very small compared with that between the K shell and $E = 0$.

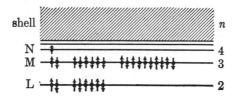

Figure 7-28. Electron configuration and energy levels of $_{29}$Cu in the ground state.

Suppose that a very energetic electron strikes the atom, thereby removing one of the two electrons in the K shell to an available higher energy level. The electron cannot be accepted in the filled L and M shells; it must, then, either go to one of the unfilled energy states or go out of the atom completely, thereby ionizing the atom. In any event the removal of the electron from the K shell has increased the energy of the atom drastically (by well over a thousand electron volts), and a vacancy exists in the K shell. The "hole" thus created may be filled by a transition of one of the eight electrons from the L shell to the K shell, where it will then be more tightly bound. This transition, which reduces the energy of the atom by more than a thousand electron volts, gives rise to the emission of the so-called K_α x-ray line. Because the difference in energy is typically of the order of thousands of electron volts, the photon created in such a transition is an x-ray photon with a wavelength between 0.1 and 10 angstroms.

Still other transitions can occur. The vacancy in the K shell can be filled through a somewhat less probable transition, in which an electron in the M shell jumps inward to the K shell; the corresponding emitted photon is labeled K_β. The transitions from successively higher energy states, all *terminating* at the K shell, are identified in the x-ray notation by K_α, K_β, K_γ, K_δ, . . . , as shown in Figure 7-29. This group of K x-ray lines comprises the K *series*.

Other series of x-ray lines having smaller energies, or longer wavelengths, also occur. When an L electron jumps to the K shell to fill the vacancy created by the removal of a K electron, a vacancy is created in the L shell. This hole can be filled by electron transitions from still higher states, giving rise to the L series, L_α, L_β, L_γ, L_δ, . . . , the symbols again

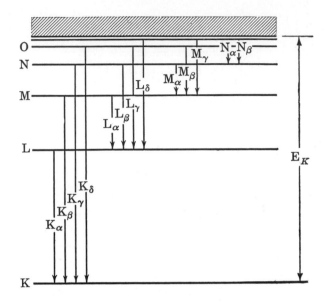

Figure 7-29. Inner-electron transitions giving rise to characteristic x-ray lines.

indicating transitions terminating in the L shell and originating in the respective higher energy states.

The minimum energy necessary to excite a K electron is close to the ionization energy *for the K shell*. The ionization energy for the K shell, E_K, is the energy required to remove a K electron completely out of the atom, such that the freed electron and the atom remain at rest; the atom is then ionized. The energy E_K is only *slightly* greater than the energy required to bring a K electron to *any* of the unoccupied optical levels.

The energy required to produce x-ray ionization from the L shell is called E_L. Because E_K is ordinarily much greater than E_L, the x-ray lines in the K series have appreciably shorter wavelengths than those in the L series (for Z greater than 30, lines in the K series have wavelengths of less than 1 angstrom, and lines in the L series have wavelengths of less than 10 angstroms). Ordinarily the lines originating in still higher transitions, in the M, N, . . . , series, are still weaker and of longer wavelength.

The x-ray ionization energies E_K, E_L, . . . , are related in a simple way to the frequencies of the x-ray emission lines. Consider the K_α line. If an energy E_K removes a K electron, the atom then has an energy increased by the amount E_K; similarly, if an electron is removed from the L shell, the atom's energy is increased by E_L. These two conditions correspond respectively to the situations before and after the emission of the K_α line. The energy of an emitted K_α photon, $h\nu$, is simply $E_K - E_L$. Therefore,

$$K \text{ series} \begin{cases} h\nu_{K\alpha} = E_K - E_L \\ h\nu_{K\beta} = E_K - E_M \\ h\nu_{K\gamma} = E_K - E_N \\ \text{etc.} \end{cases} \qquad [7\text{-}23]$$

$$L \text{ series} \begin{cases} h\nu_{L\alpha} = E_L - E_M \\ h\nu_{L\beta} = E_L - E_N \\ h\nu_{L\gamma} = E_L - E_O \\ \text{etc.} \end{cases} \qquad [7\text{-}24]$$

We can now interpret the characteristic x-ray lines that appear when the target in an x-ray tube is struck by electrons having energies of the order of thousands of electron volts. Figure 7-30 shows the measured intensity of

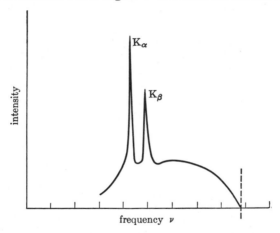

Figure 7-30. X-ray spectrum of molybdenum.

emitted x-radiation from a molybdenum target. There is a smoothly varying, continuous x-ray spectrum arising from bremsstrahlung collisions of electrons with the target; the continuous spectrum has a well-defined maximum frequency, determined solely by the accelerating potential of the x-ray tube (see Section 4-3). Superimposed on the x-ray continuum are sharp peaks in the intensity, characteristic of the x-ray spectrum of molybdenum. Those peaks are identified as the K_α and K_β lines; the lines of the L series, having much longer wavelengths and lower intensity, do not appear.

The breaking down of an x-ray spectrum into its component wavelengths is typically made with an x-ray crystal spectrometer. A single crystal having a known crystalline structure can be used to separate the various wavelengths, and the wavelength can be computed from the Bragg law (see Section 5-2). The intensity of the x-radiation can be measured with a chamber which is sensitive to the ionization effects produced by x-rays passing through a gas (Section 8-2).

The frequency or wavelength of the K_α line can be calculated approximately on the basis of a rather simple theoretical analysis involving only the Bohr atomic theory. The wavelength λ of lines emitted by one-electron, or hydrogenic, atoms, is given by the Rydberg formula,

[6-15]
$$\frac{1}{\lambda} = RZ^2 \left(\frac{1}{n_l^2} - \frac{1}{n_u^2} \right)$$
[7-25]

where R is the Rydberg constant, $(k^2 e^4 m/4\pi\hbar^3 c)$, n_u and n_l are the principal quantum numbers of the upper and lower states of the transition, respectively, and Z is the atomic number of the one-electron atom. When a K electron, $n_l = 1$, has been removed from the atom of a heavy element, an electron in the L shell, $n_l = 2$, will "see" the nuclear electric charge Ze shielded by the charge $-e$ of the one remaining K electron. Electrons in the M, N, and higher states do not penetrate appreciably the region between the K and L shells. Therefore, an L electron will approximate closely the single electron in a hydrogenic atom, moving in the electric field of the nucleus plus the K electron, which has an *effective* atomic number, $Z - 1$. Equation 7-25 then yields, for the frequency $\nu_{K\alpha}$ of the K_α line emitted when an L electron jumps to the hole in the K shell,

$$\nu_{K\alpha} = \frac{c}{\lambda} = cR(Z - 1)^2 \left(\frac{1}{1^2} - \frac{1}{2^2} \right)$$

$$\boxed{\nu_{K\alpha} = (3cR/4)(Z - 1)^2}$$
[7-26]

A plot of $\nu_{K\alpha}^{1/2}$ versus the atomic number Z of the emitting x-ray elements should, therefore, yield a straight line. The first comprehensive study of the characteristic x-ray frequencies was made by H. G. J. Moseley in 1913. Moseley found that Equation 7-26 represented the data on the K lines very well. In fact, it was his measurements that first established clearly the values of the atomic numbers of the elements. If the chemical elements in the periodic table are listed in the order of their atomic *weights*, the resulting list is (with a few notable exceptions) identical with a listing by atomic number. One such exception is found in the ordering of the elements cobalt and nickel. The work of Moseley established that, although $_{27}$Co has a greater atomic weight than $_{28}$Ni (58.93 as against 58.71), its atomic number is smaller.

Our discussion of atomic structure has heretofore been restricted to free atoms of a gas and not to atoms strongly interacting with one another, as in molecules, liquids, or solids. Why is it proper in the theory of x-ray emission to consider the atoms essentially free when actually x-ray target materials are in the form of solids? The answer is, of course, that x-ray transitions involve the innermost, tightly bound electrons, not the outer electrons, and that the latter have their configurations and energies changed when atoms are brought close together in a solid, while the inner, tightly bound electrons are hardly influenced by the state of the material, whether solid, liquid, or gas.

7-10 Summary   For a particle subject to an inverse-square force of attraction the classical constants of the motion (having a continuum of possible values) are quantized in the quantum theory of the atom.

The possible values of the principal quantum numbers are

$$n = 1, 2, 3, 4, \ldots$$
$$K, L, M, N, \ldots$$

For a given n:

$$l = 0, 1, 2, 3, 4, \ldots n - 1 \qquad (n \text{ possible values})$$
$$s, p, d, f, g, \ldots$$

For a given l:

$$m_l = l, l - 1, \ldots, -(l - 1), -l \qquad (2l + 1 \text{ possible values})$$

For a given m_l:

$$m_s = +\tfrac{1}{2}, -\tfrac{1}{2} \qquad (2 \text{ possible values})$$

When the valence electron of a hydrogen-like atom is in a state for which l is small, the energy of the atom is lowered with respect to the corresponding hydrogen energy level. The selection rule giving the allowed transitions is $\Delta l = \pm 1$.

The ratio of the magnetic moment to the angular momentum, called the magnetogyric ratio, is:

$$\mu_l/L = (e/2m) \qquad \text{for orbital motion}$$
$$\mu_s/L_s = 2(e/2m) \qquad \text{for electron spin}$$

The change in the magnetic energy of a state for a magnetic moment in a magnetic field B is:

$$\Delta E_m = m_l(e\hbar/2m)B = m_l\beta B \qquad \text{for an orbital magnetic moment}$$
$$\Delta E_s = m_s(2e\hbar/2m)B = m_s(2\beta)B \qquad \text{for a spin magnetic moment}$$
$$\beta \text{ (the Bohr magneton)} = (e\hbar/2m) = 0.9273 \times 10^{-23} \text{ J/(Wb/m}^2)$$

The normal Zeeman effect arises from the interaction of the *orbital* magnetic moment with a magnetic field. The magnetic field causes each line in the spectrum to split into three equally spaced lines. The selection rule for allowed transitions is $\Delta m_l = 0, \pm 1$.

Table 7-4

Constant of the Motion	Quantum Number	Allowed Values
Energy	n (principal quantum number)	$E_n = -Z^2 E_I / n^2$ (for a single electron, ignoring spin-orbit interaction)
Magnitude of the orbital angular momentum	l (orbital angular-momentum quantum number)	$L = \sqrt{l(l+1)}\hbar$
Component of the orbital angular momentum along Z	m_l (orbital magnetic quantum number)	$L_z = m_l \hbar$ Space quantization: $\cos\theta = m_l / \sqrt{l(l+1)}$
Magnitude of the spin angular momentum	s (electron-spin quantum number)	$L_s = \sqrt{s(s+1)}\hbar = \tfrac{1}{2}\sqrt{3}\hbar$
Component of the spin angular momentum along Z	m_s (spin magnetic quantum number) $s = \tfrac{1}{2}$	$L_{s,z} = m_s \hbar$ Space quantization: $\cos\theta = m_s / \sqrt{s(s+1)}$

The Stern-Gerlach experiment, in which atoms with a net electron spin pass through an inhomogeneous magnetic field, shows directly the phenomenon of space quantization.

The fine structure of spectral lines has its origin in the interaction between L and L_s, spin-orbit interaction.

The spectroscopic nomenclature for atoms having one or more electrons is:

total orbital angular-momentum $L = 0, 1, 2, 3, 4, \ldots$
    quantum number $S, P, D, F, G, \ldots$

total spin angular-momentum $S = \tfrac{1}{2}$ (for one electron)
    quantum number $S = 0$ or 1 (for two electrons)
                                 $J = j = l + s$ or $l - s$

The Pauli exclusion principle, the basis for understanding the periodic table of chemical elements, specifies that no two electrons in the same atom can have the same set of the four quantum numbers n, l, m_l, m_s.

BIBLIOGRAPHY

HEITLER, W., *Wave Mechanics*. Oxford: Clarendon Press, 1946. The rules for angular-momentum quantization are developed in elementary fashion in Chapter 4.

LEIGHTON, R. B., *Principles of Modern Physics*. New York: McGraw-Hill Book Company, Inc., 1959. The wave functions of the hydrogen atom are derived in detail in Chapter 5; Chapters 7 and 8 treat of the periodic table and many-electron atomic structure.

PROBLEMS

7-1 Show that the angular momentum of an extended, symmetrical object spinning about its axis of symmetry is independent, not only of the choice of axis for computing angular momentum, but also of the inertial frame.

7-2 Which transition in the potassium atom has the shorter wavelength, $6S \rightarrow 4P$ or $6D \rightarrow 4P$? Explain why.

7-3 Calculate the approximate energy of photons emitted in radiation from triply ionized titanium, $_{22}\text{Ti}^{3+}$, for the transition $5D \rightarrow 4P$.

7-4 List all possible downward transitions in sodium atoms initially in the $5S$ state (see Figure 7-9).

7-5 In general, an atom initially in an excited state remains in that state for such a short time (about 10^{-8} sec on the average) that the probability of its absorbing a photon and jumping to a still higher state is very small. Explain on this basis why only the P series (*principal* series) is ordinarily observed in the *absorption* spectrum of potassium.

7-6 (a) Prove that an electron moving in a classical circular orbit of radius r has a magnetic moment whose magnitude is $\mu = (ke^4r/4m)^{1/2}$ (b) Show that the Bohr magneton $eh/2m$ is the orbital magnetic moment of the hydrogen atom in the first Bohr orbit.

7-7 Show that the difference in frequency between adjacent magnetic sublevels in a normal Zeeman splitting is $\beta B/h$.

7-8 A particle with a mass of 10^{-6} kg moves in circle of radius 10^{-2} m at a speed of 10^{-1} m/sec. (a) What is the orbital angular-momentum quantum number l of this particle? (b) What is the maximum angular difference between the allowed orientations of the orbital angular-momentum vector?

7-9 The magnetic moment of a proton is about $10^{-3}\beta$, where β is the Bohr magneton. The electron and proton of the hydrogen atom interact, giving rise to two relative magnetic-moment orientations: electron and proton magnetic moments aligned and antialigned. For this reason the $n = 1$ state of hydrogen consists of two distinct, hyperfine energy levels separated in energy by an amount corresponding to a photon with a wavelength of 21 cm. (a) Given that the magnetic field at a distance r from a magnetic moment μ is $\sim (10^{-7}\text{Wb/A} - \text{m})\mu/r^3$, compute the approximate energy difference for the two sublevels of hydrogen. (b) Show that the corresponding photon wavelength is of the order of 21 cm.

There is appreciable 21 cm radiation from hydrogen atoms making transitions between the two hyperfine levels, from intergalactic hydrogen clouds and stellar sources. Indeed, the observation of the radiation is a principal basis of radio astronomy. One might expect inhabitants of other planets attempting communication with the Earth to broadcast signals at 21 cm wavelength.

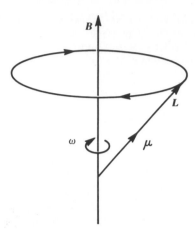

Figure 7-31. Classical gyromagnet processing about a magnetic field.

7-10 * A classical gyromagnet, an object with angular momentum L and magnetic moment μ, is immersed in an external field B, as shown in Figure 7-31. One may imagine the gyromagnet to consist of rotating charge particles with a magnetogyric ratio of $\mu/L = e/2m$. The gyromagnet is subject to a magnetic torque at right angles to its angular momentum in the same fashion that a spinning top is subject to a gravitational torque at right angles to its angular momentum. (a) Show that the gyromagnet precesses about the direction of B at the angular frequency $\omega = (\mu/L)B$, the so-called Larmor precession frequency. (b) Show that the precession frequency of a classical gyromagnet about an external field is the same as the difference in angular frequency between magnetic sublevels in the normal Zeeman effect.

7-11 Assume that an electron moves in a classical circular orbit with an angular velocity ω_0, under the influence of a force of magnitude $m\omega_0^2 r$ directed toward the center of the circle. A magnetic field B is then applied at right angles to the plane of the orbit. (a) Show that, if the radius r remains the same, the angular frequency of the particle's motion becomes $\omega = [\omega_0^2 + (eB/2m)^2]^{1/2} \pm eB/2m$. (b) In all cases of interest, $eB/2m \ll \omega_0$; using this approximation, show that $\nu = \nu_0 \pm eB/4\pi m$ (comparing this result with Equations 7-15, we see that the frequencies for the *normal* Zeeman effect can be accounted for by a classical calculation). The change in frequency, $eB/4\pi m$, is known as the *Larmor frequency*.

7-12 How large must the orbital angular-momentum quantum number l be for the difference between the magnitude of the orbital angular momentum and its maximum component to be no more than 1 part in 10^6?

7-13 The separation between adjacent normal Zeeman components of radiation emitted at 4,500 Å is 0.0849 Å when the atoms are in a magnetic field of 0.900 Wb/m². What is the value of e/m computed from these data? (The fact that the value of e/m computed from Zeeman-effect experiments agreed with the value found independently from cathode-ray experiments indicated early in the development of atomic theory that the motion of electrons rather than of more massive particles in atoms was responsible for the radiation from atoms.)

7-14   Draw an energy-level diagram and compute the energy difference (eV) between the adjacent normal Zeeman components for a transition between the $4D$ and $3P$ states. The magnetic field is 1.0 Wb/m².

7-15   Suppose a certain spectrometer can resolve spectral lines in the visible region (say, 6,000 Å) that are separated by 0.1 Å. Approximately what minimum magnetic field B is necessary to permit the resolution of the normal Zeeman effect?

7-16   Show that the maximum component of the spin magnetic moment of the electron along the direction of the magnetic field is equal to the Bohr magneton.

7-17 *   Assume the electron to be a spherical shell of radius 2.8×10^{-15} m, whose mass and charge are uniformly distributed over its surface. (a) What must the angular velocity of the spinning electron be, if the magnitude of its spin angular momentum is $\frac{1}{2}\sqrt{3}\hbar$? (b) Compute the spin magnetic moment of the electron for this model (fictitious), and compare it with the correct value.

7-18   A beam of free electrons passes perpendicularly into a uniform magnetic field B, whose magnitude is 3.0×10^{-1} Wb/m². Calculate the difference in energy between electrons aligned and antialigned with the magnetic field.

7-19   The spin angular momentum and spin magnetic moment of the *nucleus* of the atom can give rise to a hyperfine splitting of the emitted spectral lines. Taking a typical nuclear-spin magnetic moment to be approximately $10^{-3}\beta$, where β is the Bohr magneton of the electron, (a) show that the difference between energy levels, due to nuclear spin, is of the order to 10^{-5} eV, and (b) show that the corresponding difference in wavelength of visible light is $\Delta\lambda \approx 10^{-2}$ Å.

7-20 *   In a spin-orbit interaction for an electron l is 20 and s is, of course, $\frac{1}{2}$. (a) Show that the spin and orbital angular-momentum vectors are nearly at right angles to one another for both of the two possible j values. (b) Show that the total magnetic-moment vector lies essentially along the line of the total angular-momentum vector.

7-21   (a) Show that the difference in energy between the two allowed electron-spin orientations in a magnetic field B is given by $2\beta B$. (b) What is the frequency of radiation that can induce transitions (spin flips) between these two states when $B = 0.30$ Wb/m²? This effect, in which photons flip electron spins, and for which $h\nu = 2\beta B$, is called *electron-spin resonance*.

7-22   Under certain circumstances transitions (magnetic-dipole) can be induced between the fine-structure components arising from spin-orbit interaction by the absorption of radiation. Because the energy differences are very small, the corresponding frequencies are relatively low, and the *direct* study of fine structure and hyperfine structure from transitions between the multiplet components lies in the area of radiofrequency or microwave spectroscopy. What is the frequency of radiation that can induce transitions between the $3^2P_{1/2}$ and $3^2P_{3/2}$ states of sodium? The wavelengths of the sodium D lines are 5,889.95 Å and 5,895.92 Å.

7-23 * An "antiatom" is one in which *all* of the elementary particles are replaced with their corresponding antiparticles. Show that the lower energy state of a spin-orbit doublet is still $j = l - s$. (An "antiuniverse" cannot be distinguished from the universe simply by examining the electromagnetic radiation from it and inferring the energy levels of atoms.)

7-24 Find the angle between the total and the orbital angular-momentum vectors for the $^2D_{5/2}$ state.

7-25 Show with a vector diagram that the vector sum of the orbital magnetic moment $\boldsymbol{\mu}_l$ and spin magnetic moment $\boldsymbol{\mu}_s$ does *not* lie along the same line as the sum of the orbital angular momentum L and spin angular momentum L_s.

7-26 * Using the law of cosines, show that

$$\cos(l, j) = \frac{j(j+1) + l(l+1) - s(s+1)}{2\sqrt{j(j+1)}\,\sqrt{l(l+1)}}$$

where $\cos(l, j)$ is the cosine of the angle between the orbital and total angular momenta. See Figure 7-20.

7-27 * (a) Knowing that the orbital magnetic moment is $\mu_l = (e\hbar/2m)[l(l+1)]^{12/}$ and the spin magnetic moment is $\mu_s = 2(e\hbar/2m)[s(s+1)]^{1/2}$, show that the *component* of the total magnetic moment $\boldsymbol{\mu}_j$ along the direction of the total angular momentum P_j is given by

$$\mu_j = \sqrt{j(j+1)}\,(eh/2m)\left[1 + \frac{j(j+1) + s(s+1) - l(l+1)}{2j(j+1)}\right]$$

See Problem 7-26. (b) The quantity in the square brackets is called the Lande g factor. Show that the Lande g factor gives the magnetic moment, in units of the Bohr magneton, divided by the total angular momentum, in units of h.

7-28 In a certain Stern-Gerlach experiment a beam of potassium atoms emerges from an oven at a temperature of 150 °C. The atoms pass through an inhomogeneous magnetic field, whose gradient is 1.2×10^4 $(Wb/m^2)/cm$ for a distance of 2.0 cm, and continue through field-free space for 10.0 cm before being deposited on a collector plate. What is the maximum distance between the two lines at the detector?

7-29 Find the total angular momentum and total magnetic moment of (a) $_5B$ and (b) $_{37}Rb$ in their ground states.

7-30 The ground-state electronic configuration of a divalent atom is $4P$. What is the element?

7-31 An atom of $_3Li$ atom is in its ground state. (a) What are the four quantum numbers for each of the three electrons? (b) What are the quantum numbers of the third electron for the two lowest excited states of this atom?

7-32 Show that the total angular momentum and total magnetic moment of an element with closed subshells is zero.

7-33 Show, in the fashion of Figure 7-27, the occupied states of $_{17}Cl$ in the ground state. What are the corresponding electron configurations?

7-34   Which of the following elements can show a normal Zeeman effect; $_7$N, $_{14}$Si, $_{17}$Cl, $_4$Be?

7-35   Show that Equation 7-21, which gives the force on an electron spin in the Stern-Gerlach experiment, is consistent with Figure 7-22 insofar as the magnetic force is in the direction of the region of strong magnetic field.

7-36   What is the approximate energy (keV) of the K_α x-ray photon emitted from $_{102}$No?

7-37   Calculate the wavelength of the K_α line in $_{79}$Au.

7-38 *   Is the slope of the line obtained by plotting the square root of the frequencies of K_α lines (as ordinates) against the corresponding atomic numbers greater than or less than the slope of the line for the K_β frequencies?

7-39   (a) With what energy would a free $_{29}$Cu atom recoil upon emitting a K_α photon? (b) What is the ratio of the kinetic energy of the recoiling atom to the energy of the emitted K_α photon?

7-40   X-ray fluorescence is that process in which the absorption of a photon of relatively high energy in a material results in the emission of a number of x-ray photons of lower energy. Show that the complete x-ray fluorescence of a material can be produced only if the material is irradiated with characteristic x-rays produced by a target of *higher* atomic number.

7-41   The critical accelerating potential for excitation of all lines in the x-ray spectrum never exceeds by a large amount the K_α photon's energy divided by the electron's charge. Show that this is a good rule of thumb.

E I G H T

INSTRUMENTS AND ACCELERATING
MACHINES USED IN NUCLEAR PHYSICS

Advances in atomic and nuclear physics have depended on the development of devices for studying submicroscopic phenomena. Our understanding of the structure of the atom, derived in large measure from the study of spectral lines, has depended as much on spectroscopic observations as on the development of the quantum theory. Nuclear physics had its origin in the discovery, made by H. Becquerel in 1896, that uranium salts can produce a darkening of photographic plates, but the development of a detailed, if still somewhat incomplete, knowledge of the nucleus—an object so minute that it is observed only indirectly—has come from a variety of experiments with instruments of which some are remarkably simple and others extraordinarily complex, subtle, ingenious, and costly. In this chapter we shall set forth the physical principles on which a number of important devices in nuclear physics operate: detectors of nuclear radiation, devices for measuring the mass, velocity, and momentum of charged particles, and high-energy particle accelerators. Our discussion will be confined to the physical laws underlying the operation of these devices; technical matters, however important they may be in the actual construction of the instruments, are beyond the scope of this book.

The particles with whose detection, control, and acceleration we shall be concerned in this chapter are the proton, deuteron, alpha particle, electron, and photon. The proton is, of course, the nucleus of an ordinary hydrogen atom. The *deuteron* is the nucleus of the deuterium atom, or heavy hydrogen atom; it consists of a proton and a neutron, so its charge is equal to that of the proton, but its mass is approximately twice that of the proton. The alpha particle has already been described as one of the particles emitted, typically with energies of a few million electron volts, from radioactive materials; it is the nucleus of the helium atom, having a double positive charge and a mass roughly four times that of the proton. Beta rays and gamma rays are emitted from the nuclei of radioactive materials. Beta-particles are high-speed electrons or positrons with kinetic energies up to several million electron volts. Gamma rays are photons emitted from nuclei with energies measured in thousands or millions of electron volts. The properties of radioactive nuclei and the characteristics of their nuclear radiation are treated in some detail in Chapter 9.

We shall not discuss in this chapter the detection of the neutron, a constituent of atomic nuclei. The neutron has a zero electric charge and a mass nearly equal to that of the proton. Because it carries no charge and is incapable of producing ionization effects or of being deflected by electric or magnetic fields, it cannot be studied with the same directness as charged particles. For this reason we postpone discussion of neutron detection until Section 10-6, when the nuclear reactions in which it participates have been explored.

The term *nuclear radiation* refers to the radiation of any type of particle, including the photons of electromagnetic radiation, emitted from the nuclei of atoms. Experiments in nuclear physics must deal with the measurement of such properties as the mass, energy, and momentum of particles of nuclear radiation. The particles generally have energies as great as several million electron volts, and since such energies are considerably greater than those encountered in atomic physics, which are never more than a few hundred thousand electron volts, the detection and measurement of nuclear radiation require special experimental techniques.

8-1 Ionization and absorption of nuclear radiation It is worth recognizing at the outset that the detection and control of nuclear particles pose difficult experimental problems by virtue of the very minuteness of the particles. (An electron's mass is a mere 9.11×10^{-31} kg and its electric charge only 1.60×10^{-19} coulomb). None of the particles are "seen" directly and, moreover, their influence on instruments is usually an extremely subtle one. The chief problem of experimental atomic and nuclear physics is to infer the properties and structure of submicroscopic particles and to control the particles, all with macroscopic apparatus.

If a particle is identified and known to be at a certain place at a certain time, we can say that we have detected it. The problem of detecting a particle is, then, one of being able to establish that it is present or absent in some detecting device. What is required is that the detecting instrument be of such sensitivity that a minute change produced by the particle's presence will influence a large-scale, easily observed characteristic of the instrument. We have an example of such a delicate measurement in the Millikan oil-drop experiment, in which the electron's charge was first directly determined. A tiny, uncharged oil drop, observed through a microscope, falls slowly under the influence of gravity and the retarding effects of the air. If it acquires any excess electrons and so becomes charged, an electric field, applied so as to produce an upward electric force on the charge, can be made to balance out the downward gravitational force, and the entire drop can be brought to rest. By equating the two forces the electric charge on the drop can be computed.

Detectors of such particles as electrons, protons, and alpha particles depend basically on the fact that these particles have electric charge. The photon has, of course, no electric charge, but it does interact strongly with charged particles, producing ionization, so that an instrument sensitive to the effects of electric charges can detect the presence of a photon if it responds to electrons produced by photons in the photoelectric effect, the Compton effect, or pair production (see Section 4-7).

Consider the ionization effects produced by a moving charged particle whose mass is large compared with that of the electron. The probability that such a particle will have a close encounter or collision with a nucleus in the material is very slight (see Section 6-1), and therefore its energy is influenced almost entirely by interactions with the electrons of the atom. For the most part a charged particle collides with and transfers some energy to electrons it encounters. Thus, an electron bound to an atom can be excited to a higher energy state or, if the energy gain is sufficiently great, it can even be removed from its parent atom, leaving behind an ion. Inasmuch as the massive particle does work on the electrons in exciting or removing them, its energy decreases, and it slows down. Its direction of travel is, however, not appreciably changed by the collisions, because its mass greatly exceeds that of an electron. As the particle continues through the material in a nearly straight line, it leaves a track of ionized atoms and freed electrons along its path. It finally comes to rest when all of its kinetic energy has been transferred to atoms of the material. The number of *ion pairs* (an ion plus the detached electron comprise one ion pair) produced by a massive particle increases greatly near the end of the path. This is because the ionizing particle is then moving slowly, and the time it spends in the vicinity of any one atom and its attached electrons increases correspondingly.

When a charged particle is stopped through the process just described, we can say that it has been absorbed in the material. A monoenergetic beam of massive charged particles has a well-defined *range* of passage through a given absorbing material. This serves as a simple means of determining the initial energy of the particles composing the beam. As might be expected from the difference in density of the absorbing materials, the range of a massive particle of given energy is considerably greater in a gas than in a solid, since the particle encounters less atoms per unit length in a gas than in a solid. For example, an alpha particle with an energy of several MeV is stopped by a few centimeters of air but by a fraction of a millimeter of an absorber of relatively high density, such as aluminum.

The ionization produced by a charged particle is related closely to the average energy required to produce an ion pair. For absorption in gases the mean loss of kinetic energy from the charged particle in producing an ion pair ranges from 25 to 40 electron volts, depending on the characteristics of the gas. This does not mean that the ionization potential for some one gas is, say, 25 eV; it means, rather, that an ionizing particle loses, on the average, that much energy in producing a single ion pair, whether in excitation or in ionization collisions. Because the number of ion pairs produced in a material is directly proportional, therefore, to the kinetic energy lost by the ionizing particle, a measurement of the total ionization leads, not only to a detection of the charged particle, but also to a measurement of its initial kinetic energy.

The absorption of electrons in an absorbing material is more complicated than the absorption of massive charged particles, because the ionizing particle's mass now equals that of the particle to which its energy is imparted in collisions, the electron of the atom. An energetic electron is deflected appreciably in collisions, and its path through an absorbing material is not a straight line, and the various electrons of a monoenergetic beam may trace out quite different paths. Nevertheless, one can attribute a range to a collection of monoenergetic electrons, too; it is the thickness of the absorber required to stop essentially all electrons. The range of electrons is roughly inversely proportional to the density of the absorber (the number of atomic electrons per unit volume in any absorber is very closely proportional to the density of the absorber). For a given kinetic energy and a given absorber the range of an electron is appreciably greater than that of a heavy charged particle.

The processes by which photons are absorbed—the photoelectric effect, the Compton effect, and pair production—were discussed in Section 4-7. Recall that one cannot assign a precise range to a photon of a particular energy. The absorption of photons is characterized by the absorption coefficient μ, whose reciprocal gives the thickness of absorber for which the number of photons in a beam is reduced to $1/e$ of the initial number. The intensity of a photon beam is reduced by exponential attenuation according to $I = I_0 e^{-\mu x}$. Therefore, the intensity of the beam is truly zero, *all* photons having undergone collisions, only after the beam has passed through an *infinite* absorber thickness.

Note the fundamental difference between the absorption of a photon beam and the absorption of charged particles. A photon loses *all* of its energy in a *single* collision,† it *always* moves at speed c, and its absorption *cannot* be characterized by a range. A charged particle, on the other hand, loses its energy little by little in many collisions, its speed gradually decreases, and its absorption is characterized by a definite range. Photon absorption is accompanied by ionization effects, which can be detected electrically. The electrons (and positrons, in pair production), to which energy is imparted in photon collisions, can themselves produce ions in the absorbing material. Photons are far more penetrating than electrons or heavy charged particles of the same energy.

Table 8-1 gives the ranges for the absorption of alpha particles, protons, and electrons in air and in aluminum for certain kinetic energies. For comparison the table also gives that thickness of aluminum absorber, $1/\mu$, required to reduce the intensity of a photon beam to $1/e$ of its initial intensity. It is seen that all types of nuclear radiation are more readily absorbed in a solid than in a gas, that gamma rays are more penetrating than beta rays, which are, in turn, more penetrating than protons or alpha rays, and that the penetration of charged particles increases with increasing energy.

Table 8-1

Ranges, in centimeters, of α-particles, protons, and electrons in air and in aluminum. The values listed for γ-ray absorption in aluminum are the reciprocals of the absorption coefficients, $(1/\mu)$.

ENERGY, MEV	RANGE, CM						RANGE, $1/\mu$: GAMMA RAY IN AL
	Alpha particle		Proton		Electron		
	Air	Al	Air	Al	Air	Al	
1	0.5	0.0003	2.3	0.0014	314	0.15	6.1
5	3.5	0.0025	34.	0.019	2,000	0.96	13.1
10	10.7	0.0064	117.	0.063	4,100	1.96	16.0

8-2 Detectors Every detector of nuclear radiation, whether energetic charged particles or photons, ultimately yields an electric signal, or voltage pulse, to be fed into a counting circuit, which then registers the arrival of

† In a Compton collision the incident photon is annihilated and the scattered photon is created.

the particle in the detecting device. The medium in which the incident particles produce effects that may be converted finally to electric signals can be of various forms. In this section we describe briefly the most commonly used detectors for experiments in nuclear physics: gas-filled, semiconductor, scintillation, and Cerenkov detectors.

GAS-FILLED DETECTORS   The simplest detector sensitive to the ionization effects of nuclear radiation through a gas is an electroscope. When an electroscope is charged, a gold leaf or some other light-weight conductor is displaced, by mutual electrical repulsion, from the fixed conductor to which it is attached, the displacement being a measure of the charge on the electroscope. Nuclear radiation passing through an initially charged electroscope ionizes the air, and the electroscope is discharged as ions collect on and neutralize it. Electroscopes are relatively insensitive, and they are not used as commonly as the gas-filled detectors, to which we now turn. The three general classes of gas-filled detectors are the *ionization chamber*, *proportional counter*, and *Geiger counter*.

Consider the device shown in Figure 8-1. The gas-filled chamber has

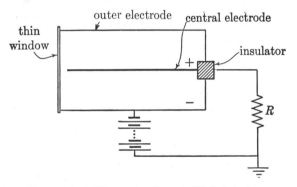

Figure 8-1 Elements of a gas-filled detector.

two electrodes, an outer cylinder and a thin wire along the cylinder axis. The wire is maintained at a high positive electric potential with respect to the cylinder. The wall of the chamber, whether of glass, metal, or mica, is sufficiently thin to permit the entry of charged particles or photons from the outside. Various gases may be used in the chamber, and the pressure may range from a fraction of an atmosphere to several atmospheres. The electric field between the two electrodes is highly inhomogeneous and is very strong near the central wire. All gas-filled detectors operate on the following principle: (a) nuclear radiation ionizes some of the gas molecules within the chamber, (b) the electric field pulls the ionized particles to the electrodes, producing a current in the circuit, and (c) the resulting current through a resistor is measured by electrical instruments.

A plot showing the number of ions collected as a function of the applied voltage in a typical gas-filled detector is shown in Figure 8-2. The number of ions collected at any particular applied voltage will depend on the volume of the detector, and the details in the curve may differ according to the gas used. Two curves for the lower voltages are shown, one for the ionization effects of alpha particles and one for the ionization effects of high-speed electrons, or beta particles. The various types of gas-filled detector can best be understood by considering separately each of the four regions A, B, C, and D, of Figure 8-2.

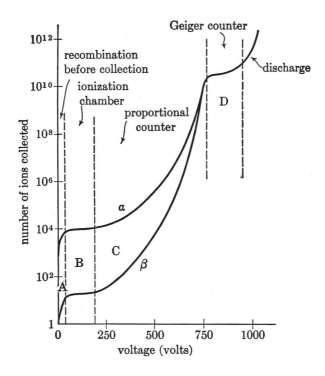

Figure 8-2 Number of ions collected as a function of applied voltage for a typical gas-filled detector of alpha particles (α) and beta particles (β).

In region A, where the applied voltage is relatively small, ions created by the passage of charged particles or photons within the detector are subject to a relatively weak electric field. Therefore, some of them recombine into neutral atoms or molecules before they reach an electrode. In region A the current due to the collection of the ions is so small that a gas-filled detector cannot operate efficiently.

A gas-filled detector operated in region B is called an *ionization chamber*. In this region, where the applied voltage has been increased, practically all ions formed by the radiation are collected on the electrodes before recombination can take place. Recall that the energy required to produce one ion pair in a gas is typically 25 to 40 eV.

Ordinarily the ionization produced by the nuclear radiation is so small that the formation of a single ion pair and its attraction to the electrodes cannot be detected as a single, abrupt change in the current through the circuit. Instead, the combined ionization effects of many nuclear particles produce a nearly constant current, which can be measured as a voltage drop across the high resistance R by amplification in electronic circuits. The current from the ionization chamber is a direct measure of the intensity of the ionizing radiation; for this reason ionization chambers are frequently used to measure the intensity of x-ray or gamma ray photon beams. Another characteristic of an ionization chamber is that it can distinguish between the ionization effects produced by alpha particles and beta particles; we see from Figure 8-2 that an alpha particle produces many more ion pairs than a beta particle of the same energy. An ionization chamber does not, however, measure the energy of charged particles.

The low-energy portion of region C is the basis of operation of the *proportional counter*. The applied voltage and, therefore, also the electric field are greater than in region B. In region C the multiplication of ions becomes evident. Thus, when an ion pair—usually an electron and positive ion—is produced by nuclear radiation through the gas, the electrons are strongly attracted to the wire in the center and the ions move toward the outer electrode. An electron can now gain enough kinetic energy, as it is accelerated toward the wire, to produce still more ions in its collisions with gas molecules. In fact, a single ion pair produced directly can, through the process of ion multiplication, increase the total number of ions by a factor of 10^5 to 10^6. This increase produces a markedly enhanced current or voltage pulse, and it is possible under such conditions to register incoming nuclear particles one by one, that is, to count pulses directly. The size of the pulse is directly proportional to the energy of the ionizing particle (that is how the counter gets its name). The pulses from alpha particles are considerably greater than those from beta particles, and it is possible to arrange the circuitry of a proportional counter so that only they are registered.

In region D the Geiger counter, sometimes called a G-M tube or Geiger-Müller counter, operates. The behavior of the gas-filled detector at relatively high voltages (about 1,000 volts) changes fundamentally. The applied voltage and the electric fields within the detector are now so high that *any* nuclear particle producing a single ion pair within the gas can initiate an avalanche of electrons by the multiplication of ions. The current pulses are now *independent* of the energy of the initiating particle. It is not possible to distinguish between various types of nuclear radiation with a Geiger counter, inasmuch as alpha, beta, and gamma rays produce similar electron avalanches (see Figure 8-2). Geiger counters are used to count x-rays and beta and gamma rays, but usually not alpha rays; beta-ray counters must have relatively thin windows to permit the easily stopped electrons to enter the tube. A typical Geiger counter is filled with an inert gas, such as argon, to a pressure of about 10 cm Hg; a small amount (0.1 percent) of halogen gas, such as bromine, is added to quench the discharge in the tube quickly after it has been registered. The duration of a pulse is about a millionth of a second.

We see from Figure 8-2 that when voltages greater than those in region D are applied to a gas-filled chamber, the gas is continuously conducting; spontaneous electrical discharge takes place between the electrodes without ionizing radiation's entering the chamber.

SEMICONDUCTOR DETECTORS   Among the most useful, precise, and efficient of contemporary particle detectors is the recently developed semiconductor, or solid-state, detector. In its simplest form it consists of a solid, semiconducting material, such as germanium (usually with a lithium impurity), sandwiched between two electrodes at which the output pulse appears. Whereas gas-filled detectors operate with ion pairs that consist each of a free electron and atomic ion, the semiconductor detector operates with "ion pairs" that consist each of an electron and a "hole."

The conduction properties of semiconducting materials will be treated in some detail in Section 12-10. Suffice it to say here that the electrons of a pure semiconducting or insulating material are ordinarily bound to their parent atoms and cannot wander through the solid as charge carriers. In such materials charge carriers are produced by thermal excitation, by appropriate impurity atoms, or, in detecting devices, by energetic particles passing through. If an incident charged particle or a photon gives sufficient energy to a bound electron, the electron is freed to move. At the same time, the removal of a bound electron from the crystalline lattice results in a so-called hole, a place where an electron is missing. The hole can be filled when a near-by electron shifts into it, in which case another hole appears where the shifted electron had originally been. The process may be repeated; it may be described as a hole moving through the material in a direction opposite from that of the motion of the electrons, much as if the hole were a positively charged particle, for which reason the electron-hole pair is called an "ion" pair. An electron-hole pair can be accelerated by an external electric field and so produce still more pairs, which finally register as measurably large pulses at the electrodes.

The pulse size for a semiconductor counter is linearly related to the particle's energy over a wide range, and counters can be made sensitive enough to count electrons with kinetic energies as small as 20 keV and heavy ions with kinetic energies as large as 200 MeV. The detectors' efficiency in registering particles traversing the sensitive region is nearly 100 percent and substantially greater than that of gas-filled detectors. The fast rise time of the pulses, of the order of 1 nanosecond (10^{-9} sec), permits the counters to be used at high counting rates.

SCINTILLATION DETECTORS The operation of the scintillation detector depends on the fact that certain materials, called *phosphors*, emit visible light when they are struck by particles or irradiated by ultraviolet light or x-rays. When a particle collides with a phosphor, it excites an electron into a higher energy state. The de-excitation of the phosphor and the return to the ground state is accompanied by the emission of photons lying in the visible region of the spectrum.

A familiar example of scintillation, or phosphorescence, is found in the cathode-ray oscilloscope or television picture tube, in which high-speed electrons strike a phosphor and cause the emission of visible radiation. One of the earliest means of detecting the presence of alpha particles was through their scintillation effects on the phosphor zinc sulphide. In the original Rutherford scattering experiments a zinc sulfide screen was viewed through a microscope as an alpha-particle detector (see Section 6-1). The tedium and relative insensitivity of the method, in which the scintillations are counted in direct visual observation of bright light flashes, are eliminated in modern scintillation detectors, which employ a remarkable electronic tube, the *photomultiplier*.

Consider the schematic diagram, Figure 8-3, of a scintillation detector with photomultiplier. The phosphor, a transparent material, may be sodium iodide with a trace of thallium (for gamma rays), an organic substance,

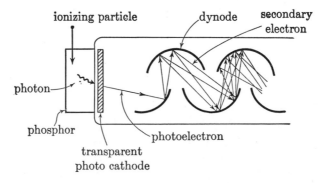

Figure 8-3 Schematic diagram of a scintillation detector with photomultiplier tube.

such as anthracene (for electrons), or zinc sulfide with a trace of silver (for massive charged particles, such as alpha particles). The phosphor produces light flashes after their atoms are excited by collisions with particles or photons. The phosphor is sealed in a light-tight envelope, and photons reach the photocathode of the photomultiplier tube, possibly after reflections within the phosphor. A photon striking the cathode undergoes a photoelectric collision, and one electron is dislodged from the cathode surface. This photoelectron is accelerated by a potential difference of about 100 volts to the first *dynode* of the photomultiplier tube. When it collides with the surface of the dynode, now with kinetic energy of at least 100 electron volts, secondary electron emission occurs, and two or more electrons are released from the surface by the kinetic energy they gain from the initial electron. The secondary electrons are then accelerated to the second dynode, through another 100-volt potential difference, and there multiplication of the electrons by secondary emission again occurs. A typical photomultiplier tube has ten dynodes, or ten stages of electron amplification. The original photoelectron can produce at the final dynode a readily measured pulse of current due to the arrival of as many as a million electrons.

An important feature of the scintillation detector is that the output voltage pulse from the photomultiplier tube is very nearly proportional to the energy of the particle or photon that initiates scintillation in the phosphor; then not only can particles be detected with a scintillation detector, but also their energies can be measured. Scintillation detectors have other advantages; they are capable of handling very high counting rates, with pulse durations as short as 1 nsec (10^{-9} sec), and their efficiency in counting gamma rays is nearly 100 percent.

A scintillation detector together with a pulse-height analyzer, an electronic device that sorts the output pulses from a photomultiplier according to their size, constitute a *scintillation spectrometer*, by which the energies of monochromatic gamma rays in particular may be measured straightforwardly with high precision. The voltage of the output pulse is directly proportional to the kinetic energy of the *electrons* produced by the three processes of the photoelectric effect, the Compton effect, and electron-positron pair production (Chapter 4), in which gamma rays interact with the scintillation material.

Consider the pulse-height distribution, or spectrum, shown in Figure 8-4. The number of detected pulses for a given pulse height is displayed as a function of the pulse height, which is measured in volts but shown here as kinetic energy of the electrons in MeV. The monochromatic gamma-ray source in this case consists of radioactive ^{40}K atoms, each one of which emits a photon of 1.48 MeV as the unstable nucleus decays.

The peak of highest energy originates from the photoelectric effect. Since the binding energy of atomic electrons is only a few electron volts,

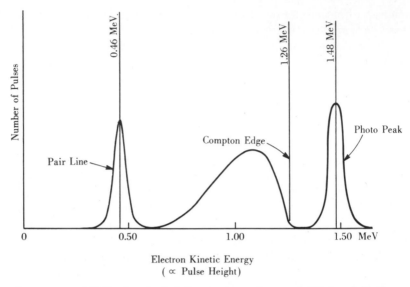

Figure 8-4 Idealized pulse-height spectrum for a scintillator detecting 1.48 MeV photons.

small compared with the photons' energy, and consequently the photoelectrons have essentially the entire photon energy, the energy at the so-called "photopeak" is almost exactly the same as the gamma-ray energy. The second peak arises from the Compton effect. When a 1.48 MeV photon collides head on with an essentially free atomic electron, the Compton electron recoils in the forward direction with a kinetic energy of 1.26 MeV (computed from Equation 4-17), while the scattered photon travels in the reverse direction with the remaining energy, 1.48 − 1.26, or 0.22, MeV. Compton collisions that are not head-on produce less energetic electrons and more energetic scattered photons. Therefore, the Compton peak has a relatively sharply defined high-energy edge, in the figure corresponding to 1.26 MeV; it trails off gradually on the low-energy side because of the Compton collisions producing electrons with less than the maximum kinetic energy. The third peak in the scintillation spectrum originates from electron-positron pair production. Since the rest energy of an electron or positron is 0.51 MeV, a total of 1.02 MeV is needed to bring a pair into existence. The difference in energy, 1.48 − 1.02 = 0.46 MeV, is the sum of the kinetic energies of the electron and positron (see Section 4-5); this total kinetic energy, after exciting scintillator electrons, produces the pulses at the pair-production peak.

The relative sizes of the three peaks described depend on the energy of the photons and the size, shape, and identity of the scintillation material. Still other peaks may be found. For example, gamma rays with an energy above the threshold energy of 1.02 MeV for pair production will produce positrons, and if the positrons are annihilated with electrons before leaving the scintillator, annihilation photons of 0.51 MeV are produced (Section 4-5), and these photons also can give rise to photoelectric and Compton peaks.

THE CERENKOV DETECTOR   Visible light is emitted when a charged particle travels through a transparent medium at a speed that exceeds the speed of light *in that medium*; such light is called Cerenkov radiation, after its discoverer. An energetic charged particle traveling in a straight line through the medium may be thought of as displacing from their equilibrium positions one by one a series of atomic electrons lying along its path. The radiation fields from the displaced electrons combine to form a strong outgoing electromagnetic wave, in the same fashion that a shock wave is produced in an elastic medium by an object traveling through it at a speed greater than that of the speed of sound in the medium.†

The speed of a charged particle through the medium is v_p; the speed of light (the group velocity) through the medium is c/n, where n is the index of refraction in the medium. Then, when the particle has advanced a distance $v_p t$ past some one displaced atomic electron, the electron has emitted light that has traveled a distance $(c/n)t$; see Figure 8-5. The Cerenkov emission, on the expanding cone of a "shock wave," is radiated at the angle θ with respect to the particle velocity v_p. From the geometry of the figure we see that its propagation direction is given by

$$\cos \theta = (c/n)/v_p = c/n v_p \qquad [8\text{-}1]$$

Note that no radiation is produced unless $v_p > c/n$.

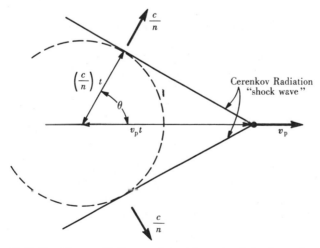

Figure 8-5 Cerenkov radiation produced by a particle of speed v_p traveling through a medium of refractive index n.

† See Section 42-5, Weidner and Sells, *E.C.P.*

A Cerenkov counter typically contains a transparent plastic block (refractive index 1.5) and a photomultiplier tube that registers the radiation. If, in addition, the angle of emission θ is measured, the detector serves to determine the particle's speed. In Lucite the particle's speed must be at least $c/1.5 = 2 \times 10^8$ m/sec, for the counter to discriminate effectively against low-speed particles.

8-3 Track-recording devices   Whereas the detectors described in the foregoing section will register a count that indicates that a charged particle or photon has passed somewhere within the detector's active material, they do not yield a detailed record of the particle's path. Among the devices by which it is possible to photograph in three dimensions or otherwise record the trail of ions produced by a charged particle traversing a medium are the *cloud chamber, bubble chamber, spark chamber,* and *nuclear photographic emulsions.*

Before turning to these devices we consider how two or more single detectors, each capable of defining the position of the detected particle within some limited region of space, may be used in combination to register, at least approximately, the path of a particle through space. Consider the so-called *counter telescope* in Figure 8-6; two separated detectors A and B are so connected that a count is registered only if both produce signal pulses

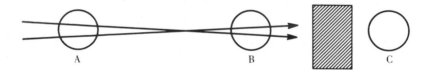

Figure 8-6 Simple form of a counter telescope.

simultaneously. Suppose that a high-speed charged particle produces ions in A and then, essentially in coincidence, also in B. The coincidence circuit to which detectors A and B are connected will, in recording the event, imply that the particle's path is like that shown in the figure. We may ensure that the particle first goes through detector A, then goes through detector B, and then stops in an absorber, rather than the reverse, with the use of a third detector, C, in anticoincidence with A and B; that is, an event is recorded only if A and B register counts in coincidence while C registers no count. To account for the finite travel time between the two or more detectors the detectors may be operated in delayed coincidence, the event now being registered only if the sequence of the pulses in time satisfies prescribed intervals.

THE CLOUD CHAMBER   The cloud chamber, invented by C. T. R. Wilson in 1907, is the earliest of the track-recording devices. Its operation depends on the behavior of a supersaturated vapor. When a vapor is in thermal equilibrium with a liquid, its pressure is the saturated-vapor pressure. Typically, the saturated-vapor pressure increases as the temperature of the liquid rises. Suppose a saturated vapor is suddenly expanded adiabatically, so that no thermal energy leaves or enters it. Its temperature falls, but its pressure is now too high for the reduced temperature and, if dust particles or ions are present, it will condense around them, so as to keep its pressure equal to the saturated-vapor pressure. If the vapor is free from dust and ions, however, the liquid droplets cannot form, and the adiabatic expansion produces a supersaturated vapor; an ionizing particle passing through the supersaturated vapor leaves a trail of ions, about which condensation can take place, and the tracks of the liquid droplets, about 10^{-5} m in radius, may easily be seen or, better still, photographed.

The elements of a cloud chamber are shown in Figure 8-7. The chamber,

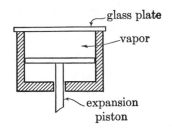

Figure 8-7 Simple elements of a cloud chamber.

whose volume may be as large as a cubic foot, operates with such mixtures as air and water vapor or argon gas and alcohol. To produce the supersaturated vapor the piston is suddenly retracted when a counter telescope placed near the chamber signals the approach or passage of particles. A track of droplets defines a passing charged particle's path. At this instant the chamber is illuminated, and a camera photographs the track. Using two or more cameras for stereophotography permits the paths to be analyzed in three dimensions.

The path of a single particle is of limited interest. Of far more importance are nuclear events, in which an incident particle collides with particles within the chamber, possibly creating new particles, or in which an unstable incident particle decays, or explodes, in flight into other particles. Thus, a nuclear event is typically one in which the tracks of both incident and emerging particles appear (a photon or electrically neutral particle leaves no tracks, of course). By measuring the momenta of the particles (by measuring their curvature r in a magnetic field B through the relation $p = mv = QrB$ and the relative directions of the tracks) and by applying the laws of energy and momentum conservation, one may analyze the event in detail; Figure 4-21 is a cloud-chamber photograph.

Cloud chambers have serious shortcomings. The density of a gas is so low that the probability that an incident particle will collide and interact with particles within the gas is low. The recycling time is long; after an expansion one must wait as long as a minute for ions to be cleared by an electric field and the chamber readied for the next expansion.

The diffusion type of cloud chamber operates continuously, however, without expansion. The bottom is maintained at a considerably lower temperature than the top, a heavy gas fills the chamber, and a light vapor is introduced at the top. As the vapor diffuses downward it cools and becomes supersaturated; the chamber is at all times sensitive in the region of the supersaturated vapor.

THE BUBBLE CHAMBER   The shortcomings of the cloud chamber are largely overcome in the *bubble chamber*, invented by D. A. Glaser in 1952. It has replaced the cloud chamber in most contemporary experiments in high-energy physics.

Since it operates with a superheated liquid rather than a supersaturated gas, the density of the active material in a bubble chamber is substantially greater than that of a cloud chamber, and the probability of finding interesting events increases correspondingly. A bubble chamber is, in one sense, a cloud chamber turned inside out: it utilizes vapor droplets formed in a liquid rather than liquid droplets formed in a vapor. See Figure 8-8. A typical bubble chamber uses liquid hydrogen, which boils at 20 °K at atmospheric pressure. When the pressure is increased to 5 atmospheres, the temperature of the liquid rises to 27 °K. Then, if the pressure is suddenly reduced, the liquid becomes *superheated*, its temperature being momentarily greater than the boiling point.

Triggering devices, particularly counters in coincidence, may be used with bubble chambers to ensure that photographs are taken when interesting events may be occurring. The dimensions of bubble chambers may be of the order of meters. The chambers are always operated with external magnetic fields to separate positively and negatively charged particles and to measure the momentum of the particles.

THE SPARK CHAMBER   In the photographic type of spark chamber the path of a charged particle is registered by a series of sparks, which can be photographed. In its simplest form a spark detector operates as follows. A high potential difference is applied across a pair of electrodes immersed in an inert gas. A charged particle passes through the region, forming ions, and the ions multiply through intermolecular collisions under the influence of the accelerating electric field, until a visible spark flashes between the

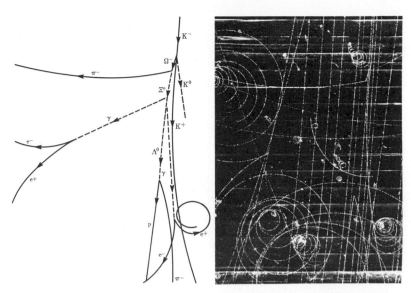

Figure 8-8 Photograph taken in the 80-inch liquid-hydrogen bubble chamber at Brookhaven National Laboratory. It shows a track produced by the negatively charged omega particle (Ω-), which decays after a lifetime of approximately 10^{-10} sec to a Ξ^0 particle and $\pi-$ particle. These and subsequent events are identified in the sketch; neutral particles, which produce no bubbles in the liquid hydrogen and therefore leave no tracks, are shown by dashed lines. The existence of the Ω^- had been predicted on theoretical grounds in advance of observation. Characteristics of these and other esoteric particles are treated in Chapter 11. (Courtesy Brookhaven National Laboratory.)

electrodes. Residual ions then are swept away by a clearing electric field, and the spark counter is ready to register again.

A spark chamber is merely a collection of spark counters. Parallel plates separated by several millimeters are immersed in an inert gas such as neon; see Figure 8-9. The region between the plates is viewed edge on by a camera. *After* the particle whose track is to be photographed has passed transversely through the plates, as signalled by separate counters, an electric potential of tens of kilovolts is applied to alternate electrodes, the ions initially formed by the passing charged particle multiply, sparks form in the gaps between adjacent plates, and a photograph is taken. As Figure 8-10 shows, two or more tracks may be registered simultaneously in a spark chamber. Although lacking the very high spatial resolution of the bubble chamber, the special advantage of the spark chamber is its very short insensitive time interval between successive firings, or dead time (as short as 10 μsec) and the consequent high ratio of interesting events to background events available from high-intensity beams.

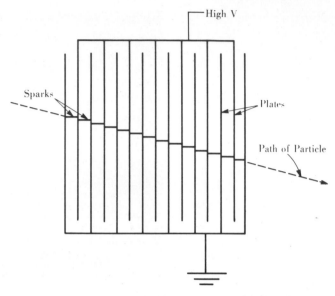

Figure 8-9 Schematic diagram of a spark chamber.

Figure 8-10 Two tracks in a spark-chamber photograph used in experiments to establish the existence of the neutrino associated with the muon. (Courtesy of Brookhaven National Laboratory.)

A more sophisticated device is the *wire spark chamber*, in which the uniform electrode plates of the photographic spark chamber are replaced with layers of uniformly spaced parallel wires. Wires in alternate layers are parallel and connected to a high potential, with the second set of wires at right angles to the first, which is connected to ground. When a spark initiated by the passage of a charged particle jumps between two wires in adjacent layers, electric signals travel at constant speed along the two wires, and the respective times of arrival at the wire ends of the two signals, typically indicated by a magnetic effect, correspond to the respective distances of the spark from the wire ends; see Figure 8-11. Indeed, a series of sparks resulting from the passage of a particle through the several layers of the

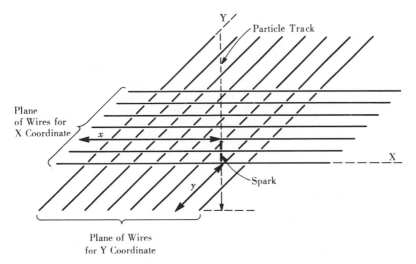

Figure 8-11 Two layers of uniformly spaced, parallel wires in a wire spark chamber.

spark chamber produce corresponding signals in still other wires. The identity of the wires carrying signals and the times of arrival of the signals may then be fed into a computer, which can reconstruct the path of the particle in three dimensions. Since the wire spark chamber is completely electronic, there is no delay arising from the development of a photographic record, and the system may be triggered to record events as frequently as a hundred times a second.

Nuclear Emulsions   A photographic emulsion used to record the tracks of charged particles is called a *nuclear emulsion*; see Figure 8-12. The emulsion, usually thicker and more sensitive than emulsions used in ordinary photography, renders the trail of ions visible upon development, because a latent image can be produced by the track of a charged particle traversing the sensitive volume. A particle's range in a nuclear emulsion depends on its energy, and the measurement of the range may be used to determine the particle's energy. For example, in a typical emulsion a proton of 10 MeV produces a track 0.5 mm long, whereas one of 20 MeV pro-

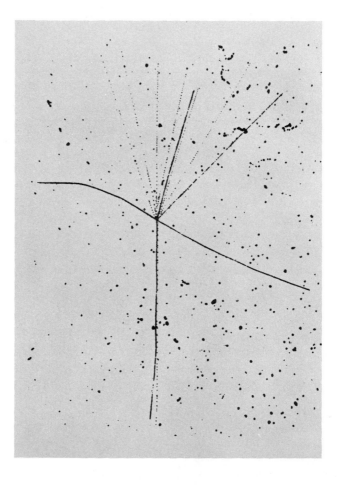

Figure 8-12 Tracks produced in a nuclear emulsion plate by the interaction of high-energy cosmic-ray particles with emulsion grains. (Courtesy Brookhaven National Laboratory.)

duces a track 2.0 mm long. The mass of the particle is related to the density of grains of the emulsion along the track; moreover, the number of grains increases as any one particle slows down. Like cloud and bubble chambers, a nuclear emulsion permits collisions and nuclear reactions to be analyzed through the measurement of the energies, masses, and relative directions of the participating particles. Although the microscopic examination of emulsions for particle tracks is relatively tedious, these track-recording devices have the advantages of small size, light weight, and simplicity. Moreover, a nuclear emulsion is continuously sensitive.

8-4 Devices for measuring velocity, momentum, and mass It is possible to determine such characteristics of a particle as its identity and energy from its absorption in materials or from its ionization effects in detecting instruments. All such measurements are, however, of rather limited precision. In this section we discuss the physical principles of instruments with which the velocity, momentum, mass, and energy of charged particles can be measured with very great precision.

A charged particle can be appreciably influenced in its motion through a vacuum only by an electric force $F = Q\mathcal{E}$ and a magnetic force $F = Q\boldsymbol{v} \times \boldsymbol{B}$ arising from external electric and magnetic fields. All devices for measuring velocity, momentum, and mass involve merely the use of electric and magnetic fields, singly or in combination, to determine the path of a charged particle. Each instrument consists of three parts: a source or beam of charged particles, a region in which electric or magnetic

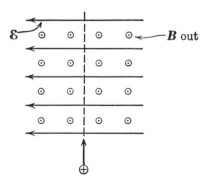

Figure 8-13 A velocity selector, consisting of crossed electric and magnetic fields.

fields act on the particles, and a detector for registering their arrival. What is done in every instrument is to set up, so to speak, an obstacle course for the charged particles in such a way that, if the particles succeed in moving from the source to the detector, one can infer from a knowledge of the electric or magnetic fields acting on the particle some quantity of interest, such as the velocity of the particle.

THE VELOCITY SELECTOR   Consider first a velocity selector; see Figure 8-13. A narrow beam of charged particles is projected into a region of space where a uniform electric field $\mathcal{E}$ acts to the left, and simultaneously a uniform magnetic field $\boldsymbol{B}$ is applied in the direction out of the paper. The incident beam is composed of particles which may have a variety of masses, charges (magnitude and sign), and velocities. A particle of mass m and charge $+Q$ entering the region of the *crossed* electric and magnetic fields $\mathcal{E}$ and $\boldsymbol{B}$ at right angles to them is acted on by an electric force $Q\mathcal{E}$ to the left and a magnetic force QvB to the right, where v is the speed of the particle: If the particle is to travel through the selector undeflected, the net force on it must be zero; that is,

$$Q\mathcal{E} = QvB$$

$$\boxed{v = \mathcal{E}/B}$$ [8-2]

Thus, only those particles with speeds equal to the ratio $\mathcal{E}/B$ will emerge from the selector without having been deflected to the left or right; when $\mathcal{E}$ and $\boldsymbol{B}$ are known, so too is the velocity of particles in the emerging beam. Note that *all* particles with a velocity of magnitude $\mathcal{E}/B$, despite differences in mass or in sign or magnitude of electric charge, pass through undeviated.

THE MOMENTUM SELECTOR   Now consider a device for measuring the momentum of a charged particle. Only a uniform magnetic field is required. This field is directed into the paper in Figure 8-14 and negatively charged

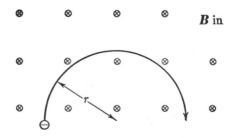

Figure 8-14 A momentum selector, consisting of a uniform magnetic field.

particles move at right angles to the magnetic field lines. The magnetic force acts at right angles to the velocity, deflecting the particle into a circular path of radius r, where

$$QvB = mv^2/r$$

[3-9]
$$\boxed{mv = QBr}$$
[8-3]

The momentum p is directly proportional to the radius r; all particles having the same charge Q and momentum mv will move in paths having the same radius of curvature. It should be recalled that the mass m appearing in Equation 8-3 is the *relativistic* mass and, therefore, mv is the relativistic momentum (see Section 3-1). The quantity Br, to which the relativistic momentum is proportional for particles of a given charge Q, is sometimes called the *magnetic rigidity*.

If a charged particle's identity—its charge Q, rest mass m_0, (or rest energy E_0)—is known, then a determination of its momentum $p = QBr$ through a measurement of its curvature r in a known magnetic field B permits the particle's relativistic kinetic energy $E_k = E - E_0 = E - m_0c^2$ to be computed directly. We use the general relativistic relation between energy and momentum:

[3-14]
$$E^2 = (pc)^2 + E_0^2$$

or
$$(E_k + E_0)^2 = (QBr)^2c^2 + E_0^2$$
[8-4]

Thus, the measurement of the curvature of tracks in a bubble-chamber photograph permits the particles' energies to be computed from Equation 8-4. The density of a track, determined by the rate dE/dx at which a charged particle loses energy in passing through a given medium, is uniquely related to the particle's mass, and the particle's identity is thereby established.

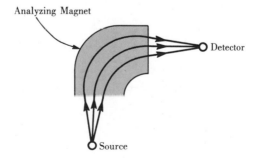

Figure 8-15 An analyzing magnet focusing the particles diverging from the source and converging to the detector.

Magnetic-momentum analyzers are usually designed to accept particles traveling a variety of paths from source to final detector; see Figure 8-15. Particles diverge from a small source, travel in circular arcs through a uniform magnetic field, and then converge to a small region at the detector. The beam of particles may be thought to be focused, as well as deflected, by the magnetic field, and the source and detector may be thought of as equivalent to an optical point object and point image. The obvious advantage of such an arrangement is that more particles can be accepted from the source and focused on the detector, thereby improving the sensitivity of the magnetic analyzer.

One form of magnetic spectrograph is the *beta-ray spectrometer*. It may be used to measure the momentum of electrons emitted from nuclei with energies up to a few MeV or to measure the momentum of electrons released in photoelectric or Compton collisions of x-rays and gamma rays.

The kinetic energy of a particle of high energy is most easily determined by measuring its momentum with a magnetic field. In principle one could measure the energy of electrons of 1 MeV by finding that they were brought to rest by a retarding potential of 1 million volts. This is, of course, impossible in practice, and one must resort to the indirect determination of the energy of a very-high-speed particle by a measurement of its momentum.

THE MASS SPECTROMETER   A device for measuring the mass of an ionized atom is a mass spectrometer. We shall see that it is of great importance in nuclear physics to know the masses of atoms to an accuracy of a few parts in a hundred thousand; such high precision can be achieved in mass spectrometry. Although mass spectrometers can take on a variety of forms, we shall discuss only one of the simpler types.

Inasmuch as a particle's linear momentum p is mv, it is obvious that a mass selector, or mass spectrometer, can be constructed by combining a velocity selector and a momentum selector. Consider the device shown schematically in Figure 8-16. Ions from a source pass through a slit S_1 and

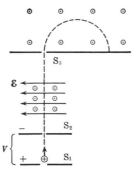

Figure 8-16 Simple form of mass spectrometer, consisting of a velocity selector followed by a momentum selector.

are accelerated through a potential difference V. After passing through slit S_2, they enter a velocity selector. Only those ions moving with a velocity $\mathcal{E}/B_1$ emerge through slit S_3, where $\mathcal{E}$ is the uniform electric field between vertical plates and B_1 is the uniform magnetic field, directed out of the paper, which is confined to the region of the velocity selector. The surviving ions leaving S_3 enter a second uniform magnetic field B_2, directed out of the paper, and are deflected so as to move in a circle of radius r. We have, from Equations 8-2 and 8-3,

$$\frac{m}{Q} = \frac{B_2 r}{v} = \frac{B_2 r}{\mathcal{E}/B_1}$$ [8-5]

from which the mass-to-charge ratio, m/Q, can be computed directly. If the charge of the ion is known (for a singly ionized atom, $Q = e$), the mass itself can be evaluated. The mass m is directly proportional to the radius r. Note that the mass of an electrically charged ion is directly measured, but if one corrects for the deficiency of electrons, the mass of the neutral atom can be determined. When ions of various masses fall on a photographic plate (*mass spectrograph*), the mass spectrum of the ions is recorded. Alternatively, if the ions are collected in a detector located behind a slit at a fixed distance, $2r$, from the entrance slit S_3, a plot of collector current versus variable magnetic field B_2 yields the mass spectrum.

All types of mass spectrometers, although differing in certain features, include an electric field and a magnetic field, either simultaneously or in succession. The first mass spectrometer was developed by J. J. Thomson in 1912; he found that any given chemical element may consist of atoms having several discrete values of atomic mass. Such atoms, which have the same atomic number Z and are therefore chemically indistinguishable, but which have different values of atomic mass, are known as *isotopes*.

Consider, for example, the element chlorine, $_{17}Cl$, whose chemical atomic weight, as found in nature, is 35.453. Mass spectrometry shows that chlorine has two isotopes with the atomic masses 34.969 and 36.966 u. By definition, the mass of one neutral atom of the carbon isotope ^{12}C is exactly 12 u. Natural chlorine, a mixture of the two isotopes, has a mass of 35.453, not at all close to an integer, whereas the two separate isotopes, ^{35}Cl and ^{37}Cl, with relative abundances of 75.53 and 24.47 percent respectively, have atomic masses that are very close to the integers 35 and 37, the so-called *mass numbers*; the mass spectrum of chlorine, as measured by a mass spectrometer, is shown in Figure 8-17. Every chemical element is found to consist of one or more isotopes, whose masses in atomic units are very close, but not equal, to integers. These slight departures of the atomic masses from integral values yield valuable information on the structure of nuclei.

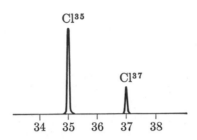

Figure 8-17 Mass spectrum of natural atomic chlorine.

8-5 High-energy accelerators   Our understanding of the structure of matter has always advanced hand in hand with the development of machines capable of accelerating charged particles to increasingly higher energies. We have already seen that the bombardment of atoms by electrons accelerated to several electron volts can excite or ionize their outer, weakly bound electrons and induce optical photon emission; from such experiments the excitation and ionization energies of atoms can be determined and the outer-electron structure of the atom deduced. When atoms are bombarded with electrons accelerated to energies of 10^3 or 10^4 electron volts, their innermost, tightly bound electrons can be dislodged, and x-ray photon emission can be induced; from such experiments the inner-electron structures of atoms can be determined. In all these experiments the nucleus of the atom behaves as a positively charged, but otherwise inert, point mass having no internal structure. This is not to say that the atomic nucleus is truly a simple point charge and point mass but, rather, that the bombardment of the atom by particles having energies no greater than several thousand electron volts produces no perceptible changes in any internal structure the nucleus may possess.

As we shall see in Chapter 9, the constituent particles of the nucleus are bound together with energies of several *million* electron volts; therefore, if the internal structure and arrangement of the nuclear constituents is to be altered, so that the structure of the nucleus may be studied, the nucleus must be given energies of the order of millions of electron volts. The most direct means of altering the structure of nuclei is to bombard targets containing atoms (and therefore also nuclei) with particles that have been accelerated to very high energies. Progress in nuclear physics and in the physics of elementary particles has, therefore, depended upon the invention and design of machines that can accelerate charged particles to kinetic energies measured in mega electron volts or even in several hundred giga electron volts ($1 \text{ GeV} = 10^9 \text{ eV}$).

The principal motivation for constructing such very-high-energy accelerators is that the particles may be used to create unstable particles not easily found in nature, and these may be studied. For example, antiprotons are created by protons of 6 GeV striking protons at rest. Moreover, as a particle's energy and momentum are increased, its wavelength $\lambda = h/p$ is reduced, so that, for example, an electron of 20 GeV has a wavelength of less than 10^{-16} m, whereas a typical nuclear size is about 10^{-14} m. Indeed, high-energy electrons may be used to probe the distribution of electric charge within a nucleus or even within a proton.

An ideal accelerating machine produces a beam of charged particles with a well-defined high energy and with a high beam intensity, or large number of particles. The beam energy must be high, because only then can the nuclear structure be appreciably changed by particles colliding with target nuclei or creating new particles; the beam intensity should, ideally, be high, because the probability of a collision between an incoming particle and a target nucleus is very small by virtue of the extremely small target area.

All charged-particle accelerators are based on the fact that a charged particle has its energy changed when it is acted on by an *electric* field. A *constant* magnetic field does *no* work on a moving charged particle and cannot change its energy; on the other hand, a *changing* magnetic field produces an electric field, which in turn can accelerate a charged particle. Therefore, all high-energy accelerators change the energy of charged particles by subjecting them to an electric field derived either directly from charged particles or indirectly from a changing magnetic field.†

Before describing the basic types of accelerators we point out two formidable technical problems that must be solved in the design of any of them. They are the maintenance of a very high *vacuum* in the interior of the machine and the *focusing* of the beam of accelerated particles by electric or magnetic fields. A high vacuum reduces the probability of collisions with gas molecules and the consequent loss of useful beam intensity. Focusing ensures that those accelerated particles which deviate slightly from the ideal design path (which may be as long as many miles between the ion source and the target) will be returned to the path and so kept in

---

† An accelerating machine that utilizes a changing magnetic field to produce an electric field is the betatron, an accelerator of high-energy electrons. See Section 34-6, Weidner and Sells, *E. C. P.* for the basis of its operation. We omit discussion of its features here, inasmuch as the betatron is no longer used primarily as a research tool in nuclear physics; it is more frequently used to produce x-rays with highspeed electrons.

the useful beam. Although high-vacuum and focusing problems are crucial in the design of all accelerators, we shall concern ourselves only with the basic principles underlying the acceleration of particles (some aspects of focusing are dealt with in Problems 8-28 to 8-32).

The two general classes of charged-particle accelerators are the *linear accelerators*, in which the charged particles move along a straight line, and the *cyclic accelerators*, in which the charged particles move in curved paths and are recycled. The linear accelerators described herein are the Van de Graaff generator and the drift-tube accelerator; the cyclic accelerators described are the cyclotron, the synchrocyclotron, and the synchrotron.

Linear Accelerators   A number of relatively low-energy accelerating machines (accelerating particles to energies no greater than 1 MeV) are based on such conventional devices as step-up transformers, or capacitors charged in parallel and then connected in series, to achieve high voltages. All such machines are, however, ultimately limited—by electrical discharge—to approximately one million volts.

Linear accelerators are colloquially called "linacs."

The most successful machine for accelerating charged particles along a straight line by applying a *single* large potential difference is the *Van de Graaff electrostatic generator*, invented by R. J. Van de Graaff in 1931. It can accelerate singly charged particles to energies of about 30 MeV. Its chief virtue is a large beam intensity (a few milliamperes) and a precisely controlled energy (to within 0.1 percent).

The physical principle on which the machine is based is that electric charge placed within a hollow metal conductor must always move to the outer surface, irrespective of the quantity of charge already residing on that surface.† We concentrate here on the recently developed *tandem* Van de Graaff accelerator, in which is used a single high electric potential difference to accelerate particles *twice* by changing the sign of the particle's charge midway through the acceleration process. Figure 8-18 is a diagram of the principal parts of the tandem machine, and Figure 8-19 shows a tandem machine with its associated instruments. A charging belt carries electrons away from a terminal at the center of the machine; this terminal is a hollow conductor whose positive potential may reach 10 megavolts. An ion source produces negative ions of hydrogen, H⁻, each consisting of a proton and *two* bound electrons. The negative ions enter the acceleration chamber at ground potential, acquire a high kinetic energy, and finally arrive at the positively charged central terminal. Inside this terminal they pass through a thin foil or a gas (the stripper) and lose their two electrons, to emerge as positively charged bare protons. The protons are then accelerated a second

† See Section 28-7, Weidner and Sells, *E. C. P.*

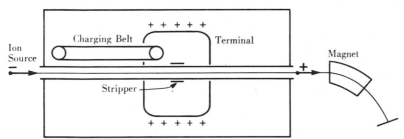

Figure 8-18 Principal parts of a tandem Van de Graaff accelerator.

time as they go from the high potential to the exit of the accelerator at ground potential. Thus, a terminal potential of 10 million volts produces protons of 20 MeV. The charged particles then pass through a magnet, which deflects them and also focuses them into a beam of monoenergetic particles, which then strike a target.

A Van de Graaff accelerator can produce a continuous, high-intensity beam of positive ions with energies as great as 30 MeV. It can serve also as an x-ray generator by accelerating electrons and bringing them to rest at the target. The voltage difference and, therefore, the particle energy in this accelerator can be precisely controlled by adjusting the leakage of charge from the positive terminal; the maximum particle energy, however, is limited finally by the unavoidable leakage of charge.

The two general types of linear accelerator in which charged particles are accelerated several times along a straight line are the *drift-tube accelerator* (R. Widerøe, 1929) and the *waveguide accelerator* (D. W. Fry, 1947). In the drift-tube machine the particles are repeatedly accelerated by an electric

Figure 8-19 A tandem Van de Graaff accelerator and its associated deflecting, analyzing, and focusing magnets. (Courtesy Rutgers News Service.)

field between insulated conductors; in the waveguide machine they are accelerated by an electric field guided through a hollow conductor. We shall discuss only the first type in detail.

Charged particles enter a long, straight, evacuated tube within which are a number of hollow conducting cylinders of increasing length; see Figure 8-20. The cylinders are connected alternately to the opposite termi-

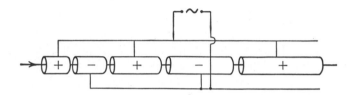

Figure 8-20 Simple form of drift-tube linear accelerator.

nals of a radiofrequency generator; thus a sinusoidally varying electric field exists in the region between any two adjacent cylinders. Suppose that positive ions drift through the first cylinder at a constant velocity. When they pass into the gap between the first two cylinders during that part of the cycle in which the second cylinder is negative with respect to the first, they are accelerated forward by the electric field there. They then enter and pass through the second cylinder at a constant but higher velocity. The length of the second cylinder is so chosen that by the time the ions have emerged from it the polarity of the cylinders has reversed—that is, the time of travel through the cylinder is exactly one half-cycle—and again the electric field accelerates the particles forward to the next cylinder.

Whenever a charged particle is in the interior of a cylinder, it is shielded from the electric field. Because the frequency of the alternating voltage applied to the drift tube is constant, it is necessary that the particles spend the same amount of time drifting through each tube, so that they may arrive at the spaces between the tubes at just the right moment to be further accelerated. For this reason the tubes are made progressively longer.

The final energy of the particles depends on the energy gained at each gap and on the number of gaps and, therefore, on the overall length of the accelerator. The beam striking the target consists of pulses of particles; the number of such pulses arriving at the target during each second is equal to the frequency of the alternating voltage applied to the drift tubes. In linacs of the drift-tube type protons can be accelerated to kinetic energies approaching 100 MeV.

The $100 million electron linac at the Stanford Linear Accelerator Center is the largest of the waveguide type. It produces electrons of 20 GeV with a beam current of 30 milliamperes. See Figure 8-21. Very-high-frequency electromagnetic waves are guided down a tube, and electrons may be thought of as riding on them, while an electric field steadily increases their kinetic energy. In the Stanford machine, 2 miles in overall length, the accelerating electromagnetic wave is produced by 245 klystron microwave oscillators, each with a power output of 24 megawatts at a frequency of 2.9 gigahertz (2,900 megacycles per second). The electrons enter the main accelerating tube after preliminary acceleration, first to 80 keV and then to 30 MeV. After leaving the main accelerator they enter a beam switchyard and magnetic spectrometer (one with 1,700 tons of iron), from which they can produce interactions at a variety of targets, including spark and bubble chambers.

CYCLIC ACCELERATORS   The class of accelerators known as cyclic accelerators include the *cyclotron, synchrocyclotron,* and *synchrotron.* In these machines multiple accelerations are given to charged particles that are restricted to motion in circular arcs by a magnetic field.

The basic relation for a particle of relativistic mass m and charge Q moving at right angles to a magnetic field B in a circular arc of radius r is

[3-9] $$p = mv = QBr$$

The particle's angular velocity ω is given by

$$\omega = v/r = (Q/m)B$$

and the frequency $f = \omega/2\pi$ of the motion, the number of revolutions per unit time, is given by

$$f = (Q/2\pi m)B \qquad\qquad [8\text{-}6]$$

The frequency given by this equation is known as the *cyclotron frequency;* the expression applies to all cyclic accelerators. Note that f depends on the charge-to-mass ratio and the magnitude of the magnetic field, but not on the particle's speed or the radius of its circular path. Thus, all particles of a given type circle the magnetic field lines at the same frequency, quite apart from differences in their speeds or energies. Strictly, the cyclotron frequency is independent of a particle's kinetic energy only if the relativistic mass m does not differ appreciably from the rest mass m_0.

The simplest cyclic machine is the *cyclotron.*

The cyclotron was invented by E. O. Lawrence and M. S. Livingston in 1932. In this accelerator a charged particle is subjected to a *constant* magnetic field, which bends it into a circular path, while it is accelerated each half-cycle by an electric field.†

Positive ions, such as protons, deuterons, and alpha particles, are injected into the central region, point C in Figure 8-22, between two flat,

† See Section 32-5; Weidner and Sells, *E. C. P.*

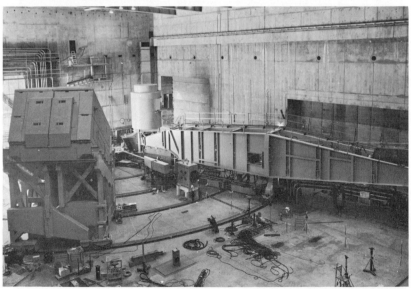

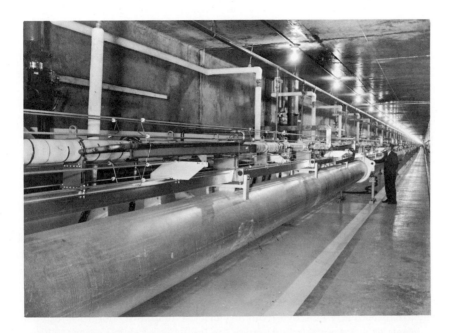

Figure 8-21 The 20 GeV Stanford electron linear accelerator: (a) the target area at the end of the two-mile-long accelerator, where electrons are deflected and magnetically analyzed and are directed to such devices as spark and bubble chambers; (b) at the target area an 8 GeV magnetic spectrometer in the foreground and a 20 GeV spectrometer in the rear; and (c) interior view of the subsurface accelerator housing with accelerator waveguide and beam within the large cylindrical tube. (Courtesy Stanford Linear Accelerator Center, Stanford University.)

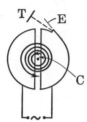 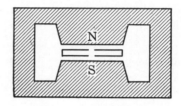

Figure 8-22 Cyclotron accelerator: top view (left); side view (right).

D-shaped, hollow metal conductors (called "dees"). An alternating high-frequency voltage is applied to the dees, producing an alternating electric field in the region between them. During the time that the left dee is positive and the right dee is negative the ions are accelerated to the right by the electric field between the dees. Upon entering the interior of the right dee they are electrically shielded from any electric field and therefore move in a semicircle at a constant speed under the influence of the constant magnetic field. When they emerge from the right dee, they are further accelerated across the gap, if the left dee is now negative. This requires that the frequency of the alternating voltage applied to the dees be equal to the orbital, or cyclotron, frequency of the ions, given by Equation 8-6. During each acceleration the ions gain energy, move at a higher speed, and travel in semicircles of larger radii. As the ions spiral outward in the dees they remain in resonance with the a-c source of constant frequency, inasmuch as the time for an ion to move through 180° is independent of its speed or **radius,** provided only that its mass m in Equation 8-6 remain essentially equal to the rest mass. When the accelerated particles reach the perimeters of the dees, they are deflected by the electric field of an ejector plate E and strike the target T. Their final kinetic energy E_k (for E_k much less than E_0 the rest energy) is

$$E_k = \tfrac{1}{2}mv_{max}^2 = \tfrac{1}{2}m(QBr_{max}/m)^2$$
$$E_k = Q^2B^2r_{max}^2/2m$$

We see that the final kinetic energy of the particle depends on the square of the radius of the dees and on the square of the magnetic field B. To achieve the greatest possible energies the quantities B and r_{max} are made as large as possible. When the greatest possible magnetic field (about 2 Wb/m²) is used, the frequency f, by means of Equation 8-6, is of the order of megacycles per second (radiofrequencies). The diameter of the dees, which is also the diameter of the electromagnet's pole faces, may be as large as 8 ft; this is enormous (400 tons of iron) and expensive. A typical alternating voltage across the dees is 200 kilovolts.

Massive particles—protons, deuterons, and alpha particles—can be accelerated in a cyclotron to energies of about 25 MeV. The final kinetic energies of all such ions are much less than their rest energies (a proton's final energy is about 1 GeV.) Therefore, the mass does not increase appreciably, and the particles, if protons, can remain in synchronism with the alternating voltage up to about 12 MeV and, if deuterons, to about 25 MeV. Electrons can be rather easily accelerated to relativistic speeds (their rest energy is only 0.5 MeV); such light particles cannot be synchronized with the applied voltage and therefore cannot be accelerated to high energies by a cyclotron.

We now consider the *synchrocyclotron*.

An ordinary fixed-frequency cyclotron will work only if the accelerated particle's kinetic energy remains small compared with its rest energy. The cyclotron frequency $f = (Q/2\pi m)B$ of the orbiting particles is constant and in resonance with the alternating electric field between the dees, only if the relativistic mass m appearing in Equation 8-6 is always essentially equal to the rest mass m_0. As a particle's speed and kinetic energy increase, the relativistic mass increases, and its cyclotron frequency in a constant magnetic field decreases. Therefore, as particles spiral outward in a cyclotron with fixed magnetic field and frequency, they fall increasingly behind the applied frequency and finally arrive at the gap between the dees so late that they are no longer accelerated by the electric field. This limitation is overcome in the synchrocyclotron; a photograph of a synchrocyclotron is shown in Figure 8-23.

In this accelerating machine, too, the particles (ions) start at the center of an electromagnetic producing a constant magnetic field but, as they move to increasingly larger radii, the applied frequency is *decreased* continuously in such a way as to compensate for the decrease in the particles' cyclotron frequency with increased speed. The particles can then remain in synchronism with the alternating electric field. Because the frequency is changed as the ions are accelerated and move in increasingly larger radii, this type of machine is sometimes referred to as an FM, or frequency-modulated, cyclotron.

The success of synchrocyclotrons in accelerating particles to kinetic

Figure 8-23 A 184-inch (dee diameter) synchrocyciotron capable of accelerating protons to 0.7 GeV. The lower pole of the cyclotron magnet is below the floor and not visible. (Courtesy Lawrence Radiation Laboratory, University of California, Berkeley.)

energies (for example, 700 MeV for protons) comparable to the rest energy is crucially dependent upon the phenomenon of *phase focusing*. In order that particles may be accelerated continuously in a machine whose accelerating electric field changes frequency they must always arrive at the gap precisely when the phase of the alternating electric field is proper. Or so it might seem; actually, particles that arrive late at the accelerating gap receive a somewhat greater acceleration, so that they tend to make up the lost time and arrive more nearly on time at the next gap crossing, whereas particles that arrive early receive a lesser acceleration and also tend to arrive on time at the next gap crossing. Through this phase-focusing effect, first introduced by V. Veksler and E. M. McMillan, the bunches of accelerated particles are kept in the useful beam during the acceleration cycle; this consideration is important, because the number of particles that survive the entire acceleration cycle—a very long trip with appearances required at check points on schedule—is so small under the most favorable circumstances that the many particles that inevitably fail to follow the ideal route must be restored by correction (or focusing) procedures.

Although a synchrocyclotron can accelerate particles to much higher energies than a cyclotron, its output beam current is much less, because only one pulse of particles can be accelerated in the machine at one time. Theoretically there is no limit on the size and, therefore, the energy of a synchrocyclotron, but it becomes economically prohibitive to build machines of this design for accelerating particles to energies of more than about 1 GeV.

We finally consider the *synchrotron*.

To increase a particle's final kinetic energy in a cyclic accelerating machine one must increase its final relativistic momentum $p = QBr$. There is a limit on the magnitude of the magnetic field B attainable over moderately large regions of space; because of the properties of magnetic materials, B cannot exceed about 2 Wb/m^2. Thus, the only way to increase substantially a particle's momentum and thereby its kinetic energy in a cyclic machine is to make the final orbital radius large. In a synchrocyclotron the particles start at the center of the electromagnet and spiral outward to the final radius; the electromagnet produces a magnetic field over this entire region. So, if a particle's final kinetic energy in a synchrocyclotron is to be increased, the radius of the final orbit and, consequently, the radius of the electromagnet must be increased correspondingly. A machine accelerating protons to about 0.7 GeV has a dee diameter of about 5 m; to produce a large magnetic field over the entire inner region requires an electromagnet of about 4,000 tons. Still larger sizes and energies become economically unfeasible. Therefore, the synchrotron, which utilizes magnetic fields only at one orbital radius, has been devised.

Particles, preaccelerated to a fairly high kinetic energy, are injected into the synchrotron and thereafter move in an orbit of *fixed* radius. The basic relations governing the particle motion are

[8-3] $p = QBr$

[8-6] $f = (Q/2\pi m)B$

Since the radius r in Equation 8-3 is fixed, the particle momentum p will increase only if the magnetic field B increases. Equation 8-6, however, shows that if B changes, so too must the frequency f of the accelerating electric field with which the orbiting particles are to remain in synchronism. Thus, in the synchrotron accelerator *both* the magnetic field and the frequency of the accelerating electric field increase with time as the accelerated particle, moving in a fixed circle, gains kinetic energy.

Figure 8-24 shows schematically the principal parts of a proton synchrotron, and Figure 8-25 is a photograph of one. Protons first are accelerated to an energy of several MeV by a linac serving as an injection accelerator (either a Van de Graaff machine or a resonant linear accelerator), as shown in Figure 8-26. Then they enter a doughnut-shaped, evacuated tube,

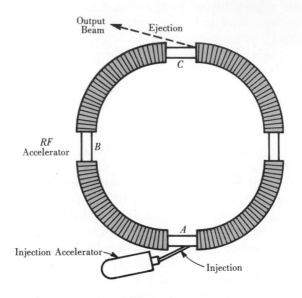

Figure 8-24 Schematic diagram of a synchrotron.

not more-than about 1 m in transverse dimensions, which is contained within an electromagnet producing a deflecting magnetic field at and near the tube but not at interior points. Energy is supplied to the particles once in each revolution by an alternating electric potential difference supplied by a variable radiofrequency source. As the particles acquire speed, momentum, and kinetic energy in successive orbits, the magnitude of the deflecting magnetic field and the frequency of the accelerating electric field both increase with time, so that the particles continue to travel in a path of constant radius and also arrive at the energizing gap at the right time for further acceleration. After the magnetic field has reached its maximum magnitude and the particles their maximum kinetic energy, the particles are deflected and strike an external target. A plan of the 200 GeV (and later, with additional magnets, 500 GeV) synchrotron to be constructed at the National Accelerator Laboratory, Weston, Illinois, is shown in Figure 8-27.

The design and construction of synchrotrons capable of accelerating protons to final energies of tens and, eventually, hundreds of GeV involve very precise focusing of the beam. We can appreciate the importance of focusing by noting that in a synchrotron designed for 30 GeV protons with an orbital diameter of 0.2 km the particles travel a total distance of about 10^7 km while confined within a vacuum chamber whose transverse dimension is as small as 0.1 m. Clearly, particles that depart from the ideal path must be returned to, or focused toward, the center of the vacuum chamber,

Figure 8-25 Aerial view of the 33 GeV alternate gradient synchrotron at Brookhaven National Laboratory. The accelerating tunnel underground has a diameter of 0.84 km. The building at "3 o'clock" houses an 80-inch liquid-hydrogen bubble chamber, at "6 o'clock" the service, target, and experimental buildings, and at "9 o'clock" a 10-ton spark chamber. (Courtesy Brookhaven National Laboratory.)

if the number surviving the entire trip is to be adequate. The strong focusing is achieved by means of alternating-gradient magnets: the particles pass through *nonuniform* magnetic deflecting fields that alternate in asymmetry (see Problems 8-30 and 8-31). The principle of *alternate-gradient focusing* was introduced in 1952 by E. Courant, M. S. Livingston, and H. Snyder and, independently, by N. Christofilos.

The remarks above apply primarily to synchrotrons for accelerating massive particles, such as protons. Synchrotrons can, however, be designed for accelerating electrons to energies of a few GeV. The radiation losses arising from the acceleration (bremsstrahlung) of electrons traveling in a circular path preclude still higher energies; hence, the use of linac machines for electrons with energies of hundreds of GeV. An electron synchrotron first accelerates the particles according to the betatron principle—an electric field produced by a changing magnetic flux—and then, the particles traveling at essentially the speed c, it accelerates them by the process described above. If the magnetic field is increased with time to compensate

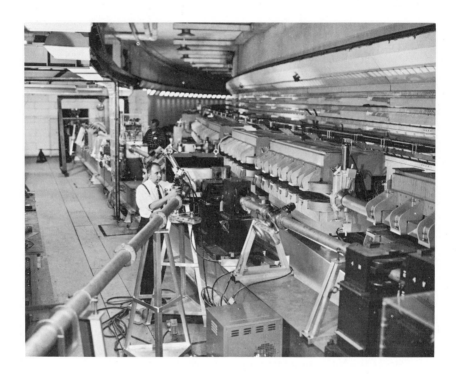

Figure 8-26 The conjunction of the linear accelerator and synchrotron magnet ring inside the tunnel of the synchrotron shown in Figure 8-25. The 50 MeV proton beam leaves the linac behind the shielding wall (left rear) and travels along the 4-inch pipe to the lower right, while passing through a series of focusing lenses and steering magnets onto the orbit of the main synchrotron magnet ring. The pipe extending to the left is used to determine the energy spread of protons leaving the linac. (Courtesy Brookhaven National Laboratory).

for the increase in the electrons' relativistic momentum, the particle's constant orbital frequency can be kept in resonance with an oscillator of constant frequency.

8-6 Summary   Nuclear detectors are devices which are sensitive to the passage of nuclear radiation (charged particles and photons) through the detector. Charged particles lose about 30 electron volts in creating a single ion pair in a gas. Nuclear radiation has the following general properties: it is more readily absorbed in a solid or liquid than in a gas; the degree of penetration *decreases*, for a given energy, in the order gamma rays, beta rays, and alpha rays, and the range of charged particles increases with increasing energy.

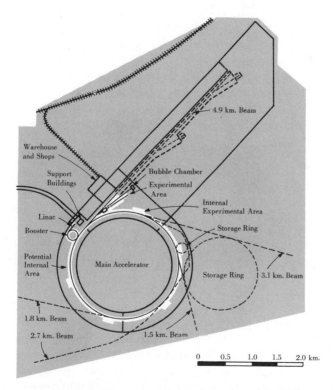

Figure 8-27 Master plan for the 200 GeV proton synchrotron to be constructed at the National Accelerator Laboratory, Weston, Illinois. Protons will first be accelerated to 0.2 GeV by a linac, then to 10 GeV in the booster ring (a synchrotron), and finally to 200 GeV in the main synchrotron ring with a circumference of four miles. Note that the beam can exit into a number of target areas or be stored in a large or small storage ring.

The types of charged-particle detector are listed in Table 8-2.

Table 8-2

Detectors of Charged Particles and Photons

Type	Reacting medium	Special characteristics
Cloud chamber	*Supersaturated vapor*	*Particle tracks*
Bubble chamber	*Superheated liquid*	*Particle tracks (high density of absorber)*
Spark chamber	*Gas*	*Fast recycling*
Nuclear emulsion	*Photographic emulsion*	*Particle tracks (continuously sensitive)*
Ionization chamber	*Gas*	*Ionization proportional to radiation intensity*
Proportional counter	*Gas*	*Pulse size proportional to radiation intensity*
Geiger counter	*Gas*	*Same size pulse initiated by any type of ionizing radiation*
Scintillation counter	*Solid (or liquid)*	*Very short resolution time*
Semiconductor (solid-state) detector	*Semiconductor*	*Energy-pulse linearity, high efficiency*
Cerenkov detector	*Transparent solid or liquid*	*Sensitive to high-speed particles only*

Measuring devices and selectors are the velocity selector (crossed electric and magnetic fields, $v = \mathcal{E}/B$), the momentum selector (uniform magnetic field, $mv = QBr$), and the mass spectrometer (at least one electric and one magnetic field, in its simplest form a combination of a momentum selector and a velocity selector).

Charged-particle accelerators, all of which energize particles by electric fields, are of two classes: linacs, which include the Van de Graaff, drift-tube, and traveling-wave resonant linear accelerators, and cyclic accelerators, which include the cyclotron (fixed frequency, fixed magnetic field, increasing particle radius), the synchrocyclotron (decreasing frequency, fixed magnetic field, increasing particle radius), and the synchrotron (increasing frequency, increasing magnetic field, fixed particle radius).

BIBLIOGRAPHY

Bacon, D. F., and W. F. Nash, in *Contemporary Physics*, 4, 356 (1963). An account of spark chambers.

Baker, W., in *Physics Today*, **20**, 41 (July, 1967). An account of wire spark chambers and associated apparatus.

Livingston, M. S., *High-Energy Accelerators*. New York: Interscience Publishers, Inc., 1954. Written by an early collaborator of E. O. Lawrence in the development of the cyclotron. This small book gives a fairly detailed account of the principle of alternate-gradient focusing.

Livingston, M. S., Editor, *The Development of High-Energy Accelerators*. New York: Dover Publications, Inc., 1966. A collection of twenty-eight original papers on basic developments in accelerating machines.

Lapp, R. E., and H. L. Andrews, *Nuclear Radiation Physics*, 3rd edition. Englewood Cliffs, New Jersey: Prentice-Hall, Inc., 1963. Further technical details of detectors and the associated electronic circuits and of accelerating machines are given at an elementary level in this book.

Portis, Alan M., *Laboratory Physics, Part A; Berkeley Physics Laboratory*. New York: McGraw-Hill Book Company, 1964. The first four experiments deal with electron ballistics, the behavior of electron beams in a cathode-ray tube under the influence of electric and magnetic fields, including their focusing properties.

Ritson, D. M., Editor, *Techniques of High-Energy Physics*. New York: Interscience Publishers, Inc., 1961. See Chapters 1 (Particles and Radiation), 3 (Bubble Chambers), 4 (Nuclear Emulsions), 6 (Ionization Counters), 7 (Scintillation and Cerenkov Counters), and 9 (Beam Optics).

Wilson, R. R., and R. Littauer, *Accelerators, Machines of Nuclear Physics*. Garden City, New York: Anchor Books, Doubleday & Company, Inc., 1960. A paperback giving an elementary account of the development of accelerating machines.

Yount, D., "The Streamer Chamber," *Scientific American* (October, 1967). Characteristics of bubble and cloud chambers.

PROBLEMS

8-1 The average energy required to produce one ion pair in air at STP is 35 eV. (a) How many ion pairs are produced by one 7.0 MeV proton absorbed in air? (b) What is the magnitude of total charge of either sign produced by the proton? (c) If the two kinds of charge were collected on opposite plates of a capacitor with a capacitance of 2.0×10^{-14} F, by how much would the potential difference between the plates change?

8-2 A 10 MeV alpha particle is stopped in a gas in which the mean energy for the production of an ion pair is 25 eV. Suppose that all ions of one sign are collected by electrodes having a capacitance of 100 pF. What is the change in potential across the electrodes?

8-3 The thickness of an absorber, or the range of a particle in an absorber, is often expressed in terms of the *areal density*, the product of the actual absorber thickness t and the absorber density ρ. The range of 10 MeV protons in a copper absorber is 0.21 g/cm², and that of 100 MeV protons is 12 g/cm². What thickness of copper (in centimeters) will stop protons of (a) 10 MeV and (b) 100 MeV? The density of copper is 8.9 g/cm³.

8-4   The roentgen, the practical unit of radiation dosage, is defined in terms of ionization effects: 1 roentgen produces 1 statcoulomb of ions of either sign in 1 cm³ of dry air under standard conditions (273°, 1 atm). The mean energy needed to produce a pair of ions in air is 35 eV. The statcoulomb is the unit for electric charge in the Gaussian, or esu, system of units, in which 1 statcoulomb = $1/(3 \times 10^9)$ coulomb. Show that a dosage of one roentgen is equal to an energy of 1.2×10^{-8} J absorbed in 1 cm³ of air.

8-5   A *pocket dosimeter* is a small, well-insulated, air-filled electroscope, whose discharge through the ionizing effects of nuclear radiation can be used to measure radiation dosage. One such dosimeter, having a capacitance of 0.20 pF and an effective sensitive volume of 0.8 cm³, is charged initially to a potential difference of 150 V. What potential difference will be read after the dosimeter has been exposed to a radiation dose of 100 mR? (See Problem 8-4 for the definition of the roentgen.)

8-6   Radioactive ^{24}Na decays by the emission of 1.38 and 2.76 MeV gamma rays. When gamma rays of these two energies are studied with a scintillation spectrometer, what five peak (electron) energies are expected in the pulse-height distribution?

8-7   Monochromatic photons with an energy of 2.48 MeV are detected with a scintillation spectrometer. Assuming that a pulse height of 100 V corresponds to an electron energy of 1.00 MeV, at what voltage in the pulse-height distribution would one expect to find (a) the photopeak, (b) the Compton edge, and (c) the pair-production peak?

8-8   A direct way of calibrating the energies of the pulses registered in a scintillation spectrometer is to use a material emitting photons of *two* well-known energies, such as the 1.17 MeV and 1.33 MeV gamma rays from radioactive ^{60}Co. The difference in energy between the photopeaks is exactly the difference between the energies of the two photons. Moreover, the pulse height varies linearly with energy. If the most energetic pulses from a ^{60}Co source have a height of 133 V, at what other voltages does one expect to find peaks (or edges, in the Compton effect)?

8-9   A typical photomultiplier tube has 10 dynodes with a potential difference of 125 V across each pair of adjoining dynodes, approximately 1.0 cm apart. What is the total time interval between the arrival of electrons at the first dynode and the appearance of a pulse at the last dynode, assuming that secondary electrons are released instantaneously and with negligible energy?

8-10   (a) Show that a Cerenkov counter made of Lucite (refractive index, 1.5) can register only those electrons whose kinetic energy exceeds 0.17 MeV. (b) What is the threshold kinetic energy of a Lucite Cerenkov counter for protons?

8-11   Protons traveling through Lucite (refractive index, 1.5) produce strong Cerenkov radiation at an angle of 30° with respect to the beam direction. What is their kinetic energy?

8-12   A counter telescope consisting of two counters is to register 5.0 MeV protons. The two detectors are separated by 1.0 m and operated in a coincidence circuit. What is the minimum duration of the signal pulses from each of the two detectors needed to obviate the delayed coincidence counting?

8-13   Particles with a rest energy E_0, kinetic energy E_k, and charge e move at right angles to the magnetic field lines of the magnetic field B. Show that the particles' radius of curvature in meters is given by $r = [E_k(E_k + 2E_0)]^{1/2}/300B$, where the energies E_k and E_0 are measured in MeV and the field B is given in Wb/m².

8-14   Show that the radius of curvature, in centimeters, of a particle with charge z (in multiples of the electronic charge e) and with a momentum P (in MeV/c) when traveling at right angles to a magnetic field B (in gauss), is given by $r = (3.33 \times 10^3)P/zB$.

8-15   (a) Show that in a magnetic field B the radius of curvature of a charged particle, whose kinetic energy E_k is much less than its rest energy E_0, is given by $r = (2E_kE_0)^{1/2}/QBc$. (b) Show that the radius of curvature of a particle whose kinetic energy greatly exceeds its rest energy is given by $r = E_k/QBc$.

8-16   What are the radii of curvature in a magnetic field of 1.0 Wb/m² of (a) 1.0 keV electrons, (b) 1.0 GeV electrons, (c) 1.0 keV protons, and (d) 1.0 GeV protons?

8-17   In a velocity selector charged particles are sent through crossed electric and magnetic fields. What would be the path of a charged particle sent through (a) two crossed uniform electric fields and (b) two crossed uniform magnetic fields?

8-18   A velocity selector contains a magnet with a field of 0.50 Wb/m² and a parallel-plate capacitor with plates separated by 0.50 cm. What potential difference must be applied to the capacitor in order to select charged particles having a speed $v/c = 1/100$?

8-19   Suppose that a velocity selector is to be built with crossed electric and magnetic fields for use with charged particles having a kinetic energy equal in magnitude to their rest energy ($E_k = 0.51$ MeV for electrons, $E_k = 0.94$ GeV for protons, etc.). (a) Show that the required ratio of the electric field to the magnetic field, ε/B, is $(\sqrt{3}/2)c$. (b) Taking the magnetic field to be of magnitude 2.0 Wb/m², the largest readily obtained over reasonably large regions of space, show that the required electric potential difference across parallel-plate electrodes separated by 2.0 cm is approximately 10^7 V under these circumstances. The extremely high electric potential differences required for high-speed particles precludes the use of crossed-field velocity selectors.

8-20   A magnetic spectrometer is to be used with singly charged particles having a momentum centered at 1.0 GeV/c. It is to operate with a magnetic field of 1.0 Wb/m², detect particles after turning them through 90°, and distinguish between particles differing in momentum by 1 percent by a spatial separation of 1.0 mm. What are the approximate overall dimensions of the spectrometer (taken to be equal to the diameter of the particles' radius of curvature)?

8-21   What are the kinetic energies of (a) electrons and (b) protons that will be registered in a magnetic spectrometer adjusted for a particle momentum of 5.0 MeV/c?

8-22   A cloud-chamber photograph reveals the path of a charged particle before and after its passage through a thin lead plate located within the cloud chamber; see Figure 8-28. From the density of the droplets it is established

Figure 8-28

that the particle has the same mass as that of an electron. The radii of curvature of the particle above and below the lead plate are 7.0 cm and 10.0 cm, respectively. Assume that the particle is traveling perpendicularly to the constant magnetic field of 1.0 Wb/m² directed into the paper. (a) In which direction is the particle moving? (b) Is the particle a positron or an electron? (c) How much energy was lost by the particle in traversing the lead plate?

8-23   One simple form of a beta-ray spectrometer, a device for separating the high-speed electrons emitted from radioactive nuclei, is shown in Figure 8-29. Electrons with a variety of energies pass from a radioactive source

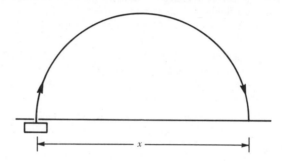

Figure 8-29

through a slit into a uniform magnetic field perpendicular to the plane of the paper, and the electrons are bent into circular paths so as to strike a photographic plate. Derive a relation giving the relativistic kinetic energy E_k of an electron in terms of the magnetic field B, electron charge e, electron rest energy E_0, and distance x from the slit to the point on the photographic plate where the electron strikes.

8-24   *   The energies of electrons produced by the interaction of 1.33 MeV photons with a relatively light-weight material are measured with a magnetic analyzer operating with a magnetic field of 1.0 Wb/m². What is the radius of curvature of (a) electrons released by photoelectric collisions, (b) the most energetic electrons produced in Compton collisions, and (c) electrons created in pair production?

8-25   *   In the 1955 experiments that first established the existence of antiprotons the sign of the particle charge was determined by the direction of deflection in a magnetic field, the mass was determined by simultaneous measurements of the particle momentum mv (by deflection in a magnetic field) and particle speed v (with a Cerenkov detector), and the antiproton's speed was checked independently by measuring the particle's time of flight from one scintillation detector to another, the two separated by a known distance and operated in delayed coincidence. The antiprotons (rest energy, 938 MeV) had a speed of $v/c = 0.78$. (a) What was the angle between the direction of propagation of the Cerenkov radiation and the particle path in the Cerenkov detector of Lucite (refractive index, 1.5)? (b) What was antiproton momentum (in MeV/c)? (c) What approximate size of the deflecting magnets (taken as the diameter of curvature) was needed for deflecting the antiprotons through 90° in a field of 1.5 Wb/m^2? (d) If the scintillation detectors were separated by 13 m, by what time interval was the signal from the first detector delayed so as to coincide in time with the signal from the second detector in the delayed-coincidence circuit?

8-26 * A magnetic spectrometer is used to measure the energy of gamma-ray photons by having the rays strike a so-called radiator, in which photo-electric emission takes place. A source of radioactive cobalt, which emits gamma rays of 1.17 MeV and 1.33 MeV, is used with a lead radiator. The spectrometer detects electrons moving in a fixed radius of curvature when the electric current through a solenoid is changed. The photoelectric emission from lead involves the removal of a K-shell electron, bound with an energy of 0.0891 MeV. If the spectrometer detects the photoelectron from the 1.17 MeV gamma ray when the current is set for 1.50 A, what is the current setting for detecting the photoelectron from the 1.33 MeV gamma ray?

8-27 Carbon has two stable isotopes, ^{12}C and ^{13}C. The collector in a mass spectrometer registers peak currents of 197.8 and 2.2 μA, respectively, for the ions of the isotopes that reach it. (a) What is the relative abundance of the two isotopes? (b) Compute the chemical atomic weight of carbon. (Carbon in living organic material also contains 1 part in 10^{12} of ^{14}C, a radioactive isotope useful in dating dead organic materials; see Section 9-12.)

Problems 8-28 to 8-32 deal with some simpler aspects of the focusing of beams of charged particles by electric and magnetic fields.

8-28 A simple type of electrostatic focusing lens is shown in Figure 8-30. It consists of a left cylindrical ring at electric potential V_1 and a coaxial right cylindrical ring at a higher potential V_2. The electric field lines are as shown: essentially parallel to the axis of symmetry of the lens at its center

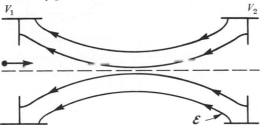

Figure 8-30 An electrostatic focusing lens.

and with sizable radial components at the ends. A positively charged particle entering the lens along the symmetry axis is undeflected, although it will be slowed in passing through the lens by an electric field whose direction is opposite to that of its velocity. A positively charged particle entering the lens above the axis is deflected upward by the radial component of the electric field as it enters the lens, slowed down as it passes through the central region of the lens, and finally deflected downward as it leaves the lens. (a) Show, on a qualitative basis, that the net effect of the electric field is to bring the particle closer to the symmetry axis on its emergence from the lens; that is, show that the lens produces a net convergence on a beam of finite transverse dimensions incident upon the lens. (b) Suppose now that the electric potentials applied to the two elements of the electrostatic lens are reversed, with the left element at a higher potential than the right one, so that the direction of the electric field is reversed; show that a beam of positively charged particles is again made to converge in traversing the lens. (c) Suppose that the beam of positively charged particles is replaced with a beam of negatively charged particles; show that once again the lens is convergent for either polarity of the two lens elements. In short, an electrostatic lens is always convergent.

8-29 Consider Figure 8-31, which shows the fringing magnetic field at the boundaries of the pole pieces of an electromagnet. Positively charged particles passing into the plane of the paper along the median plane travel at right angles to the magnetic-field lines and are consequently affected by a magnetic force acting to the right. Show that particles that pass through the region of the fringing magnetic field above or below the median plane are focused: that is, show that a particle entering at point A above

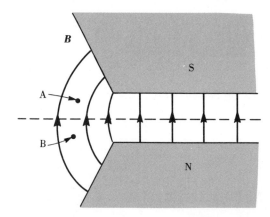

Figure 8-31

the median plane, where the magnetic field has a component to the right, is deflected downward toward the median plane and that a particle entering at point B below the median plane, where the magnetic field has a component to the left, is deflected upward toward the median plane. Since the magnitude of the magnetic-field component parallel to the median plane increases with distance from the median plane, the deflection increases with the distance of a particle from the median plane, and a dispersed beam of particles is converged to a focus at the median plane. Actually, the beam is alternatively focused and defocused along the median plane, and the beam undergoes oscillations, since the particles diverge after converging to a focus.

8-30 * Figure 8-32 shows the two north and two south magnetic poles of a *magnetic quadrupole lens*. The pole surfaces being in the shape of rectangular hyperbolas (xy = constant), it can be shown that the magnitude of B_x, the magnetic-field component along X, is proportional to the coordinate $-y$, while the magnitude of B_y, the component along Y, is proportional to the coordinate x. Under these conditions the magnitude of the magnetic field produced by the lens is zero at points along the lens's symmetry axis (perpendicular to the plane of the paper) and increases with increasing distances from the symmetry axis. (a) Suppose that a beam of positively charged particles enters the magnetic lens, traveling into the plane of the figure. Show, by using the relation for the magnetic force on a charged particle, that particles entering the lens from off the symmetry axis along X are deflected toward the central region of the symmetry axis, while particles entering from off the axis along Y are deflected away from the central region of the symmetry axis; that is, show that positively charged particles are focused along X but defocused along Y. (b) Suppose that a beam of particles passes through a pair of coaxial magnetic quadrupole

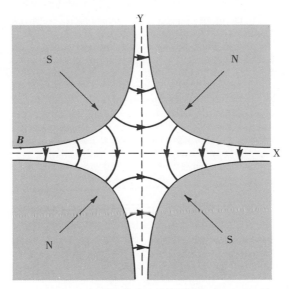

Figure 8-32 Magnetic quadrupole lens.

lenses in tandem, the second quadrupole lens rotated 90° relative to the first. Show that all particles of a beam entering the quadrupole pair are focused and then defocused, or conversely. The behavior is like that of a beam of light first passing through a converging lens and then through a diverging lens of the same focal length, or conversely. (c) It can be shown (see Problem 8-31) that, in general, a lens combination consisting of a converging lens of focal length f followed by a diverging lens of focal length $-f$ is always converging. Using this result, show that a pair of identical coaxial quadrupole lenses appropriately separated and with a relative angular displacement of 90° will act as a focusing device for a beam of charged particles.

8-31 * Consider a lens combination consisting of one thin lens of focal length f_1 followed by a second thin lens of focal length f_2 separated from it by a distance d. The focal length F of the combination is given by: $1/F = 1/f_1 + 1/f_2 - d/f_1 f_2$.† (a) Show that, if the two lenses have equal focal-length magnitudes, but one converges and the other diverges ($f_2 = -f_1$), then $F = f^2/d$. The focal length of the pair of lenses is *always positive*; that is, the combination always acts as a converging lens. (b) Show that a continuous sequence of lenses alternately converging and diverging is always converging. (*Hint:* A series of converging lenses must be converging; a single pair of converging and diverging lenses is converging.)

Since a nonuniform magnetic field acts as a converging or diverging lens for charged particles, depending upon the relative directions of the particle velocity and the magnetic-field gradient, a series of magnetic lenses, alternating in the gradient of the magnetic field, as shown in Figure 8-33, will have a net focusing effect. The use of the alternate-gradient focusing property is essential in the design of high-energy synchrotrons; indeed, all synchrotrons accelerating particles to energies higher than 1 GeV are of the AGS type ("alternate-gradient synchrotron").

8-32 Particles of mass m and charge Q are accelerated from rest by an electric potential difference V and are fired along the direction of the lines of a uniform magnetic field B (produced, for example, in the interior of a solenoid); see Figure 8-34. Actually, some particles enter the magnetic field at speed v at an angle slightly off the symmetry axis. These particles travel in a helical path; they coast along the direction of B at constant speed while moving at constant speed in a circle at right angles to B. Show that, if the angle θ between the particle's direction of velocity v at point A and the direction of B is small, all particles in the slightly diverging beam are brought to a focus a distance d from point A along the symmetry axis, where $d = (2\pi/B)(2mV/Q)^{1/2}$ and the particles are nonrelativistic. Note that the arrangement shown in Figure 8-34 permits the particle's mass m to be measured directly; it was first used by H. Busch in 1922 in measuring the e/m of an electron.

8-33 A drift-tube linac for accelerating protons to a final kinetic energy of 10 MeV is to employ oscillating electric fields with a frequency of 20 MHz and a maximum voltage of 100 kV. (a) What is the length of the final (longest) electrode? (b) If the protons are injected into the linac at an energy of 200 keV, what is the length of the first (shortest) electrode?

† See Chapter 44, Weidner and Sells, *E. C. P.*

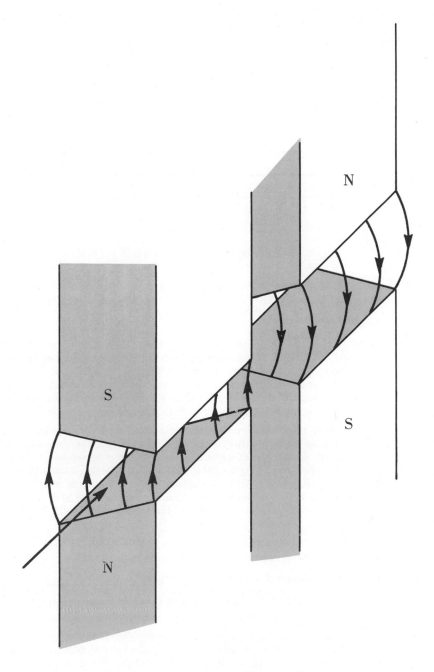

Figure 8-33 Alternating-gradient focusing.

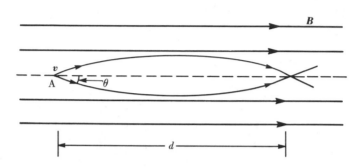

Figure 8-34

(c) How many acceleration gaps between adjacent electrodes must be used to achieve the final energy of 10 MeV? (d) Find the approximate overall length of the accelerator, ignoring the gaps between adjacent electrodes.

8-34 Electrons of 2.0 MeV kinetic energy are directed into a linear accelerator composed of 200 drift tubes connected alternately to a 3 GHz oscillator. (a) If the electrons are to emerge with a final energy of 50 MeV, what must be the lengths of the second and the last drift tube? (b) What would be the approximate overall length of the 100 MeV linear accelerator, assuming the spacing between adjacent drift tubes to be negligible?

8-35 In the 20 GeV linear electron accelerator at Stanford University electrons are accelerated from 30 MeV to 20 GeV along the 2-mile accelerating tube. (a) By what percentage is the final electron speed less than c? (b) What is the overall length of the accelerating tube as measured by an observer traveling with a 20 GeV electron? (c) The electron beam at the target has an electron current of 15 μA and a power of 0.50 MW. What is the average number of electrons striking the target per second?

8-36 (a) What is the design frequency for protons in a cyclotron with dees 1.0 m in diameter and a magnetic field of 1.0 Wb/m²? (b) What is the maximum kinetic energy attainable with such a cyclotron?

8-37 A cyclotron is adjusted to accelerate deuterons. (a) Show that it can, with only a small change in frequency or magnetic field, also accelerate alpha particles. (b) Assuming the magnetic field to remain unchanged, by what approximate factor must the frequency be changed to accelerate protons?

8-38 A cyclotron is adjusted to accelerate protons. (a) If the cyclotron frequency remains fixed, by what factor must the magnetic field be changed to permit the machine to accelerate deuterons? (b) What is the ratio of the maximum energy of the deuterons to that of protons (assume the deuteron mass to be twice that of the proton)?

8-39 A cyclotron has an electromagnet 1.0 m in diameter producing a field of 2.0 Wb/m². What is the oscillator frequency for accelerating (a) protons, (b) deuterons, and (c) alpha particles? What is the maximum energy of (d) protons, (e) deuterons, and (f) alpha particles?

8-40 A synchrocyclotron 6.0 m in diameter accelerates protons to 700 MeV. (a) What is the magnitude of the magnetic field? (b) What is the final oscillator frequency?

8-41 A synchrocyclotron having a magnetic field of 2.0 Wb/m² accelerates 2 MeV protons to an energy of 300 MeV. What are (a) the initial and (b) the final frequencies of the oscillator?

8-42 In the Bevatron synchrotron accelerator at the University of California at Berkeley protons are injected with a kinetic energy of 9.8 MeV and achieve a final kinetic energy of 6.2 GeV. The orbit radius is 15.2 m throughout. Compute the (a) initial and (b) final frequencies of the radio-frequency source.

8-43 At the Bevatron, the synchrotron at Berkeley, protons are injected into an orbit 15.2 m in radius at a kinetic energy of 9.8 MeV and emerge at 6.2 GeV. The protons gain 1.5 keV in energy at each revolution. (a) How many revolutions do the protons make? (b) How far does a proton travel during acceleration? (c) What is the frequency of the accelerating oscillator when protons achieve their maximum energy?

8-44 The alternating-gradient synchrotron (AGS) at Brookhaven National Laboratory employs a circular accelerating tunnel 840 m in diameter and accelerates protons to a kinetic energy of 33 GeV. What is the magnitude of the final magnetic field in the acceleration cycle?

8-45 Protons from a linear accelerator are injected at 50 MeV into the synchrotron at CERN, the European nuclear research center near Geneva, Switzerland. The protons emerge with a kinetic energy of 30 GeV. By what percentage is a proton's speed increased by the synchrotron?

8-46 Compute the approximate diameter of the 200 GeV proton synchrotron, to be constructed at Weston, Illinois, taking the maximum magnetic field to be 0.9 Wb/m².

8-47 * Imagine that a proton synchrotron has a diameter that of the Earth, 1.26×10^4 km, and a maximum magnetic field of 1.6 Wb/m²; the field guides protons along a path circling the Earth. (a) What is the maximum proton kinetic energy for this, the "ultimate" high-energy earth-bound particle accelerator? (b) The projected cost of the 200 GeV proton synchrotron at Weston, Illinois, is $0.260 billion; assuming very conservatively for simplicity that the cost of an accelerator is proportional to the kinetic energy of the accelerated particles or, equivalently, to the radius of the orbit, compute the approximate cost of the "ultimate" accelerator in units of the 1970 U.S.A. Gross National Product (approximately $1 trillion). (c) At what approximate date might the maximum energy be achieved, according to extrapolation from the following facts: starting with a machine for 1 MeV particles in 1932, the development of high-energy accelerators has advanced such that the maximum particle energy attainable has increased by a factor of 20 over a decade.

8-48   When particles from an accelerator collide with target particles that are at rest and of the same rest mass, at least half of the kinetic energy is "wasted" because of the requirement of momentum conservation. (a) A classical particle collides completely inelastically with an identical particle initially at rest, and the two particles may be imagined to stick together after collision. What fraction of the initial kinetic energy is dissipated in the collision? (b) By what factor is the dissipated energy in part (a) increased if the particle initially in motion collides head on in completely inelastic collision with a second identical particle moving in the opposite direction at the same speed?

To achieve the maximum dissipation of energy in a collision between two particles—or, in terms of high-energy physics, to make available the maximum kinetic energy for the creation of particles—the collision must take place in the reference frame in which the system's center of mass is at rest and the total momentum of the system is zero before and after collision. This is most readily accomplished by having the particles in two oppositely directed beams collide head on. For example, charged particles in two "storage rings," each consisting of a magnetic field guiding particles from an accelerator in a fixed circular path, can be made to collide head on. See Problem 8-49.

8-49 *   A colliding-beam accelerating machine has been proposed for construction at Novosibirsk, Siberia. In this machine a beam of protons accelerated to a kinetic energy of 25 GeV collides head on with a beam of antiprotons moving in the opposite direction with the same kinetic energy through the *same* acceleration chamber. All 52 GeV of energy entering each collision (1 GeV from each of the rest energies of the proton and antiproton and 25 GeV in kinetic energy from each colliding particle) may be consumed in the collision to create new particles. The system's total momentum is zero. On the other hand, when a 25 GeV proton collides with a second proton at rest, the total momentum before collision is approximately 25 GeV/c, and the total momentum must remain 25 GeV/c after collision, to preserve momentum conservation. Therefore, only a portion of the incident particle's kinetic and rest energy can be consumed in the reaction; the remainder is unavailable because it is required to conserve the system's momentum (see Problem 8-48).

The general relation is this: When a particle of rest energy E_0 and relativistic kinetic energy E_k collides head on with an identical particle at rest, the energy in the center-of-mass reference frame is $[(E_k + 2E_0)2E_0]^{1/2}$. To derive this relation one may use the fact that $E_0^2 = E^2 - (pc)^2$ is the same invariant quantity in every inertial frame, where E and p represent the total relativistic energy and momentum of the entire system. With what minimum kinetic energy must a proton strike a target proton at rest to make the same energy available as when oppositely directed protons, each of 25 GeV kinetic energy, collide head on?

N I N E

NUCLEAR STRUCTURE

Insofar as atomic structure is concerned the atomic nucleus may be regarded as a point mass and a point charge. The nucleus contains all of the positive charge and nearly all of the mass of the atom; it provides, therefore, the center about which electron motion takes place. Although the nucleus influences atomic structure primarily through its Coulomb force of attraction with electrons, some rather subtle effects in atomic spectra can be attributed to the nucleus. We recall that the Rydberg constant for a particular element is changed slightly by differences in the mass of the isotopes. Furthermore, hyperfine structure, the very closely spaced spectral lines in atomic spectra, has its origin in the angular momentum and the very small magnetic moment of the nucleus.

The fundamental alpha-particle scattering experiments of Rutherford established that for distances greater than 10^{-14} m the nucleus interacts with other charged particles by the inverse-square Coulomb force. It was found, however, that when the alpha particles approached the nuclear center closer than 10^{-14} m, the distribution of the scattered particles could not be accounted for simply in terms of Coulomb's law. These experiments showed then that a totally new type of force, the nuclear force, acts at distances smaller than 10^{-14} m.

In this chapter we shall explore some of the simpler aspects of nuclear structure: the fundamental nuclear constituents, their interactions, the properties of stable nuclei, and the properties and decay characteristics of unstable nuclei. We shall see that, apart from the tremendous difference in their relative sizes, 10^{-10} m for atoms but less than 10^{-14} m for nuclei, nuclear structure is different from atomic structure in several significant respects.

Whereas atoms can be excited so that they emit their optical or x-ray spectra through gaining an energy never greater than 100 keV, nuclei generally remain inert until they gain energies of the order of a few million electron volts. Some aspects of atomic structure can be understood on the basis of the Bohr model; no such simple model of nuclei exists. The primary force between the particles comprising the atom is the well-understood Coulomb force; additional forces act between the constituents of nuclei and these forces are only partially understood. An atom typically loses energy of excitation by emitting photons; an excited nucleus can lose its energy of excitation by emitting particles as well as by emitting photons. Despite these differences there are a number of fundamental laws that are found to apply equally well to atoms and to nuclei; these are the rules of the quantum theory and the laws of the conservation of mass-energy, linear momentum, angular momentum, and electric charge.

9-1 The nuclear constituents The particles of which all nuclei are composed are the proton and the neutron. We shall describe here some fundamental properties—charge, mass, spin, and nuclear magnetic moment—of these particles.

CHARGE The proton is the nucleus of the atom $^1_1$H, the light isotope of hydrogen; it carries a single positive charge, equal in magnitude to the charge of the electron.

The neutron is so named because it is electrically neutral. Because it carries no charge, it shows only a feeble interaction with electrons, it produces no direct ionization effects, and it is, therefore, detected and identified only by indirect means (see Section 10-6). The existence of the neutron was not clearly established until 1932, when J. Chadwick demonstrated its properties in a series of classic experiments, which will be discussed in Chapter 10.

MASS We list below the masses of the proton (the bare nucleus of the $^1_1$H atom) and the neutron in unified atomic mass units (see Section 3-6), together with the rest energies of these particles in units of MeV.

$$\text{proton rest mass} = 1.00727663 \pm 0.00000008 \text{ u}$$
$$\text{proton rest energy} = 938.256 \pm 0.005 \text{ MeV}$$
$$\text{neutron rest mass} = 1.0086654 \pm 0.0000004 \text{ u}$$
$$\text{neutron rest energy} = 939.550 \pm 0.005 \text{ MeV}$$

The proton and neutron have nearly the same mass, the neutron mass exceeding the proton mass by slightly less than 0.1 percent. Both particles have rest energies of about 1 GeV. Because the proton carries an electric charge, its mass can be measured directly with high precision by the methods of mass spectrometry; electric and magnetic fields have virtually no effect on a neutron, and its mass is inferred indirectly from experiments to be described shortly.

SPIN   An important property of both the proton and the neutron is the intrinsic angular momentum, or the so-called *nuclear spin*. Since spin angular momentum is independent of orbital motion, the nuclear spin can be visualized, as in the case of electron spin, in terms of the spinning of the particle as a whole about some internal rotation axis. The nuclear spin angular momentum L_I corresponds to the nuclear spin quantum number I; its magnitude is given by

$$L_I = \sqrt{I(I+1)}\,\hbar \qquad\qquad [9\text{-}1]$$

which is analogous to Equation 7-16, giving the spin angular momentum of the electron.

The nuclear spin quantum numbers of both the proton and the neutron are $\frac{1}{2}$:

> proton spin: $I = \frac{1}{2}$
> neutron spin: $I = \frac{1}{2}$

The nuclear-spin angular momentum is space-quantized by an external magnetic field, the permitted components along the direction of the magnetic field being $+\frac{1}{2}\hbar$ and $-\frac{1}{2}\hbar$, as shown in Figure 9-1. The magnitude of the spin angular momentum of a proton or neutron, as well as the components of the angular momentum along the space-quantization direction, are precisely the same as those for an electron.

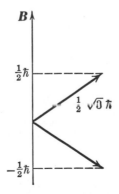

Figure 9-1. Space quantization of a proton spin or a neutron spin.

NUCLEAR MAGNETIC MOMENT The component of the magnetic moment associated with electron spin along the direction of an external magnetic field is one Bohr magneton (Section 7-6), $\beta = e\hbar/2m = 0.92732 \times 10^{-23}$ J/(Wb/m²). Because the electron has a negative electric charge, the electron-spin magnetic moment points in the opposite direction to that of the electron-spin angular momentum.

Now consider the magnetic moment associated with proton spin. Nuclear magnetic moments are measured in units of the *nuclear magneton* β_I, which is defined as

$$\beta_I = e\hbar/2M_p = (5.05050 \pm 0.00013) \times 10^{-27} \text{ J}/(\text{Wb/m}^2) \qquad [9\text{-}2]$$

where M_p, the proton mass, replaces the electron mass m in the Bohr magneton. Since the proton mass is 1,836.10 times that of the electron, the nuclear magneton is smaller than the Bohr magneton by this factor. The nuclear magnetic moment of the proton is found by experiment to be

$$\text{proton magnetic moment} = +(2.79276 \pm 0.00002)\beta_I$$

The plus sign indicates that the proton's magnetic moment points in the same direction as its nuclear spin; the magnitude of the nuclear moment gives the *component* of the proton's magnetic moment along the space-quantization direction in units of the nuclear magneton. It is significant that the size of the proton magnetic moment is *not* one nuclear magneton, but is, instead, nearly three times larger than what one might expect simply on the basis of the proton mass.

Despite the fact that the neutron as a whole carries no net electric charge, it does have a magnetic moment whose value is found to be

$$\text{neutron magnetic moment} = -1.191315\beta_I$$

The negative sign indicates that the neutron magnetic moment is *opposite* to the direction of the neutron angular momentum, as shown in Figure 9-2.

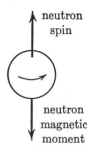

Figure 9-2. Representation of the relative orientations of the neutron spin and magnetic moment.

Because the proton moment is *not* one β_I and the neutron moment is *not* zero, the proton and neutron are more complicated entities than the electron. The non-zero magnetic moment of the neutron implies that, although it has zero total charge, there is a non-uniform charge distribution within the neutron.

9-2   The forces between nucleons   All nuclei consist of protons and neutrons bound together to form more or less stable systems; therefore, it is important to have some knowledge of the forces that act between these fundamental nuclear constituents. Consider first the force between two protons. The most direct way to examine this force is by means of a proton-proton scattering experiment. In such an experiment monoenergetic protons from a particle accelerator strike a target containing mostly hydrogen atoms and, therefore, protons. From the angular distribution of the scattered protons one can infer the force acting between the incident particles and the target particles—in this instance, both protons. Proton-proton scattering experiments show that the force can be represented approximately by the potential curve shown in Figure 9-3. At large distances of separation

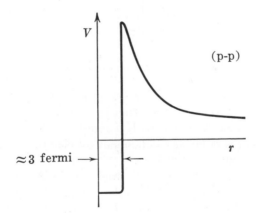

Figure 9-3. Proton-proton potential.

the protons repel one another by the Coulomb inverse-square force. At a separation distance of approximately 3×10^{-15} m there is a fairly sharp break in the potential curve. It indicates the onset of the *nuclear force* between a pair of protons. The force is strongly attractive at smaller distances (although there is evidence of a repulsive "core" at very small distances). The "size" of the proton can be taken as the *range*, 3×10^{-15} m, of the nuclear proton-proton force. The customary unit for measuring nuclear dimensions is the fermi, where

$$1 \text{ fermi} = 10^{-15} \text{ m}$$

The force between a neutron and a proton can be investigated by neutron-proton scattering experiments. In these experiments a mono-energetic neutron beam (neutrons from a nuclear reaction) bombards a target containing protons. Again the distribution of the scattered neutrons is analyzed for the force acting between the neutron and the proton, or the potential whose (negative) derivative gives this force. The interaction between a neutron and proton can be represented approximately by the potential curve shown in Figure 9-4. At large distances of separation there

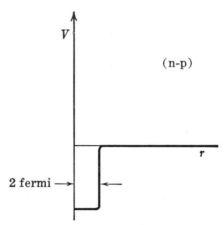

Figure 9-4. Neutron-proton potential.

is *no* force between the two particles, but at a distance of about 2 fermi the neutron and proton attract one another by a strong nuclear force having a fairly well-defined range, again with a repulsive inner core. Clearly, this nuclear attraction is in no way dependent on electric charge, inasmuch as the neutron is a neutral particle.

The nuclear force between two neutrons cannot be investigated directly by a neutron-neutron scattering experiment, because it is impossible to prepare a target consisting of free neutrons, but a variety of indirect evidence indicates that the force between two neutrons is approximately equal to the force between a neutron and a proton and also to the nuclear force between a pair of protons. Because a neutron and a proton are nearly equivalent in their interactions (apart from the Coulomb force between protons), it is customary to refer to a neutron *or* a proton as a *nucleon*. The term designates either a proton or a neutron when the distinction between them is of little importance. The independence of the nuclear force from the charge of the particular participating nucleons is known as the *charge independence* of the nuclear force. More sophisticated treatments of the proton-neutron interactions show that it is possible to consider the proton and neutron as two different charge states of the *same* particle.

9-3   **The deuteron**   The simplest nucleus containing more than one particle is the *deuteron*, the nucleus of the deuterium atom. The deuteron consists of a proton and a neutron bound together by the attractive nuclear force to form a stable system. The deuteron has a single positive charge, $+e$. Its mass is approximately twice that of the proton or neutron; more precisely,

$$\text{deuteron rest mass} = 2.013553 \text{ u}$$

It must be emphasized that the deuteron mass given here is that of the bare deuterium nucleus; the mass of the neutral deuterium atom exceeds that of the deuteron by the mass of an electron, 0.000549 u and is, therefore, 2.014102 u.

It is interesting to compare the mass of the deuteron, M_d, with the sum of the masses of its constituents, the proton and neutron, M_p and M_n:

$$M_p = 1.007277 \text{ u}$$
$$M_n = 1.008665 \text{ u}$$
$$M_p + M_n = 2.015942 \text{ u}$$
$$M_d = 2.013553 \text{ u}$$
$$M_p + M_n - M_d \text{ (mass difference)} = 0.002389 \text{ u}$$

The total mass of the proton and neutron when separated *exceeds* the mass of the two particles when they are bound together to form a deuteron. This difference is easily interpreted on the basis of the relativistic conservation of mass-energy (see Section 3-3).   When *any* two particles attract one another, the sum of their separate masses exceeds that of the bound system, inasmuch as energy (or mass) must be added to the system to separate it into its component particles. The added energy is called the binding energy; its value can be computed from the mass difference by using the mass-energy conversion factor

$$1 \text{ u} = 931.5 \text{ MeV}/c^2.$$

Thus, the binding energy E_b of the neutron-proton forming a deuteron is given by

$$E_b + M_d c^2 = (M_p + M_n)c^2 \qquad\qquad [9\text{-}3]$$
$$E_b = (M_p + M_n - M_d)c^2$$
$$E_b = (0.002389 \text{ u})(931.5 \text{ MeV}/c^2)c^2 = 2.225 \text{ MeV}$$

If 2.225 MeV is added to a deuteron, the neutron and proton can be separated from one another, beyond the range of the nuclear force, both particles being left at rest and thus having no kinetic energy.

A mass difference arises in *any* system of bound particles. For an atomic system such as the hydrogen atom the difference in mass between the atom and its separated parts is so small, 1 part in 10^8 indispensible, that it cannot be measured directly. The binding energy is manifested as a measurable mass difference in nuclear systems because the nuclear force is very strong and the binding energy is very great. In fact, the nuclear binding energy, 2.225 MeV, of two nucleons forming a deuteron is roughly a *million* times greater than the electrostatic binding energy, 13.58 eV, of a proton and an electron forming a hydrogen atom.

Recall that the binding energy of a hydrogen atom in its lowest, or ground, state (the ionization energy of the hydrogen atom), can be determined from the energy of the photon whose absorption in the photoelectric effect frees the bound electron from the hydrogen nucleus. A completely analogous measurement can be made of the deuteron binding energy. Deuterium gas is irradiated with a beam of high-energy monoenergetic gamma-ray photons. If the energy of the photons is equal to the deuteron's binding energy, photon absorption will produce a free neutron and a proton. If it exceeds the binding energy, the deuteron will be dissociated into a neutron and proton, each particle having kinetic energy. This *nuclear reaction* may be written as follows:

$$\gamma + d \rightarrow p + n \qquad [9\text{-}4]$$

Mass-energy conservation requires that

$$h\nu + M_d c^2 = M_p c^2 + M_n c^2 + K_p + K_n \qquad [9\text{-}5]$$

where K_p and K_n are the kinetic energies† of the freed proton and neutron, respectively. This process, in which the proton and neutron are detached from one another by the absorption of a photon, is a nuclear photoelectric effect, or a nuclear *photodisintegration*. The threshold for the reaction corresponds to $K_p = 0$ and $K_n = 0$; then,

$$h\nu_0 = (M_p + M_n - M_d)c^2 = E_b \qquad [9\text{-}6]$$

That is, the energy of the photon is equal to the binding energy of the deuteron.‡ If the threshold photon energy $h\nu_0$ is measured, the values of M_p and M_d being known, the neutron mass can be computed from Equation 9-6. This is one of several ways in which the neutron mass can be measured by applying energy conservation to nuclear reactions.

† Kinetic energy is denoted by K, rather than the conventional symbol E_k, throughout this chapter to avoid double subscripts.
‡ Strictly, the photon threshold energy for the photodisintegration of a deuteron initially at rest slightly *exceeds* the deuteron binding energy because of the requirement of momentum conservation: the total momentum of proton and neutron resulting from collision must equal the photon's momentum $h\nu/c$ entering into the collision. A more detailed analysis (Section 10-3) shows that the photon threshold energy is $h\nu = E_b/(1 - E_b/M_d c^2)$, greater than the deuteron binding energy by about 1 part in 10^3.

The inverse reaction of the deuteron photodisintegration is this: a neutron and proton at rest combine to form a deuteron in an excited state which decays to the ground state with the emission of a photon, of 2.22 MeV,

$$p + n \rightarrow d + \gamma \qquad [9\text{-}7]$$

Note that this nuclear reaction is merely that of Equation 9-4 with the arrow reversed.

A *nuclear energy-level diagram* of the deuteron is shown in Figure 9-5. Unlike all atoms and all other nuclei, the deuteron is found to have only

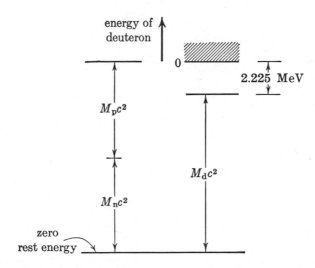

Figure 9-5. Energy-level diagram of the neutron-proton system, the deuteron.

one bound state; it can exist as a bound system only in this, the ground, state. In the continuum of unbound states the proton and neutron are free. The deuteron has no bound excited states. The rest masses and rest energies of the deuteron, proton, and neutron are also shown (but not to scale) in the diagram. It is useful to compare this diagram of the simplest of all bound nuclear systems with that of the simplest two-particle atomic system, the hydrogen atom. The simplified (and grossly exaggerated) energy-level diagram of the bound proton-electron system is shown in Figure 9-6, where the masses of the electron and proton are also displayed.

The hydrogen atom has, of course, a whole series of possible excited states, which is to say that the rest mass of the bound electron-proton system can assume any one of a large number of possible quantized values (compare Figure 9-6 with Figure 3-8). Because the binding energy for any one of the possible energy states of the hydrogen atom is small (less than

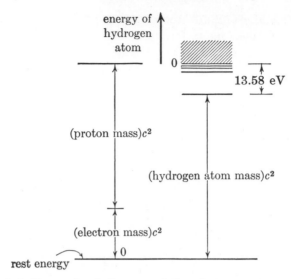

Figure 9-6. Energy-level diagram of the electron-proton system, the $^{1}_{1}$H atom.

13.58 eV), it is not possible in practice to determine the quantized energies of the hydrogen atom by measuring its mass, but the large binding energies of nucleons in nuclear systems permit the binding energy of nuclei to be determined directly from the difference between the rest masses of the constituent particles and the mass of the bound nuclear system.

9-4 Stable nuclei   We now consider the stable nuclei containing more than two nucleons. The number of protons in a nucleus is represented by the *atomic number* Z, the total number of nucleons is represented by the *mass number* A, and the number of neutrons is represented by $N = A - Z$. The term *nuclide* designates a particular species of nucleus having the same values of Z, N, or A. Species having the same proton number Z are nuclides known as *isotopes*, those having the same neutron number N are nuclides known as *isotones*, and those having the same nuclear number A are nuclides known as *isobars*. For example, $^{37}_{17}$Cl, which has 17 protons, 20 neutrons, and 37 nucleons, is an isotope of $^{35}_{17}$Cl, an isotone of $^{39}_{19}$K, and an isobar of $^{37}_{18}$Ar.

   The *stable* nuclides found in nature are plotted in Figure 9-7, where neutron number N is plotted against proton number Z. Each point represents a particular stable nuclide, that is, a combination of protons and neutrons forming a stable bound system. If we concentrate on its overall features, we can see a number of interesting and significant regularities in this diagram.

   Only those combinations of protons and neutrons which appear as points in the figure are found in nature as stable nuclides in their ground states;

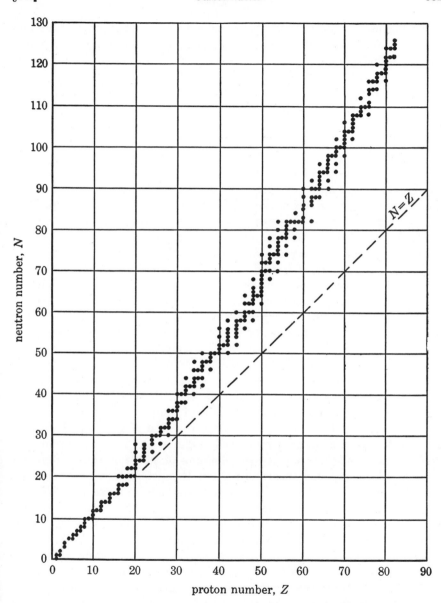

Figure 9-7. Neutron number versus proton number for the stable nuclides.

all other possible combinations of nucleons are to some degree unstable in that they decay, or disintegrate, into other nuclei. For example, the nuclides $^{16}_{8}O$, $^{17}_{8}O$, and $^{18}_{8}O$, all isotopes of oxygen, exist as stable nuclear systems, but the isotopes $^{15}_{8}O$ and $^{19}_{8}O$ are unstable.

The location of the stable nuclides can be represented approximately by a *stability line*. Such a line does not, of course, pass through each point; rather, it indicates the general region in which the most stable nuclides fall. We see that at small values of N and Z the stable nuclides lie close to the $N = Z$ line at 45°. For example, $^{16}_{8}O$ has $N = Z = 8$. The most stable light nuclides for a given mass number A are those whose number of protons is nearly equal to the number of neutrons. We might say that light nuclei prefer to have equal numbers of protons and neutrons because such aggregates are more stable than those in which there is a decided excess of protons or of neutrons. For the heavier nuclides the stability line bends increasingly away from the 45° line; that is, $N > Z$ at large A. For example, the stable nuclide $^{208}_{82}Pb$ has $Z = 82$ and $N = 126$. Thus heavy nuclides show a decided preference for neutrons over protons.

The neutron excess can be accounted for through the repulsive Coulomb force that acts between protons. If we start with a moderately heavy nucleus and attempt to construct from it a heavier nucleus by adding one nucleon, the binding of the additional neutron will usually be stronger than the binding of an additional proton. This follows from the fact that the neutron is only attracted by the nuclear force, whereas the proton is both attracted by the nuclear force and repelled by the Coulomb repulsive forces of the protons already in the heavy nucleus. The repulsive Coulomb effect competes noticeably with the strong nuclear attractive force only in heavy nuclides. One might say that, if protons had no electric charge but were otherwise distinguishable from neutrons, then the heavy, stable nuclides would have approximately equal numbers of protons and neutrons.

We can understand the near equality of Z and N at small A and the greater N than Z at large A by considering how the Pauli exclusion principle (Section 7-8) operates in the building of stable nuclides. Both the proton and the neutron separately follow this principle: no two identical particles can be placed in the same quantum state in a nucleus. We need not concern ourselves here with details of the quantum theory of nuclear structure, but we shall simply recognize that, if two protons are in a state having the same three spatial quantum numbers (not necessarily the quantum numbers n, l, and m_l appearing in atomic structure), then the protons must differ in their magnetic spin quantum numbers. This implies that two protons can occupy the same quantum state only if their nuclear spins are antialigned. The same rule applies to neutrons: only two neutrons, one with spin up and one with spin down, can occupy a quantum state that is identical in the three spatial quantum numbers. Apart from the Coulomb interaction between protons, the states available to a proton or a neutron are very nearly the same, since the proton and neutron are essentially equivalent in their nuclear interactions.

Consider Figure 9-8, which shows in a schematic fashion the states available to protons and neutrons as they combine to form stable nuclei.

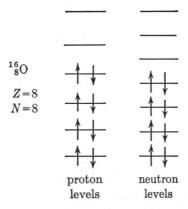

$^{16}_{8}O$

$Z = 8$
$N = 8$

proton   neutron
levels   levels

Figure 9-8. Schematic representation of the proton and neutron states of $^{16}_{8}O$.

For simplicity the states are shown nearly equally spaced and with one set of levels for protons and a second set for neutrons. The spacing between proton levels increases as the levels get higher, to correspond to the Coulomb force between protons. The neutron levels are equally spaced. We suppose that two protons, one with spin up and one with spin down, can be accommodated in each proton level and two neutrons in each neutron level.

The first proton level and the first neutron level are filled when a nucleus is formed of two protons and two neutrons. This corresponds to the very stable nuclide $^{4}_{2}He$. With further nucleons forming stable nuclides of larger A we should expect the proton and neutron levels to be nearly equally populated. Thus, at small A the stable nuclides will have $Z \approx N$, in accord with observation. As the number of nucleons increases, the most stable nuclides will again be formed when the lowest energy levels available to the protons and neutrons are filled first. This requires that there be a neutron excess, or $N > Z$, for large A. We see, then, that the general features of the stability line can be accounted for by applying the Pauli exclusion principle to the building up of stable nuclides.

9-5 Nuclear radii   The radius of a nucleus can be defined and evaluated in a number of ways. A nuclear radius is given approximately by the results of alpha-particle scattering experiments. Although the distribution of the scattered particles is accounted for by the Coulomb interaction alone for distances greater than 10^{-14} m, deviations from Coulomb's law occur when the alpha particles come within approximately that distance from the nuclear center. A nuclear radius can be defined, then, as the distance from the nuclear center at which the nuclear force becomes important.

The nuclear radius can, however, be inferred more directly and with higher precision from scattering experiments in which high-energy neutrons bombard target nuclei. Neutrons are not repelled by a Coulomb force;

they are deviated from their incident directions or absorbed by the target nucleus only when they come within the range of the nuclear force of the bombarded nuclei. We can define the *nuclear-force* radius as that distance from the center of the nucleus at which a neutron first feels the nuclear attractive force. Because the range of the nuclear force is quite definite, the nuclear interaction being effectively zero for greater separation distance, neutron scattering experiments do not have the complicating effect of the Coulomb force, which must be subtracted out in an analysis of the scattering data.

Like all particles, the neutron has a wavelength associated with it. Unless the neutron's wavelength is small enough for the neutron's position to be quite precisely specified with respect to nuclear dimensions, neutron scattering experiments cannot be interpreted simply. Neutrons of 100 MeV have a wavelength of about 1 fermi. Many experiments have been designed to measure the absorption of high-energy neutrons in a variety of targets. The results may be summarized by the following relation, in which the nuclear radius R is given as a function of the nuclear mass number A :

$$R = r_0 A^{1/3} \qquad [9\text{-}8]$$

where $r_0 = 1.4$ fermi is the nuclear-force radius. The radius of any nucleus, defined in terms of its nuclear interaction with a neutron, can be computed from this equation. The radius R of even the most massive nuclei is found to be no larger than about 10 fermi.

The scattering of very-high-energy electrons provides another means of assigning a nuclear radius. An electron of 10 GeV has a wavelength of only 0.1 fermi, *less* than the size of even the smallest nucleus. Such a well-localized particle is a suitable probe for studying nuclear radii, and experiments with high-energy electrons (particularly in the linear electron accelerators at Stanford University) have led to information concerning the distribution of electric charge within a nucleus and even within a single proton. Whereas neutrons are scattered only by the nuclear force in nuclear interactions, electrons are scattered only by the charges within nuclei in electric interactions, not by the nuclear force. The results of high-energy electron-scattering experiments may be summarized by the relation

with
$$R = r_0 A^{1/3}$$
$$r_0 = 1.1 \text{ fermi} \qquad [9\text{-}9]$$

which is precisely the same form as Equation 9-8. Note, however, that the value of the charge, or electromagnetic, radius r_0 is somewhat smaller than the value of the nuclear-force radius r_0. Figure 9-9 shows the distribution of electric charge within nuclei as measured by the scattering of high-energy electrons.

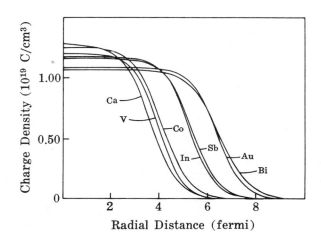

Figure 9-9. Nuclear electric-charge density as a function of radial distance for several elements, as determined from scattering experiments with 183 MeV electrons.

The relationship for the nuclear radius leads to an important conclusion concerning the density of nuclear material. Cubing Equation 9-8 and multiplying by $4\pi/3$, we have

$$4\pi R^3/3 = (4\pi r_0^3/3)\, A \qquad\qquad [9\text{-}10]$$

The quantity $4\pi R^3/3$ is the volume of the nucleus, assumed to be a sphere, or a near sphere, and we can take $4\pi r_0^3/3$ to be the volume of a single nucleon. Therefore, Equation 9-10 becomes

(volume of the nucleus) = (volume of a nucleon) $\times$ (number of nucleons)

The total volume of a nucleus is merely the sum of the volumes of the several nucleons composing it. This relation holds for all nuclei. Moreover, all nucleons have nearly the same mass. Therefore, we conclude that *all* nuclei have the *same density* of nuclear matter. It is easily found that the density of nuclear material is 2×10^{17} kg/m³, or about 10^9 tons per square inch (this extraordinarily high density is, of course, consistent with the fact that the radii of atoms are approximately a hundred thousand times that of nuclei).

We are now in a position to discuss a question that has not been raised so far, namely, why electrons are not constituents of nuclei. Before the discovery of the neutron in 1932 it was thought that nuclei consisted of protons and electrons and that, for example, a nucleus of $^{14}_{7}$N would consist of 14 protons and 7 electrons. The hypothesis that electrons existed in nuclei was strengthened by the observation that radioactive materials undergoing beta decay actually emit electrons from their nuclei.

If an electron were confined and localized within a nuclear dimension, say 1 fermi, then the wavelength of the electron could be no greater than this distance. Now, an electron of 1 GeV has approximately this wavelength. Therefore, if it were contained within a nucleus, it would have a kinetic energy of at least 1 GeV; however, an electron of that energy can be bound and have a negative total energy only if its potential energy is less than -1 GeV. Thus, an attractive potential of at least that much must exist for electrons if they are to be bound within a nucleus. There is no evidence whatsoever of so strong an attractive force on an electron; we must, therefore, conclude that electrons cannot exist within a nucleus. We shall later discuss other equally compelling arguments against electrons as nuclear constituents. A nucleon can, however, be localized within a nuclear dimension when its kinetic energy is only a few MeV; for example, a nucleon of 10 MeV has a wavelength of about 1 fermi.

9-6 The binding energy of stable nuclei The nuclear force is so strong that the mass of a bound nuclear system is measurably smaller than the sum of the masses of its components. Thus, information on the binding energy of nuclear systems can be arrived at directly from a comparison of masses.

The masses of atoms can be measured with considerable precision (better than 1 part in 10^5) by the methods of mass spectrometry (Section 8-4). Appendix II gives the masses of the *neutral* atoms in unified atomic mass units (u). All measured atomic masses are very close to the integral mass number A; this is called the *whole-number rule*. An atom of $^{12}_{6}$C has a mass of precisely 12 u by definition. The mass of a nucleus is the atomic mass less Z electron masses (since the number of electrons equals the number of protons). Because the energy binding the atomic electrons to the nucleus is usually quite small compared with the atom's rest energy, we can take the neutral atom's mass to be the mass of the nucleus plus the masses of the electrons.

Consider the nucleus of $^{12}_{6}$C, which has 6 protons and 6 neutrons. We wish to calculate the *total* binding energy; that is, the energy required to separate a $^{12}_{6}$C nucleus into its 12 component nucleons, each nucleon being at rest and effectively out of the range of the forces of the other nucleons. In the following computation we shall use the mass of a *neutral hydrogen atom*, 1.007825 u and the mass of an electron, 0.000549 u.

$$6 \text{ protons} = 6(1.007825 - 0.000549) \text{ u}$$
$$6 \text{ neutrons} = 6(1.008665) \text{ u}$$

$$\text{total nucleon masses} = 12.098940 - 6(0.000549) \text{ u}$$
$$^{12}_{6}\text{C nuclear mass} = 12.000000 - 6(0.000549) \text{ u}$$

$$\text{mass difference} = 0.098940 \text{ u}$$
$$\text{total binding energy} = 0.098940 \text{ u} \times 931.5 \text{ MeV/u} = 92.16 \text{ MeV}$$

Note that, because the electron masses cancel out, we can use the masses of the *neutral* atoms of hydrogen and carbon 12 rather than the masses of the proton and the carbon 12 nucleus.

We see that 92.16 MeV must be added to a carbon nucleus to separate it completely into its constituent particles; therefore, the twelve nucleons of the carbon atom are bound together with a total binding energy $E_b = 92.16$ MeV to form the nucleus in its lowest energy state. The *average* binding energy per nucleon, E_b/A, is 92.16/12, or 7.68 MeV; this is not the binding energy of every nucleon but is the average of the twelve binding energies.

We can write a general relationship giving the total binding energy E_b of any nucleus having an atomic mass M and composed of Z protons of *atomic* mass M_H and $A - Z$ neutrons of mass M_n:

$$\boxed{E_b/c^2 = ZM_H + (A - Z)M_n - M} \qquad \text{[9-11]}$$

Now, let us compute the energy needed to remove *just one proton* from $^{12}_{6}$C, leaving a nucleus with 5 protons and 6 neutrons, namely, the nucleus of $^{11}_{5}$B. The energy binding the last proton to the remaining 11 nucleons, *the separation energy*, can likewise be computed by using the rest masses of the particles (again we use the masses of *neutral* atoms):

$$\text{mass of } ^1_1\text{H} = 1.007825 \text{ u}$$
$$\text{mass of } ^{11}_{5}\text{B} = 11.009305 \text{ u}$$
$$\text{mass of } ^1_1\text{H} + ^{11}_{5}\text{B} = 12.017130 \text{ u}$$
$$\text{mass of } ^{12}_{6}\text{C} = 12.000000 \text{ u}$$

$$\text{mass difference} = 0.017130 \text{ u}$$

$$\text{separation energy} = 0.017130 \text{ u} \times 931.5 \text{ MeV/u} = 15.96 \text{ MeV}.$$

We see that in $^{12}_{6}$C the binding energy, 15.96 MeV, of one particular nucleon (the least tightly bound proton) is *not* the same as the *average* binding energy of a nucleon, 7.68 MeV, although they are of the same order of magnitude (the separation energy of the least tightly bound *neutron* in $^{12}_{6}$C is 18.72 MeV).

Removing the last proton from a nucleus corresponds, in atomic structure, to removing the least tightly bound valence electron from an atom by ionization. We know that the ionization energy of an outer, valence electron in an atom is usually several orders of magnitude less than that of an inner, tightly bound electron (visible light for the former, x-rays for the latter); thus we see that, unlike the case of electrons bound by electric interaction, the particles of a stable nucleus are all bound with at least approximately the same energy.

The average binding energy per nucleon, E_b/A, can be computed for any stable nucleus by using Equation 9-11. When the computed values of E_b/A are plotted against the corresponding values of the atomic mass A, we obtain the results shown in Figure 9-10. The characteristics of the curve

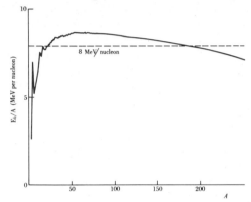

Figure 9-10. Average binding energy per nucleon as a function of mass number, for the stable nuclides.

may be summarized as follows. Apart from sharp peaks for the especially stable nuclides with groups of 2 protons and 2 neutrons, $^4_2$He, $^{12}_6$C, $^{16}_8$O, the curve rises sharply from the lightest stable nuclides to values of $A \approx 20$. At $A > 20$ the curve rises slowly, reaches a maximum near the element $^{56}_{26}$Fe, and then drops slowly toward the heaviest nuclides. It is approximately horizontal from $A = 20$ onward, E_b/A being roughly constant:

$$\boxed{\text{for} \quad A > 20 \qquad E_b/A \approx 8 \text{ MeV/nucleon}} \qquad [9\text{-}12]$$

Iron and nuclides close to it represent the most stable configurations of nucleons found in nature; in all elements lighter or heavier than iron the typical nucleon is bound with less energy.

9-7 Nuclear models Because a nucleus consists of many particles *all* strongly interacting, no single theoretical model successfully describes all aspects of nuclear behavior, but a number of nuclear models that account for the nuclear properties have been found. We discuss here the liquid-drop model, the single-particle and shell models, and the collective model.

LIQUID-DROP MODEL   Excluding for the moment the initial rise in the curve of Figure 9-10, the value of E_b/A is nearly a constant. Therefore, the total binding energy E_b is closely proportional to A, the total number of nucleons. This simple dependence of binding energy on number of bound particles finds a simple interpretation in the nuclear model known as the *liquid-drop model*, proposed by N. Bohr in 1936. In this model the binding between the nucleons in a nucleus is treated as similar to the binding of molecules in a liquid. We know that the total binding energy of a liquid is directly proportional to the mass of the liquid (for example, to boil 2 kg of water requires twice the energy needed to boil 1 kg) and if the density of a liquid is constant, the total binding energy of a liquid is also proportional to the volume of the liquid. Nuclei show the same behavior: the binding energy E_b and the nuclear volume $4\pi R^3/3$ are both directly proportional to the number of nucleons, A. This simple behavior is related to the forces between nucleons.

Each nucleon interacts with other nucleons by a strong, *short-range* nuclear force; that is, any one nucleon interacts only with its immediate neighboring nucleons. The nuclear force shows *saturation*: after a nucleon is completely surrounded by a full complement of neighbors with which it interacts, it exerts no substantial force on other, more distant nucleons. At the surface of a nucleus, however, the force of a nucleon is unsaturated, since a surface nucleon is not completely surrounded. This corresponds to the phenomenon of surface tension in liquids. The surface effect is most marked among the lightest nuclides, for which many of the nucleons are at the surface; it is less marked among the heavy nuclides, for which a smaller fraction of the nucleons are at the surface.

Although the attractive nuclear force shows saturation, each nucleon interacting only with its immediate neighbors, this is not true of the repulsive Coulomb force between protons in a nucleus. Each proton in a nucleus interacts with *every other* proton with a Coulomb potential energy E_e given by

$$E_e = ke^2/r \qquad [9\text{-}13]$$

where $k = 1/4\pi\epsilon_0$, e is the proton charge, and r is the distance between a pair of protons. Taking r to be 3 fermi as a typical, average distance between a pair, we find from this equation that $E_e \approx 0.5$ MeV. This energy is small compared with the value of $E_b/A \approx 8$ MeV; so the Coulomb energy is not an important influence in the lightest nuclei.

Among the heavy nuclides with large Z, the Coulomb energy becomes significant. Every proton interacts with *every* other proton in the nucleus, according to Equation 9-13, so the *total* Coulomb energy depends on the number of proton pairs, that is, the total number of protons taken two at a time, or $Z(Z - 1)/2$. In a heavy nucleus the Coulomb effect, which represents a tendency of the protons to disrupt the stable nucleon configuration consequently varies approximately as Z^2.

According to the liquid-drop model, the total binding of nucleons is influenced principally by the following three effects:

The volume effect: $E_b/A \approx$ constant; therefore, the binding energy E_b is proportional to A and to the nuclear volume.

The surface effect: The *unbinding* energy is proportional to the surface area of the nucleus and therefore to R^2, or to $A^{2/3}$.

The Coulomb effect: The *unbinding* energy is proportional to the total number of proton pairs, $Z(Z-1)/2$, and inversely proportional to the nuclear radius R; the total unbinding Coulomb energy is, therefore, proportional to $Z^2 A^{-1/3}$.

It is possible to fit fairly well the curve of Figure 9-10 to the total of the volume, surface, and Coulomb effects. The volume effect makes a *positive*

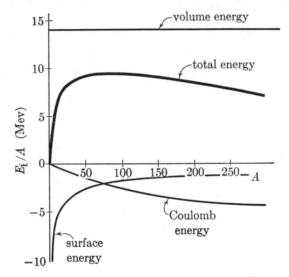

Figure 9-11. Contributions of the volume energy, surface energy, and Coulomb energy to the average binding energy per nucleon, as a function of mass number.

contribution to the total binding energy; the surface and Coulomb effects make *negative* contributions. The three separate curves and their algebraic sum are shown in Figure 9-11. Because the liquid-drop model is capable of accounting so well for the principal features of the curve of binding energy per nucleon, the assumptions contained in it must correspond, at least approximately, to the true nature of the interactions between nucleons. The liquid-drop model emphasizes the ways in which all nucleons are alike, inasmuch as it treats the proton and neutron as identical (apart from the Coulomb force between protons). The model is not successful, however, in accounting for some of the finer details of nuclear structure.

THE SINGLE-PARTICLE AND SHELL MODELS   With regard to atomic structure the quantum levels and chemical properties of a so-called one-electron atom, such as the sodium ion Na^+ with one valence electron outside closed shells of inner electrons (in the electron configuration $1s^2 2s^2 2p^6 3s^1$), can be attributed primarily to this "last" valence electron. Similarly, with regard to nuclear structure such properties as the nucleus' angular momentum and magnetic moment can, under some circumstances, be accounted for primarily in terms of a "last" odd nucleon. To see how such a single-particle nuclear model accounts for nuclear properties, consider first how the stable (or very long-lived and nearly stable) nuclides are distributed among even-even, even-odd, odd-even, and odd-odd proton-neutron numbers, Z-N, as shown in Table 9-1.

Table 9-1

NUCLIDE TYPE, Z-N	NUMBER OF STABLE NUCLIDES	(NUMBER OF VERY LONG-LIVED NUCLIDES)
Even-even	155	11
Even-odd	53	3
Odd-even	50	3
Odd-odd	4	5

Almost 60 percent of the stable, or very nearly stable, nuclides have an even number of protons and of neutrons. Clearly, nuclei have a greater stability when both the proton and neutron levels are full (see Figure 9-8) than when there is an odd number of protons or neutrons. In fact, the only examples of *stable* odd-odd nuclides are the lightest possible nuclides of this type, $_1^2H$, $_3^6Li$, $_5^{10}B$, and $_7^{14}N$, and all of these have $Z = N$.

The shell model is fairly successful in predicting the total nuclear angular momentum of stable nuclides. The total angular momentum of any nucleus consists of contributions from three sources: the intrinsic angular momentum, or nuclear spin, of the protons, $\frac{1}{2}\hbar$, the intrinsic angular momentum, or nuclear spin, of the neutrons, $\frac{1}{2}\hbar$, and the orbital angular momentum of the nucleons arising from their motion in the nucleus. These three contributions are combined by rules of vector addition (see Figure 7-20) to give the total, or resultant, nuclear angular momentum (misleadingly called *the* nuclear spin), represented by the symbol I.

The nuclear spins of the four categories of stable nuclides are given in Table 9-2.

Table 9-2

Nuclide type Z-N	Nuclear spin
Even-even	0
Even-odd $\rbrace$ Odd-even $\rbrace$	$\frac{1}{2}, \frac{3}{2}, \frac{5}{2}, \frac{7}{2}, \dots$
Odd-odd	1, 3

The fact that all even-even nuclides have zero total nuclear angular momentum is interpreted as follows. The protons fill the available proton levels in pairs of antialigned proton spins; the contribution of proton-spin angular momentum, therefore, is zero. Similarly, the neutrons are antialigned in pairs, producing zero neutron-spin angular momentum. Finally, the angular orbital momentum of the protons and neutrons is zero, indicating that these nucleons are in closed shells analogous to the closed shells and subshells of atomic structure. Furthermore, all even-even nuclides have a zero nuclear magnetic moment. Just as the zero angular momentum and magnetic moment of inert-gas atoms is attributed to the pairing off of electron spins and orbital momenta, so too the zero nuclear angular momentum and the zero nuclear magnetic moment of even-even nuclides is attributed to the pairing off of neutron spins and proton spins.

In the even-odd or odd-even nuclides one odd nucleon combines its half-integral intrinsic spin with the integral orbital angular-momentum quantum number of the nucleus yielding half-integral I values. The nuclear magnetic moment of these nuclides is of the order of the nuclear magneton. This is the basis of another argument against electrons' being nuclear constituents: if electrons were to exist in the nucleus, the magnetic moment of the nucleus would be of the order of a Bohr magneton, roughly a thousand times larger than the observed nuclear magnetic moments.

The odd-odd nuclides have an odd proton and an odd neutron, each with spin $\frac{1}{2}$; therefore, the total nuclear spin I is integral. It is interesting to consider what the nuclear spin of an odd-odd nuclide such as the deuteron, $^2_1$H, would be if the nucleus consisted of protons and electrons. In the proton-electron nuclear model the deuteron would consist of two protons and one electron, each of the *three* particles with spin $\frac{1}{2}$. Therefore, this model predicts a *half*-integral value of I. On the other hand, the proton-neutron nuclear model, with *two* particles each of spin $\frac{1}{2}$, predicts that I be *integral*. The nuclear spin I of the deuteron is experimentally found to be 1. On this basis the proton-electron nuclear model is again untenable.

The nuclear shell model of M. G. Mayer and J. H. Jensen, first introduced in 1948, accounts for the special stability of nuclides whose number of protons or neutrons equals 2, 8, 20, 28, 50, 82, and 126 (the "magic" numbers). The basic assumption is that single-particle quantum states are split appreciably by spin-orbit interaction (see Section 7-6). Thus, the six p states available to a proton or neutron are divided, through the interaction of the orbital angular momentum and the intrinsic proton or neutron angular momentum, into two $p_{1/2}$ states and four $p_{3/2}$ states. (The letter indicates the orbital angular-momentum quantum number, and the subscript gives the total nuclear angular momentum; thus, $p_{3/2}$ implies that the orbital angular-momentum quantum number is 1, the nuclear spin I is 3/2, and the total number of available states is $2I + 1 = 2(3/2) + 1 = 4$.) Table 9-3 lists nucleon configurations according to the shell model up to Z or $N = 82$. Groups of levels, or shells, between which there are sizable energy gaps, are bracketed, and the total number of nucleons producing closed shells are seen to be the magic numbers.

Table 9-3

Nucleon configuration	Nucleon numbers		Total number of nucleons
$2d_{3/2}$	4		
$3s_{1/2}$	2		
$1h_{11/2}$	12	32	82
$2d_{5/2}$	6		
$1g_{7/2}$	8		
$1g_{9/2}$	10		
$2p_{1/2}$	2	22	50
$1f_{5/2}$	6		
$2p_{3/2}$	4		
$1f_{7/2}$	8	8	28
$1d_{3/2}$	4		
$2s_{1/2}$	2	12	20
$1d_{5/2}$	6		
$1p_{1/2}$	2	6	8
$1p_{3/2}$	4		
$1s_{1/2}$	2	2	2

Besides yielding the magic numbers, the shell model predicts nuclear spins. The observed spins of many nuclides, in both ground and excited states, are found to be in accord with the predicted values.

THE COLLECTIVE MODEL   The collective nuclear model, suggested by A. Bohr and B. Mottelson in 1953, is intermediate between the nuclear-drop model, in which the nucleons are all taken to be equivalent, and the shell model, in which each nucleon is taken to be in a distinctive quantum state. This model emphasizes the collective motion of nuclear matter, particularly the vibrations and rotations, both quantized in energy, in which large groups of nucleons can participate. Even-even nuclides with proton or neutron numbers close to magic numbers are particularly stable configurations with nearly perfect spherical symmetry; the excitation energies of the excited nuclear energy states may be ascribed to the vibration of the nucleus as a whole. On the other hand, even-even nuclides far from magic numbers depart substantially from spherical symmetry (they are said to have a large electric quadrupole moment); the excitation energies of their excited nuclear states may be ascribed to the rotation of the nucleus as a whole in quantized rotational energy states.

9-8 The decay of unstable nuclei   Thus far we have discussed only stable nuclei which, when left to themselves, will exist indefinitely without change. Just as an atom can exist in any one of a number of excited energy states, so too a nucleus has a set of discrete, quantized, excited nuclear energy states. Research in nuclear physics over the past years has yielded voluminous experimental data on the energy states and decay schemes of somewhat more than twelve hundred nuclides, and although a complete theoretical understanding of nuclear structure is still wanting, many important aspects of it have been established through a study of unstable nuclei.

In addition to the laws of conservation of mass-energy, linear momentum, angular momentum, and charge, which hold for nuclear systems, there are other conservation laws that have been found to apply to nuclear transformations. The only one that will concern us at this time is the following:

Law of *conservation of nucleons: the total number of protons and neutrons entering a reaction must equal the total number of nucleons leaving the reaction.*

Therefore, the mass-energy, linear momentum, angular momentum, electric charge, and number of nucleons before a reaction or decay must all be equal to the respective quantities after the reaction or decay.

We shall see that there are several important differences between unstable nuclei and unstable atoms:

The spacing of nuclear energy levels is much greater than that of atomic energy levels.

The average time that an unstable nucleus spends in an excited state can range from 10^{-14} sec to 10^{11} years, whereas atomic lifetimes are usually about 10^{-8} sec.

Whereas excited atomic systems almost invariably emit photons upon de-excitation, an unstable nucleus may emit photons or particles of nonzero rest mass (for example, alpha particles or beta particles).

Just as in the decay of excited atomic systems, all nuclear decays, whatever their differences in particles emitted or rates at which they take place, follow a single law: the *law of radioactive decay*. We shall call the initial unstable nucleus the parent and the nucleus into which the parent decays the daughter. The death of the parent gives birth to the daughter. The probability that an unstable or excited nucleus will decay spontaneously into one or more particles of lower energy is independent of the parent nucleus' past history, is the same for all nuclei of the same type, and is very nearly independent of external influences (temperature, pressure, etc.).

There is no way of predicting the time that any one unstable nucleus will decay, its survival being subject to the laws of chance, but during an infinitesimally small time interval dt the probability that it will decay is directly proportional to this time interval. Thus,

$$\text{probability that nucleus } decays \text{ in time } dt = \lambda \, dt$$

where the proportionality constant λ is called the *decay constant* or the *disintegration constant*. Since the total probability that a nucleus will either survive or decay in the time dt is 1 (100 percent),

$$\text{probability that nucleus } survives \text{ time } dt = 1 - \lambda \, dt$$

$$\text{probability that nucleus } survives \text{ time } 2 \, dt$$
$$= (1 - \lambda \, dt)(1 - \lambda \, dt) = (1 - \lambda \, dt)^2$$

Consider now the probability of the nucleus' surviving n time intervals, each of duration dt:

$$\text{probability that nucleus survives time } n \, dt = (1 - \lambda \, dt)^n \qquad [9\text{-}14]$$

Then putting $n \, dt = t$, the total time elapsed, and remembering that, as $dt \rightarrow 0$, $n = t/dt \rightarrow \infty$, we have

$$\text{probability that nucleus survives time } t = \lim_{n \to \infty} (1 - \lambda t/n)^n \qquad [9\text{-}15]$$

Now, the definition of e^{-x}, where e is the base of the natural logarithms, is

$$e^{-x} \equiv \lim_{n \to m} (1 - x/n)^n \qquad [9\text{-}16]$$

Comparing Equations 9-15 and 9-16, we see that

$$\text{probability that nucleus survives time } t = e^{-\lambda t} \qquad [9\text{-}17]$$

This equation is the necessary consequence of the assumption that the decay of nuclei in unstable states is independent of the nucleus' present condition and past history. Although we cannot say precisely when a *single* nucleus will decay, we can predict the statistical decay of a *large* number of identical unstable nuclei. If there are initially N_0 unstable nuclei undergoing a decay process characterized by the decay constant λ, then the number N surviving a period of time t is merely N_0 times the probability that any one nucleus will have survived. Therefore, from Equation 9-17 we have

$$N = N_0 e^{-\lambda t} \qquad [9\text{-}18]$$

This exponential decay law holds, not only for unstable nuclei, but also for any unstable system (such as atoms in excited states) that is subject to decay by chance.

It is customary to measure the rapidity of decay in terms of the *half-life*, $T_{1/2}$, which is defined as the time in which one half of the original unstable nuclei have decayed and one half still survive. Therefore, $t = T_{1/2}$ when $N = \frac{1}{2}N_0$, and Equation 9-18 gives

$$\tfrac{1}{2}N_0 = N_0 e^{-\lambda T_{1/2}}$$

$$T_{1/2} = (ln_e 2)/\lambda = 0.693/\lambda \qquad [9\text{-}19]$$

Thus, if a radioactive material decays with a half-life of 3 sec, after 3 sec one half of the initial nuclei remain, after 6 sec one quarter of the initial nuclei remain, and after 9 sec one eighth of the initial nuclei remain. The decay constant λ has the units of reciprocal time (for example, $\sec^{-1}$), which follows from its definition as the probability per unit time for decay.

The half-life is *not* the same as the *average lifetime*, or mean life T_{av}, of an unstable nucleus; a straightforward calculation (see Problem 9-21) shows that

$$T_{av} = 1/\lambda = T_{1/2}/ln_e 2 \qquad [9\text{-}20]$$

The decay of the parent nuclei and the concomitant growth in the number of daughter nuclei with time are shown in Figure 9-12. The number of daughter nuclei produced after a time t is $N_0 - N = N_0(1 - e^{-\lambda t})$, where N_0 is again the initial number of parent nuclei.

Another useful quantity describing radioactive decay is the *activity*, which is defined as the number of decays per second. It follows from Equation 9-18 that

$$dN/dt = -\lambda N_0 e^{-\lambda t} = -\lambda N$$

$$\text{activity} = -dN/dt = \lambda N = (\lambda N_0)e^{-\lambda t} \qquad [9\text{-}21]$$

The minus sign appearing in this equation indicates that the number of unstable nuclei *decreases* with time. The activity λN, originally λN_0, falls

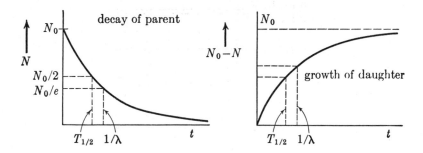

Figure 9-12. Decay in the number of radioactive parent atoms and growth in the number of (stable) daughter atoms, as functions of time.

off as $e^{-\lambda t}$. The activity of unstable nuclei that radiate particles or photons, the *radioactivity*, can be measured with a nuclear-radiation counter over periods of time that are short compared with the half-life of the decay. This provides, then, a simple and direct method of measuring λ or $T_{1/2}$.

The common unit for measuring activity is the *curie*, which is defined as exactly 3.7×10^{10} disintegrations per second; a related unit, the milli-curie is 3.7×10^7 sec^{-1}. Another unit sometimes used for activity is the *rutherford*, defined as 10^6 disintegrations per second.

9-9 Gamma decay All stable nuclides are ordinarily in their lowest, or ground, states. If such nuclei are excited and gain energy by photon or particle bombardment, they may exist in any one of a number of excited, quantized energy states. Furthermore, all radioactive nuclides are initially in energy states from which they decay with the emission of photons or particles. We shall be concerned here with the decay of a nucleus from an excited state by the emission of a photon. A photon emitted from a nucleus in an excited state is called a gamma ray.

The nuclear energy levels of the radioactive element thallium, $^{208}_{81}\text{Tl}$, are shown in Figure 9-13, where the energy of the nucleus in the ground state is chosen as zero. The figure also shows the transitions giving rise to γ-rays. The spacings of nuclear energy levels range from tens of thousands of electron volts to a few million electron volts, in contrast to the much smaller separations associated with atomic energy levels. The nuclear energy levels can be inferred from the γ-ray spectrum emitted when excited nuclei make downward quantum jumps to lower states.

Several methods may be used in γ-ray spectroscopy to measure the energy of γ-rays; the simplest is the scintillation spectrometer (Section 8-2).

Only those nuclear transitions occur in which the conservation laws are satisfied. In the downward transition from an upper nuclear energy state

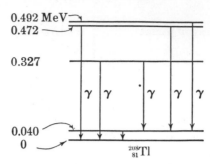

Figure 9-13. Nuclear energy-level diagram and gamma-ray transitions of $^{208}_{81}\text{Tl}$.

E_u to a lower state E_l through the emission of a γ-ray photon of energy $h\nu$ the conservation of energy requires that†

$$h\nu = E_u - E_l \qquad [9\text{-}22]$$

Conservation of linear momentum requires that the total linear momentum following the γ-decay equal the linear momentum before the decay. If the decaying nucleus is originally at rest, it must recoil, when the photon is emitted, with a momentum equal to the momentum of the photon, $h\nu/c$. Thus,

$$h\nu/c = mv \qquad [9\text{-}23]$$

where mv is the momentum of the recoiling nucleus.

In γ-decay the particle is created as the nucleus in the excited state, $^A Z^*$, decays to a lower state, say, the ground state $^A Z$. We use here the conventional notation, in which a nucleus in an excited state is labeled with an asterisk. We can write symbolically

$$^A Z^* \rightarrow {}^A Z + \gamma$$

The decay is consistent with the conservation of charge (Ze before, Ze after), and the conservation of nucleons (A before, A after).‡

It is useful to have a criterion for judging the relative rapidity with which nuclear decays take place. For this purpose we may speak of a *nuclear time* t_n as the time required for a typical nucleon, having an energy of several million electron volts and traveling at a speed $\approx 0.1c$, to travel a nuclear

† Equation 9-22 is approximate; see "The Mössbauer Effect" below for the rigorously correct relation.

‡ Another process that competes with gamma decay is *internal conversion*. In this process a nucleus in an excited state converts its excitation energy internally (within the atom) to one of the inner atomic electrons, bound with an energy E_b; therefore, $E_u - E_l = E_b + K_e$, where K_e is the kinetic energy of the freed electron.

distance, ≈ 3 fermi. It follows that $t_n = (3 \times 10^{-15}\text{ m})/(3 \times 10^7\text{ m/sec}) \approx 10^{-22}$ sec. It is expected, then, that any rapid nuclear decay will have a half-life that is not more than a few orders of magnitude larger than 10^{-22} sec, an immeasurably short time.

The half-life in a typical γ-decay is predicted by theory to be of the order of 10^{-14} sec; such a fast decay cannot be followed in time, but some γ-decays are so strongly forbidden that the half-life is greater than 10^{-6} sec, which can readily be measured. Such nuclides, having a measurably long half-life in γ-decay, are called *isomers*. An isomer is not chemically distinguishable from the lower-energy nucleus into which it slowly decays. An extreme example of isomerism is that of niobium, $^{91}_{41}\text{Nb}$, which undergoes γ-decay with a half-life of 60 days.

The γ-decay of excited nuclei serves as a direct means of signaling the instability of the nuclei. An analysis of the γ-ray energies allows nuclear energy-level diagrams, such as Figure 9-13, to be constructed. Any success-ful nuclear theory must, of course, be capable of predicting in detail the energy levels of nuclei, and although no complete theory yet exists, the energy-level diagrams of many nuclides are at least partially understood on the basis of the quantum theory.

The Mössbauer effect   When a nucleus in an excited state and initially at rest decays with the emission of a photon, energy conservation yields

$$E_u - E_l = h\nu + E_k$$

where $\frac{1}{2}mv^2 = E_k$ is the kinetic energy of the recoiling nucleus. Because of momen-tum conservation we have $p = mv = h\nu/c$, and the kinetic energy of recoil may be written $E_k = p^2/2m = (h\nu)^2/2mc^2$. Then, the energy difference $E_u - E_l$ between the upper and lower energy states becomes

$$E_u - E_l = h\nu + (h\nu)^2/2mc^2 = h\nu(1 + h\nu/2mc^2)$$

Consider an $^{57}\text{Fe}^*$ nucleus, which decays from an excited state with a mean life of 6.9×10^{-8} sec with the emission of a gamma ray of 14.4 keV. The nucleus, if free and initially at rest, recoils upon photon emission with a kinetic energy of

$$E_k = (h\nu)^2/2mc^2 = (14.4\text{ keV})^2/(2 \times 57\text{ u} \times 0.93\text{ Gev/u}) = 2.0 \times 10^{-3}\text{ eV}$$

Now suppose that the 14.4 keV photon is incident upon a second free ^{57}Fe nucleus initially at rest and in its nuclear ground state. Can it be absorbed by the second nucleus in the process of *resonant absorption*? That is, can de-excitation from an excited state to the ground state of one nucleus, with the emission of a photon, be followed by the excitation of a second nucleus, from the ground state to an excited state, by bombardment from the same photon? As the energy relation above shows, the answer is no, because the difference between the two quantized energy levels *exceeds* the photon energy by $E_k = 2.0 \times 10^{-3}$ eV. The photon can be resonantly absorbed only if the second nucleus is initially in motion toward the photon with a kinetic energy of 2.0×10^{-3} eV. All told, the difference in energy between the emit-ting nucleus and absorbing nucleus is $2E_k$.

We have supposed implicitly that the upper and lower nuclear energy levels are infinitely sharp. Since the excited state of ^{57}Fe has a *finite* average lifetime of 6.9×10^{-8} sec, the uncertainty relation requires that the quantized state's energy be indefinite by at least an amount ΔE (the natural linewidth), where

[5-14] $\Delta E = \hbar/\Delta t = (1.1 \times 10^{-34}$ J-sec$)/(6.9 \times 10^{-8}$ sec$) = 1.0 \times 10^{-8}$ eV

We see that the intrinsic "fuzziness" of the quantized energy levels, $\Delta E = 1.0 \times 10^{-8}$ eV, is smaller than the recoil energy $E_k = 2.0 \times 10^{-3}$ eV by a factor of 200,000. The failure of the photon energy to match exactly the energy-level difference by virtue of recoil is *not* compensated for by the indefiniteness of the participating energy levels.

Nevertheless, R. L. Mössbauer found in 1958 that resonant absorption did occur between a source of ^{57}Fe* nuclei *in the crystalline lattice of a solid* and an absorber of ^{57}Fe nuclei, also in a crystalline lattice. The explanation of this, the *Mössbauer effect*, lies in the phenomenon of *recoilless emission* of gamma rays. Since each nucleus in a solid is bound to a lattice of atoms, whose possible energies are determined by quantum conditions (Section 12-8), the recoil momentum of a nucleus emitting a photon is transmitted to the entire lattice of atoms. To put it differently, the recoil energy $E_k = (h\nu)^2/2mc^2$ is negligibly small, because the mass m is effectively that of the entire lattice of atoms, not merely one atom. The photon energy then matches exactly the quantized nuclear energy difference (within the linewidth ΔE); in other words the γ-ray photons are limited in energy definition by the natural width ΔE only, not by the recoil effect. Thus, the line of 14.4 keV for ^{57}Fe*, with $\Delta E = 1.0 \times 10^{-8}$ eV, is extremely sharp, the spread $\Delta E/h\nu$ in γ-ray energies being less than 1 part in 10^{12}.

Suppose that a photon emitter is in motion with speed v. Then, according to the Doppler effect† the photon frequency ν is changed by an amount $\Delta\nu$, where

$$\Delta\nu/\nu = v/c$$

A photon absorber in motion follows the same rule. Taking v to be a mere 3 cm/sec, we find that $\Delta\nu/\nu = v/c = 10^{-10}$. Thus, for this relatively low speed the fractional change in photon frequency is 10 times greater than the photon frequency resolution (1 part in 10^{12}) achievable through the Mössbauer effect with a ^{57}Fe* source. It is possible, then, by moving a γ-ray source at a low speed, to measure extremely small changes in photon frequency or, equivalently, extremely small changes in nuclear energy levels. One noteworthy example is the experiment that R. V. Pound and G. A. Rebka, Jr., made in 1960: a change in photon frequency of 2 parts in 10^{15}, arising when a photon interacts gravitationally with Earth, as it falls 20 m, was confirmed (see Problem 9-29).

9-10 Alpha decay Gamma decay clearly demonstrates that excited nuclear energy states are discrete. Another decay mode of unstable nuclei, also verifying the discreteness of nuclear energy states, is alpha decay. Certain radioactive nuclei, those for which $Z > 82$, spontaneously decay into a daughter nucleus and a helium nucleus. Since the α-particle has a very stable configuration of nucleons, it is perhaps not surprising that such a group of particles might exist within the parent nucleus prior to α-decay.

† See Section 42-4, Weidner and Sells, *E. C. P.*

The laws of conservation of charge and of nucleons require that

$$\boxed{\alpha \text{ decay:} \quad {}_{Z}^{A}\text{P} \rightarrow {}_{Z-2}^{A-4}\text{D} + {}_{2}^{4}\alpha}$$ [9-24]

where P and D refer to the parent and daughter nuclei, respectively. The subscripts and superscripts give the electric charge in units of e and nucleon numbers, respectively; the conservation laws require that the sums on both sides of the reaction equation be equal. For example, bismuth 212 decays by α-emission to thallium 208:

$$_{83}^{212}\text{Bi} \rightarrow {}_{81}^{208}\text{Tl} + {}_{2}^{4}\alpha$$ [9-25]

If the radioactive parent is taken to be initially at rest, the conservation laws of energy and of linear momentum yield

$$M_P c^2 = (M_D + M_\alpha)c^2 + K_D + K_\alpha$$ [9-26]

$$M_D v_D = M_\alpha v_\alpha$$ [9-27]

where the M's are the atomic rest masses of the parent, daughter, and α-particle, and the K's and v's are the kinetic energies and velocities of the daughter and α-particle. Nonrelativistic expressions for kinetic energy and momentum may be used in these equations because the energy released in α-decay is never greater than 10 MeV, whereas the α-particle rest energy is about 4 GeV.

Obviously, the kinetic energies K_D and K_α can never be negative; therefore, α-decay is energetically possible, by Equation 9-26, only if

$$M_P > M_D + M_\alpha$$ [9-28]

If this inequality is not satisfied, α-decay simply cannot occur.

The energy released in the decay, $K_D + K_\alpha$, is called the *disintegration energy* and is represented by the symbol Q. Using Equation 9-26, we can write

$$\boxed{Q = K_D + K_\alpha = (M_P - M_D - M_\alpha)c^2}$$ [9-29]

Decay is energetically possible only for $Q > 0$.

When one observes an α-decay, it is the energy of the α-particle, K_α, that is usually measured; this can be done, for instance, by finding the range of the particle or by measuring its radius of curvature in a magnetic field. Let us see how this measured energy K_α is related to the total energy Q released in the decay. Squaring Equation 9-27 and multiplying by $\frac{1}{2}$ gives

$$M_D(\tfrac{1}{2}M_D v_D^2) = M_\alpha(\tfrac{1}{2}M_\alpha v_\alpha^2)$$

$$M_D K_D = M_\alpha K_\alpha$$ [9-30]

In atomic mass units the daughter and alpha masses are approximately $A - 4$ and 4u, respectively. Then this equation becomes

$$(A - 4)K_D = 4K_\alpha$$

but
$$Q = K_\alpha + K_D = K_\alpha[1 + 4/(A - 4)]$$

therefore
$$K_\alpha = \left(\frac{A - 4}{A}\right) Q \qquad [9\text{-}31]$$

This equation shows that in *two-particle* emission from an initially unstable nucleus at rest the α-particle emerges with a *precisely defined energy*: since Q has a precise value, so does K_α. The energy spectrum of the α-particles emitted from a radioactive substance in a simple α-decay is shown in Figure 9-14. The α-particles are *monoenergetic*.

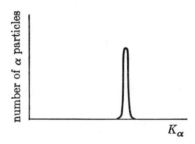

Figure 9-14. Energy spectrum of alpha-particles from a radioactive substance.

Radioactive materials unstable to α-decay are heavy elements with $A \gg 4$. Equation 9-31 shows that K_α is only slightly less than Q; for this reason nearly all of the energy released in the decay is carried away as kinetic energy by the light particle.

Most α-emitters show a group of discrete α-particle energies, rather than a single energy. This is easily understood in terms of a nuclear energy-level diagram, such as Figure 9-15 for the decay of bismuth 212 (see Equation 9-25). The parent nucleus can decay by α-emission to a number of energy states, the ground state and excited states. The most energetic α-particles correspond to those transitions involving decay to the ground state of the daughter; the Q used in our analysis is defined for just this case, in that the mass of the daughter was taken to be its mass in the ground state.

A decay to an excited state of a daughter is followed by one or more γ-emissions leading to the ground state. Because the half-life for γ-decay is usually extremely short, the γ-rays appear to be coincident in time with the α-decays. The energies of the γ-rays are found to be completely consistent with the differences in the energies of the emitted α-particles.

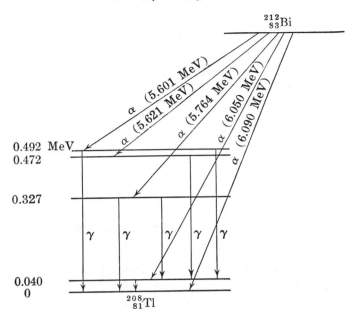

Figure 9-15. Nuclear energy-level diagram showing the decay of bismuth 212 by alpha-emission to the ground and excited states of thallium 208.

About 160 α-emitters have been identified. The emitted α-particles have discrete energies ranging from about 4 to 10 MeV, a factor of 2, but half-lives ranting from 10^{-6} sec to 10^{10} years, a factor of 10^{23}. Short-lived α-emitters have the highest energies, and conversely, as indicated by the examples in Table 9-4.

Table 9-4

Alpha emitter	K_α, MeV	$T_{1/2}$, sec	λ, sec^{-1}
$^{238}_{92}$U	4.19	1.42×10^{17}	5.6×10^{-18}
$^{212}_{83}$Bi	6.05; 6.09	3.64×10^4	1.90×10^{-5}
$^{215}_{85}$At	8.00	10^{-4}	10^4

THEORY OF ALPHA DECAY   We wish to examine some of the details of the decay of uranium 238 to thorium 234 by α-emission. Consider Figure 9-16, which shows the potential energy of the daughter as seen by an α-particle. When the α particle is at a greater distance from the center of the nucleus than R, the range of the nuclear force (about 10^{-14} m), the force between the particles is given by Coulomb's law. This is established by α-particle scattering experiments, in which α-particles having energies as great as 8 MeV are scattered from the thorium nuclei by the Coulomb repulsive force. At distances less than R an α-particle is subject to a strong

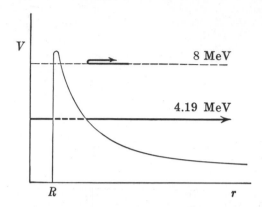

Figure 9-16. Potential energy of the nucleus of thorium 234 as seen by an alpha particle.

attractive force that holds it to the thorium nucleus. But this bound system, composed of the daughter nucleus $^{234}_{90}$Th and an α-particle, is just the parent nucleus, $^{238}_{92}$U. It is assumed, therefore, that two protons and two neutrons unite to form an α-particle within the parent, which exists for a time that is long compared with the nuclear time, 10^{-22} sec.

It is known from experiment that uranium 238 emits α-particles with a kinetic energy of 4.19 MeV; see Figure 9-16. Since the potential energy is zero when the α-particle is very far from the daughter nucleus, this kinetic energy also represents the *total* energy of the particle at any distance from the nucleus. Within the nucleus the total energy of the α-particle is again 4.19 MeV, the algebraic sum of the potential energy (negative) and the kinetic energy (positive). Classically, if the α-particle is confined within nuclear "walls," it moves back and forth between them indefinitely, striking them roughly 10^{21} times per second; it cannot penetrate the walls and escape, for it cannot have a negative kinetic energy. On this basis, it would be impossible for α-decay to take place!

Because α-decay does indeed occur, the classical argument is inapplicable; however, α-decay is readily understood in terms of the wave-mechanical phenomenon known as the *tunnel effect* (Section 5-10), first proposed by G. Gamow (1928) and R. W. Gurney and E. U. Condon (1928).

In wave mechanics the probability of locating an α-particle is related to its wave function $\psi(r)$. The wave function for the potential of Figure 9-16 is that shown in Figure 9-17: oscillatory within the attractive potential-energy well, drastically attenuated through the potential barrier, and again oscillatory outside the nucleus, with a small, but finite, amplitude. This means that there is a very small, but finite, probability that an alpha particle originally within the nucleus will be at some time outside the nucleus. The probability of tunneling through the barrier is strongly depen-

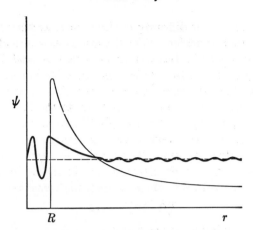

Figure 9-17. Wave function corresponding to the penetration of an alpha particle through a nuclear barrier.

dent on the height and thickness of the barrier, being greater the greater the particle's energy.

One way of visualizing the decay is to imagine the particle as bouncing between the nuclear walls until it finally escapes by penetrating the potential-energy barrier. Let us compute the number of tries the particle must make before it breaks through the potential barrier. The half-life of uranium 238 is about 10^{17} sec; on the average then, an α-particle must make 10^{21} tries per second for 10^{17} sec, or 10^{38} tries altogether, before it escapes.

9-11 Beta decay Beta decay may be defined as that radioactive decay process in which the charge of a nucleus is changed without a change in the number of nucleons.

For an example of β instability consider the three nuclides boron 12, carbon 12, and nitrogen 12, whose proton and neutron occupation levels are shown schematically in Figure 9-18. These three nuclides are isobars,

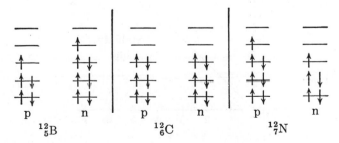

Figure 9-18. Proton and neutron occupation levels of boron 12, carbon 12, and nitrogen 12.

all having 12 nucleons, but differing in the proton and neutron numbers Z and N. Only the carbon nucleus, with 6 protons and 6 neutrons, is stable. Evidently the boron nucleus has too many neutrons, and the nitrogen nucleus too many protons, to be stable. The unstable boron nucleus decays to a lower energy state by changing one of its nucleons from a neutron into a proton, the last neutron jumping, as it were, to the lowest available proton level. In this process the $^{12}_{5}\text{B}$ nucleus has been transformed into the stable $^{12}_{6}\text{C}$ nucleus, and to conserve electric charge one unit of negative charge must be created. We know that an electron cannot exist *within* the nucleus; therefore, the created electron, or β-particle, must be emitted from the decaying nucleus, according to the transformation

$$^{12}_{5}\text{B} \rightarrow {}^{12}_{6}\text{C} + \beta^{-}$$

where the minus sign indicates the negative charge.

The decay of nitrogen 12 is analogous. This isotope of nitrogen has too many protons and too few neutrons to be stable. Therefore, it decays to a lower energy state by converting one of its nucleons from a proton into a neutron, the last proton jumping to the lowest available neutron level. In this decay the unstable $^{12}_{7}\text{N}$ nucleus is transformed into the stable $^{12}_{6}\text{C}$ nucleus, and charge is conserved by the creation of a positive beta particle, the positron. Because a positron cannot exist within a nucleus, it must be emitted. The decay may be shown as

$$^{12}_{7}\text{N} \rightarrow {}^{12}_{6}\text{C} + \beta^{+}$$

These decay processes are also shown in Figure 9-19 on a plot of N versus Z. The carbon nucleus lies on the stability line; the boron lies above it and

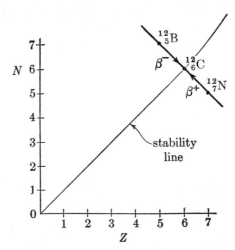

Figure 9-19. The β^{+} decay of nitrogen 12 and the β^{-} decay of boron 12 to carbon 12.

the nitrogen below it. The β-decay transformations occur along an isobaric ($-45°$) line in such a way as to bring the unstable nuclides closer to the stability line.

Another type of beta decay is *electron capture*. In electron capture an atomic orbital electron combines with a proton of the nucleus to change it into a neutron. Again the number of nucleons is unchanged, but a proton is converted into a neutron, as in β^+-decay. The electrons of the atom have a finite probability of being at the nucleus (see Figure 7-7), and one of the innermost, or K, electrons has the highest probability of being captured within the nucleus. Beta decay resulting from the nuclear capture of a K-shell electron is often referred to as K *capture*.

No charged particle is emitted in the decay by electron capture. The absorption and annihilation of a particle is equivalent to the creation and emission of its antiparticle; in K capture an electron is absorbed, but in β^+-decay an electron anti-particle, or positron, is emitted. Both processes change a proton into a neutron. An example of electron capture is the decay of unstable beryllium 7 to lithium 7:

$$e\,\bar{_K} + {^7_4}\text{Be} \rightarrow {^7_3}\text{Li}$$

Electron capture cannot, of course, be identified by an emitted charged particle. It may be inferred from the change in the chemical identity of the element undergoing the decay, or it may be detected by observing the *x-ray photons* emitted when the decay takes place. When a K electron is absorbed into the nucleus there is a hole, or vacancy, in the K shell; this vacancy is filled as electrons in outer shells make quantum jumps to inner vacancies, thereby emitting characteristic x-ray spectra. Because the x-ray emission must take place *after* the K vacancy is created, that is, after the nuclear decay has occurred, the x-rays are characteristic of the *daughter* element, not the parent.

Many hundreds of nuclides are known to decay by emitting an electron or a positron or by capturing an orbital electron. In fact, nearly all unstable nuclides with Z less than 82 decay by at least one of the three beta processes.

Beta decay differs from alpha and gamma decay in several respects:

The parent and daughter have the same number of nucleons.

As in γ-emission, the electron or positron is created at the time it is emitted.

Whereas γ-ray photons and α-particles are emitted with a discrete spectrum of energies, β-particles have a continuous energy spectrum.

The half-lives in β-decay are never less than about 10^{-2} sec, in contrast to γ-decay (as small as 10^{-17} sec) and α-decay (as small as 10^{-7} sec).

β^--DECAY   Let us consider β^--decay in somewhat more detail. By the conservation of electric charge and the conservation of nucleons, the decay of a parent nucleus P into the daughter D may be represented by

$$\substack{A \\ Z}P \rightarrow \substack{A \\ Z+1}D + \substack{0 \\ -1}e \qquad [9\text{-}32]$$

For example, boron 12 decays into carbon 12 and an electron with a half-life of 2.0×10^{-2} sec.

$$\substack{12 \\ 5}B \rightarrow \substack{12 \\ 6}C + \substack{0 \\ -1}e$$

Mass-energy conservation requires that the rest mass of the parent *nucleus*, $M_P - Zm_e$, exceed the rest masses of the daughter nucleus, $M_D - (Z + 1)m_e$, and the electron m_e, where M_P and M_D are the *neutral atomic* masses of the parent and daughter respectively. Any excess energy Q that is, energy released in the decay, appears as kinetic energy of the particles emerging from the decay. Therefore,

$$(M_P - Zm_e) = [M_D - (Z + 1)m_e] + m_e + Q/c^2$$

or, for β^--decay,

$$\boxed{M_P = M_D + Q/c^2} \qquad [9\text{-}33]$$

Equation 9-33 shows that β^--decay is energetically possible whenever $M_P > M_D$, that is, mass of the parent atom exceeds the mass of the daughter atom. Moreover, it is found that when β^--decay is energetically possible, it does occur, although the probability may be small and the half-life extremely long.

Conservation of linear momentum requires that the vector sum of the linear momenta of the particles emerging from the decay be zero if the decaying nucleus is initially at rest. Recall this implies that in α-decay, the α-particle and the daughter nucleus leave the site of the decay in opposite directions, the energy Q being shared between the two particles in such a way that they each have the same magnitude of linear momentum. Thus they each have precisely defined and *discrete* energies.

Now, if β^--decay really were similar to alpha decay in that the parent nucleus did decay into just *two* particles, as we have assumed so far, then their energies would both be precisely defined, with $m_e v_e = M_D v_D$ and $Q = K_e + K_D$. Because the mass of the electron is at least several thousand times smaller than that of the daughter nucleus, essentially all of the released energy would be carried by the electron, and the kinetic energy of the recoiling daughter nucleus would be negligible by comparison (the magnitudes of the momenta of the two particles would, of course, be equal). This implies that if β^--decay were altogether analogous to α-decay, one heavy and one light particle being produced by an initially unstable nucleus, the electron would have a precisely defined kinetic energy, approximately equal to Q. With $M_D \gg m_e$ we have

$$Q = K_e + K_D \approx K_e$$

We can compute Q for the β^--decay of boron 12 to carbon 12 directly from atomic masses by using Equation 9-33:

$$\text{mass } {}^{12}_{5}\text{B} = 12.014354 \text{ u}$$
$$\text{mass } {}^{12}_{6}\text{C} = \underline{12.000000 \text{ u}}$$
$$M_P - M_D = 0.014354 \text{ u}$$
$$Q = 0.014354 \text{ u} \times 931.5 \text{ MeV/u} = 13.37 \text{ MeV}$$

We might expect, then, to find *all* electrons emitted with a kinetic energy $K_e \approx Q = 13.37$ MeV. Is this what is observed?

The distribution in energy of the emitted β^- particles from any particular radioactive element can be measured with a magnetic spectrometer (see Section 8-4). The result for boron 12 decay is shown in Figure 9-20. The

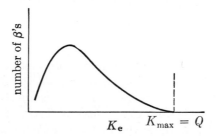

Figure 9-20. Distribution in energy of emitted β^- particles in boron 12 decay.

emitted electrons are *not* monoenergetic! Instead, there is a distribution of electron energies from zero up to the maximum, $K_{max}; = 13.37$ MeV. The very few electrons having this maximum energy, and only those electrons, carry the kinetic energy expected on the basis of a two-particle decay; that is, the measurements show that

$$K_{max} = Q \qquad [9\text{-}34]$$

All other electrons—and this means almost all of the emitted electrons—seem to have too little kinetic energy. In short, there is an apparent violation of the conservation of energy! Furthermore, observations of individual β^- decays show that the electron and daughter do *not* necessarily leave the site of the disintegration in opposite directions. There is an apparent violation of the conservation of linear momentum! In addition, the angular momentum of the parent nucleus (integral spin, since A is even) *cannot* equal the sum of the angular momenta of the daughter (integral spin) and the electron (half-integral spin). There is an apparent violation of the conservation of angular momentum!

We hasten to assure the reader that the fundamental laws of the conservation of energy, linear momentum, and angular momentum are, in fact, not violated in β^--decay. This is so because of the *neutrino* ("little neutral one"), also emitted in β^--decay, which we discuss next. The existence of the neutrino was first suggested by W. Pauli in 1930 as an alternative to abandoning the conservation principles; its existence was directly confirmed by experiment in 1956. It is now known that a radioactive nucleus decays in β^--emission to *three* particles: the daughter nucleus, the electron, and the neutrino. We shall see that all of the difficulties we have mentioned above disappear by virtue of the neutrino's participation in β^--decay.

THE NEUTRINO   The neutrino has electric charge 0, rest mass 0, linear momentum, p, *total* relativistic energy $E = pc$, and intrinsic angular momentum $\frac{1}{2}\hbar$.

The neutrino has zero electric charge; charge is conserved in β^--decay-*without* the neutrino. The neutrino cannot interact with matter by producing ionization. It interacts very, very weakly with nuclei, and is virtually undetectable.†

As we have seen, energy *is* conserved for those very few electrons in β^--decay which are emitted with the maximum kinetic energy $K_{max} = Q$. Therefore, the neutrino mass must be very small compared with the electron mass, and there are good theoretical reasons for taking it to be *exactly zero*. Since the neutrino has a zero rest mass and rest energy, it must, like a photon, always travel at the speed of light. Therefore, a neutrino's total relativistic energy E is related to its relativistic momentum p by $E = pc$ (see Equation 3-15).

Consider again the conservation of energy and of linear momentum in β^--decay, assuming now that a neutrino, as well as an electron, is created in the decay and carries away energy and momentum. The conservation of energy requires that

$$Q = K_D + K_e + K_v \approx K_e + K_\nu \qquad [9\text{-}35]$$

Note that the kinetic energy of a neutrino, K_ν, is also its total energy: $E_\nu = K_\nu$. The conservation of linear momentum requires that the total *vector* momentum of the three particles add up to zero, as shown in Figure 9-21. If three particles are emitted in the decay process, it is no longer necessary that they leave the site of the decay along the *same* straight line; now there are a variety of ways in which the separate momentum vectors can be arranged to add up to zero, satisfying Equation 9-35 in every in-

† Strictly, the massless particle emitted in β^--decay is the antineutrino, whereas the massless particle emitted in β^+-decay is the neutrino.

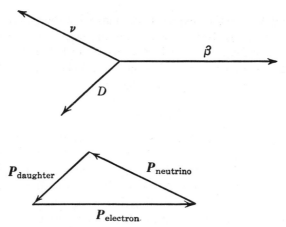

Figure 9-21. Linear momentum vectors of the daughter nucleus, electron, and neutrino in β^--decay.

stance. The electron and daughter nucleus will usually *not* move along the same straight line in opposite directions, but if they do, the neutrino momentum and energy can be zero and from Equation 9-35 we will have $K_e = K_{max} = Q$, in agreement with observation for the most energetic electrons. In all other decays the virtually unabsorbable neutrino will carry energy and momentum, and the electron will necessarily have a kinetic energy less than K_{max}. In two-particle decay the emerging particles are monoenergetic; in three-particle decay they are polyenergetic.

Consider finally the angular momentum, or spin, of the neutrino. It is $\frac{1}{2}$ in units of $\hbar$. In the β^--decay of $^{12}_5\text{B}$ to $^{12}_6\text{C}$, the parent and daughter nuclei both have integral nuclear spins; the electron has a spin of $\frac{1}{2}$. Therefore, when the neutrino's angular momentum is included, total angular momentum is conserved in β^--decay.

β^+-DECAY The general relation giving the β^+-decay is

$$\boxed{{}^A_Z P \rightarrow {}^{\;\;A}_{Z-1} D + {}^0_{+1}e + \nu}$$ [9-36]

A neutrino is emitted in β^+-decay as well as in β^--decay. Positron decay can occur only if mass-energy is conserved. This means that the rest mass of the parent *nucleus* must exceed the sum of the rest masses of the daughter nucleus and the positron (the neutrino rest mass is zero). Any excess energy appears as the kinetic energy of the three particles emerging from the decay. Therefore,

$$(M_P - Zm_e) = [M_D - (Z - 1)m_e] + m_e + Q/c^2$$

or, for β^+-decay,

$$\boxed{M_P = M_D + 2m_e + Q/c^2}$$ [9-37]

where M_P and M_D are the *neutral atomic* masses of the parent and daughter, respectively, m_e is the rest mass of the positron (or electron), and the energy Q is the energy released in the decay and shared by the positron, daughter nucleus, and neutrino. We see from this equation that β^+ decay is energetically possible (Q is greater than zero) only if

$$M_P > M_D + 2m_e \qquad \text{[9-38]}$$

Positron decay is possible, then, only if the mass of the parent atom *exceeds* the mass of the daughter atom *by at least two electron masses*, $2(0.000549)$ u or its energy equivalent, 1.02 MeV (there is nothing especially significant in the appearance here of the two electron masses; it merely reflects the fact that neutral *atomic* masses rather than *nuclear* masses are used).

Let us compute the Q of the positron decay of nitrogen 12 (half-life 0.0110 sec) to carbon 12:

$$
\begin{aligned}
\text{mass } {}^{12}_{7}\text{N} &= 12.018641 \\
\text{mass } {}^{12}_{6}\text{C} &= 12.000000 \\
\hline
M_P - M_D &= 0.018641 \\
2m_e &= 0.001097 \\
\hline
Q/c^2 &= 0.017544 \text{ u}
\end{aligned}
$$

$$Q = 0.017544 \text{ u} \times 931.5 \text{ MeV/u} = 16.34 \text{ MeV}$$

This energy, 16.34 MeV, is shared among the decay products, the positron, neutrino, and carbon nucleus. When positron energies are measured with a beta-ray spectrometer, it is found that there is a distribution of energies up to a maximum, in agreement with the mass differences.

In actuality the masses of short-lived radioactive electron or positron emitters cannot be easily measured; it is possible to compute the mass of a radioactive element by measuring the maximum energy of the emitted beta particle. The β^+ decay can be readily identified, because an emitted positron will undergo annihilation with an electron and produce two annihilation photons, each with an energy of 0.51 MeV, the rest energy of an electron (or positron). Thus, β^+ decay is always characterized by the appearance of annihilation quanta of 0.51 MeV.

ELECTRON CAPTURE   The general relation for electron capture is written

$$\boxed{{}^{0}_{-1}e + {}^{A}_{Z}P \rightarrow {}^{A}_{Z-1}D + \nu} \qquad \text{[9-39]}$$

which shows that an orbital electron is captured by the parent nucleus ${}^{A}_{Z}P$, and the products of decay are the daughter nucleus ${}^{A}_{Z-1}D$ and a neutrino.

Mass-energy is conserved when the energy Q released in the decay is equal to the sum of the rest masses entering the reaction less the sum of the rest masses leaving the reaction. Therefore,

$$m_e + (M_P - Zm_e) = [M_D - (Z - 1)m_e] + Q/c^2$$

or, for electron capture,

$$\boxed{M_P = M_D + Q/c^2}$$ [9-40]

where M_P and M_D are again the neutral atomic masses of the parent and daughter, respectively. This equation shows that electron capture is energetically possible if the atomic mass of the parent exceeds that of the daughter.

Consider our earlier example of the decay of beryllium 7 (half-life 53 days) to lithium 7 through electron capture:

$$\text{mass } {}^7_4\text{Be} = 7.016929$$
$$\text{mass } {}^7_3\text{Li} = 7.016004$$
$$M_P - M_D = Q/c^2 = \overline{0.000925} \text{ u}$$
$$Q = 0.000925 \text{ u} \times 931.5 \text{ MeV/u} = 0.861 \text{ MeV}$$

(Note that β^+-decay is energetically forbidden to ${}^7_4$Be.) In this decay 0.861 MeV is released. Where does it go? Unlike β^+- and β^--decay, electron capture produces only *two* particles. By the conservation of momentum these two particles, the neutrino and the daughter nucleus, must move in opposite directions with the same momentum magnitude, the sum of their kinetic energies being the disintegration energy $Q = 0.861$ MeV. Because only two particles appear in electron capture, they each have precisely defined energies. The neutrino's rest mass is zero; therefore, almost all of the energy is carried by a virtually unobservable neutrino, and the nucleus recoils with an energy of only several electron volts. Nevertheless, some very delicate experiments have confirmed that the recoiling nuclei are mono-energetic and that their energy is precisely the amount required to satisfy the laws of momentum and energy conservation. Without the accompanying neutrino in electron capture this decay process is completely inexplicable.

Figure 9-22 is an energy-level diagram of the decay of boron 12 and nitrogen 12 to the stable nuclide carbon 12. By convention a nuclide undergoing β^--decay is shown to the left of the daughter, and the nuclide undergoing β^+-decay or electron capture is shown to the right (Z increases toward the right). We see that the decay of the boron consists of electron emission to two states of the carbon, the ground state and an excited state 4.433 MeV above the ground state. Decay from the excited state to the ground state by the emission of a γ-ray photon is essentially simultaneous with the corresponding β^- decay. This near coincidence of the electron and photon emission can be verified experimentally by using two detectors, one for electrons and one for photons, and by noting that the pulses in the

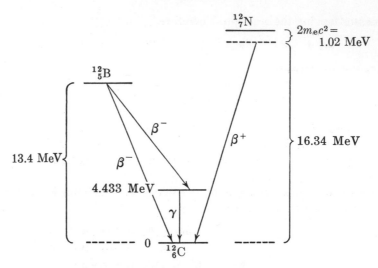

Figure 9-22. Energy-level diagram showing the decay of boron 12 and nitrogen 12 to carbon 12.

two detecting systems are coincident in time (within the resolving time of the detecting instruments).

An energy-level diagram of the radioactive element copper 64, which decays by β^- emission to zinc 64 and also by β^+ emission and electron capture to nickel 64, is shown in Figure 9-23.

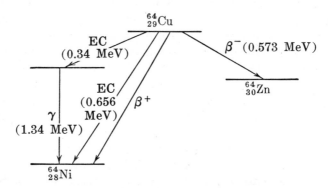

Figure 9-23. Energy-level diagram showing the decay of copper 64 by β^- emission, β^+ emission, and electron capture.

Note a general rule that applies to any two isobaric nuclides that differ in Z by 1. Clearly, the atomic mass of one nuclide must exceed that of the other. Therefore, the nucleus of the more massive atom can decay to the nucleus of the lighter atom either by decay or by β^- electron capture. It follows that no two neighboring isobars can both be stable against β-decay, and this indeed is in accord with observation of the known nuclides (see Figure 9-7).

The four basic reactions associated with beta decay are the following:

$$
\begin{aligned}
\beta^-\text{-decay:} & \quad n \rightarrow p + e + \bar{\nu} \\
\beta^+\text{-decay:} & \quad p \rightarrow n + \bar{e} + \nu \\
\text{electron capture:} & \quad e + p \rightarrow n + \nu \\
\text{neutrino absorption:} & \quad \bar{\nu} + p \rightarrow n + \bar{e}
\end{aligned}
\qquad [9\text{-}41]
$$

The symbol e represents the electron (charge, -1), $\bar{e}$ represents the positron (charge, $+1$), the electron's antiparticle, ν represents a neutrino, and $\bar{\nu}$ represents an *antineutrino*.

Up to this point we have recognized only one type of neutrino; there are in reality two, one the antiparticle of the other.† This distinction may seem to be completely formal, but it is not. It has been confirmed in subtle experiments that the antineutrino, the neutrino's antiparticle, has the direction of its spin, or intrinsic angular momentum, along the direction of its linear momentum. For an antineutrino the sense of its spin is clockwise, when viewed from behind, giving it a "right-handed" *helicity*, or *spirality*. On the other hand, the neutrino's angular momentum and linear momentum are in opposite directions, giving it a left-handed helicity. The sense of its spin is counterclockwise when viewed from behind. Nature thus distinguishes between the neutrino and antineutrino. This lack of symmetry —the neutrino is *only* left-handed and the antineutrino is *only* right-handed—is a manifestation of the *non-conservation of parity*, predicted by C. N. Yang and T. D. Lee, and experimentally confirmed in 1957 by C. S. Wu *et al*. The principle that nature does *not* distinguish between left and right, the conservation of parity, is violated in β decay. (See Section 11-4.)

The basic process of β^- decay, the decay of the neutron into a proton, electron, and antineutrino, given by Equations 9-41, occurs in a *free neutron*, not merely a neutron bound within a nucleus. The decay is energetically allowed because the neutron mass exceeds that of the hydrogen atom, ^{1}H, the Q being 0.78 MeV. The half-life of this decay is found, in experiments of extreme difficulty, to be 12 minutes. Because a free neutron is typically absorbed in less than 10^{-3} sec when it passes through materials, the decay of a neutron is usually unimportant in situations involving free neutrons.

The basic β^+ decay, in which a proton is converted into a neutron, positron, and neutrino, is *not* permitted for a free proton, inasmuch as the mass

---

† In fact, things are actually still more complicated: a distinctive neutrino and antineutrino are associated with beta decay via electron or antielectron emission. Other distinctive neutrinos and antineutrinos are associated with the decay of the unstable elementary particles known as muons (see Table 11-5).

in the left-hand side of the reaction is less than that in the right-hand side. Positron decay is possible only when protons are bound within a nucleus.

Electron capture is closely related to the β^+ decay, of course. Note that in Equations 9-41 the second reaction becomes the third reaction when the antielectron is transferred to the left side, thereby becoming an electron. This follows the general rule that the emission of a particle is equivalent to the absorption of an antiparticle, and conversely. By using this rule together with the permitted reversal of the arrow it may be seen that all four beta reactions are equivalent.

The last reaction in Equations 9-41 is that in which an antineutrino combines with a proton to become a neutron and a positron. Although the relative probability of neutrino capture is extremely small, the capture was observed directly, with the very large neutrino flux from a nuclear reactor, by C. L. Cowan and F. Reines in 1956, thereby directly confirming the existence of the neutrino (strictly, the antineutrino). The antineutrino of the absorption is identified by observing the neutron and the positron produced simultaneously when the antineutrino is captured by a proton; the neutron is detected by observing the photon emitted from an excited nucleus that has absorbed the neutron, and the positron is detected by observing annihilation photons. The difficulty of this experiment may be appreciated from the fact that a neutrino or antineutrino has only 1 chance in 10^{12} of being captured while traveling completely through the Earth. Because neutrinos have such a very small probability of interacting with matter and being absorbed, a large fraction of the energy released in all beta-decay processes is effectively lost.

9-12 Natural radioactivity We have discussed the three common modes of radioactive decay, alpha, beta, and gamma, without concern as to how unstable nuclides are produced. It is customary to divide radioactive nuclides into two groups: the unstable nuclides found in nature, which are said to exhibit *natural radioactivity*, and the unstable nuclides made by man (usually by bombarding nuclei with particles), which are said to exhibit *artificial radioactivity*. So far approximately 1,000 artificially radioactive nuclides have been produced and identified. The number of identified isotopes of a given element varies: hydrogen has two stable isotopes and one unstable; xenon has nine stable and fourteen unstable isotopes. Nuclear reactions and the radioactivity that can be produced by them will be discussed in Chapter 10; here we discuss only the naturally radioactive nuclides.

It is believed that a cataclysmic cosmological event occurred about 10 billion years ago, at the time of the formation of the universe, in which *all* nuclides, stable and unstable, were formed in varying amounts. Those

unstable nuclides with half-lives much less than 10×10^9 years have long
since decayed into stable nuclides; however, there are twenty-one unstable
nuclides whose half-lives are comparable to, or greater than, the age of the
universe, and which, therefore, are still found in measurable amounts in
nature. These long-lived, naturally radioactive materials are listed in
Table 9-5.

Table 9-5.

Naturally Radioactive Nuclides with Half-Lives Comparable to or
Greater Than the Age of the Universe ($\sim 10^{10}$ yr $\simeq 3 \times 10^{17}$ sec)†

NUCLIDE (Z-SYMBOL-A)	DECAY MODE	DAUGHTER (Z-SYMBOL-A)	HALF-LIFE (IN SEC)
19 K 40	β^-, EC	20 Ca 40	4.10×10^{16}
23 V 50	β^-, EC	24 Cr 50	1.89×10^{23}
37 Rb 87	β^-	38 Sr 87	1.48×10^{18}
49 In 115	β^-	50 Sn 115	1.58×10^{22}
52 Te 123	EC	51 Sb 123	3.79×10^{20}
57 La 138	β^-, EC	58 Ce 138	3.47×10^{18}
58 Ce 142	α	56 Ba 138	1.58×10^{23}
60 Nd 144	α	58 Ce 140	7.57×10^{22}
62 Sm 146	α	60 Nd 142	3.79×10^{15}
62 Sm 147	α	60 Nd 143	3.35×10^{18}
62 Sm 148	α	60 Nd 144 (Unstable, α)	3.79×10^{20}
62 Sm 149	α	60 Nd 145	1.26×10^{22}
64 Gd 152	α	62 Sm 148 (Unstable, α)	3.47×10^{21}
71 Lu 176	β^-	72 Hf 176	6.94×10^{17}
72 Hf 174	α	70 Yb 170	1.36×10^{23}
75 Re 187	β^-	76 Os 187	1.26×10^{18}
78 Pt 190	α	76 Os 186	2.21×10^{19}
82 Pb 204	α	80 Hg 200	4.42×10^{24}
90 Th 232	α	88 Ra 228 (Unstable, α)	4.45×10^{17}
92 U 235	α	90 Th 231 (Unstable, α)	2.25×10^{16}
92 U 238	α	90 Th 234 (Unstable, α)	1.42×10^{17}

† H. A. Enge, *Introduction to Nuclear Physics*, Addison-Wesley, 1966.

The first eighteen nuclides in Table 9-5 all decay into stable daughters
(or granddaughters or great granddaughters). The last three are all very
massive; they decay into daughters which are themselves radioactive, and
which decay in turn into still other radioactive daughters, through several
generations, until finally a stable nuclide is reached. These are the three
naturally *radioactive series*. Each series begins with a very long-lived
nuclide, whose half-life exceeds that of any of its descendants. The final
stable nuclides into which they decay are all isotopes of lead, $^{208}_{82}\text{Pb}$, $^{207}_{82}\text{Pb}$,
and $^{206}_{82}\text{Pb}$. The age of the Earth can be estimated by measuring the relative

amounts of the long-lived parent of the series and the appropriate stable
isotope lead.

Figure 9-24 shows the complete decay scheme of all the unstable nuclides
in the so-called *thorium series*, plotted on a neutron-versus-proton diagram.

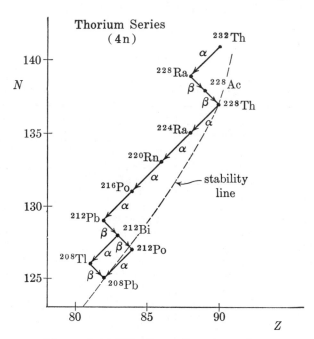

Figure 9-24. Thorium radioactive series.

A decrease of 2 in Z and in N represents an α-decay, and an increase of 1 in
Z and decrease of 1 in N represents a β^- decay. The stability line represents
the least unstable nuclides for the particular value of A. Both α- and β^-
decay often produce daughter nuclei in excited nuclear states, which leads
to subsequent decay (see Figures 9-15 and 9-22).

All nuclides with $A > 209$ are unstable. We might say that all such nuclides are too big to be stable and must lose nucleons to become more stable.
The only mode of decay in which a heavy, naturally radioactive nucleus
loses nucleons is α emission, in which both Z and N are reduced by 2. We
see from Figure 9-24 that α-decay tends, however, to displace the daughter
to the left of the stability line; β^- decay is needed to bring the nucleus back.
Some nuclides, such as $^{212}_{83}$Bi in the thorium series, tend to be unstable to
both alpha and beta decay, and a *branching* of the series then occurs.

The first nuclide in the thorium series has a mass number of 232, which
is divisible by 4, and all other nuclides in this series also have A values that
are divisible by 4, since the only decay that changes the number of nucleons

is α decay, in which it is reduced by 4. Therefore, the A values of any of the members of the *thorium series* may be written as $4n$, where n is an integer. The members of the so-called *actinium series*, beginning with uranium 235, have A values given by $4n + 3$, and the members of the *uranium series*, beginning with uranium 238, have A values given by $4n + 2$.

There is a fourth radioactive series whose members have A values given by $4n + 1$. None of its members, however, has a half-life comparable to the age of the universe. Therefore, nuclides in this series do not occur naturally, but they can be produced by nuclear reactions with the very heavy elements of the other series (for example, the capture of a neutron by uranium 236, followed by a β^- decay). This series is named the *neptunium series*, after the longest-lived nuclide in it, $^{237}_{93}\text{Np}$, which decays with a half-life of 2.14×10^6 years. The decay modes and half-lives of the neptunium, uranium, and actinium series are shown in Figure 9-25.

The naturally radioactive materials show a tremendous range of half-lives, from thorium 232 with $T_{1/2} = 1.41 \times 10^{10}$ years to polonium 213 with $T_{1/2} = 4.0 \times 10^{-6}$ sec. How are such extraordinarily long or short half-lives measured? Clearly, it is impractical to measure $T_{1/2}$ by following in time the change in the activity of the decaying nuclei, and indirect methods must be resorted to.

Consider first the measurement of very long half-lives. The fundamental radioactive-decay law is

$$[9\text{-}21] \qquad\qquad \text{activity} = \lambda N = \lambda N_0 e^{-\lambda t} \qquad\qquad [9\text{-}42]$$

This equation can be rearranged to

$$\lambda = \frac{\text{activity}}{N} \qquad\qquad [9\text{-}43]$$

The decay constant λ can be computed from this equation if the activity and the number N of radioactive nuclei are known. If $T_{1/2}$ is very long compared with t, the period of observation, we have $\lambda t \ll 1$; then $N = N_0 e^{-\lambda t} \approx N_0$. That is, if a radioactive material decays very slowly, the number of atoms present is essentially constant over the period of observation.

For example, measurements show that a 1.0 mg sample of uranium 238 emits 740 alpha particles per minute. If the atomic mass is taken as 238, the number of uranium atoms N in 1 mg is $(10^{-3}\text{ g})/(238)(1.67 \times 10^{-24}\text{ g})$ $= 2.52 \times 10^{18}$ atoms. Using Equation 9-43, we have

$$\lambda = \frac{(740/60) \text{ disintegrations/sec}}{2.52 \times 10^{18} \text{ atoms}} = 4.90 \times 10^{-18} \text{ sec}^{-1}$$

$$T_{1/2} = 0.693/\lambda = 4.51 \times 10^9 \text{ yr}$$

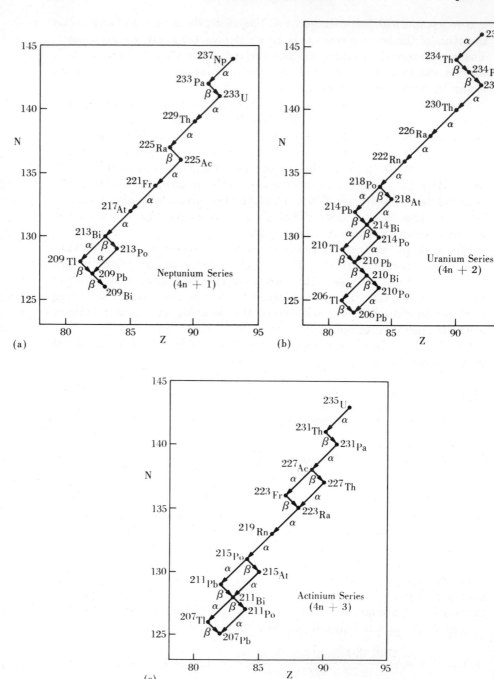

Figure 9-25. The neptunium, uranium, and actinium radioactive series.

Now consider the measurement of the half-life of a very short-lived member of a radioactive series. Assume that the radioactive descendants of the first member remain with the original material. Then, after sufficient time has elapsed, *all* members of the series will be present together, nuclei of any particular member being formed by its parent while other nuclei of this member decay into its daughter. The relative amounts of the several nuclides will be constant when the decay series reaches *radioactive equilibrium*, each nuclide decaying at the same rate at which it is formed. This means, then, that the activity λN of each member of the series is precisely the same as that of any other member:

$$(\text{activity})_1 = (\text{activity})_2 = (\text{activity})_3, \quad \text{etc.}$$

$$\lambda_1 N_1 = \lambda_2 N_2 = \lambda_3 N_3, \quad \text{etc.} \qquad [9\text{-}44]$$

$$\frac{N_1}{(T_{1/2})_1} = \frac{N_2}{(T_{1/2})_2} = \frac{N_3}{(T_{1/2})_3}, \quad \text{etc.} \qquad [9\text{-}45]$$

The half-life, $(T_{1/2})_s$, of a very *short-lived* radionuclide in equilibrium with a *longer*-lived nuclide of the same series, having $(T_{1/2})_1$, is given, then, by

$$(T_{1/2})_s = (T_{1/2})_1 (N_s/N_1) \qquad [9\text{-}46]$$

where N_s/N_1 is the relative numbers of these two members. Equation 9-45 shows that the relative numbers of atoms of the several members of a naturally radioactive series in equilibrium are directly proportional to their respective half-lives. Therefore, long-lived nuclides will be relatively abundant and short-lived nuclides scarce.

A sample of a naturally radioactive substance emits alpha, beta, and gamma rays simultaneously, because *all* members of the radioactive series are present and decaying. The alpha and beta emissions result in changes in Z or A or both; the gamma emissions result in changes in energy level. The early investigators of radioactivity distinguished among the three types of radiation emitted from radioactive substances by noting the deflection of the emitted rays in a magnetic field. The α-rays were deflected in the same direction as positively charged particles, the β-rays were deflected in the same direction as negatively charged particles, and the γ-rays were undeflected. Furthermore, it was observed that the penetration of the radioactive emanations increased in the order alpha, beta, and gamma; thus these rays were labeled by the first three letters of the Greek alphabet. All three types of nuclear radiation from naturally radioactive materials have energies of up to several MeV, and until the development of high-energy particle accelerators in the early nineteen-thirties these radioactive materials were the only sources of high-energy nuclear particles for bombarding other nuclei.

Uranium 238 is the heaviest nuclide found in nature. Still heavier and relatively short-lived nuclides, corresponding to *transuranic elements*, are man-made in that they can be produced by bombarding heavy elements with energetic particles. Transuranic elements up to mendelevium 258, $^{258}_{101}$Mv, have been produced, at least momentarily, and identified.

The term *natural radioactivity* usually refers to those radioactive materials produced in the very distant past and to their descendants. There are, in nature, however, radioactive materials *continuously* being produced in nuclear collisions of high-energy cosmic-ray particles with nuclei in the Earth's upper atmosphere. An example of this is the production of carbon 14 by the collision of neutrons with nitrogen nuclei, according to the reaction

$$^{14}_{7}\text{N} + ^{1}_{0}\text{n} \rightarrow ^{14}_{6}\text{C} + ^{1}_{1}\text{p}$$

This radioactive isotope of carbon, *radiocarbon*, decays by β^- emission with a half-life of 5,740 years:

$$^{14}_{6}\text{C} \rightarrow ^{14}_{7}\text{N} + \beta^-$$

A small fraction of the CO_2 molecules in the air thus will contain radioactive carbon 14 atoms in place of stable carbon 12 atoms. Living organisms exchange CO_2 molecules with their surroundings, utilizing both types of carbon in their structure. When the organisms die, their intake of carbon 14 ceases, and from that moment on the carbon 14 atoms relative to the carbon 12 atoms decrease in number by virtue of the ^{14}C decay, only half of the original ^{14}C atoms being present after 5,740 years. This offers a very sensitive method of determining the age of organic archeological objects: one merely determines the relative numbers of the two isotopes. The number of carbon 14 atoms is determined by measuring their activity and using Equation 9-43. This ingenious method of measuring the age of organic relics many thousands of years old was originated by W. F. Libby in 1952 and is known as *radiocarbon dating*.

A second cosmic-ray nuclear reaction continuously producing a naturally radioactive element is

$$^{14}_{7}\text{N} + ^{1}_{0}\text{n} \rightarrow ^{12}_{6}\text{C} + ^{3}_{1}\text{H}$$

where $^{3}_{1}$H, called *tritium* (with a nucleus known as a *triton*), is a heavy radioactive isotope of hydrogen. Tritium decays into the stable helium isotope, $^{3}_{2}$He, with a half-life of 12.4 years by β^- emission.

$$^{3}_{1}\text{H} \rightarrow ^{3}_{2}\text{He} + \beta^-$$

9-13   Summary

Table 9-6

Properties of the Nuclear Constituents

PROPERTY	PROTON	NEUTRON
Mass, u	1.007277	1.008665
Charge, e	1	0
Spin, $\hbar$	$\frac{1}{2}$	$\frac{1}{2}$
Magnetic moment, $e\hbar/2M_pc$	+2.79	−1.91

PROPERTIES OF THE NUCLEAR FORCE

Attractive and much stronger than the Coulomb force

Short-range, ≈ 3 fermi (3×10^{-15} m)

Charge-independent; all three nucleon interactions, n-p, p-p, and n-n, are approximately equal.

NOMENCLATURE

Nucleon: proton or neutron

Atomic number, Z: number of protons

Neutron number, N: number of neutrons

Mass number, A: total number of nucleons $(Z + N)$

Nuclide: nucleus with a particular Z and a particular N

Isotopes: nuclides with same Z

Isotones: nuclides with same N

Isobars: nuclides with same A

PROPERTIES OF THE NUCLIDES

Stable nuclides: $N \approx Z$ at small A, and $N > Z$ at large A.

The nuclear radius is given by $R = r_0A^{1/3}$, where $r_0 = 1.4$ fermi (neutron scattering) or $r_0 = 1.1$ fermi (electron scattering). All nuclei have the same nuclear density.

The total binding energy E_b of a nucleus ^AZ is given by

$$E_b/c^2 = ZM_H + (A - Z)M_n - M$$

where all masses are those of the neutral atoms. For $A > 20$ the energy is $E_b/A \approx 8$ MeV per nucleon.

In the liquid-drop model of the nucleus, the forces between nucleons are assumed to be analogous to the forces between molecules in a liquid; the important contributions to the binding energy are the volume energy, the surface energy (important for low A), and the Coulomb energy (important for high A). In the single-particle and shell models of the nucleus the quantum aspects of the nucleons are used to account for nuclear spins and magnetic moments. The collective model emphasizes nuclear vibration and rotation.

In the decay of all unstable nuclei, the laws of conservation of electric charge, nucleons, mass-energy, and momentum are satisfied.

The law of radioactive decay is $N = N_0 e^{-\lambda t}$, where the decay constant λ, the probability per unit time that any one nucleus will decay, is related to the half-life by $T_{1/2} = 0.693/\lambda$.

Table 9-7

Radioactive Decay Modes

	ALPHA (helium nucleus)	BETA (electron, positron)	GAMMA (photon)
Half-lives	10^{-6} sec to 10^{10} yr	$> 10^{-2}$ sec	10^{-17} to 10^5 sec (isomer)
Energies	4 to 10 MeV	a few MeV	keV to a few MeV
Decay mode	$^A_Z P \rightarrow ^{A-4}_{Z-2} D + ^4_2 \alpha$	β^-: $^A_Z P \rightarrow _{Z+1}^A D + _{-1}^0 e + \bar{\nu}$ β^+: $^A_Z P \rightarrow _{Z-1}^A D + _{+1}^0 e + \nu$ EC: $_{-1}^0 e + ^A_Z P \rightarrow _{Z-1}^A D + \nu$	$^A Z^* \rightarrow ^A Z + \gamma$
Disintegration energy equation (all neutral atom masses)	$M_P = M_D + M_\alpha + Q/c^2$	β^-: $M_P = M_D + Q/c^2$ β^+: $M_P = M_D + 2m_e + Q/c^2$ EC: $M_P = M_D + Q/c^2$	$E_u = E_l + h\nu$
Energy distribution of decay products	Monoenergetic	β^- and β^+: polyenergetic EC: monoenergetic	Monoenergetic

NEUTRINO PROPERTIES

mass: 0

charge: 0

spin: $\frac{1}{2}$

neutrino capture: $\bar{\nu} + p \rightarrow n + \beta^+$

Table 9-8

Natural Radioactivity

SERIES NAME	LONGEST-LIVED MEMBER	TYPE	NUMBER OF MEMBERS
Thorium	$^{232}_{90}$Th	$4n$	13
Actinium	$^{235}_{92}$U	$4n + 3$	15
Uranium	$^{238}_{92}$U	$4n + 2$	18
Neptunium	$^{237}_{93}$Np	$4n + 1$	13

BIBLIOGRAPHY

Beyer, R. T., Editor, *Foundations of Nuclear Physics*. New York; Dover Publications, 1949. A collection of original research papers dealing with fundamental discoveries in nuclear physics.

Preston, M. A., *Physics of the Nucleus*. Reading, Massachusetts; Addison-Wesley Publishing Company, Inc., 1962.

Boorse, H. A., and L. Motz, Editors, *The World of the Atom*. New York; Basic Books, Inc., 1966. Volume 2 of this collection of papers and commentary on the investigators contains a number of items relating to nuclear physics.

Evans, R. D., *The Atomic Nucleus*. New York; McGraw-Hill Book Company, Inc., 1955. An advanced and thorough 972-page treatise.

Livesey, D. L., *Atomic and Nuclear Physics*. Waltham, Massachusetts; Blaisdell Publishing Company, 1966. The treatment of nuclear physics is somewhat more sophisticated than that given in this text.

PROBLEMS

See Appendix I for values of the atomic masses.

9-1   Show that the wavelength of any particle whose kinetic energy is large compared with its rest energy is given by $\lambda = 1.24$ GeV-fermi$/E$, where E is the particle's total energy in GeV.

9-2   Although the neutron is electrically neutral as a whole, it has a negative nuclear magnetic moment, the direction of which is opposite to the direction of its nuclear-spin angular momentum. What sort of distribution of separated positive and negative charge within a neutron—positive on the inside and negative on the outside, or negative on the inside and positive on the outside—would correspond to the observed magnetic moment?

9-3   A free proton in an external magnetic field B has two possible orientations of its spin and associated magnetic moment relative to the magnetic field lines because of the space quantization of the proton nuclear spin. A photon whose energy is equal to the difference in energy between the two proton states can induce the proton to make a transition from one state to the other. The phenomenon is known as *nuclear magnetic resonance* (NMR). Compute the proton resonance frequency for free protons in a magnetic field of 3,000 gauss.

9-4   The nuclear magnetic moment of the deuteron in its ground state is $+0.8574$ nuclear magnetons: its nuclear spin is $I = 1$. Show by comparing the magnetic moment of the deuteron with the separate magnetic moments of the proton and neutron that the deuteron can be assumed to exist in a $^3S_1$ state, that is, a quantum state of zero orbital angular momentum, with intrinsic angular momenta of proton and neutron so aligned as to produce a net deuteron nuclear spin of one unit.

9-5 *   The equality of the neutron-neutron and proton-proton nuclear forces can be verified by considering *mirror nuclides*. One nuclide of a pair of mirror nuclides becomes the other nuclide by the interchange of proton and neutron numbers: for example, ^{11}B ($Z = 5, N = 6$) and ^{11}C ($Z = 6$, $N = 5$) are mirror nuclides. If it were not for the neutron-proton mass difference and the difference in Coulomb energy arising from the difference in Z, the total binding energies and masses of a pair of mirror nuclides would be identical, assuming the internucleon forces to be the same. The average Coulomb energy for a *pair* of protons, each of whose charge is distributed uniformly throughout a nucleus of radius R, is given by $(6/5)ke^2/R$. The radius R is given by $R = r_0A^{1/3}$, with $r_0 = 1.4$ fermi (Equation 9-8). Compute the mass of ^{11}C from the mass of ^{11}B by (a) assuming the charge independence of the nuclear force as applied to mirror nuclides and (b) utilizing the observed fact that ^{11}C decays into ^{11}B by the emission of positrons having a maximum kinetic energy of 0.96 MeV.

9-6   Show that in a proton-proton or a neutron-proton elastic scattering experiment no particles are scattered from the forward direction by more than 90° (take the neutron and proton masses to be equal, and assume the incident particle kinetic energy to be small compared with the rest energy).

9-7 * A photon produces a photodisintegration of a deuteron initially at rest. The proton emerges at right angles to the direction of the incident photon with a kinetic energy of 3.00 MeV. (a) In what direction does the neutron move relative to the incident photon's direction? (b) What is the neutron's kinetic energy? (c) What is the photon's energy?

9-8   A 2.0 MeV proton collides head on with a 2.0 MeV neutron and produces a deuteron. (a) What is the energy of the photon emitted? (b) With what kinetic energy does the deuteron recoil upon emitting the photon? Take the neutron and proton masses to be equal.

9-9   Show that the quantity ke^2 (the Coulomb force constant multiplied by the square of the electron charge) is equal to 1.44 MeV-fermi.

9-10   (a) Show that the so-called *classical electron radius*, ke^2/m_ec^2, where m_e is the electron rest mass, is of the order of a nuclear dimension. (b) Show that two point charges, each of magnitude e, separated by a distance equal to the classical electron radius, have a Coulomb energy equal to the rest energy of an electron.

9-11   (a) Show that an even-Z nuclide usually has many more stable isotopes than an odd-Z nuclide. (b) Between $^{16}_8$O and $^{32}_{16}$S there are one stable isotope for each odd-Z nuclide and three stable isotopes for each even-Z nuclide. Explain this in terms of the filling of neutron and proton shells.

9-12   Show that in $^{12}_6$C the separation energy of the least tightly bound neutron is 18.72 MeV.

9-13   (a) Compute the separation energies of the least tightly bound nucleons in the stable nuclides $^{24}_{12}$Mg, $^{23}_{11}$Na, $^{22}_{10}$Ne, $^{21}_{10}$Ne, $^{20}_{10}$Ne, and $^{19}_9$F. (b) How does the separation energy of a nuclide with even A compare with that of the neighboring nuclides of odd A? (c) Explain this in terms of the filling of proton and neutron levels.

9-14   What stable nuclide has a nuclear radius one half that of Mendelevium 258, the most massive nuclide observed thus far?

9-15   Show that the density of nuclear matter is approximately 2×10^{17} kg/m³ $\approx 10^9$ tons/inch³.

9-16   Use the nuclear shell model (Table 9-3) to predict the nuclear spin of the following nuclides; (a) $^7_3$Li, (b) $^{15}_7$N, (c) $^{41}_{20}$Ca, and (d) $^{55}_{26}$Fe.

9-17 By examining the neutron-proton chart of the stable nuclides in Figure 9-7 find the (a) isotopes and (b) isotones with the greatest numbers of stable nuclides and compare them with the magic numbers of the nuclear shell model. (c) What nuclides are "doubly magic," that is, have closed shells of both protons and neutrons?

9-18 * The collective model of the nucleus can be used to predict the energies of excited nuclear states for certain even-even nuclides. An object having a moment of inertia I about a rotation axis has rotational kinetic energy $E = \frac{1}{2}I\omega^2 = (I\omega)^2/2I = L^2/2I$, where L is the rotational angular momentum. With the angular-momentum quantization rule $L^2 = J(J + 1)\hbar^2$, where the rotational quantum number J is 0, 1, 2, . . . , (see Section 7-2), the permitted rotational kinetic energies are given by $E = J(J + 1)\hbar^2/2I$. Quantum restrictions on the nuclear wave functions allow only the states of even J: $J = 0, 2, 4, \ldots$. Show that the excitation energies of the first four excited, nuclear, rotational states relative to the ground state are in the ratios 1, 10/3, 7, and 12.

9-19 The activity of a certain radioactive material drops by a factor of 4 in a time interval of 1 min. What is the decay constant of this radionuclide?

9-20 A certain radionuclide emits radiation at the rate of 6.40 μW at one instant of time and 0.40 μW one day later. What is its half-life?

9-21 Show that the mean life T_{av} of a radionuclide having a decay constant λ is given by $T_{av} = \int_{N_0}^{0} t \, dN / \int_{N_0}^{0} dN = 1/\lambda$.

9-22 What fraction of the $^{232}_{90}$Th atoms in existence at the creation of the universe 10 billion years ago still survive? The half-life of $^{232}_{90}$Th is 4.45×10^{17} sec.

9-23 Show that 1 g of radium 226 ($T_{1/2} = 1,620$ yr) has an activity of 1.00 curie. (This was the basis of the original definition of the curie.)

9-24 * What is the probability that a free neutron with a kinetic energy of (1/25) eV will decay to a proton in traveling a distance of 1.0 km? The neutron's half-life is 12 min.

9-25 How many grams of carbon-14 (half-life 5,740 yr) will produce an activity of 1 millicurie?

9-26 The nuclide ^{226}Ra decays into ^{222}Rn by alpha emission. Some decays are to the ground state, and others to an excited state, of the daughter nucleus. The measured α-particle kinetic energies are, respectively, 4.863 MeV and 4.673 MeV. What is the excitation energy of the excited nuclear state of ^{222}Rn?

9-27 An α-emitter decays with the emission of two distinct groups of α-particles having respective kinetic energies of K_1 and K_2. Show that γ-rays having an energy of $(K_1 - K_2)(A - 4)/A$, where A is the mass number of the parent nucleus, are expected to be emitted.

9-28 Iridium 191, a suitable radionuclide for Mössbauer experiments, decays from an excited nuclear state of mean life 1.5×10^{-10} sec with the emission of a 129 keV γ-ray. (a) What is the natural linewidth (in eV) associated with this transition? (b) What is the resolution of the photons emitted by iridium 191, as measured by the natural linewidth divided by the photon energy?

9-29   That a photon has not only a mass $m = h\nu/c^2$ but also a weight $mg = (h\nu/c^2)g$ was established in the 1960 experiment of R. V. Pound and G. A. Rebka, Jr., through the use of the Mössbauer effect. In a vertical fall toward Earth through a distance y the photon frequency increases from ν to ν' according to the energy-conservation relation $h\nu + mgy = h\nu'$, or $h\nu + (h\nu/c^2)gy = h\nu'$. Assuming the frequencies ν and ν' to be nearly equal, one obtains $\nu' = \nu(1 + gy/c^2)$. (a) Show that for $y = 20$ m, as it was in the Pound-Rebka experiment, the fractional change in photon frequency is 2 parts in 10^{15}. (b) If the 14.4 keV photons from an ^{57}Fe* source in a crystalline lattice fall 20 m downward, the peak in the gamma-ray line of the gamma-ray source at the top does not match exactly the peak in the absorption line of an ^{57}Fe absorber at the bottom, because of the frequency shift of 2 parts in 10^{15} arising from the gravitational interaction with the photon. In what direction (up or down) and with what speed must the absorber be moved if the emission and absorption peaks are to correspond exactly?

9-30   What is the maximum possible kinetic energy of the electron emitted in the decay of $_1^3$H?

9-31   What modes of decay are energetically possible for the following unstable nuclides; (a) $_{17}^{36}$Cl, (b) $_{20}^{41}$Ca, (c) $_{23}^{48}$V, and (d) $_{25}^{54}$Mn?

9-32   The nuclide $_5^{12}$B decays by β^- emission with a half-life of 0.020 sec. What are the total energies radiated from an initially 100 μg sample of ^{12}B in (a) the first millisecond, (b) the thousandth millisecond, and (c) the first second?

9-33   Lead 214 has a half-life of 27 min and emits electrons with a maximum kinetic energy of 1.03 MeV. What is the radioactive power output, in microwatts, of a 1-millicurie sample of this lead?

9-34   Beryllium 7 decays by electron capture. What are the (a) energy and (b) momentum of the emitted neutrinos? (c) What is the recoil kinetic energy of each lithium-7 nucleus?

9-35   A $_4^8$Be* nucleus may decay to the ground state with the emission of a 17.6 MeV gamma ray. With what kinetic energy does it recoil? (The beryllium 8 nucleus is highly unstable and decays rapidly to two α-particles.

9-36   The unstable nuclide $_4^7$Be decays by electron capture to the ground state of $_3^7$Li. Some of it decays, however, to a 0.48 MeV excited state of $_3^7$Li. What monoenergetic (a) neutrinos and (b) photons are emitted by a sample of $_4^7$Be?

9-37   The unstable nuclide $_{20}^{41}$Ca decays by electron capture. (a) What is the total energy released in this $_{20}^{41}$Ca decay? (b) What is the energy of the neutrino? (c) What is the recoil kinetic energy of the $_{19}^{41}$K nucleus? (d) What fraction of the energy released is carried by the daughter nucleus?

9-38   What is the minimum energy an antineutrino may have for capture by a proton so as to produce a neutron and positron?

9-39 * Free neutrons at rest decay by β^- emission. What is the maximum possible kinetic energy of (a) the protons, (b) the electrons, and (c) the antineutrinos?

9-40 In the naturally radioactive series beginning with uranium 238 there are five successive alpha decays, beginning with $^{234}_{92}U$ and ending with $^{214}_{82}Pb$. (a) Show that the emission of a nucleus of $^{20}_{10}Ne$ by $^{234}_{92}U$ is energetically allowed. (b) Considering the tunnel effect operating in alpha decay, why is ^{20}Ne emission much more improbable than the emission of five ^4_2He particles in sequence?

9-41 A certain organic relic containing 200 g of carbon has a carbon-14 activity of 1,890 disintegrations per minute. The carbon-14 activity of a living organism is 12 disintegrations per minute for each gram of carbon. At what date did the organism die?

T E N

NUCLEAR REACTIONS

10-1 Low-energy nuclear reactions In the last chapter we saw that unstable nuclei will decay spontaneously, changing their nuclear structure without external influence. One can, however, induce a change in the identity or characteristics of nuclei by bombarding them with energetic particles. The change is known as a *nuclear reaction*.

Thousands of nuclear reactions have been produced and identified since Rutherford observed the first one in 1919. The bombarding particles were, until the development of charged-particle accelerators in the nineteen-thirties, those emitted from radioactive substances. It is now possible to accelerate charged particles to energies of nearly 100 GeV. When particles of such great energy strike nuclei, they severely disrupt them and may create new and strange particles. These so-called *high-energy* reactions and the particles participating in them will be discussed in Chapter 11.

We shall be concerned in this chapter with *low-energy* nuclear reactions, reactions in which the incident particles have energies no greater than, say, 20 MeV. All such reactions have several features in common:

The bombarding particle is typically a light-weight particle: an alpha particle, gamma ray, proton, deuteron, or neutron.

The reactions typically involve the emission of *one* other of such particles.

No such particles as mesons or baryons are created.

We shall illustrate several types of nuclear reaction with examples that have been important in the development of nuclear physics.

In the first observed nuclear reaction (1919) Rutherford used alpha particles of 7.68 MeV from the naturally radioactive element $^{214}_{84}$Po. When the alpha particles were sent through a nitrogen gas, most of them were either undeflected by the nitrogen nuclei or elastically scattered in close encounters with them. Rutherford found, however, that in a few collisions (about 1 in 50,000) protons were produced, according to the nuclear reaction

$$^{14}_{7}N + ^{4}_{2}He \rightarrow ^{1}_{1}H + ^{17}_{8}O$$

In this reaction an α-particle strikes a nitrogen-14 nucleus, producing a proton and an oxygen-17 nucleus. Rutherford identified the emitted light-weight particles as protons by measuring their range, which exceeded that of the incident α-particles (see Section 8-1). That the particles emitted in this reaction are protons has since been established by measurements of the charge-to-mass ratio with a magnetic field. A cloud-chamber schematic of the reaction, Figure 10-1, shows the tracks of the incident α-particle, the

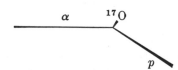

Figure 10-1. Representation of a cloud-chamber photograph of the reaction, $^{14}_{7}N(\alpha, p)^{17}_{8}O$.

emitted proton, and the recoiling oxygen nucleus. The reaction represents *induced transmutation* of the element nitrogen into a stable isotope of oxygen; α- or β-radioactive decay represents, of course, *spontaneous transmutation* of one element into another.

The laws of conservation of electric charge and of nucleons are satisfied in all nuclear reactions; therefore, the presubscripts giving the electric charge of the particles and the presuperscripts giving the number of nucleons in each particle each sum to the same amount on both sides of the equation. The reaction may be written in abbreviated form as follows:

$$^{14}_{7}N(\alpha, p)^{17}_{8}O$$

where the light particles going into and out of the reaction are written in parentheses between the symbols for the target and product nuclei.

Until 1932 all nuclear reactions were produced by the relatively high-energy α-particles or γ-rays from naturally radioactive materials. In that year J. D. Cockcroft and E. T. S. Walton, using a 500 keV accelerator, observed the first nuclear reaction produced by artificially accelerated charged particles. They found that α-particles were emitted when a lithium target was struck by protons with energies of 500 keV, according to the reaction

$$_3^7\text{L} + {}_1^1\text{H} \rightarrow {}_2^4\text{He} + {}_2^4\text{He}$$
$$_3^7\text{Li} \, (p, \alpha)_2^4\text{He}$$

The emitted α-particles each had an energy of 8.9 MeV; thus, an energy of 0.5 MeV had been put into the reaction, and 17.8 MeV was released as kinetic energy of the emerging particles. Here is a striking example of the release of nuclear energy. The total amount of energy released was trifling, of course, since most of the collisions between the incident protons and target nuclei did *not* result in nuclear distintegrations.

In the two reactions described above the product nuclei were stable. The first nuclear reaction leading to an unstable product nucleus was observed by I. Joliot-Curie and F. Joliot in 1934. In the reaction an aluminum target is struck by α-particles, leading to

$$_{13}^{27}\text{Al} + {}_2^4\text{He} \rightarrow {}_0^1\text{n} + {}_{15}^{30}\text{P}$$
$$_{13}^{27}\text{Al} \, (\alpha, n)_{15}^{30}\text{P}$$

The product nuclide is not stable but decays with a half-life of 2.6 minutes into a stable isotope of silicon by β^+ emission:

$$_{15}^{30}\text{P} \rightarrow {}_{14}^{30}\text{Si} + \beta^+ + \nu$$

where ν is a neutrino. The production of unstable nuclides that spontaneously disintegrate by the law of radioactive decay is a feature of many nuclear reactions. The nuclides are said to exhibit *artificial radioactivity*. Indeed, nuclear reactions are the only means of obtaining artificial radioactive isotopes, or *radioisotopes*. The radioisotopes are chemically identical with the element's stable isotopes. If a small amount of radioisotope is added to stable nuclides of the same element, it can serve, through its radioactivity, as a *tracer* of the element; that is, the presence and concentration of the element can be determined by measuring the radioisotope's activity.

The discovery of the neutron came as a result of a nuclear reaction observed in 1930 by W. Bothe and H. Becker, the bombardment of beryllium by alpha particles:

$$_4^9\text{Be} + {}_2^4\text{He} \rightarrow {}_0^1\text{n} + {}_6^{12}\text{C}$$
$$_4^9\text{Be} \, (\alpha, n)_6^{12}\text{C}$$

It was thought at first that the products were a γ-ray and the stable nucleus $^{12}_{6}C$, rather than a neutron and $^{12}_{6}C$, because an extremely penetrating radiation was found to result. Then Curie and Joliot in 1932 found that when the resulting radiation fell on paraffin (which consists largely of hydrogen), protons with energies of about 6 MeV were emitted. This at first was interpreted in terms of the Compton effect, in which a gamma-ray photon makes a Compton collision with a proton and ejects it from the paraffin. The photon energy required to transfer 6 MeV to protons is easily found from Equation 4-17 to be nearly 60 MeV. It is easy to show from the conservation of mass-energy that *less* than this amount of energy would be released in a $^{9}_{4}Be(\alpha, \gamma)^{13}_{6}C$ reaction. Therefore, the photon hypothesis was untenable.

The proper interpretation of these experiments was given by J. Chadwick in 1932, who showed that all experimental results were consistent with the assumption that an uncharged, and therefore highly penetrating, particle having a mass nearly that of the proton was being emitted. By the conservation of mass-energy, such a particle would be emitted with an energy of about 6 MeV, and when the neutron struck a proton head on, it would come to rest, transferring its momentum and energy to the proton.

Neutrons are emitted in many nuclear reactions and can themselves be used as bombarding particles. One of the important neutron-induced reactions is that in which a neutron is captured by a target nucleus and a γ-ray photon is emitted. This reaction is known as neutron *radiative capture*. For example,

$$^{27}_{13}Al + ^{1}_{0}n \rightarrow \gamma + ^{28}_{13}Al$$
$$^{27}_{13}Al(n, \gamma)^{28}_{13}Al$$

The product nucleus, an unstable isotope of the target nucleus, decays by β^{-} decay:

$$^{28}_{13}Al \rightarrow ^{28}_{14}Si + \beta^{-} + \bar{\nu}$$

where $\bar{\nu}$ is an antineutrino.

Since the neutron has no electric charge, the neutron radiative capture process can occur when a neutron of almost any energy strikes (almost) any nucleus; the heavier isotope thus produced frequently is radioactive, and the absorption of neutrons is, therefore, a common means of producing radioisotopes.

Another important type of reaction resulting from neutron bombardment is that in which a charged particle, such as a proton or α-particle, is emitted. Such a reaction offers a method of detecting neutrons, because the emitted charged particles produce detectable ionization. One reaction frequently used in neutron detection is

$$^{10}_{5}B + ^{1}_{0}n \rightarrow ^{4}_{2}He + ^{7}_{3}Li$$
$$^{10}_{5}B(n, \alpha)^{7}_{3}Li$$

Photodisintegration is the nuclear reaction in which the absorption of a γ-ray photon results in the disintegration of the absorbing nucleus. An example is

$$^{25}_{12}\text{Mg} + \gamma \rightarrow {}^{1}_{1}\text{H} + {}^{24}_{11}\text{Na}$$
$$^{15}_{12}\text{Mg}(\gamma, \text{p}){}^{24}_{11}\text{Na}$$

followed by ${}^{24}_{11}\text{Na} \rightarrow {}^{24}_{12}\text{Mg} + \beta^- + \bar{\nu}$.

A special type of low-energy nuclear reaction is that of *nuclear fission*. In this reaction, which we shall discuss in more detail in Section 10-7, a low-energy neutron is captured by a very heavy nucleus, and the resulting aggregate splits into two moderately heavy nuclei along with a few neutrons.

We have listed only a few of the many known nuclear reactions. One general statement concerning low-energy nuclear reactions involving the light particles (p, n, d, α and γ) either bombarding or emerging, may be made: nuclear reactions with essentially all possible combinations of in-going and outgoing light particles occur.

10-2   The energetics of nuclear reactions   Consider the generalized nuclear reaction X(x, y)Y, where X is the target nucleus, x is the bombarding particle, y is the emergent light-weight particle, and Y is the product nucleus. The target nucleus is assumed to be at rest ($K_X = 0$), and the kinetic energies of x, y, and Y are denoted by K_x, K_y, and K_Y, respectively.

The disintegration energy, or *Q value*, of a radioactive decay has been defined as the total energy released in the decay (Equation 9-29). In a similar way the *Q* value of a nuclear reaction is defined as the total energy released in the reaction; that is, *Q* is the kinetic energy coming out of the reaction less the kinetic energy going into the reaction:

$$Q = (K_y + K_Y) - K_x \qquad [10\text{-}1]$$

The total relativistic energy of a particle is the sum of its rest energy and its kinetic energy; the conservation of mass-energy requires, then, that

$$(m_x c^2 + K_x) + M_X c^2 = (m_y c^2 + K_y) + (M_Y c^2 + K_Y) \qquad [10\text{-}2]$$

where m_x, M_X, m_y, and M_Y are the *rest* masses. Combining the two equations gives

$$Q/c^2 = (m_x + M_X) - (m_y + M_Y) \qquad [10\text{-}3]$$

This equation shows that Q/c^2, the mass equivalent of the energy released in the reaction, is simply the total rest mass going into the reaction less the total rest mass coming out of the reaction. Thus, the nuclear energy released in a reaction can be computed directly from the masses of the participating particles or, if one of the masses (most often that of the product heavy nucleus) is not known with precision, it can be computed if the Q value is determined from measurement of particle kinetic energies.

Nuclear energy is released in a reaction when $Q > 0$; such a reaction, in which mass is converted into the kinetic energy of the outgoing particles, is known as an *exothermic*, or *exoergic*, reaction. A reaction in which nuclear energy is absorbed, or consumed, with $Q < 0$, is called *endothermic*, or *endoergic*. An endothermic reaction may be thought of as an inelastic collision in which the identity of the colliding particles changes and kinetic energy is at least partially converted into mass.

A rather special sort of reaction is that in which the incoming and outgoing particles are identical, x = y and X = Y. If no kinetic energy is lost ($Q = 0$), the reaction is an elastic collision; if energy is lost ($Q < 0$), the reaction is an inelastic collision.

Let us compute the Q of the reaction $_3^7\text{Li}(\text{p}, \alpha)_2^4\text{He}$ in which y = Y, a somewhat atypical reaction. We may use the *neutral atomic* masses of the four particles because in the change from nuclear masses to atomic masses an equal number of electron masses is added to both sides of Equation 10-2.

$$\text{mass } _1^1\text{H} = 1.007825$$
$$\underline{\text{mass } _3^7\text{L} = 7.016004}$$
$$m_\text{x} + M_\text{X} = 8.023829 \text{ u}$$

$$\text{mass } _2^4\text{He} = 4.002603$$
$$\underline{\text{mass } _2^4\text{He} = 4.002603}$$
$$m_\text{y} + M_\text{Y} = 8.005206 \text{ u}$$

$$Q/c^2 = (m_\text{x} + M_\text{X}) - (m_\text{y} + M_\text{Y}) = 8.023829 - 8.005206 = 0.018623 \text{ u}$$

$$Q = 0.018623 \text{ u} \times 931.5 \text{ MeV/u} = 17.35 \text{ MeV}$$

This reaction is exothermic, 17.35 MeV being released; thus, the total kinetic energy of the two outgoing α-particles exceeds the kinetic energy of the incoming proton by that amount. In the original Cockcroft-Walton experiment the incident protons had an energy of 0.50 MeV; therefore, the total energy carried by the two α-particles was expected to be $17.35 + 0.50 = 17.85$ MeV, or about $\frac{1}{2}(17.85) = 8.93$ MeV for each α-particle. The measured energy of the α-particles was in good agreement with the expectation. This and all other reactions between particles whose masses and kinetic energies are known gives striking confirmation of the relativistic mass-energy equivalence.

Because y = Y in this reaction, the two particles emerging from the collision have nearly equal kinetic energies and momenta (magnitude). When a reaction involves masses $M_\text{Y} \gg M_\text{y}$, then the energies are $K_\text{Y} \ll K_\text{y}$, most of the kinetic energy being carried by the light particles.

Energy is released in an exothermic reaction; therefore, it is energetically possible for an exothermic reaction to occur even when the energy of the bombarding particle is nearly zero, although the probability of its occurrence may be very small. On the other hand, an endothermic reaction cannot occur unless the incident particle carries kinetic energy. At first thought it might appear that an endothermic reaction with a Q of, say, -5 MeV would be energetically possible if 5 MeV kinetic energy were carried into the collision by the bombarding particle, but this is *not* so. The value of K_x must, in fact, exceed the magnitude of Q for the reaction to go. The reason is that linear momentum must be conserved in every nuclear reaction, and because of this a fraction of the incident particle's energy is unavailable.

10-3 The conservation of momentum in nuclear reactions The total linear momentum of any isolated system is constant in magnitude and direction; momentum conservation holds as well in nuclear collisions and reactions as in macroscopic systems. Therefore, the total vector momentum of particles in a nuclear reaction must be the same before and after the reaction.

If the target nucleus X is at rest in the laboratory, the total momentum of the system before the collision is simply $m_x v_x$, the momentum of the incident particle (we assume that the energies of the particles are never more than a few MeV, so that the classical expressions for momentum and kinetic energy apply). The momenta of particles y and Y emerging from the reaction must, therefore, add as vectors to yield a vector along the direction of the incident particle whose magnitude is $m_x v_x$, as shown in Figure 10-2.

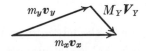

Figure 10-2. Linear momenta of the incident particle x and the emerging particles y and Y in a nuclear reaction.

This means that it is impossible for both the resulting particles y and Y to be at rest, for then the total momentum after the reaction would be zero.

Now consider the reaction from the point of view of an observer in a reference frame in which the system's center of mass is at rest. By definition, the center-of-mass reference frame is that reference frame in which the system's total momentum is zero.† Then

$$M v_{cm} = m_1 v_1 + m_2 v_2$$

where M is the system's total mass, v_1 and v_2 are the respective velocities in the laboratory reference frame of masses m_1 and m_2, and v_{cm} is the velocity

† See Equation 8-24, Weidner and Sells, *E. C. P.*

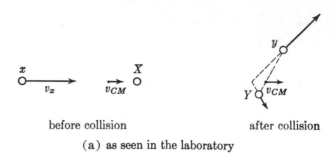

before collision   after collision

(a) as seen in the laboratory

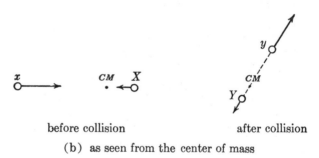

before collision   after collision

(b) as seen from the center of mass

Figure 10-3. Nuclear collision or reaction as seen in the laboratory and from the center of mass reference frame.

of the center of mass relative to the laboratory. Applied to the reaction of Figure 10-2, with particle X at rest in the laboratory, this relation becomes

$$(m_x + M_X) v_{cm} = m_x v_x \qquad [10\text{-}4]$$

Figure 10-3 shows the reaction as seen by an observer at rest in the laboratory and as seen by an observer in the center-of-mass reference frame. In the laboratory the center of mass travels at the constant velocity v_{cm} both before and after the collision. In the center-of-mass reference frame the center of mass remains at rest; particles x and X approach it in opposite directions with momenta of equal magnitudes before the collision, and particles y and Y recede from it in opposite directions with momenta of equal magnitudes after the collision.

If a reaction is to take place at all, it must be energetically allowed in the center-of-mass reference frame. In a perfectly elastic reaction ($Q \doteq 0$) the total kinetic energy of the particles leaving the site of collision is the same as that of the particles approaching. In an exoergic, or explosive, reaction $(Q > 0)$ the total kinetic energy of the particles leaving the collision exceeds that of the particles approaching. In a perfectly inelastic, or endoergic, reaction $(Q < 0)$ the particles leaving the collision are at rest in the center-of-mass reference frame.† Now, if particles y and Y are at rest in the center-of-mass reference frame, they are clearly in motion, with nonzero kinetic energy, in the laboratory reference frame. Since they must be in motion in the laboratory frame in order to ensure momentum conservation, not all of the energy that goes into the collision as viewed in the laboratory, $K_x = \frac{1}{2}mv_x^2$, is available to be consumed, or dissipated, in an endoergic reaction. Only a portion of K_x can be consumed; the remainder is energy that may be thought of as being carried by the system's center of mass.

The kinetic energy K_{cm} of the system's center of mass is given by

$$K_{cm} = \tfrac{1}{2}(m_x + M_X)v_{cm}^2$$

which becomes, through the use of Equation 10-4,

$$K_{cm} = \tfrac{1}{2}(m_x + M_X)\left(\frac{m_x v_x}{m_x + M_X}\right)^2 = \tfrac{1}{2}m_x v_x^2 [m_x/(m_x + M_X)]$$

$$= K_x\left(\frac{m_x}{m_x + M_X}\right)$$

Then the *available energy* K_a, that portion of K_x which is not carried by the center of mass, is given by

$$K_a = K_x - K_{cm} = K_x - K_x m_x/(m_x + M_X)$$

$$= K_x\left(\frac{M_X}{m_x + M_X}\right) \qquad\qquad [10\text{-}5]$$

This equation shows that only a fraction, $M_X/(m_x + M_X)$, of the incident particle's kinetic energy is available for dissipation in the reaction. If a reaction is endoergic, with $Q < 0$, it cannot take place unless an amount of energy equal in magnitude to Q is supplied to the colliding particles; that is, it can occur only if $K_a = -Q$ (note that Q is intrinsically *negative*). Then the value of K_x for which the reaction becomes energetically just possible, the *threshold energy*, is $K_x = K_{th}$. Making these substitutions in Equation 10-5, we have

$$Q - K_{th}\left(\frac{M_X}{m_x + M_X}\right)$$

$$\boxed{K_{th} = -Q\left(\frac{M_X + m_x}{M_X}\right)} \qquad\qquad [10\text{-}6]$$

† See Section 12-4, Weidner and Sells, *E. C. P.*

It must be emphasized that this equation applies only when the colliding particles move at speeds small compared with c and when the magnitude of Q is small compared with the rest energies of particles x, X, y, and Y. In other words, this threshold-kinetic-energy relation was arrived at by classical mechanics.

Consider the endothermic reaction ${}^{14}_{7}\text{N}(\alpha, \text{p}){}^{17}_{8}\text{O}$. From a comparison of the masses of the participating particles it is easy to show that $Q = -1.18$ MeV. We can take M_X to be 14 and m_x to be 4. Then the threshold energy, or the minimum alpha-particle energy required for this reaction, is, from Equation 10-6, $K_{\text{th}} = -(-1.18)(18/14) = 1.52$ MeV. This result is confirmed by experiment. When α-particles with energies less than this strike nitrogen, no protons are released; after the threshold has been reached and exceeded, the reaction takes place, as is indicated by the appearance of protons (see Figure 10-4). The Q values of endothermic reactions can, there-

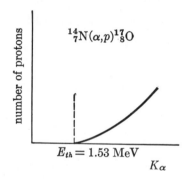

Figure 10-4. Number of protons from the ${}^{14}_{7}\text{N}(\alpha, \text{p}){}^{17}_{8}\text{O}$ reaction as a function of the α-particle energy, indicating a threshold of 1.52 MeV.

fore, be determined quite directly by observing the threshold energy of the reaction and applying Equation 10-6.

To derive the general, relativistic relation for the threshold kinetic energy of the incident particle in an endoergic reaction we recognize that, whereas a particle's relativistic momentum $\boldsymbol{p} = m\boldsymbol{v}$ and total relativistic energy $E = mc^2$ depend upon the reference frame in which these quantities are measured, the particle's rest energy $E_0 = m_0c^2$ is an *invariant* and has the same value for all observers (Section 3-4):

[3-14] $$E_0^2 = E^2 - (pc)^2$$

More generally, the total rest energy of an isolated *system* of particles is invariant for observers in all inertial frames if E and p represent the *system's* total relativistic energy and (vector) momentum. Thus, both before or after a reaction X(x, y)Y has taken place, the total rest energy of the system is the same in the laboratory reference frame, in which the target particle X is free and initially at rest, as in the center-of-mass reference frame, in which the total momentum is, by definition, always zero. Therefore,

$$E_0^2 = E_{lab}^2 - (p_{lab}c)^2 = E_{cm}^2 - (p_{cm}c)^2$$

Moreover, since we are considering an endoergic reaction in which the incident particle x has just enough kinetic energy, as measured in the laboratory, to allow the reaction to take place (the threshold energy K_{th}), we know that the system's total kinetic energy after the reaction, as measured in the center-of-mass reference frame, is exactly zero.

In the center-of-mass reference frame the system's total momentum is

$$p_{cm} = 0$$

and, after the reaction has occurred at the threshold, its total relativistic energy is

$$E_{cm} = E_{0y} + E_{0Y}$$

where E_{0y} and E_{0Y} are the respective rest energies of particles y and Y. Note that the kinetic energies of y and Y are zero.

In the laboratory reference frame the system's total momentum before the reaction is just that of particle x,

$$p_{lab} = p_x$$

since particle X is initially at rest in the laboratory. The total relativistic energy before the reaction, as measured in the laboratory, is

$$E_{lab} = E_x + E_{0X} = (E_{0x} + K_{th}) + E_{0X}$$

where we recognize that the total energy E_x of particle x is its rest energy E_{0x} and kinetic energy K_{th}. The kinetic energy of X is zero.

Then, substituting the relations for p_{cm}, E_{cm}, p_{lab}, and E_{lab} in the general relation for total rest-energy invariance, we have

$$E_{lab}^2 - (p_{lab}c)^2 = E_{cm}^2 - (p_{cm}c)^2$$

$$(E_{0x} + K_{th} + E_{0X})^2 - (p_x c)^2 = (E_{0y} + E_{0Y})^2 - 0$$

However, we know that for particle x alone

$$E_{0x}^2 = E_x^2 - (p_x c)^2 = (E_{0x} + K_{th})^2 - (p_x c)^2$$

Then, by eliminating $(p_x c)^2$ between the two equations above, we have

$$(E_{0x} + K_{th} + E_{0X})^2 + [E_{0x}^2 - (E_{0x} + K_{th})^2] = (E_{0y} + E_{0Y})^2$$

Solving for K_{th} we finally obtain

$$K_{th} = \frac{(E_{0y} + E_{0Y})^2 - (E_{0x} + E_{0X})^2}{2E_{0X}} \qquad \text{[10-7a]}$$

If we use the symbols m_x, M_X, m_y, and M_Y to denote the *rest* masses of the particles (omitting the zero subscript), we can write the threshold kinetic energy of particle x in terms of rest masses as follows:

$$K_{th} = \frac{[(m_y + M_Y)^2 - (m_x + M_X)^2]c^2}{2M_X} \qquad [10\text{-}7b]$$

Recalling that the total reaction Q is defined as $Q/c^2 = (m_x + M_X) - (m_y + M_Y)$, we find that an alternate form of Equation 10-7b is

$$K_{th} = -\frac{Q(m_x + M_X + m_y + M_Y)}{2M_X} \qquad [10\text{-}7c]$$

The minus sign appears here because the reaction is endoergic and Q is intrinsically negative (note that with $m_x + M_X \approx m_y + M_Y$ and the reaction Q then small compared with the rest energy of any of the particles the equation reduces to the classical approximation given in Equation 10-6).

Although we have been concerned with a reaction that produces only two outgoing particles, it is a simple matter to generalize our results to situations in which three or more particles may emerge. We note that within the parentheses of Equation 10-7c appears the total rest mass of *all* particles entering into and emerging from the reaction. The equation may then be written more generally as

$$K_{th} = -\frac{Q \left(\begin{array}{c} \text{rest energy of \textit{all} particles entering and} \\ \text{leaving the reaction} \end{array} \right)}{2(\text{rest energy of target particle})} \qquad [10\text{-}7d]$$

Equations 10-7, a to d, are, of course, merely alternative forms of the same basic relation for the threshold kinetic energy.

Example 10-1 With what minimum kinetic energy must a proton collide with a second, free proton at rest in order to create a proton-antiproton pair according to the reaction

$$p^+ + p^+ \rightarrow p^+ + p^+ + (p^+ + p^-)$$

where p^+ denotes a proton and p^- an antiproton?

We call the rest energy of a proton or an antiproton E_0. Since two additional particles, each of rest energy E_0, are created in the reaction, we have $Q = -2E_0$. The total rest energy of all particles entering into the reaction (2 protons) and leaving the reaction (3 protons and 1 antiproton) is $6E_0$. Then with the use of Equation 10-7d we find

$$K_{th} = -\frac{(-2E_0)(6E_0)}{2E_0} = 6E_0$$

The incident proton's kinetic energy must be at least *six* times its rest energy, or $6E_0 = 6(0.94 \text{ GeV}) = 5.64 \text{ GeV}$, to create an antiproton (together with a proton). On the other hand, when two protons, each with a kinetic energy E_0 of only 0.94 GeV collide head on in the laboratory, an additional proton and antiproton may be created in the collision; in this instance the laboratory reference frame *is* the center-of-mass reference frame, and none of the kinetic energy of the colliding particles is "wasted," or made unavailable, in order to conserve momentum. Since only a fraction of the incident particle's kinetic energy is available for creating particles when the target particle is at rest in the laboratory, consideration has been given to the use of colliding beams of particles moving in opposite directions.

Example 10-2 What is the minimum energy of a photon needed to create an electron-positron pair through interaction with a free *electron* initially at rest?

We know that when a photon interacts with a massive particle, such as a nucleus, and produces an electron-positron pair, its threshold energy $h\nu_{\min}$ is $2E_0 = 2(0.51$ MeV$) = 1.02$ MeV, where E_0 is the rest energy of an electron or positron (Section 4-5). The massive particle serves to carry away some of the incident photon's momentum but hardly any of its energy, so that essentially all of the photon's energy $h\nu$ is available for the creation of an electron-positron. For the following reaction, however,

$$h\nu + e^- \rightarrow e^- + (e^- + e^+)$$

we must invoke the general relativistic threshold relation.

The most convenient equation to use is Equation 10-7d. The total reaction energy is $Q = -2E_0$. The total rest energy of all particles entering and leaving the reaction is $4E_0$, since 1 electron enters the reaction (the incident photon has zero rest energy), and 2 electrons and 1 positron leave the reaction. Thus, we have, through the use of Equation 10-7d,

$$h\nu_{\min} = K_{\text{th}} = -\frac{(-2E_0)(4E_0)}{2E_0} = 4E_0 = 2.04 \text{ MeV}$$

which is *twice* the minimum photon energy for pair production by interaction with a massive particle.

10-4 Cross section The decay of unstable nuclei is characterized, not only by the energy released in the decay products, but also by the half-life, or decay constant, of the disintegration process. For an unstable nucleus the decay constant λ gives a measure of the probability of the occurrence of the decay *in time*. We wish to introduce a quantity, called the reaction *cross section*, that measures the probability of occurrence *in space* of a nuclear reaction. The conservation laws of energy and momentum tell us whether the reaction is possible; the cross section tells us whether the reaction is probable and how probable it is.

Consider Figure 10-5, which shows a number of target nuclei X exposed to an incident beam of particles x. Each X nucleus has associated with it an area σ, called the cross section, which is imagined to be oriented at right angles to the incidence of the particles (which are regarded as point masses). Each cross-sectional area is assumed to be so small that in a reasonably thin target material no one nucleus is hidden from the incident particles by any other nucleus. The area of the cross section is so chosen that, if an inci-

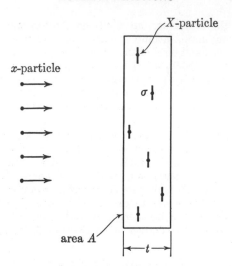

Figure 10-5. Target nuclei X in a target of thickness t, area A, and cross section σ, being struck by x particles.

dent particle strikes the area σ, the reaction $X(x, y)Y$ takes place, and if it misses, the reaction does not take place. The intrinsic probability of the occurrence of a nuclear reaction is, therefore, directly proportional to its cross section σ.

We take the number of incident particles in a thin foil of thickness t and area A to be n_i. The number of these particles undergoing the nuclear reaction $X(x, y)Y$ is n_r, which therefore represents the number of y, or Y, particles produced. The number of target nuclei per unit volume is N, each with nuclear-reaction cross section σ. Since the total number of nuclei in the target foil is $N(At)$, the total exposed area resulting in reactions is σNAt. The ratio n_r/n_i of the x particles undergoing reactions to the total number incident on the foil must be equal to the ratio of the total exposed area σNAt to the total foil area A; then $n_r/n_i = \sigma NAt/A$, or

$$\boxed{n_r/n_i = \sigma Nt} \qquad [10\text{-}8]$$

This derivation of the reaction cross section is analogous to that of the scattering cross section, described in Section 6-1. It shows that the probability n_r/n_i that an incident particle will undergo a nuclear reaction is proportional to the reaction cross section σ, the number N of target nuclei per unit volume, and the thickness t of the target foil. The common unit for measuring nuclear cross sections is the *barn*, which is $10^{-24}\,\text{cm}^2 = 10^{-28}\,\text{m}^2 = 100$ fermi^2. As nuclear cross sections go, one of $10^{-28}\,\text{m}^2$ is relatively large; for an incident particle to hit a nuclear target having a cross section of 1 barn is as easy as hitting the side of a barn. Cross-sections vary from one reaction to another. Furthermore, they are usually dependent on the energy of the bombarding particle.

Example 10-3   Consider the radiative capture of 500 keV neutrons by aluminum in the reaction $^{27}_{13}\text{Al}$ (n, γ) $^{28}_{13}\text{Al}$. The neutron-capture cross section in aluminum has been measured as 2 millibarns $= 2 \times 10^{-31}$ m^2. Suppose that a neutron flux of 10^{10} neutrons/(cm^2-sec) is incident on an aluminum foil 0.20 mm thick. What is the number of neutrons captured per second in a 1 cm^2 area of the foil?

We can compute the density N of aluminum nuclei from the ordinary density of aluminum, 2.70 g/cm^3, Avogadro's number, and the atomic weight of aluminum, 27. Then,

$$N = (2.7 \text{ g/cm}^3)(6.02 \times 10^{23} \text{ atoms/mole})/(27 \text{ g/mole})$$
$$= 6.02 \times 10^{22} \text{ nuclei/cm}^3$$

From Equation 10-8 we have

$$n_r = n_i \sigma N t$$
$$n_r = [10^{10} \text{ neutrons/(cm}^2\text{-sec)}](2 \times 10^{-27} \text{ cm}^2)$$
$$(6.02 \times 10^{22} \text{ nuclei/cm}^3)(2 \times 10^{-2} \text{ cm})$$
$$n_r = 2.4 \times 10^4 \text{ neutrons/(cm}^2\text{-sec)}$$

Since there were 10^{10} incident particles per square centimeter per second, only 2.4 out of every 10^6 neutrons striking the foil are captured in the reaction $^{27}_{13}\text{Al}$ (n, γ) $^{28}_{13}\text{Al}$.

Because the cross section gives a measure of the probability that the nuclear reaction will occur, its measurement and the interpretation in the light of nuclear structure have been important activities in nuclear physics. In reaction cross-section experiments monoenergetic x particles strike a target; the cross section is measured by determining either the number of y particles or Y particles produced by a known number of x particles. The y particles emerging from a target can be counted by particle detectors, and the Y particles (often unstable) can be counted by measuring the radioactivity resulting from their decay. Chemical quantitative analysis of the Y atoms is difficult because their concentration is typically very small.

A few general remarks concerning reaction cross sections are made in the following paragraphs.

In an endothermic reaction, one that cannot proceed unless energy is added to the combining particles, the reaction cross section is necessarily zero until the threshold energy is exceeded.

Reactions in which the incident particles are neutrons, particularly the radiative-capture reactions (n, γ), may show large cross sections even when the energy of the bombarding particle is extremely small. Unlike a charged particle, a neutron is undeflected by the electric charge of the nucleus, and it can quite easily come within the range of the nuclear force and react with the nucleus at slow speeds. A typical (n, γ) cross section is shown in Figure 10-6 as a function of the neutron energy. It is seen that apart from the quite

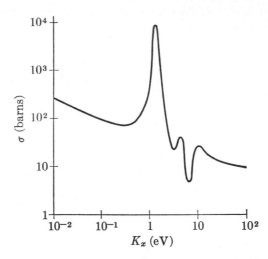

Figure 10-6. Neutron capture cross section for indium as a function of neutron energy.

pronounced peaks the cross section increases as the energy or speed of the neutrons decreases. In fact, it is found to be closely proportional to $1/v$, where v is the neutron speed. This $1/v$ law may be stated as follows: the probability that a neutron will be captured is directly proportional to the time it spends in the vicinity of any one bombarded nucleus, or inversely proportional to its speed. The peaks in the cross-section curve are referred to as *resonances*; their interpretation, to be discussed in Section 10-5, gives information on nuclear energy levels.

When *charged* particles strike a target nucleus, the size of the reaction cross section is influenced by the fact that they are repelled by the Coulomb force. If it were not for the phenomenon of the tunnel effect, or *barrier penetration* (Sections 5-10 and 9-10), low-energy charged particles could not come within the range of the nuclear force of the target nucleus, the nuclear reaction could not occur, and the reaction cross section would be zero. Incident charged particles with energies even less than 1 MeV (much less than the height of the Coulomb potential barrier), do undergo nuclear reactions, indicating that the Coulomb barrier has been penetrated. The probability of barrier penetration depends very much on the barrier height and thickness. The more energetic the incident charged particle, the more easily it can penetrate the barrier; see Figure 10-7. It follows that the reaction cross section will, in general, increase with the energy K_x, as shown in Figure 10-8

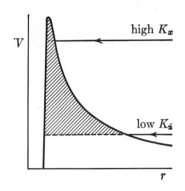

Figure 10-7. Representation of the relative nuclear barriers to be penetrated by low-energy and by high-energy incident charged particles.

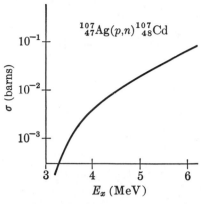

Figure 10-8. Increase in the cross section of a nuclear reaction with proton energy.

10-5   The compound nucleus and nuclear energy levels   For an introduction to the concept of the compound nucleus let us compute the energy with which the "last" (least tightly bound) neutron in the stable cadmium nuclide $^{114}_{48}\text{Cd}$ is bound to the other 113 nucleons. This separation energy is just the amount of energy that must be added to the nuclide to separate the last neutron, leaving the stable isotope $^{113}_{48}\text{Cd}$. The separation energy E_s is found directly by comparing the masses of $^{1}_{0}\text{n} + {}^{113}_{48}\text{Cd}$ and $^{114}_{48}\text{Cd}$:

$$E_s = [(1.008665 + 112.904409) - (113.903361)] \text{ u} \times 931.5 \text{ MeV/u}$$
$$= 9.048 \text{ MeV}$$

Therefore, if 9.05 MeV of energy is absorbed by the $^{114}_{48}\text{Cd}$ nucleus, a free neutron and a $^{113}_{48}\text{Cd}$ nucleus are formed, both particles being at rest. Symbolically,

$$^{114}_{48}\text{Cd} + 9.05 \text{ MeV} \rightarrow {}^{113}_{48}\text{Cd} + {}^{1}_{0}\text{n}$$

Now imagine the process to be reversed, so that we bring together a neutron and a $^{113}_{48}\text{Cd}$ nucleus, both with zero kinetic energy, to form a $^{114}_{48}\text{Cd}$ nucleus. No energy need be added to the particles to make them amalgamate, since the neutron will be attracted by the nuclear force of the nuclide when it is sufficiently close to it. The cadmium-114 nucleus then formed will *not*, however, be in its ground state; instead, it will be in an excited state, with an excitation energy of 9.05 MeV. The nucleus $^{114}_{48}\text{Cd}^*$ (the asterisk denotes an excited state) is unstable and will quickly decay to its ground state by the emission of a gamma-ray photon of 9.05 MeV. The overall process may be written

$$^{113}_{48}\text{Cd} + {}^{1}_{0}\text{n} \rightarrow {}^{114}_{48}\text{Cd}^* \rightarrow \gamma(9.05 \text{ MeV}) + {}^{114}_{48}\text{Cd}$$

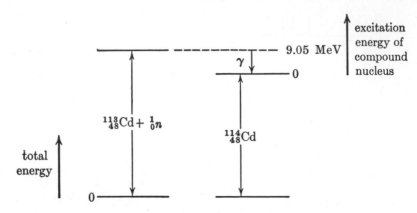

Figure. 10-9. Energy-level diagram of a neutron radiative-capture reaction.

We have just described the neutron radiative-capture reaction $^{113}_{48}$Cd (n, γ) $^{114}_{48}$Cd. This reaction takes place in *two* stages: the amalgamation of the two original particles to form a single nucleus in an excited state and the decay from this intermediate state to the products of the reaction. The energetics of the process are shown in Figure 10-9, where the total energies of the particles going into and coming out of the reaction are displayed.

The neutron radiative-capture reaction illustrates a feature that is common to most low-energy nuclear reactions: the formation and decay of a compound nucleus. The existence of the compound nucleus as an intermediate stage in nuclear reactions was proposed by N. Bohr in 1936. The assumptions are these:

(a) For the reaction $X(x, y)Y$ the particles x and X combine to form the compound nucleus C, invariably in an excited state: $X + x \rightarrow C^*$. The energy carried into the reaction by x is quickly shared among all the nucleons in the compound nucleus.

(b) The compound nucleus C^* exists for a long time compared with the nuclear time ($\approx 10^{-22}$ sec), the time for a nucleon with a few MeV of energy to traverse a nuclear dimension. The average lifetime of a typical compound nucleus is nevertheless so short that C^* is not directly observable. We may say that the compound nucleus lives so long that it has no "memory" of how it was formed: because it does not remember its formation, various x and X particles can form the same nucleus C^* in the same excited state, as shown in Table 10-1.

(c) The compound nucleus decays into the products of the reaction, $C^* \rightarrow y + Y$, as follows. After a fairly long time has elapsed (on a nuclear scale), the excitation energy of the compound nucleus, which was earlier distributed more or less equally among the several nucleons, is

Table 10-1

$$\boxed{X + x \rightarrow C^* \rightarrow y + Y}$$

$$\left.\begin{array}{c} {}^{13}_{6}C + p \\ {}^{12}_{6}C + d \\ {}^{10}_{5}B + \alpha \end{array}\right\} {}^{14}_{7}N^* \left\{\begin{array}{l} p + {}^{13}_{6}C \\ d + {}^{12}_{6}C \\ \alpha + {}^{10}_{5}B \\ n + {}^{13}_{7}N \\ \gamma + {}^{14}_{7}N \end{array}\right.$$

finally concentrated on some one particle y, which is ejected, leaving the nucleus Y. A compound nucleus in some particular excited state may decay, then, through the formation of any one of a variety of y and Y combinations, as shown in Table 10-1. For a particular excited state of C^* one particular decay mode typically dominates all others.

(d) Inasmuch as the nuclear reaction is to be regarded as taking place in two distinct stages (the formation of C^* and the decay of C^*), the reaction cross section, which gives a measure of the probability that the *complete* reaction will take place, is proportional to *two* probabilities: the probability that x and X will amalgamate to form C^* and the probability that C^* will decay into some particular y and Y particles.

Table 10-1 shows that there are a number of ways in which the compound nucleus ${}^{14}_{7}N^*$ can be formed and a number of ways in which this nucleus can decay from an excited state. For example, when a proton of 1 MeV combines with ${}^{13}_{6}C$, the most probable reaction is ${}^{13}_{6}C(p, \gamma) {}^{14}_{7}N$, but when a proton of 6 MeV strikes the same target and forms the same compound nucleus, the reaction ${}^{13}_{6}C(p, n) {}^{13}_{7}N$ is the most likely. In the first instance the excitation energy of ${}^{14}_{7}N^*$ is about 8 MeV, and in the second it is about 13 MeV, as shown in Figure 10-10. Furthermore, when an α-particle of 2 MeV combines with ${}^{10}_{5}B$, again forming ${}^{14}_{7}N^*$ with an excitation of about 13 MeV, the observed reaction is ${}^{10}_{5}B(\alpha, n){}^{13}_{7}N$. The decay mode of the compound nucleus depends only on its excitation energy and *not* on the particles that form it.

Note that Q values of the reactions can be read directly from the energies given in Figure 10-10.

Now consider the reaction ${}^{7}_{3}Li(p, \alpha){}^{4}_{2}He$. This reaction produces the compound nucleus ${}^{8}_{4}Be^*$, which does *not* exist as a *stable* nucleus in nature. In this reaction the compound nucleus decays into two α-particles, each with about 8.8 MeV of kinetic energy. A competing reaction is ${}^{7}_{3}Li(p, \gamma){}^{8}_{4}Be$, in which the compound nucleus is again ${}^{8}_{4}Be$ in an excited state. In this reaction, however, the compound nucleus decays by γ-emission to its ground

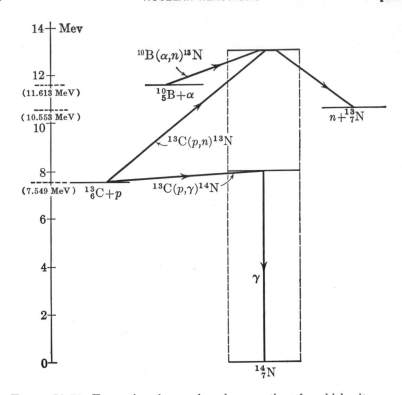

Figure 10-10. Energetics of several nuclear reactions for which nitrogen 14 is the compound nucleus. The scale gives energies with respect to the ground state of nitrogen 14 as zero.

state, emitting a very energetic photon, 17.6 MeV in energy. After this γ-decay the unstable product nucleus, ${}^{8}_{4}$Be, now in its ground state, decays into two α-particles, each with a necessarily very low energy. The energy-level diagram of these reactions is shown in Figure 10-11.

Let us return to the ${}^{113}_{48}$Cd(n, γ)${}^{114}_{48}$Cd reaction, now noting how the cross section for this reaction varies with the energy of the incident neutrons. The capture cross section for very low neutron energies is shown in Figure 10-12. It is well over 10 barns for all neutron energies, but there is a well-defined maximum, or *resonance*, at $K_x = 0.178$ eV. This means that there is a particularly high probability that the compound nucleus ${}^{114}_{48}$Cd* will be formed when the excitation energy is approximately† 0.18 eV higher than that which it has (9.05 MeV) when combined with neutrons of zero kinetic energy. It indicates further that the nucleus ${}^{114}_{48}$Cd has a well-defined quan-

---

† Strictly, the additional energy given to the compound nucleus by a neutron with $K_x = 0.178$ eV is the *available* energy $K_a = K_x[M_X/(M_X + m_x)] = (0.178)(113/114)$ eV ≈ 0.177 eV, according to Equation 10-5.

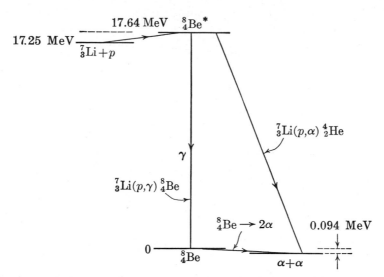

Figure 10-11. Nuclear energy-level diagram of two competing reaction.

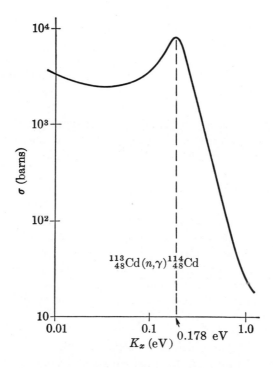

Figure 10-12. Resonance in the cross section of a nuclear reaction.

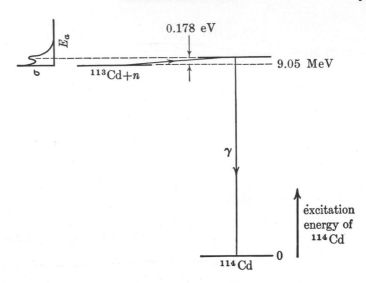

Figure 10-13. Resonance capture at an excited state of a compound nucleus in the reaction $^{113}_{48}\text{Cd}(n, \gamma)^{114}_{48}\text{Cd}$. The energy differences are *not* to scale.

tized energy level when its excitation energy is just 0.178 eV higher than 9.05 MeV, as shown in Figure 10-13. This is just one of a number of discrete excited states of this nucleus. In general, the excited states of a *compound nucleus* may be evaluated by observing the well-defined resonances in the reaction cross section, and the existence of these resonances is strong evidence of the correctness of the compound-nucleus concept.

Nuclear-reaction data can also be used for deducing the excited energy levels of the *product nucleus*. For example, consider the reaction $^{27}_{13}\text{Al}(\alpha, \text{p})$ $^{30}_{14}\text{Si}$, having the compound nucleus, $^{31}_{15}\text{P}^*$. The compound nucleus decays, not only to the ground state of the product nucleus $^{30}_{14}\text{Si}$, but also to several of its excited states, which are followed by γ-decay to the ground state; the energy-level diagram is shown in Figure 10-14. The existence of these excited states is indicated experimentally, not only by the γ-rays emitted when $^{27}_{13}\text{Al}$ is bombarded by α-particles, but also by the fact that the protons observed (at some particular angle to the incident beam) have a spectrum of energies, as shown in Figure 10-15. The several *proton groups* correspond to the several possible decay modes of the compound nucleus, and the excitation energies of $^{30}_{14}\text{S}^*$ can be evaluated by measuring the proton energies K_y.

10-6 Neutron production, detection, measurement, and moderation   In this

section we describe methods for producing and detecting neutrons, measuring their energies, and moderating them in their passage through matter.

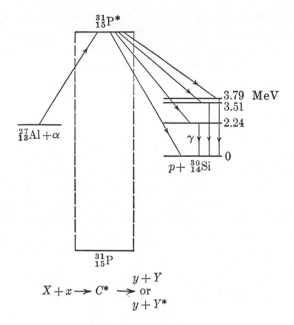

$$X + x \rightarrow C^* \xrightarrow{\text{or}} \begin{array}{c} y + Y \\ y + Y^* \end{array}$$

Figure 10-14. Energetics of the $^{27}_{13}\text{Al}(\alpha, \text{p})^{30}_{14}\text{Si}$ reaction, showing the excited states of the product nucleus.

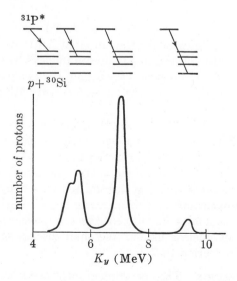

Figure 10-15. Energy spectrum of the proton groups from the reaction $^{27}_{13}\text{Al}(\alpha, \text{p})^{30}_{14}\text{Si}$.

The most distinctive property of the neutron is its electric charge, which is zero. Because a neutron is electrically neutral, it does not produce ionization directly, as do charged particles, it cannot be accelerated by electric fields, and it cannot be deflected by magnetic fields. Its only means of interacting with other particles is through its strong nuclear interaction unimpeded by a Coulomb force.

NEUTRON PRODUCTION   In the following paragraphs several means of producing neutrons are described.

A common means of obtaining neutrons is a *radium-beryllium source*, which depends on the reaction $^9_4\text{Be}(\alpha, n)^{12}_6\text{C}$. The α-particles, coming from radioactively decaying radium, collide with beryllium, with which the radium is mixed, and neutrons with a wide range of energies are emitted.

A photodisintegration reaction can also be used as a source of neutrons; a simple example is $^9_4\text{Be}(\gamma, n)^8_4\text{Be}$. The photon energy must exceed 1.67 MeV for this reaction to occur; γ-rays may be obtained from naturally or artificially radioactive materials.

Accelerated charged particles can produce nuclear reactions in which neutrons are emitted. Such reactions are particularly useful as neutron sources because the neutrons produced in them are monoenergetic. For example, the reaction $^3_1\text{H}(d, n)^4_2\text{He}$, in which deuterons are accelerated and strike a target of tritium, has a Q of 17.6 MeV. Because energy and momentum must be conserved, the energy of the neutrons depends on the angle at which they leave the target with respect to the direction of the incident deuterons.

Neutrons of very high energy can be produced by a *stripping* reaction. Deuterons having energies of several hundred MeV strike a target. The neutron is bound to the proton in a deuteron nucleus by an energy of only 2.2 MeV. When the deuteron strikes the target, the two particles may easily become separated, the neutron continuing forward with about half of the incident deuteron energy.

A still simpler means of obtaining neutrons of very high energy is a head-on collision between a proton of very high energy and a single neutron in a target nucleus. It is found, for example, that when protons of 2 GeV strike a target, neutrons of the same energy are knocked out in the forward direction, the proton having transmitted its energy and momentum to the uncharged nucleon.

The best source of a large flux of neutrons is a nuclear reactor, operating on the principle of nuclear fission. We shall discuss some properties of nuclear reactors in Section 10-7.

NEUTRON DETECTION   The operation of most particle detectors depends upon the ionization produced by charged particles. The detection of neutrons must, therefore, take place in the following way: neutrons produce charged particles by some means, and the ionization arising from these charged particles is detected. In the following paragraphs several means of detecting neutrons are described.

An ionization chamber or proportional counter is sensitive to neutrons when it is filled with a gaseous boron compound, such as boron trifluoride (BF_3), or lined with a solid boron compound. A neutron striking boron 10 can initiate the reaction $^{10}_{5}B(n, \alpha)^{7}_{3}Li$, and the ionization produced by the α-particle is detected.

The elastic collision of a neutron with a charged light-weight particle, such as a proton, can be used as a basis of neutron detection. When a neutron makes a head-on collision with a proton, it is brought to rest, and the proton moves forward with essentially the same energy as that of the original neutron. The energetic proton can be detected by its ionization.

Neutrons can be detected by the induced radioactivity that typically results from neutron radiative capture. For example, when neutrons strike a silver foil, the silver-107 nuclei are *activated* in the reaction $^{107}_{47}Ag(n, \gamma)^{108}_{47}Ag$, and the product nuclei decay according to $^{108}_{47}Ag \rightarrow {}^{108}_{48}Cd + \beta^- + \bar{\nu}$. The β^- activity may be detected and measured, and if the capture cross section, foil thickness, exposure time, and decay constant are known, the neutron flux may be computed.

MEASUREMENT OF NEUTRON ENERGY   The kinetic energy of neutrons can be measured indirectly in some of the detection methods just described, as, for example, by measuring the energy of protons. There are, however, still other methods by which neutron energies may be evaluated with con-siderable precision.

A particularly direct way of measuring a neutron's energy is to measure its speed. In the time-of-flight method one times the neutron's motion over a known distance. This can be done when neutrons are emitted in a reaction effected by pulsed charged particles from an accelerator such as a cyclotron. If one measures the time delay between the reaction collisions and the arrival of neutrons at the neutron detector, a known distance from the target, the speed of the neutrons can be computed.

The speed of a neutron can also be determined with a mechanical device known as a *neutron velocity selector*, a simple form of which is shown in Figure 10-16. In order that the rotating discs be opaque to neutrons, they

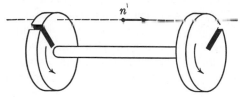

Figure 10-16. Schematic diagram of a neutron velocity selector.

are made of a material that strongly absorbs them, such as cadmium. The neutron speed is evaluated from the common angular speed of the two discs, their separation, and the angular displacement of the second slit relative to the first.

Another method of measuring neutron energies depends on the phenomenon of neutron diffraction (Section 5-3). A *neutron crystal spectrometer* is a device for measuring the wavelength of neutrons by their diffraction through a crystal with a known crystalline structure. The wavelength λ of a neutron is related to its momentum mv by the relation $\lambda = h/mv$. Therefore, if the wavelength of a neutron is known, so are its momentum and kinetic energy. Neutron diffraction is feasible only when the neutrons have energies of a fraction of an electron volt or wavelengths of several angstroms. This limitation is due to the fact that the interatomic spacing in crystalline solids is of the order of a few angstroms.

NEUTRON MODERATION   When neutrons pass through a material there are two types of nuclear interaction that usually dominate over all others: neutron radiative capture, (n, γ), and *elastic collisions* between the neutrons and the nuclei of the material. In certain materials the capture cross section is so small that the neutrons interact with the nuclei of the material primarily in elastic collisions. In passing through such materials, called *moderators*, the incident, originally energetic, neutrons are slowed down, or *moderated*.

In any elastic collision between two particles the greatest amount of kinetic energy is transferred from one particle to the other when the masses of the two particles are the same. Thus, a neutron can lose all of its kinetic energy when it makes a head-on collision with a proton. Less energy is transferred in oblique collisions. Therefore, hydrogenous materials, such as paraffin, are effective in moderating neutrons. When neutrons collide with nuclei more massive than protons, they lose only a small fraction of their kinetic energy, even in a head-on collision, and many such encounters are needed to slow them down.

Neutrons are only slowed down in a moderator, they are never brought completely to rest. The nuclei in a moderating material are in thermal motion at any finite temperature. A collection of neutrons may be said to be in the thermal equilibrium with the moderating material when a typical neutron is just as likely to gain kinetic energy as to lose it upon colliding with a nucleus within the moderator. Such neutrons, which have a distribution of speeds like that of molecules in a gas, can be assigned a temperature equal to the temperature of the moderator. The average kinetic energy of neutrons in equilibrium with a moderator at a temperature T is given by $\frac{1}{2}mv^2 = \frac{3}{2}kT$.

Neutrons in thermal equilibrium with a moderator at room temperature, 300 °K, are said to be *thermal neutrons*. Their average kinetic energy is

0.04 electron volt, their speed is 2,200 m/sec, and their wavelength is 1.80 angstroms. A beam of high-energy neutrons (several MeV) incident on a typical moderator such as graphite (carbon) or heavy water are *thermalized* in less than 1 msec. The most probable fate of moderated neutrons is capture by the nuclei of the moderator, since the capture cross section increases rapidly as the neutron energy falls. We recall that a free neutron is radio-active and decays into a proton and electron (and antineutrino) with a half-life of 12 minutes. The decay of a free neutron, although possible, occurs very infrequently in a material, because it must compete with the much faster process of neutron moderation and capture.

10-7 Nuclear fission   A special type of nuclear reaction occurs in very heavy nuclides. Unlike most low-energy nuclear reactions, in which a light particle and a heavy particle appear as products, this reaction results in the splitting, or fissioning, of the heavy nucleus into two parts of comparable masses; it is appropriately called *nuclear fission.* Identification of the nuclear-fission reaction was first made by O. Hahn and F. Strassman in 1939.

Consider the capture of a neutron of very low energy, such as a thermal neutron, by the very heavy nucleus uranium 235. The compound nucleus $^{236}_{92}U$ formed in this reaction is in an excited state with an excitation energy of 6.4 MeV. Almost all lighter excited compound nuclei formed from neutron capture decay with the emission of gamma-ray photons, the resulting heav-ier nuclei usually decaying by β^- emission, but an excited uranium-236 nu-cleus can decay also by nuclear fission, splitting into two or, less frequently, three or more moderately heavy nuclei.

The behavior of a very heavy, excited compound nucleus can be under-stood from the liquid-drop model. Recall (Section 9-7) that in this model a nucleus is regarded as analogous to a drop of liquid, which has three im-portant contributions to its total binding energy: the volume energy, the surface energy, and the Coulomb energy. The surface energy plays a role similar to that of the ordinary surface "tension" of a liquid in that it tends to minimize the surface area and thereby render the shape spherical. The Coulomb energy, on the other hand, is a disruptive influence arising from the electric repulsion between the protons.

Suppose that owing to a nuclear collision a very heavy nucleus gains energy of excitation. The nucleus as a whole will oscillate and change its shape. One probable mode of deformation is shown in Figure 10-17, in which the nucleus assumes, in turn, the shapes of sphere, prolate ellipsoid (cigar), sphere, oblate ellipsoid (pancake), etc. During the oscillations the nuclear volume does not change. The surface area changes, however, being greatest in the prolate and oblate deformations. The surface tension is manifested as a tendency of the nucleus to resume its spherical shape. On the other hand, the Coulomb repulsion increases when the nucleus assumes,

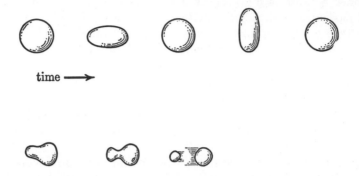

time ⟶

Figure 10-17. Stages in the deformation of an oscillating nucleus, leading to nuclear fission.

for example, the prolate ellipsoidal shape, and the positive charges at the two ends of the ellipsoid tend to increase the deformation even further. Thus, two competing influences are at work: the nuclear surface tension, which tends to keep the nucleus spherical, and the Coulomb repulsion, which tends to deform it. If the excitation is sufficiently great, the Coulomb force will succeed in shaping the nucleus into a dumbbell. With so great a distortion the surface tension is not strong enough to restore the nucleus to sphericity, and the Coulomb force increases the separation between the ends, until they split into two distinct nuclei, or *fission fragments*, usually of unequal sizes. Then the fission fragments repel one another by the Coulomb force, and they move apart, each gaining kinetic energy as the system loses potential energy.

The transformations of a fission process are shown in Figure 10-18 on the plot of N versus Z of Figure 9-7. Two fission fragments, (Z_1, N_1) and (Z_2, N_2), of a heavy compound nucleus share the protons and neutrons of the original compound nucleus (Z, N); that is, $Z = Z_1 + Z_2$ and $N = N_1 + N_2$. Both fragments fall to the *left* of the stability line; that is, both nuclei have too many neutrons to be stable. The neutron excess is so great that it is relieved almost instantaneously (in about 10^{-14} sec) by the release of two or three neutrons from the fission fragments. The nuclei still have too many neutrons, and they finally reach stability by changing neutrons into protons, that is, by β^- decay. The β^- decays are, of course, accompanied by γ-decay from excited nuclear states.

Two of the many known fission reactions resulting from neutron capture in uranium 235 are shown below with the subsequent β^- decays of the fission fragments.

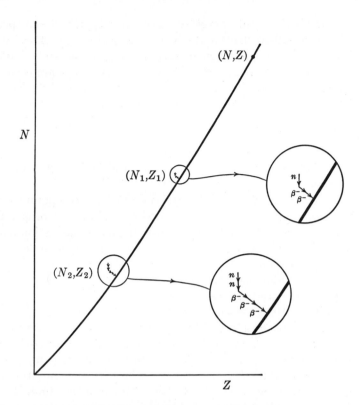

Figure 10-18. Transformations in nuclear fission as they appear on a neutron-proton diagram.

$$\ce{^{1}_{0}n} + \ce{^{235}_{92}U} \rightarrow \ce{^{236}_{92}U^*} \rightarrow \ce{^{144}_{56}Ba} + \ce{^{89}_{36}Kr} + 3\ce{^{1}_{0}n}$$

$$\ce{^{144}_{56}Ba} \xrightarrow{\beta^-} \ce{^{144}_{57}La} \xrightarrow{\beta^-} \ce{^{144}_{58}Ce} \xrightarrow{\beta^-} \ce{^{144}_{59}Pr} \xrightarrow{\beta^-} \ce{^{144}_{60}Nd}$$

$$\ce{^{89}_{36}Kr} \xrightarrow{\beta^-} \ce{^{89}_{37}Rb} \xrightarrow{\beta^-} \ce{^{89}_{38}Sr} \xrightarrow{\beta^-} \ce{^{89}_{39}Y}$$

$$\ce{^{1}_{0}n} + \ce{^{235}_{92}U} \rightarrow \ce{^{236}_{92}U^*} \rightarrow \ce{^{140}_{54}Xe} + \ce{^{94}_{38}Sr} + 2\ce{^{1}_{0}n}$$

$$\ce{^{140}_{54}Xe} \xrightarrow{\beta^-} \ce{^{140}_{55}Cs} \xrightarrow{\beta^-} \ce{^{140}_{56}Ba} \xrightarrow{\beta^-} \ce{^{140}_{57}La} \xrightarrow{\beta^-} \ce{^{140}_{58}Ce}$$

$$\ce{^{94}_{38}Sr} \xrightarrow{\beta^-} \ce{^{94}_{39}Y} \xrightarrow{\beta^-} \ce{^{94}_{40}Br}$$

The basic requirement for the occurrence of fission in the very heaviest nuclides is that the compound nucleus formed have sufficient excitation energy for it to split. Neutron capture is just one of the several ways in which nuclear fission may be induced. Fission can also result from the bombardment of heavy nuclei by protons, deuterons, alpha particles, and gamma rays (*photofission*).

Let us compute the total energy released in a typical fission process. We see from Figure 9-10 that in the very heavy elements, $A \approx 240$, the average binding energy per nucleon, E_b/A, is approximately 7.6 MeV and that in moderately heavy elements, $A \approx 120$, it is approximately 8.5 MeV. Thus, if we take the mass number A of the original nucleus to be roughly 240, the total energy released in the fission process is about

$$(240 \text{ nucleons}) \times (8.5 - 7.6) \text{ MeV/nucleon} \approx 200 \text{ MeV}$$

The total energy released in a fission reaction is very large indeed compared with the few MeV of energy released in a typical low-energy exothermic nuclear reaction.

Nuclear fission is characterized by the decay of the compound nucleus into two moderately heavy nuclei, the emission of a few neutrons, and the β^- decay of the radioactive fission fragments. In an average fission reaction about 200 MeV is released and distributed approximately as follows:

kinetic energy of fission fragments, 170 MeV

kinetic energy of fission neutrons, 5 MeV

energy of β^- and γ-rays, 15 MeV

energy of antineutrinos associated with β^- decay, 10 MeV

The light isotope of uranium, $^{235}_{92}\text{U}$, undergoes fission with thermal neutrons, the excitation energy gained by the compound nucleus $^{236}_{92}\text{U}^*$ in capturing a slow neutron being great enough to cause the fission (uranium 235 is the only *natural* nuclide that undergoes fission with slow neutrons). The much more abundant (99.3 percent) heavy isotope of uranium, $^{238}_{92}\text{U}$, will undergo fission, but only if bombarded by fast neutrons, neutrons having a kinetic energy of at least 1 MeV. Low-energy neutrons are captured by $^{238}_{92}\text{U}$, but the excited compound nucleus, $^{239}_{92}\text{U}^*$, has too little excitation energy to decay by fission, and it decays instead by gamma emission.

Uraniun 235 is fissile with both low- and high-energy neutrons. The (n, γ) reaction is less probable than fission at any energy. On the other hand, uranium 238 is fissile with high-energy neutrons only, low-energy neutrons being captured without fission. Clearly, the compound nucleus $^{239}_{92}\text{U}^*$ does not gain enough excitation energy from the capture of low-energy neutrons to decay by fission, whereas the compound nucleus $^{236}_{92}\text{U}^*$ is sufficiently excited by them to undergo fission. This difference is attributable to the fact that ^{236}U, being an even-even nuclide whose last neutron is relatively tightly bound (6.4 MeV) gains more excitation energy in capturing a zero-energy neutron than does the even-odd nuclide $^{239}_{92}\text{U}$, whose last, odd neutron is relatively weakly bound (4.9 MeV).

The fact that nuclear fission with uranium 235 can be initiated by low-energy neutrons and that on the average 2.5 neutrons are released in the fission process makes it possible to extract useful energy from uranium. The energy released in exothermic nuclear reactions produced by particle bombardment from accelerators cannot be utilized in a practical way, because the number of reactions is typically very small. The total energy released in such reactions is much less than the total energy supplied to the many accelerated particles, of which only a small fraction causes reactions. The fission process can, on the other hand, be made efficient by the possibility of a *self-sustaining chain reaction*.

In essence, the neutrons from one fission reaction may initiate other fission reactions with a further release of fission energy, which ideally continue until all of the nuclear fuel, or fissionable material, is consumed. For the fission reactions to continue, once initiated, a number of conditions must be fulfilled. These conditions are achieved in a nuclear reactor. The engineering problems connected with nuclear reactors lie in the area of nuclear technology, and we shall merely outline the physical principles on which reactor operation is based.

10-8   Nuclear reactors   The first self-sustaining nuclear-fission chain reaction was achieved by E. Fermi in 1942. The reactor used natural uranium (0.7 percent ^{235}U and 99.3 percent ^{238}U) as fuel and graphite as a neutron moderator. Although there are many different types, we shall illustrate the basic features of nuclear reactors with a simple reactor using natural uranium and a graphite moderator and based on the fission of uranium 235 by slow neutrons.

For a fission chain reaction to be self-sustaining it is required that there be, for each uranium atom split, at least one neutron that will split one more uranium atom. In the fission of uranium each decay produces about 2.5 neutrons. Therefore, no more than 1.5 neutrons can be lost without the chain reaction's stopping. The important ways in which neutrons become unavailable for uranium-235 fission are capture without fission by uranium 238 (and, to a lesser extent, by uranium 235), capture by other materials, and leakage from the interior of the reactor to the outside.

First consider the problem of neutron leakage. If the reactor (the fuel elements and the moderator) is a very small one, many of the neutrons produced in some initial fission reactions will leak out of the reactor (through the walls) before inducing further fission reactions; in a bigger reactor the neutron losses are less and the number of fission reactions greater. The fission-reaction production rate is roughly proportional to the volume of the reactor, and the leakage rate is roughly proportional to the surface area of the reactor

The fission cross section in uranium 235 increases as the neutron energy decreases (reaching 550 barns with thermal neutrons); on the other hand, the neutron-capture cross section of uranium 238 increases as the neutron energy also increases. Therefore, the problem in operating a reactor with natural uranium is to slow the high-energy neutrons (of a few MeV) emitted in the uranium-235 fission to thermal energies, at which further fission reactions in uranium 235 are more likely, without losing the neutrons by capture in uranium 238 on the way down. These conditions are met by using a moderator to slow down (but not capture) the neutrons and by properly arranging uranium fuel blocks within the moderator.

The function of the moderator, then, is to slow down neutrons without capturing them. Although hydrogen atoms, whose mass is essentially equal to that of the neutron, cause the greatest fractional loss in the kinetic energy of neutrons, they are unsuitable as moderators because of the relatively high probability of the neutron-capture reaction $_1^1H(n, \gamma)_1^2H$. The lightest usable moderator materials are heavy water (D_2O), beryllium (Be), and graphite (^{12}C); most other light materials are not usable, because of their large neutron-capture cross sections. The fuel elements are arranged as blocks in the medium of the moderator. Under ideal conditions a fast neutron from a fuel element escapes into the moderator and is slowed down, thereby avoiding capture (without fission) in uranium 238. Then the thermal neutron enters another fuel element, causing another fission in uranium 235. The whole process takes place in less than a millisecond.

When all sources of neutron loss have been minimized, it is possible for the reactor to "go critical," each fission reaction leading to at least one more fission reaction. The power level of the reactor, or the rate at which fission reactions occur in it, can be controlled by inserting such materials as cadmium, whose neutron-capture cross section is very high and which therefore readily absorbs neutrons. These materials are usually in the form of rods, called *control rods*. A reactor is said to be *subcritical* if, on the average, each fission reaction produces *less* than one further fission; the fission reaction is then not self-sustaining. On the other hand, if each fission reaction produces more than one further fission, the reactor is said to be *supercritical*; an extreme example of a supercritical fission reaction is an atom bomb.

The control of reactors by mechanically actuated control rods would be virtually impossible if the only neutrons available were the *prompt neutrons*, those released at the instant of fission, but there are in addition *delayed neutrons* (0.7 percent), which are emitted by a few of the fission fragments, usually *after* one or more β^- decays have occurred. A delayed neutron can cause a further fission about 10 sec after the fission that released it. This is in contrast with a prompt neutron, which causes a further fission in less than 1 msec.

One example of a fission-fragment decay leading to a delayed neutron is

$$\begin{matrix} & \nearrow & \beta^- \; _{36}^{87}Kr^* \rightarrow _{36}^{86}Kr + _0^1n \\ _{35}^{87}Br & & \\ (56 \text{ sec}) & \searrow & \beta^- \; _{36}^{87}Kr \xrightarrow{\beta^-} _{37}^{87}Rb \xrightarrow{\beta^-} _{38}^{87}Sr \end{matrix}$$

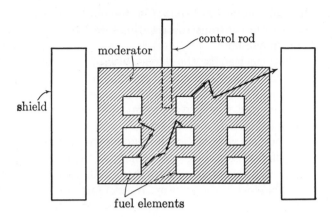

Figure 10-19. Simple elements of a nuclear reactor.

There are many designs of nuclear reactors. They may differ in the following respects: the fuel (natural uranium, uranium enriched with uranium 235, other artificially produced fissionable materials), the moderator (water, graphite, beryllium), the distribution of fuel within the moderator (homogeneous, heterogeneous), the energy of neutrons producing fission (fast, intermediate, slow), and the heat exchanger (gas, water, liquid metals). Figure 10-19 is a schematic of a nuclear reactor.

Nuclear reactors may also be classified according to their use: (a) for power generation, (b) as neutron sources, (c) for the production of radioisotopes, and (d) for the production of fissionable material:

(a) The large kinetic energy of fission fragments in a nuclear reactor is a source of thermal energy, which can be extracted through a heat exchanger to do useful work, such as generating electric energy.

(b) The interior of a reactor is a region in which the neutron flux can be as high as 10^{19} neutrons/m²-sec.

(c) Such a flux may be used in experiments in physics or for irradiating materials, so as to produce radioisotopes through (n, γ) reactions.

(d) Materials, such as uranium 238 and thorium 232, that do *not* undergo fission with low-energy neutrons can be converted in a nuclear reactor into nuclides that undergo fission with thermal neutrons. Two such reactions are:

$$_0^1\text{n} + {}_{92}^{238}\text{U} \rightarrow {}_{92}^{239}\text{U}^* \xrightarrow[\text{(23 min)}]{\beta^-} {}_{93}^{239}\text{Np} \xrightarrow[\text{(2.3 days)}]{\beta^-} \underset{\text{(24,000 yr)}}{{}_{94}^{239}\text{Pu}}$$

$$_0^1\text{n} + {}_{90}^{232}\text{Th} \rightarrow {}_{90}^{233}\text{Th}^* \xrightarrow[\text{(23 min)}]{\beta^-} {}_{91}^{233}\text{Pa} \xrightarrow[\text{(27 days)}]{\beta^-} \underset{(1.6 \times 10^5 \text{ yr})}{{}_{92}^{233}\text{U}}$$

Uranium 238 and thorium 232 *cannot* be fissioned by thermal neutrons, but when they capture neutrons the reactions lead to plutonium 239 and uranium 233, which can be.

These two reactions lead to the possibility of a *breeder reactor*. In a breeder reactor there are two fuel materials, one of which is fissionable (such as plutonium 239) and the other *fertile* (such as uranium 238) in that it can be converted in the reactor into fissionable material. In the fission of plutonium 239 there are, on the average, three neutrons released; of these one must sustain the reaction producing the fission of a plutonium-239 nucleus, and of the remaining two neutrons at least one must be captured by uranium 238, leading to plutonium 239, to maintain the same amount of fissionable fuel in the reactor. When more than one of these two neutrons is captured by uranium 238, the reactor can breed fissionable plutonium 239; that is, more fissionable material is produced than consumed.

10-9 Nuclear fusion The origin of energy radiated from the Sun and other stars is a series of exoergic nuclear reactions. The atoms participating in such reactions in the interior of the star are completely ionized, all electrons having been removed from them. Such a collection of electrically charged particles—electrons and bare nuclei—is called a *plasma*. The particles are at a very high temperature (up to 10^8 °K), move at high speeds, and make frequent collisions with one another. The average kinetic energy per particle, $\frac{3}{2}kT$, is of the order of 1 keV for $T = 10'$ °K. Therefore the Coulomb repulsion between positively charged nuclei may be overcome in internuclear collisions, so that some of the faster moving nuclei approach one another closely enough to interact through nuclear forces, and reactions take place with high probability. A nuclear reaction that occurs by virtue of the increased thermal motion of the interacting particles at a high temperature is called a *thermonuclear reaction*.

The cycle of thermonuclear reactions releasing energy in the Sun and in similar stars is the proton-proton cycle:

$$^1\text{H} + {}^1\text{H} \rightarrow {}^2\text{H} + \beta^+ + \nu$$
$$^1\text{H} + {}^2\text{H} \rightarrow {}^3\text{He} + \gamma$$
$$^3\text{He} + {}^3\text{He} \rightarrow {}^4\text{He} + 2{}^1\text{H}$$

This cycle, involving three distinct nuclear reactions, fuses four protons into an alpha particle, two positrons, and two neutrinos. The first reaction in this cycle, in which a positron is created in the collision of two protons, has a very small cross section. It occurs in the Sun's interior, because the temperature there is about 2×10^7 °K. The overall Q of the cycle is about 25 MeV or approximately 6 MeV released for each nucleon participating in the reaction (since 200 MeV is released in a typical nuclear fission reaction, the energy per nucleon in a fission reaction is about 1 MeV).

A second cycle of thermonuclear reactions, operating in some stars, is the *carbon cycle*:

$$^1H + {}^{12}C \rightarrow {}^{13}N + \gamma$$
$$^{13}N \rightarrow {}^{13}C + \beta^+ + \nu$$
$$^1H + {}^{13}C \rightarrow {}^{14}N + \gamma$$
$$^1H + {}^{14}N \rightarrow {}^{15}O + \gamma$$
$$^{15}O \rightarrow {}^{15}N + \beta^+ + \nu$$
$$^1H + {}^{15}N \rightarrow {}^{12}C + {}^4He$$

In this process the carbon-12 nucleus acts merely as a catalyst: it begins with one carbon-12 nucleus and ends with one carbon-12 nucleus; however, four protons are, in effect, fused into one alpha particle, two positrons, and two neutrinos. Since the particles entering and leaving the carbon cycle are the same as in the proton-proton cycle, the energy released is again about 25 MeV.

Why do the fission of the heaviest nuclides and the fusion of the lightest both result in highly exoergic nuclear reactions? How can both the splitting and the amalgamation lead to the release of nuclear energy? The answer may be found in Figure 9-10, which gives the average binding energy per nucleon as a function of the number of nucleons in a stable nuclide: both fission and fusion reactions lead to more tightly bound nuclear configurations. The fractional conversion of rest mass into nuclear energy is greater in a fusion reaction (0.66 percent) than in a fission reaction (0.09 percent).

Much interest has been aroused by the possibility of producing *controlled* thermonuclear-fusion reactions with the resultant very large energy release. A nuclear-fusion energy source has significant advantages over a nuclear-fission energy source: there is a virtually unlimited supply of fuel, the reactions do not result in radioactive wastes, and there is the possibility of generating electric energy more directly than through conventional heat exchangers and turbines.

Formidable technical difficulties, however, must be surmounted in achieving a power source based on controlled nuclear fusion. Chief among these are the extraordinarily high temperatures that are required to overcome the Coulomb repulsion between the interacting nuclei; a very hot plasma must be confined for long periods of time, so that many collisions may take place between the plasma particles. Ordinary containers are unsuitable, not primarily because they would be melted by the very hot plasma, but rather because they would chill the plasma below the temperature of spontaneous nuclear fusion.

The high-temperature plasma in a thermonuclear-fusion reactor may be prevented from striking the walls of its container by means of magnetic fields in the same way that charged particles are trapped within the Earth's Van Allen belts by the Earth's magnetic field.[†] The design of such containers, called magnetic bottles, is under active development. A plasma at a temperature of millions of degrees will exert an uncontainable pressure unless its density is very low indeed; therefore, the pressure of the unheated plasma must be no greater than about 10^{-4} atmosphere.

Among the reactions possible with isotopes of hydrogen (^{2}H, deuterium; ^{3}H, tritium) are the following:

$$^2\text{H} + {}^3\text{H} \rightarrow {}^4\text{He} + \text{n} \qquad Q = 17.6\,\text{MeV}$$

$$^2\text{H} + {}^2\text{H} \rightarrow {}^3\text{He} + \text{n} \qquad Q = 3.2\,\text{MeV}$$

$$^2\text{H} + {}^2\text{H} \rightarrow {}^3\text{H} + {}^1\text{H} \qquad Q = 4.0\,\text{MeV}$$

Because the Coulomb barrier between charged particles increases with increasing nuclear charge, a thermonuclear reaction with isotopes of hydrogen requires a lower temperature than one with other elements. Deuterium is particularly attractive as a nuclear-fusion fuel because it is readily available in almost unlimited quantity; for example, it is found in seawater, in which there is one D_2O molecule for every 6,000 H_2O molecules.

10-10 Summary Most low-energy nuclear reactions are of the general form $X(x, y)Y$, where x is the incident particle, X is the target nucleus, y is the emerging light-weight particle, and Y is the product nucleus (often radioactive). The nucleon number, electric charge, momentum, and mass-energy are conserved in a nuclear reaction. The net nuclear energy released in the reaction, Q, is defined by

[10-1], [10-3] $Q = [(M_X + m_x) - (M_Y + m_y)]c^2 = (K_y + K_Y) - K_x$

where the target nucleus is at rest in the laboratory. Reactions in which the x or y particles are photons are known respectively as photodisintegration and radiative capture.

Because momentum must be conserved in every nuclear reaction, only a portion of K_x is available in a nuclear reaction. The threshold energy of x for an endoergic ($Q < 0$) reaction (when Q/c^2 is small compared with the rest masses of x, y, X, and Y) is given by

[10-6] $K_{th} = -Q(M_X + m_x)/M_X$

In general, the threshold kinetic energy of the incident particle striking a target at rest is

[10-7d] $K_{th} = \dfrac{-\frac{1}{2}Q \text{ (rest energy all particles into and out of reaction)}}{\text{(rest energy of target particle)}}$

[†] See Section 32-3, Weidner and Sells, *E. C. P.*

The reaction cross section σ gives a measure of the intrinsic probability that a nuclear reaction will occur. The fractional number of x particles undergoing a reaction in a thin foil of thickness t and containing N particles per unit volume is

[10-8] $n_r/n_i = \sigma N t$

According to the concept of the compound nucleus, nuclear reactions take place in two distinct stages: the formation of the compound nucleus and the decay of the compound nucleus:

$$X + x \rightarrow C^* \rightarrow y + Y$$

The occurrence of peaks, or resonances, in the reaction cross section is a manifestation of the compound nucleus in quantized excited states.

Neutrons are detected indirectly by the ionization effects of charged particles produced by neutron-initiated reactions or by neutron collisions. Neutron energies can be evaluated by measuring their time of flight, by a mechanical velocity selector, or by neutron diffraction in crystals. Neutrons are moderated when they lose kinetic energy in elastic collisions with a material. Neutrons in equilibrium with a moderator at temperature T have an average kinetic energy of $\frac{3}{2}kT$.

In a nuclear-fission reaction an excited heavy nucleus, such as uranium 235, splits into fission fragments and several neutrons with the release of about 200 MeV, mostly in the form of kinetic energy of the fragments. The fragments are unstable and decay by β^- emission. The process of fission is best understood in terms of the liquid-drop model, in which there is competition between surface tension and Coulomb repulsion in the deformation of the heavy nucleus. The principal elements of a nuclear reactor operating on a self-sustaining nuclear-fission reaction are the fuel elements, moderator, and control rods. A reactor may be used as a source of heat or of neutrons or as a means of rendering fertile materials fissile.

A thermonuclear-fusion reaction is a highly exothermic reaction of relatively light particles in a plasma of very high temperature. The common stellar thermonuclear reactions occur in the carbon cycle and the proton-proton cycle.

BIBLIOGRAPHY

See the bibliography for Chapter 9.

Smyth, H. De W., *Atomic Energy for Military Purposes*. Princeton, New Jersey· Princeton University Press, 1945. The Smyth report gives a historical account of the remarkable scientific and technological developments leading to the first large-scale release of nuclear energy.

PROBLEMS

See Appendix II for values of the atomic masses.

10-1 By what mode are the unstable products of the following reactions likely to decay: (a) (n, γ), (b) (p, n), (c) (d, p), and (d) (α, n)?

10-2 Before the neutron had been properly identified by Chadwick in 1932, it was thought that the bombardment of $^{9}_{4}Be$ by alpha particles led to the reaction $^{9}_{4}Be\,(\alpha, \gamma)^{13}_{6}C$. It was found that, when the penetrating radiation from the bombardment struck paraffin, protons were ejected with an energy of 5.7 MeV. (a) Show that, if such protons are assumed to have been energized in a Compton collision, the energy of the gamma-ray photons must be 55 MeV. (b) Chadwick found that, whereas the penetrating radiation produced protons with an energy of 5.7 MeV, the same radiation striking nitrogen atoms imparted a kinetic energy of 1.4 MeV to a nitrogen atom. Show, by applying momentum and energy conservation to a head-on collision between a particle of penetrating radiation (really a neutron) with a proton and a nitrogen atom, with masses in the ratio of 1:14 but kinetic energies in the ratio of 5.7:1.4, that the neutron mass is essentially the same as the proton mass. (See Example 7, Chapter 12, Weidner and Sells, *E. C. P.*

10-3 Write at least three nuclear reactions in which targets made of stable nuclides may be used to produce (a) carbon 14, (b) oxygen 15, and (c) cobalt 60.

10-4 The Q of a nuclear reaction may be evaluated by measuring the kinetic energies K_x and K_y of the incident and emerging light-weight particles at some known angle between the directions of the incident x particles and the emerging y particles. Show that if y particles are observed at an angle of 90°, the reaction Q is given by $Q = K_y[1 + (m_y/M_Y)] - K_x[1 - (m_x/M_Y)]$.

10-5 Alpha particles strike an aluminum target and effect the reaction $^{27}_{13}Al(\alpha, p)^{30}_{14}Si$. The protons are observed at an angle of 90° with respect to the incident beam. If the alpha particles have an energy of 8.00 MeV, at what energies will there be peaks in the proton distribution? (See Problem 10-4 and Figures 10-14 and 10-15.)

10-6 * Deuterons 4.0 MeV of ^{14}N, and neutrons are produced in the nuclear reaction. What is the kinetic energy of neutrons emerging from the reaction in the same direction as the incident beam?

10-7 Two helium nuclei, each with a kinetic energy of 10 MeV, collide head on and produce the reaction $^{4}_{2}He(\alpha, p)^{7}_{3}Li$. What is the kinetic energy of protons emerging from the reaction?

10-8 A 1.0 MeV neutron collides head on with a 3.0 MeV helium-3 nucleus and produces two deuterons. What is the kinetic energy of any one deuteron?

10-9 What is the threshold kinetic energy of neutrons in the reaction $^{4}He(n, d)^{3}H$, assuming a target of free helium atoms at rest?

10-10 What are the minimum photon energies needed to produce the photodisintegration of a helium-3 nucleus initially at rest (a) into a deuteron and neutron and (b) into a proton and two neutrons?

10-11 * (a) What is the neutron threshold energy of the reaction ^{3}He(n, d)^{2}H? (b) Suppose that 4.0 MeV deuterons strike free deuterons at rest and that the neutron produced in the reaction travels in the opposite direction to that of the deuteron. What is the neutron's kinetic energy? (c) What is the kinetic energy of the helium-3 nucleus?

10-12 With what minimum kinetic energy must a proton strike a triton (the nucleus of the tritium atom, ^{3}H) initially at rest to produce two deuterons?

10-13 (a) With what minimum kinetic energy must deuterons strike a carbon-12 target to produce neutrons? (b) With what minimal kinetic energy must carbon-12 ions strike a target of deuterium to produce neutrons in the same nuclear reaction?

10-14 Free nitrogen-12 nuclei initially at rest decay into carbon-12. What is the maximum kinetic energy of (a) the neutrinos, (b) the positrons, and (c) the carbon-12 nuclei?

10-15 The relations giving the threshold kinetic energy of the incident particle in an endoergic nuclear reaction in which the target particle is at rest in the laboratory (Equations 10-6 and 10-7) assume the target particle to be *free*. If the target particle is bound to some degree, is the threshold energy increased or decreased?

10-16 * In the reaction X(x, y)Y the particle X is initially at rest in the laboratory. (a) Show that if E_{lab} denotes the total energy (rest plus kinetic) of the particles measured in the laboratory, E_{cm} denotes the total energy (rest plus kinetic) of the same particles measured in the center-of-mass reference frame, and E_{0x} is the rest energy of particle X, then $E_{cm}/E_{lab} = 2E_{0x}/E_{cm}$. The ratio E_{cm}/E_{lab} is a measure of the relative energies available in the center-of-mass and laboratory reference frames. (b) Protons having a kinetic energy of 200 GeV (and rest energy of about 1 GeV) will become available with synchrotron accelerators now under design. Suppose that a 200 GeV proton collides with a free proton at rest. What is the total energy in the center-of-mass reference frame, the energy that is available to create particles? (c) What fraction of the incident proton's kinetic energy is then available to create particles? (d) Suppose that two proton beams, whose protons are all of the same kinetic energy and which move in opposite directions, collide head on in the laboratory. What is the minimum proton kinetic energy of particles in either beam that will make the same energy available for creating particles as does a beam of 200 GeV protons striking free protons at rest?

10-17 Why does the neutron radiative-capture reaction (n, γ) have, for a particular target material, a much larger cross section than such competing reactions as (n, p), (n, α), and (n, d)?

10-18 (a) Compute the height (in MeV) of the Coulomb barrier encountered by a proton striking a $^7_3$Li nucleus (use Equation 9-8 for the range of the nuclear force). (b) At what minimum proton kinetic energy would one expect the reaction $^7_3$Li (p, α)$^4_2$He to take place, assuming that the nuclear barrier is not penetrated (that there is no tunnel effect)? That the reaction actually occurs at much smaller proton kinetic energies is clear evidence of the nuclear tunnel effect.

10-19 The neutron-capture cross section in the reaction ^{10}B(n, α)^{7}Li is 630 barns for neutrons with a kinetic energy of 1.0 eV. Assuming that the cross section follows the $1/v$ law, what is the neutron-capture cross section for (a) 0.1 eV neutrons and (b) 10.0 eV neutrons?

10-20 How does the cross section in high-energy neutron absorption vary with the mass number A of the target material?

10-21 The cross section in the $^{16}_{8}O(\gamma, p)^{15}_{7}N$ reaction shows a strong maximum for 22 MeV photons (a "giant resonance"). What is the corresponding nuclear excitation energy of the $^{16}_{8}O^*$ nucleus?

10-22 * A thin 10 mg foil of cadmium 112 is exposed to a beam of thermal neutrons with a neutron flux of 10^{12} neutrons/cm²-sec for a period of 1 hr. The capture cross section in cadmium 112 for thermal neutrons is 2×10^3 barns. (a) How many nuclei of cadmium 113 are formed? (b) Cadmium 113 decays with a half-life of 5 yr; what is the activity of the foil immediately after the irradiation period, assuming that a negligible number of cadmium-113 nuclei decay during irradiation? (Note that a procedure such as this permits the capture cross section to be computed if the activity is measured.)

10-23 * The cross section for antineutrino capture according to the reaction $p(\bar{\nu}, e^+)n$ is of the order of 10^{-20} barn. Show that the neutrinos in a neutrino beam are reduced in number to about half in traversing a distance of 100 l-yr through a solid. Take the density to be that of the Earth, 6 g/cm³, and assume that about half of all nucleons are protons.

10-24 * The fractional number of incident particles participating in a process with cross section σ in a very thin foil of material is given, according to Equation 10-8, by $\sigma N t$, where N is the number of target particles per unit volume and t is the foil thickness. Show that the fractional number of incident particles *emerging from* a *thick* target foil is given by $e^{-\sigma N t}$.

10-25 What targets of stable nuclides and common incident particles can be used to produce $^{15}_{7}N$ as the compound nucleus in a nuclear reaction?

10-26 (a) Show that Planck's constant divided by 2π can be expressed as 6.58×10^{-22} MeV-sec. (b) What is the approximate linewidth of an excited nuclear state with a lifetime equal to the nuclear time?

10-27 The neutron-capture cross section of a nuclide shows a resonance (Figure 10-12) with a width of 0.1 eV. What is the approximate lifetime of the corresponding nuclear excited state?

10-28 A $^{12}_{6}C$ target is struck by 180 MeV electrons. The scattered electrons are peaked at the energies 180, 176, 172, and 170 MeV. What are the excitation energies of the excited states of $^{12}_{6}C$?

10-29 A nucleus of $^{236}_{92}U^*$ decays into the fission fragments $^{140}_{54}Xe$ and $^{94}_{38}Sr$. Assume that the two fragments are spherical and just touching immediately after their formation. (a) What is the Coulomb potential energy (in MeV) of this pair of fragments? (b) Compare this Coulomb energy with the total energy released in the fission process.

10-30 What would be the temperature of a "gas" composed of fission fragments? Assume that two fragments of equal size are produced in each fission and that each fragment has a kinetic energy of 70 MeV.

10-31 (a) What is the average kinetic energy (in MeV) per particle for the temperature of 2×10^7 °K at the interior of the Sun? (b) What is the minimum separation distance between two protons having this kinetic energy and colliding head on?

10-32   All told, there are about 10^{21} kg of water on Earth, with one D_2O molecule for every 6,000 H_2O molecules. Assuming that all of the deuterium is used in the fusion reaction ${}_1^2H(d, p){}_1^3H$, what is the total amount of energy that can be extracted?

10-33 *   Approximately 10 percent of the 25 MeV released in a proton-proton cycle is carried by the two neutrinos emitted in each cycle. The intensity of the Sun's radiation at the Earth's surface is 1.4 kW/m²; the distance from the Earth to the Sun is 1.5×10^{11} m. (a) What is the rate at which neutrinos are produced in the Sun's interior by thermonuclear-fusion reactions? (b) What is the flux (number/m²-sec) of neutrinos at the Earth's surface? (c) What is the density at the Earth's surface (number/m³) of neutrinos originating from the Sun?

E L E V E N

THE ELEMENTARY PARTICLES

Man's search for the ultimate building blocks of Nature goes back to the Greek notion of four elements—earth, water, air, and fire (and possibly an ethereal fifth element, a "quintessence")—that were supposed to be the basic components of all other materials. Then came the ideas of the chemical elements—molecules and atoms—and, finally, of the particles within atoms, even within the nucleus. Underlying the quest for the elementary particles is the expectation that, if one has identified the truly fundamental particles—hopefully, of only a few distinct types—and learned the rules by which they affect one another, then the remainder of physics will be a straightforward, although possibly very difficult, exercise. At the present time all of chemistry, including the chemical properties and the periodic table, is implicit in a wave-mechanical description of atomic structure

We have not arrived at the end, though, and possibly never will. The particles that now are thought to be elementary in some sense are many, and they may be grouped in various ways to form coherent patterns, but the grand pattern still eludes physicists. Indeed, the principal motivation for constructing accelerating machines of higher and higher energies is to produce still more particles and to study the properties of those already identified. Thus, elementary-particle physics is high-energy physics.

The study of elementary-particle physics is in large measure a study of the four fundamental forces among particles: the strong, or nuclear, interaction, the electromagnetic interaction, the weak interaction, and the still weaker gravitational interaction. It is also a study of conservation laws, not merely the well-known classical laws of mass-energy, momentum, angular momentum, and electric charge, but also of certain others, somewhat more esoteric. Finally, it is concerned with how the fundamental forces, the conservation laws, the intrinsic properties of the particles, and even the properties of space and time can be fitted together to make some sense.

We shall here concentrate on the particle aspects of matter, but we recognize, of course, that each so-called particle has a wave aspect according to basic quantum theory. We take the fundamental objects to be particles when we inquire into their interactions with one another; the wave properties govern their propagation through space.

11-1 The electromagnetic interaction We begin by discussing those particles that we have already considered to be in some sense elementary, namely the electron, the proton, the photon (the particle of electromagnetic radiation), and the two antiparticles the positron (designated e^+) and the antiproton (designated p^-). Each of these elementary particles has certain intrinsic properties, such as a definite electric charge, a definite rest mass (or rest energy), a definite intrinsic (or spin) angular momentum, and a mean lifetime before decay into other elementary particles. Since all five particles are found to be stable against spontaneous decay, each has an infinite lifetime. See Table 11-1.

Table 11-1

Some Properties of Some Elementary Particles

PARTICLE	REST MASS,[a] m_e	REST ENERGY, MeV	CHARGE, UNITS OF ELECTRON CHARGE	SPIN, ANGULAR MOMENTUM, $\times h$	LIFETIME, SEC
Photon γ	0	0	0	1	∞
Electron e^-	1	0.511	-1	$\frac{1}{2}$	∞
Positron e^+	1	0.511	$+1$	$\frac{1}{2}$	∞
Proton p^+	1,836	938.256	$+1$	$\frac{1}{2}$	∞
Antiproton p^-	1,836	938.256	-1	$\frac{1}{2}$	∞

[a]In units of electron mass m_e.

How do we describe the electromagnetic interaction among these particles? As we saw in Chapter 4, we must, in treating the interaction between electromagnetic radiation and a charged particle, regard the radiation as consisting of particle-like photons and each interaction as occurring at a single point in space and in time. This was illustrated by the several photon-electron interactions of Figure 4-19. We shall see that all photon-electron interactions and, indeed, all other electromagnetic interactions are merely examples of one basic interaction between an electrically charged particle and a photon.

It is illuminating to represent these interactions on a space-time diagram, a diagram in which time as ordinate is plotted against position as abscissa. For simplicity we show the particle's spatial location in one dimension only (and, so to speak, regard all collisions as being head on); although all events occur in the three spatial and one time dimensions of four-dimensional space-time, a two-dimensional plot of time versus a single coordinate reveals all important aspects of the interactions.

The history of a particle is shown in a space-time diagram by a line, known as a *world line*. For constant velocity the line is straight. A vertical line represents a particle whose coordinate x does not change with time; it is a particle at rest. A line inclined with respect to the vertical represents a particle in motion, the angle between it and the vertical increasing with particle speed. Since a photon or any other particle with zero rest mass travels at the maximum possible speed c, the angle of its world line with respect to the vertical is the maximum.

Figure 11-1 shows space-time diagrams of the basic electron-photon interactions corresponding to those in Figure 4-19. Since time goes from past to future as the ordinate increases, we read the events on the graph from bottom to top. In the following paragraphs we shall take up each of the parts of this figure in turn.

In the *photoelectric effect* a hydrogen atom, consisting of an electron and a proton bound together, collides with a photon. After the interaction the photon has been annihilated, and the·electron and proton move away as separate particles. The space-time event characterizing the interaction corresponds to the vertex in the figure, where the incoming photon and electron lines branch into a single outgoing electron line (the proton's motion is virtually unaffected). Inasmuch as the hydrogen atom consisted initially of an electron and proton bound together, the net result of the interaction is the absorption (through the photoelectric effect) of one real photon. The total number of electrons (or of protons) going into and coming out of the interaction is unchanged.

In *bremsstrahlung* an electron creates a photon in colliding with a proton. Again the interaction is that instantaneous event occurring at the vertex on the space-time diagram, where a photon line joins an electron line; the electron line then inclines, to indicate that the electron's momentum and energy change. Indeed, we may think of the incoming electron as being

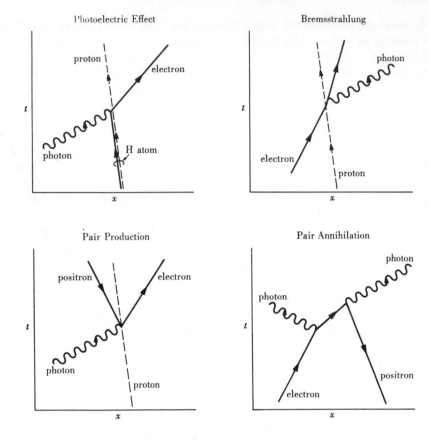

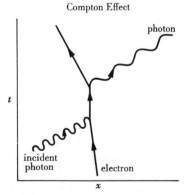

Figure 11-1. Space-time graphs of the basic electron-photon interactions. An electron is represented by a solid line, a photon by a wiggly line, and a proton by a dotted line. A positron moving forward in time corresponds to an electron moving backward in time.

annihilated at the vertex while a second outgoing electron of different momentum and energy is simultaneously created.

In *pair production* a photon is annihilated and an electron and positron are created. The positron, the electron's antiparticle, is here represented by an electron world line whose arrow is *reversed*; the antiparticle is regarded as an electron moving backward in time. Such a representation, with an antiparticle moving forward in time equivalent to a particle moving backward in time, is justified by the considerations of electromagnetic quantum field theory. So is a representation in which the creation of a particle is equivalent to the annihilation of its antiparticle. We see, then, that the electron and photon lines representing the pair-production process are basically the same as those representing the photoelectric effect and *bremsstrahlung:* an inclined electron line joined to a photon line at the vertex. These processes, and still others that we shall later treat, differ only in the orientation of the lines on the space-time graph.

In *pair annihilation* an electron and positron unite to create a photon. Typically, two or more photons are created in pair annihilation in order to conserve momentum; we may think of the production of first one photon and then another as two distinct, but nearly coincident, events.

We have thought of the *Compton effect* as that single process in which a photon interacts with a charged particle to produce a scattered photon that is deflected. Actually, as shown in Figure 11-1, the Compton effect takes place as two distinct interactions: the incident photon joins the incident electron to produce an intermediate electron; the intermediate electron then produces a photon and an electron. As before, each vertex is the point in space-time at which an electron line is joined by a photon line.

Indeed, according to quantum field theory, the basic electromagnetic interaction may be regarded as that instantaneous event in which a charged particle or its antiparticle is created and annihilated, or both are created and annihilated together, and a photon is created or annihilated; see Figure 11-2. When an electron world line changes direction, we may think of an electron with one energy and momentum as being annihilated and another electron with a different energy and momentum as being created. All photon-electron interactions involve one or more vertices on the same basic graph merely rotated in space-time. We may, of course, draw exactly similar graphs to represent the electromagnetic interactions between protons or antiprotons and photons, the solid world line representing a proton or antiproton instead of an electron or positron. Still more generally, the same graphs may be used to represent the electromagnetic interaction between any electrically charged particle and a photon.

All of the five particles listed in Table 11-1 are stable against spontaneous decay. In any interaction among them there are a number of fundamental physical properties which remain strictly conserved; we have, for

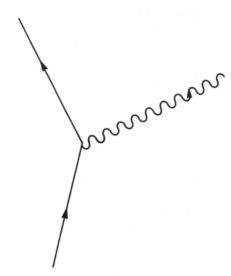

Figure 11-2. Graph of the basic electromagnetic interaction.

example, the conservation of linear momentum, of relativistic mass-energy, of angular momentum, and of electric charge. Moreover, in every interaction the number of electrons minus the number of positrons is conserved. In graphical terms this means that the world line of an electron does not end: for every electron line into a vertex there is an electron line out of it (an "electron line" going backward in time signifying a positron going forward in time). Similarly, in any interaction the number of protons less the number of antiprotons is constant; graphically, the proton lines are continuous. Although these newly discovered conservation laws govern the electron-minus-positron and the proton-minus-antiproton numbers, there is no restriction on the number of photons or on the separate numbers of electrons and protons and their respective antiparticles.

We have described the interaction between electromagnetic radiation and a charged particle in terms of the basic space-time graph. What about the interaction between two electrically charged particles, an interaction which, in classical electromagnetic theory, is familiarly described in terms of the electric and magnetic fields produced by the two particles and in terms of an electric and a magnetic force? This, too, is attributable to the creation and annihilation of photons.

Consider Figure 11-3, which shows a head-on collision between two electrons. One electron creates a photon spontaneously at vertex A (in the fashion of the *bremsstrahlung* process of Figure 11-1), and the second electron absorbs the photon at vertex B (in the fashion of the photoelectric effect of Figure 11-1). Each of the two interacting electrons has its energy

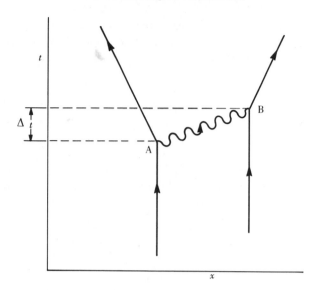

Figure 11-3. Feynman diagram of the interaction between two electrons.

and momentum changed by virtue of the exchange of a photon: each charged particle has been acted upon by an electromagnetic force. The particle whose exchange is responsible for the force between the charged particles is called a *virtual* photon, and is itself unobservable. A virtual photon travels at the speed c. Charged particles exchange such properties as energy and momentum by exchanging virtual photons. Graphical representations of interactions in space-time similar to Figure 11-3 are called *Feynman diagrams*, after R. P. Feynman who used these diagrams to represent in simple fashion and also to compute in detail the electrodynamic interactions between quantum charges.

The Coulomb force and all other electromagnetic forces between charged particles can be described in terms of the constant interchange of virtual photons between the charged particles. There is, however, a difference between virtual photons (which are the intermediary of the electromagnetic force between charged particles) and real photons. Whereas real photons are observable, virtual photons are not.

To see how an unobservable particle is responsible for an interaction we first note that, if a free electron in empty space were to emit a photon spontaneously and thereby recoil, the system's total energy and momentum would not be conserved (that is why a massive particle is required in an actual *bremsstrahlung* collision); likewise, a single free electron cannot, without violating momentum and energy conservation, absorb a photon (that is why the photoelectric effect takes place only when the particle to be freed is initially bound). Although momentum and energy conservations hold in the overall electron-electron interaction extending from vertices A to B in Figure 11-3, both cannot hold simultaneously at each of the separate vertices. It is the unobservability of the virtual photon that allows the non-conservation of energy and momentum during the time interval between photon emission and photon absorption. The violation of these two con-servation laws is consistent with the quantum theory as long as the energy ΔE and momentum Δp "borrowed" at the space-time emission event are returned within time and space intervals consistent with Heisenberg's principle of uncertainty, that is, within a time interval $\Delta t \geq \hbar/\Delta E$ and within a space interval $\Delta x \geq \hbar/\Delta p_x$. Thus, the system's total energy during the time interval Δt may exceed the initial energy of the two incoming electrons. The uncertainty principle limits the borrowed energy ΔE, by which energy conservation is violated, to

$$\Delta E \approx \hbar/\Delta t \qquad [11\text{-}1]$$

The quantity Δt (see Figure 11-3) is the time interval between the emission and the absorption of the virtual photon. Similarly, the uncertainties in momentum and position are related by $\Delta p_x \approx \hbar/\Delta x$. Note that virtual photons of all energies, from zero to infinity, may thereby be created; there-fore, the time interval and associated space interval between the emission event and the absorption event can range from very short intervals (asso-ciated with interactions separated by small distances and with virtual photons having very high energies) to very long intervals (associated with large distances and photons of very low energies).

Example 11-1   To illustrate the exchange of a virtual photon between two charged particles we consider the following interaction between two electrons, both initially at rest (see Figure 11-3). At vertex A one electron emits a virtual photon of energy E_γ (not measurable) and linear momentum p_γ (not measurable) and recoils to the left at speed v (assume $v \ll c$). At a later time, vertex B, the virtual photon is absorbed by the other electron, which recoils to the right at the same speed v. We choose the particularly simple situation (but unobservable one) in which the total linear momentum is *always* conserved: it is zero before, during, and after the exchange of the virtual photon. (a) What is the energy ΔE "borrowed" during the time Δt?; (b) If the virtual photon's energy is 1.0 eV, what is the longest time interval over which the exchange can take place? (c) What is the greatest distance separating the two electrons exchanging a 1.0 eV virtual photon?

(a) Before the emission of the virtual photon at A the system's total energy is just the total rest energy E_0 of the two electrons; its total linear momentum is zero. Assuming its total linear momentum to remain zero, the emission of the virtual photon imparts a momentum p_e to the electron:

$$p_e = mv = p_\gamma = E_\gamma/c \qquad [11\text{-}2]$$

Here m is the electron mass and E_γ and p_γ are the energy and momentum of the virtual photon. The total energy after emission but before absorption is

$$E = \tfrac{1}{2}mv^2 + E_\gamma + E_0$$

Thus, the energy ΔE borrowed during the exchange is

$$\Delta E = E - E_0 = \tfrac{1}{2}mv^2 + E_\gamma$$

or, with $E_\gamma = mvc$ from momentum conservation, Equation 11-2,

$$\Delta E = \tfrac{1}{2}mv^2 + mvc = mv(v/2 + c) \approx mvc = E_\gamma$$

where we have taken $v \ll c$. For this exchange the energy borrowed during the time interval Δt is just the energy of the virtual photon. After the time interval Δt the system's total energy is again E_0.

(b) The uncertainty principle implies that the energy ΔE may be borrowed for a time Δt given by

$$\Delta t \approx \hbar/\Delta E \approx \hbar/E_\gamma$$

If $E_\gamma = 1.0$ eV, then

$$\Delta t \approx (10^{-34} \text{ J-sec})/(1.0 \text{ eV} \times 1.6 \times 10^{-19} \text{ J/eV}) = 10^{-15} \text{ sec}$$

Electrons exchanging virtual photons of 1.0 eV energy can do so only for time intervals of the order of 10^{-15} sec. Virtual photons of less energy can, of course, exist for longer time intervals.

(c) The maximum separation distance Δx between the two electrons is determined by $\Delta x = c\Delta t$. For a 1.0 eV photon we have $\Delta t \lesssim 10^{-15}$ and

$$\Delta x \lesssim (3 \times 10^8 \text{ m/sec})(10^{-15} \text{ sec}) = 3 \times 10^{-7} \text{ m} = 0.3 \text{ Å}$$

In the computation above we assumed unrealistically that linear momentum was conserved at each instant, even during the time Δt between the emission of the virtual photon and before the absorption of this photon by the second electron. This is, of course, a possibility, but it is unverifiable, because the uncertainty principle allows for measurements of the momenta of the two electrons only before and after the exchange process. Neither momentum nor energy need be conserved during the exchange process. They clearly are not simultaneously conserved during the exchange of a virtual photon between an electron and a positive charge, such as a proton.

Consider the interaction corresponding to that of Figure 11-3 but in which one electron is replaced with a proton; see Figure 11-4. Again we assume both charges to be initially at rest. The electron emits a photon, which moves toward the proton, and the electron recoils in the *same* direction as that of the photon. The photon is later absorbed by the proton, which recoils in a direction *opposite* to that of the virtual photon: the oppositely charged particles attract one another. Obviously, the emission of the virtual photon at the first vertex is an event in which neither energy nor momentum is conserved. The nonconservation persists until the photon is absorbed by the proton which then recoils toward the electron. Again the time interval during which the virtual photon is exchanged is limited by the uncertainty principle.

In an interaction between two charged particles a virtual photon is created spontaneously by one particle and then absorbed by the other. Can the virtual photon be absorbed by the same charged particle that created it? It *can*, so long as the limits imposed by the uncertainty principle are satisfied. Figure 11-5a shows a single electron (or it may be any other electrically charged particle) emitting and then reabsorbing a virtual photon. Moreover, a photon, whether real or virtual, may spontaneously create an elec-

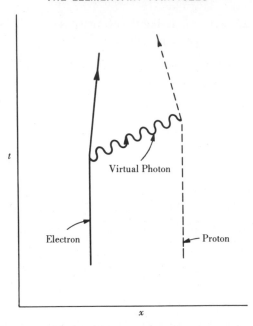

Figure 11-4. Space-time diagram of the interaction between an electron and a proton.

tron-positron pair, as shown in Figure 11-5b, even though its energy is less than the threshold energy for pair production. The process is again possible according to, and limited by, the uncertainty principle. The virtual pair may be annihilated and yield the original photon. Still more complicated processes may be constructed, as shown in the Feynman diagram of Figure 11-5c; the chain of creation-annihilation processes depicted is, of course, merely a collection of space-time graphs, whose basis is Figure 11-2. Thus, every electrically charged particle, even if isolated from other particles, may be considered to emit and reabsorb photons, which can become particle-antiparticle pairs. Although virtual particles cannot be observed directly, the validity of the conception is emphatically proved by the success of theoretical field-theory calculations of subtle electromagnetic effects, based on these ideas. The success of the field theory has, in fact, caused it to be the model for understanding fundamental forces besides the electromagnetic interaction and has led to the prediction of particles whose existence was later confirmed in experiment.

11-2 The strong interaction We have seen that the electromagnetic force between any two electrically charged particles can be ascribed to the exchange of virtual photons. To allow for the long-range character of this force—actually, an *infinite* range for an inverse-square force—necessitates

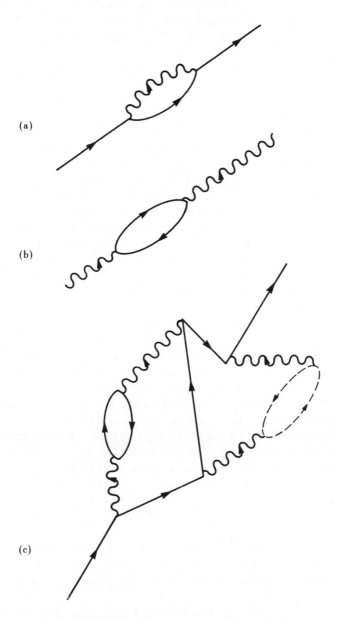

Figure 11-5. Feynman diagrams of the electromagnetic interaction: (a) an electron spontaneously creates and then reabsorbs a photon; (b) a photon spontaneously creates an electron-positron pair, and the pair is annihilated, and a photon is created; (c) a complex chain of annihilation-creation processes.

that the virtual field particles (photons) have zero rest mass. Turning now to the nuclear force, the strong force acting between protons and neutrons within a nucleus, we ask how this force field is described in terms of the exchange of virtual field particles. As we have seen (Chapters 9 and 10), the nuclear force is quite different from the electromagnetic force: whereas an electromagnetic force, such as the Coulomb force, extends throughout all space (varying as $1/r^2$), the nuclear force goes to zero at distances greater than about 1.4 fermi (see Figures 9-3 and 9-4). The nuclear force is short-range; the electromagnetic force, long-range. What properties must exchange particles have if we are to describe the short-range nuclear force in terms of the exchange of virtual particles? This question was first asked (and answered) by the Japanese physicist H. Yukawa in 1935.

Yukawa hypothesized that the nuclear force between nucleons is mediated through the exchange of virtual particles associated with the nuclear force field. The essential characteristics of these particles—now called *pi mesons* (π mesons) or simply *pions*—which act as agents of the nuclear force may be deduced by a simple argument based on the uncertainty principle. Let us describe the strong nuclear interactions between nucleons by a Feynman diagram like that depicting the electromagnetic interaction, Figure 11-3.

In the first diagram of Figure 11-6 a proton is assumed to create and emit a virtual neutral pi meson, pi-zero (π^0), at the vertex A; a short time Δt later a second proton absorbs this pion, at the vertex B. During the time Δt of existence of the pion the energy-conservation principle can be violated, so long as its violation is consistent with the uncertainty principle $\Delta E \, \Delta t \approx \hbar$, where ΔE now represents the "borrowed" energy during the exchange. When the meson is absorbed by the second proton at the later time, vertex B, the energy of the system is again restored. Similar meson exchanges are shown for the proton-neutron interactions in the other diagrams of Figures 11-6. Note that three distinct pions (pi-plus, pi-minus, and pi-zero mesons) with charges of $+1$, -1, and 0 in units of the electron charge e describe the various nucleon interactions.

All of the strong nucleon-nucleon interactions are characterized by a short-range force (Section 9-2) that extends a distance of only about 1.4 fermi. This limits the travel distance R of the virtual meson before it is again absorbed. If we assume, for simplicity, that the meson travels essentially at the speed of light, c, then it exists only for the time interval Δt of the exchange:

$$\Delta t = \frac{R}{c} = \frac{1.4 \times 10^{-15} \text{ m}}{3 \times 10^8 \text{ m/sec}} = \tfrac{1}{2} \times 10^{-23} \text{ sec}$$

Using the uncertainty principle, we find the borrowed energy to be

$$\Delta E = \frac{\hbar}{\Delta t} = \frac{10^{-34} \text{ J-sec}}{\tfrac{1}{2} \times 10^{-23} \text{ sec}} = 2 \times 10^{-11} \text{ J}$$

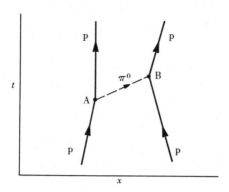

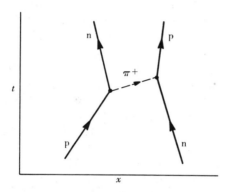

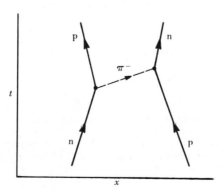

Figure 11-6. Nucleon-nucleon interactions through the exchange of virtual pions π^0, π^+, and π^-.

Taking the borrowed energy to be primarily the rest energy $E_\pi = m_\pi c^2$ of the virtual pion, we find the pion's rest mass to be

$$m_\pi = \frac{E_\pi}{c^2} \approx \frac{\Delta E}{c^2} = \frac{2 \times 10^{-11}\,\text{J}}{(3 \times 10^8\,\text{m/sec})^2} \approx 2 \times 10^{-28}\,\text{kg} \approx 200\,m_e$$

On the basis of this simple argument we expect the pion to have a mass of the order of 200 electron masses m_e, to correspond to the short-range character of the strong nuclear force.

After Yukawa predicted nuclear exchange particles would have a mass intermediate between those of electrons and protons, scientists began looking for them (calling them mesons, from the Greek *mesos*, "middle"). A virtual pion that is being exchanged between a pair of nucleons cannot, of course, be observed, but if sufficient energy, of the order of several hundred MeV, is supplied to a nuclear system, real ones can be created, and when they leave the nucleus they can be detected. Charged pi mesons (pi-plus and pi-minus mesons or, simply, charged pions) having all the properties of the nuclear exchange particles were first identified in 1947; the uncharged meson of this group, π^0, was detected three years later. Pions may be produced in collisions between high-energy nucleons in such reactions as $p + n \rightarrow p + n + \pi^- + \pi^+$. Until the nineteen-forties the high-energy reactions required for their creation were available only in the uncontrolled and infrequent events initiated by cosmic radiation. When accelerators producing particles of several hundred MeV and more were built, large numbers of charged and uncharged pions could be produced under controlled conditions in the laboratory, and our knowledge of them increased accordingly. Their properties are listed in Table 11-2.

Table 11-2

Properties of Pions

	π^+	π^-	π^0
Rest mass, m_e	273.3	273.3	264.3
Rest energy, MeV	139.58	139.58	134.97
Charge, e	+1	−1	0
Spin, $\times \hbar$	0	0	0
Magnetic moment	0	0	0
Mean lifetime, sec	2.55×10^{-8}	2.55×10^{-8}	1.8×10^{-16}
Decay modes	$\pi^+ \rightarrow \mu^+ + \nu_\mu$ (99.99%)	$\pi^- \rightarrow \mu^- + \bar{\nu}_\mu$	$\pi^0 \rightarrow \gamma + \gamma$ (98.8%)
	$\pi^+ \rightarrow e^+ + \nu_e$ (0.01%)	$\pi^- \rightarrow e^- + \bar{\nu}_e$	$\pi^0 \rightarrow e^+ + e^- + \gamma$ (1.2%)

In this chapter wherever necessary antiparticles will be designated by an overbar; for example $\bar{\nu}_\mu$ is the antiparticle of ν_μ.

Like the photon (spin 1), the pion has an integral spin (0). In fact, an integral spin angular momentum is characteristic of all field particles, every one of which has the following properties: (1) in any reaction, whether decay or collision, field particles may be created or annihilated without limit, no conservation law restricting their number; (2) any number of field particles can occupy the same quantum state, the Pauli exclusion principle not applying (see Sections 7-8 and 12-3).

The photon and pion differ in some respects: whereas the photon is electrically neutral, the pion exists in three charge states; whereas the photon has rest mass, the pion has a finite mass, to account for the short-range nuclear force; and whereas a free photon is stable, all free pions are unstable.

The decay of pions is reminiscent of the behavior of a single neutron which, when free, decays into a proton, electron, and antineutrino. From Table 11-2 we see that both decay modes of the pi-zero involve photons, one of the decays producing two photons (98.8% of all pi-zero decays) and the other producing an electron, a positron, and a photon (1.2% of all pi-zero decays). The pi-zero decay therefore takes place through the electromagnetic interaction.

We note further that the pi-zero decay through the electromagnetic interaction ($\approx 10^{-16}$ sec) is longer than the time associated with the strong, or nuclear, interaction ($\approx 10^{-23}$ sec), but much shorter than the time of the interaction responsible for neutron decay ($\approx 10^{3}$ sec) and for the charged-pion decay ($\approx 10^{-8}$ sec). Compared with the strong nuclear interaction ($\approx 10^{-23}$ sec) and the electromagnetic interaction ($\approx 10^{-21}$ sec), the decays of the neutron and of the charged pions are much weaker and take place much more slowly. This introduces another fundamental interaction between particles which, because it is much weaker than the strong or electromagnetic interactions, is called simply the *weak interaction*. It was first used by E. Fermi in the nineteen-thirties to describe the beta decay of radioactive nuclei. Compared with the strong interaction, the weak interaction is weaker by a factor 10^{13}. Even so it exceeds by a factor 10^{27} the extraordinarily weak gravitational force. See Table 11-3 for the relative strengths of the four fundamental interactions.

Table 11-3

The Fundamental Interactions

Interaction	Relative strength	Field particle
Strong	1	pion
Electromagnetic	10^{-2}	photon
Weak	10^{-13}	W particle (?)
Gravitational	10^{-40}	graviton (?)

The decay of the charged pions produces still other elementary particles. The dominant decay mode (99.99% of all pion decays) is into new particles: the muons, μ^+ and μ^-, and the neutrinos, ν_μ and $\bar{\nu}_\mu$, which are associated with

Table 11-4
A Thirteen-particle Universe

FAMILY	PARTICLE	SYMBOL	ELECTRIC CHARGE, e	SPIN, $\times \hbar$	REST MASS, m_e	REST ENERGY, MeV	INTERACTION PARTICLE PARTICIPATES IN
Baryon	neutron, antineutron	n, n̄	0	$\frac{1}{2}$	1,839	939.5	strong, electromagnetic, weak, gravitational
	proton, antiproton	p^+, p^-	+1, −1	$\frac{1}{2}$	1,836	938.2	strong, electromagnetic, weak, gravitational
Pion	π^+ meson	π^+	+1	0	273.3	139.6	strong, electromagnetic, weak, gravitational
	π^- meson	π^-	−1	0	273.3	139.6	strong, electromagnetic, weak, gravitational
	π^0 meson	π^0	0	0	264.3	135.0	electromagnetic, weak, gravitational
Lepton	electron, positron	e^-, e^+	−1, +1	$\frac{1}{2}$	1	0.5110	electromagnetic, weak, gravitational
	neutrino, antineutrino	ν_e, $\bar{\nu}_e$	0	$\frac{1}{2}$	0	0	weak, gravitational
	photon	γ	0	1	0	0	electromagnetic, gravitational
	graviton		0	2	0	0	gravitational

the muons and are of a type different from those associated with electrons (ν_e and $\bar{\nu}_e$). Charged pions are observed to decay into electrons or positrons and neutrinos or antineutrinos about once in 10,000 decays. We shall discuss the decay modes of pions and the decay products in Section 11-4.

11-3 A thirteen-particle universe Ignoring for the moment the muons and their associated neutrinos, let us consider a hypothetical universe composed of only the other elementary particles, which number thirteen. The actual universe is more complicated; however, the thirteen-particle model accounts, at least approximately, for the matter found within the real universe. Table 11-4 lists the thirteen particles in order of their rest masses. We have included the *graviton*, the exchange particle in gravitational interaction. Although it has not yet been detected experimentally, theory predicts that it will be found to have a zero rest mass (to account for the infinite range of the gravitational force) and an integral spin of 2. For completeness we should also add the exchange particle representing the weak interaction force responsible for neutron and pion decays; this has been called the *W particle*. Its existence is being pursued in the high-energy accelerator laboratories throughout the world. We exclude the *W* particle from the list because here we are assuming that the neutron and pion are stable particles.

The particles in Table 11-4 are of five distinct groups, or families. Within each family all particles have the same spin and roughly comparable masses. With respect to spin the families may be classified as those with half-integral spins and those with integral spins; according to this classification some properties of the families are given below.

Half-integral spin:

The baryons (Greek "heavy") comprise the proton, the neutron, and their antiparticles. They are by far the most massive of the elementary particles. All have spin $\frac{1}{2}$ and nearly equal masses. They participate in all four fundamental interactions. Each baryon has an antiparticle, and the total number of baryons is constant in any reaction. In the conservation law of baryons each baryon is assigned a value of $+1$ and each antibaryon a value of -1.

The leptons (Greek "light") comprise the electron, its associated neutrino, and their antiparticles. They have spin $\frac{1}{2}$ and comparable masses. The electron and positron participate in the electromagnetic, weak, and gravitational interactions; the neutrino participates only in the weak and, presumably, the gravitational interactions. Each lepton has an antiparticle, and in any reaction the total number of leptons is constant.

In the conservation law of leptons each lepton is assigned a value of $+1$ and each antilepton a value of -1.

Integral spin:

The particles in these groups are the field quanta for the various interaction forces among baryons and leptons. They can be created or annihilated in a reaction without regard to conservation of their number.

The mesons include the pions, which transmit the strong interaction among baryons. They have zero spin and comparable masses. They participate in all four fundamental interactions.

The photon family contains only the photon. It transmits the electromagnetic interaction. The photon has spin 1 and zero rest mass. It participates in the electromagnetic and gravitational interactions. The photon is its own antiparticle.

The graviton is the field quantum for the gravitational force. Although not yet detected, it is expected to have a spin of 2, a zero rest mass, and to interact through the gravitational force only.

In our part of the universe the main building blocks are the protons, neutrons, and electrons. The gravitational force (mediated by gravitons), although weak, is dominant in macroscopic systems such as the solar system, the electromagnetic forces (mediated by photons) dominate in microscopic systems such as molecules and atoms, and the strong nuclear force (mediated by pions) dominates in the subatomic systems such as nuclei.

We may make some final observations concerning the particles listed in Table 11-4. The neutron, the antineutron, and the two charged pions are stable, in the sense that they do not decay through the strong and electromagnetic interactions; however, they are unstable in the weak interaction. The neutral pion is stable in the strong interaction and unstable in the electromagnetic interaction. All the other particles listed in Table 11-4 are stable.

We see from the table that the more massive the elementary particle the more interactions in which it may participate: baryons and mesons participate in all four fundamental interactions, the leptons participate in all but the strong interaction, the photon participates in the electromagnetic and gravitational interactions, and the graviton participates in only the gravitational interaction.

The strong interaction is characterized by an energy of approximately 150 MeV (the rest energy of the pions), which is about a tenth of the rest energy of the baryons (about 1,000 MeV). The electromagnetic-interaction energy is about 1.5 MeV; this is seen by noting the rest-energy difference between the charged and uncharged members of each group in Table 11-4.

Although the thirteen-particle model is attractive and relatively simple, it does not correspond to the physical universe which we inhabit. There are many additional "elementary" particles, whose role in the structure of matter is somewhat uncertain; for instance, the charged pions decay primarily into muons, which seem to play no fundamental role. Moreover, many other particles, exotic and short-lived, have been observed, and these are apparently as elementary as the others in Table 11-4.

11-4 The fundamental particles Besides the "fundamental" particles listed in Table 11-4 many others have been observed. Except for the two muons already mentioned, they have been discovered within the last twenty years. In this section we shall describe in greater detail some of the particles of the last section and shall treat of the new ones that have been observed.

Three obvious ways in which elementary particles may differ are in charge, mass, and lifetime when they are free: Every one of the particles has an electric charge of either $+e$, $-e$, or 0; their masses vary from zero (photon and neutrino) to masses greater than 4,000 electron masses, and their lifetimes may be as short as 10^{-23} sec or as long as ∞. It is instructive to group them according to the interactions by which they decay, as in the following subsections.

STABLE PARTICLES Nine particles do not decay by any interaction: the proton and antiproton in the baryon family, the electron, antielectron, and the four different neutrinos in the lepton family; and the photon, the only stable field particle (we exclude the graviton and W particle since they have not been observed). Each of the other elementary particles is unstable and decays through the strong, the weak, or the electromagnetic interaction.

PARTICLES UNSTABLE IN THE WEAK INTERACTION Most of the elementary particles decay by the weak interaction.

We list and discuss them in order of increasing mass: (a) the muons, (b) the charged pions, (c) the charged and uncharged kaons, and (d) the neutron, antineutron, and charged and uncharged hyperons.

(a) *Muons*. The muons result from the decay of the meson field particles for the nuclear force. See Figure 11-7 for the decay of a pi-plus to a mu-plus (muon) followed by the decay of the mu-plus to a positron. The neutrinos created in these two decays are not observed since they produce no tracks. The muons are the most mysterious of all the elementary particles: there is no apparent reason for their existence. The properties of the muons are summarized in Table 11-5.

We notice that the muon-antimuon pair is analogous to the electron-positron pair: the muon has the same charge as the electron, and it inter-

Table 11-5

Properties of the Muons

	μ^+	μ^-
Rest mass, m_e	206.78	206.78
Rest energy, MeV	105.7	105.7
Charge	$+e$	$-e$
Spin, $\times h$	$\frac{1}{2}$	$\frac{1}{2}$
Magnetic moment	$1.0026(m_e/m_\mu)\beta$	$-1.0026(m_e/m_\mu)\beta$
Mean life, sec	2.20×10^{-6}	2.20×10^{-6}
Decay mode	$\mu^+ \rightarrow e^+ + \nu_e + \bar{\nu}_\mu$	$\mu^- \rightarrow e^- + \nu_e + \bar{\nu}_\mu$

acts with matter through the electromagnetic force and not through the strong nuclear force. Unlike the electron, however, it is not stable against weak interaction but decays to an electron (or positron) and two neutrinos. Its lifetime (2.2×10^{-6} sec) is very long compared with that of a nuclear interaction ($\approx 10^{-23}$ sec) or an electromagnetic interaction ($\approx 10^{-21}$ sec). All experimental evidence indicates that apart from its decay process the muon behaves exactly like a heavy electron.

(b) *Charged pions.* The properties of the charged pions are listed in Table 11-2. Both charged pions have the same lifetime and decay by means of the weak interaction. Their most frequent decay is to a muon and neutrino; very infrequently they decay to an electron and neutrino. Figure 11-7 shows the decay of a pi-plus to a mu-plus and a neutrino (the latter is unobservable). We note in Table 11-2 that the un-

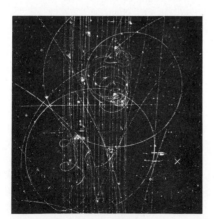
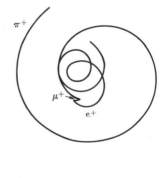

Figure 11-7. A liquid-hydrogen bubble-chamber photograph of a π^+ decaying into a μ^+, which decays into an e$^+$. (Courtesy of Brookhaven National Laboratory.)

charged pion decays in a time characteristic of the electromagnetic inter-action and thus does not partake in weak interactions.

(c) *Charged and uncharged kaons* (K mesons). The K mesons, or kaons, were observed shortly after the discovery of the pions in 1947. They have many properties similar to those of pions and are members of the same family, the meson family. There are four different kaons, all having zero spin. They decay to pions or leptons by means of the weak inter-action. As Table 11-6 shows, the number and complexity of kaon decays

Table 11-6

Properties of the K Mesons

Symbol*	Rest mass, m_e	Rest energy, MeV	Mean life, sec	Mode of decay	Probability of decay, %
$K^+(K^-)$	966.4	493.98	1.23×10^{-8}	$K^+ \to \pi^+ + \pi^0$	25
				$K^+ \to \pi^+ + \pi^- + \pi^+$	6
				$K^+ \to \pi^+ + \pi^0 + \pi^0$	2
				$K^+ \to \mu^+ + \nu$	58
				$K^+ \to \mu^+ + \pi^0 + \nu$	5
				$K^+ \to e^+ + \pi^0 + \nu$	4
$K^0(\overline{K^0})$	974.1	497.8	0.874×10^{-10}	$K^0 \to \pi^+ + \pi^-$	88
				$K^0 \to \pi^0 + \pi^0$	12
			5.3×10^{-8}	$K^0 \to \mu^+ + \pi^- + \nu$	
				$K^0 \to \mu^- + \pi^+ + \bar{\nu}$	
				$K^0 \to e^+ + \pi^- + \nu$	
				$K^0 \to e^- + \pi^+ + \bar{\nu}$	
				$K^0 \to \pi^0 + \pi^0 + \pi^0$	
				$K^0 \to \pi^+ + \pi^- + \pi^0$	

* The antikaons, K^- and $\overline{K^0}$, are in parentheses. Their decay modes are similar to the kaons; merely replace all particles with antiparticles.

arc much greater than those of pion decays. This is due in part to the ability of the kaons to decay to both pions and leptons. Explaining their decay modes, however, is another matter; for example, that a kaon sometimes decays to two pions and sometimes three violates one of the conservation laws, the conservation of parity. Figure 11-8a shows a two-particle decay of a K^-. Figure 11-8b shows a three-particle decay of a K^-.

Parity is a concept related to the symmetry of physical experiments under a reflection; that is to say, the conservation of parity requires that, if an experiment takes place, so too does its mirror image. Thus, one cannot distinguish between "left-handedness" and "right-handedness." In quan-

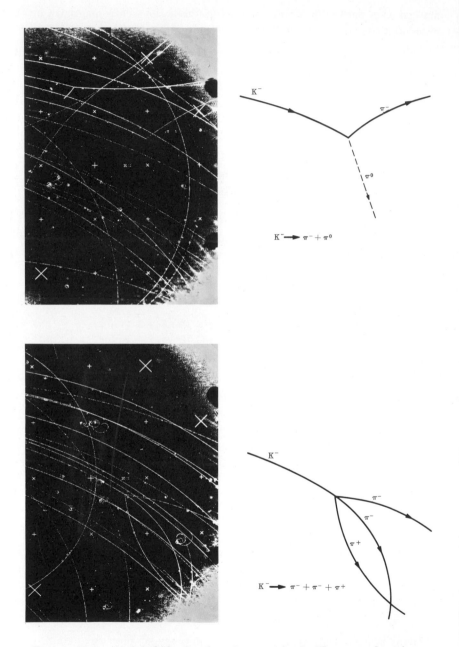

Figure 11-8. (a) A bubble-chamber photograph of a K⁻ meson decaying into two pions. (b) A bubble-chamber photograph of a K⁻ meson decaying into three pions. (Courtesy of Yale University and Brookhaven National Laboratory.)

tum mechanics the parity of a particle is simply defined in terms of the wave function, say $\psi(r)$, that describes the particle. Reflecting the position coordinates through the origin, changing r to $-r$ (such that $x \to -x$, $y \to -y$, and $z \to -z$), is equivalent to changing a right-handed system into a left-handed system. If the probability density $[\psi(r)]^2$ of the particle is to be the same whether we use a right-handed or left-handed system, we have just two possibilities for $\psi(-r)$:

$$\psi(-r) = \psi(r) \qquad \text{even parity}$$

$$\psi(-r) = -\psi(r) \qquad \text{odd parity}$$

Even parity is analogous to an even function; odd parity, to an odd function.

All elementary particles have an intrinsic parity. The electron, proton, and neutron are arbitrarily assigned an even parity; then by experiment the parity of the pion is found to be odd. It used to be believed that in any interaction the parity of a system must not change: if it was even before the interaction, it must be even after the interaction. To the kay-minus in its two-pion decay one must assign an even intrinsic parity; to the kay-minus in its three-pion decay, on the other hand, one must assign an odd intrinsic parity. Therefore, to conserve parity in the weak-interaction decay of kaons one had to assume two different kaons, a kay-minus of even parity and a distinctive kay-minus of odd parity. However, all other evidence indicated that these two kaons were one and the same.

To resolve the contradiction C. N. Yang and T. D. Lee made the bold assumption in 1956 that there is, indeed, just one kay-minus and that parity is *not* conserved in weak interactions. This hypothesis has been confirmed in many experiments since their prediction. Here, then, is a conservation law that holds in some interactions (in the strong and electromagnetic) but not in all (not in the weak). The nonconservation of parity in the weak interactions also implies that Nature actually does distinguish between right and left.

Two other features of the kaon are not found in the pion. One is that two neutral kaons are distinguishable, a kay-zero and an anti-kay-zero, K^0 and $\overline{K^0}$, whereas the antiparticle of the pi-zero, π^0, is itself. The other is that the neutral kaons do not decay by the electromagnetic interaction but by the much slower weak interaction, whereas the neutral pion decays by the electromagnetic interaction. We shall return to these points later.

Like pions, kaons can be produced by the strong interaction when two nucleons interact, but only when they interact at very short range. Both kaons and pions are field particles for the strong nuclear interaction, but the kaon's mass is more than three times the pion's. Because of this the range of virtual kaons exchanged by nucleons is much smaller than that of virtual pions. The kaons probably are exchange particles in the short-range interaction between nucleons, but the pions are the principal exchange particles in the intermediate-range interaction between nucleons. This is consistent with the experimental observation that, as the energy of a beam of incoming protons from a high-energy accelerator increases, the ratio of kaons to pions produced by the protons increases.

(d) *Neutron, antineutron, and charged and uncharged hyperons.* All the baryons except the proton constitute this group: they are the neutron, the antineutron, and the particles of the four groups lambda, sigma, xi, and omega, called the hyperons. They are more massive than the neutron and, like it, decay by the weak interaction. The neutron, which is the most familiar particle in this group, has a mass very nearly that of the proton. The hyperons are listed in Table 11-7.

All hyperons have a spin of $\frac{1}{2}$, as do nucleons. Except for the neutral sigma particles, which are included in the table simply as a convenience in listing the hyperons, they all decay by the weak interaction. The hyperons fall into the four groups according to their masses.

The creation and subsequent decay of a hyperon, lambda-zero, and an antihyperon, anti-lambda-zero, are shown in Figure 11-9. A hyperon also can be created without the simultaneous creation of an antihyperon; for example, in Figure 11-10 is shown the creation of a lambda-zero and a kay-zero. The reaction is

$$p + p \rightarrow p + \pi^+ + \Lambda^0 + K^0$$

We shall discuss the production of hyperons and kaons further in Section 11-5, where the strange manner in which they are produced is described in terms of a new conservation law, the conservation of strangeness.

Figure 11-11 shows the production of the omega-minus, the most massive of the hyperons; this photograph shows the tracks of two hyperons and three kaons.

PARTICLES UNSTABLE TO ELECTROMAGNETIC INTERACTION   Three elementary particles, all with zero electric charge, are unstable in the electromagnetic interaction: the pi-zero, the sigma-zero, and the anti-sigma-zero (π^0, Σ^0, and $\overline{\Sigma}^0$). Their lifetimes are, therefore, much shorter than those of particles decaying by the weak interaction. The pi-zero (Table 11-2) has a lifetime of $\approx 10^{-16}$ sec and decays to two photons or to one photon, an electron, and a positron. The sigma-zero (Table 11-7) has a lifetime of $< 10^{-14}$ sec and decays to a lambda-zero and a photon. The anti-sigma-zero has the same lifetime as its antiparticle and decays to an anti-lambda-zero and a photon.

One might well wonder how it is possible to ascertain that these particles have actually existed, inasmuch as they do not travel measurable distances

Table 11-7

The Hyperons

Particle* and Antiparticle		Rest mass, m_e	Rest energy, MeV	Mean life, sec	Principal mode of decay
Lambda	Λ^0, $\overline{\Lambda}^0$	2,183	1,115.5	2.52×10^{-10}	$\Lambda^0 \rightarrow p + \pi^-$, or $n + \pi^0$
Sigma	Σ^0, $\overline{\Sigma}^0$	2,334	1,192.2	$<10^{-14}$	$\Sigma^0 \rightarrow \Lambda^0 + \gamma$
	Σ^+, $\overline{\Sigma}^-$	2,327	1,189.5	0.81×10^{-10}	$\Sigma^+ \rightarrow p + \pi^0$ or $n + \pi^+$
	Σ^-, $\overline{\Sigma}^+$	2,343	1,197.4	1.7×10^{-10}	$\Sigma^- \rightarrow n + \pi^-$
Xi	Ξ^-, $\overline{\Xi}^+$	2,586	1,321	1.7×10^{-10}	$\Xi^- \rightarrow \Lambda^0 + \pi^-$
	Ξ^0, $\overline{\Xi}^0$	2,573	1,315	2.9×10^{-10}	$\Xi^0 \rightarrow \Lambda^0 + \pi^0$
Omega	Ω^-, $\overline{\Omega}^+$	3,272	1,672	1.1×10^{-10}	$\Omega^- \rightarrow \Xi^0 + \pi^-$, or $\Xi^- + \pi^0$

* Note that each particle has a distinct antiparticle. For example, the antiparticle of Σ^- is $\overline{\Sigma}^+$, which is distinct from Σ^+.

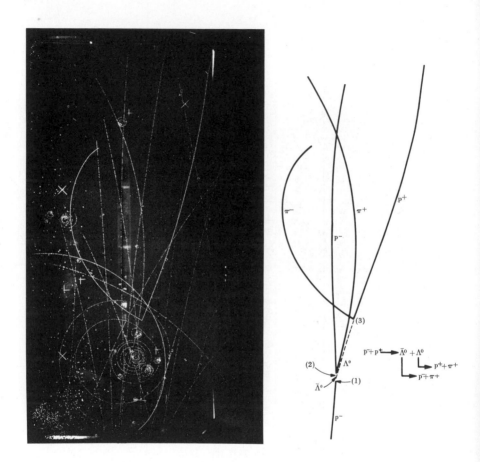

Figure 11-9. A bubble-chamber photograph of a 3.3 GeV antiproton entering the bubble chamber from the bottom and colliding with a proton at point 1 to create a hyperon (Λ^0) and an antihyperon ($\overline{\Lambda^0}$). The Λ^0 particle decays into a proton and π^--pion at point (3); the $\overline{\Lambda^0}$ antiparticle into an antiproton and π^+-pion at point (2). (Courtesy of Brookhaven National Laboratory.)

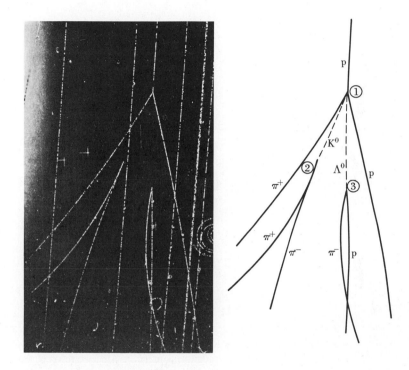

Figure 11-10. A bubble-chamber photograph of a 2.85 GeV proton colliding with a proton and creating a K° and a Λ°. The K° decays to two pions.
(Courtesy of Brookhaven National Laboratory.)

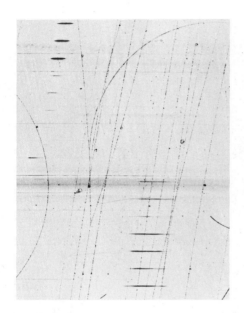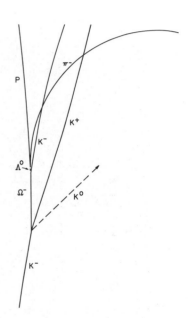

Figure 11-11. A bubble-chamber photograph and sketch of the production of a negatively-charged Omega-meson (Ω^-). An incoming K^--meson collides with a stationary proton with the resultant production of a K°, K^+, and Ω^-. The photograph also shows the subsequent decay of the Ω^- into a Λ° and K^-, and the decay of the Λ° into a proton and negative pion. (Courtesy of Brookhaven National Laboratory.)

in their short lifetimes. To understand this we may examine the longer lifetimes and correspondingly longer path lengths of particles decaying by the weak interaction.

Consider a kay-plus meson that decays to two pions (see Table 11-6)

$$K^+ \rightarrow \pi^+ + \pi^0 \qquad [11\text{-}3]$$

The pi-zero rapidly decays ($\ll 10^{-16}$) to two photons:

$$\pi^0 \rightarrow \gamma + \gamma \qquad [11\text{-}4]$$

For simplicity we view the decays from the reference frame in which the initial kay-plus is at rest. The distance x traveled by the pi-zero can easily be estimated. Assuming it to travel at the speed $\frac{1}{10}c$, we have

$$x = ct = (3 \times 10^7 \text{ m/sec})(10^{-16} \text{ sec})$$
$$= 3 \times 10^{-9} \text{ m} = 30 \text{ Å}$$

Such a small distance cannot be observed in a bubble-chamber photograph, and it might appear that the kay-plus decays directly into a pi-plus and two photons:

$$K^+ \rightarrow \pi^+ + \gamma + \gamma \qquad [11\text{-}5]$$

How, then, can we distinguish between the direct decay of the kay-plus given by this equation and the two-step decay of the kay-plus given by Equations 11-3 and 11-4?

In the two-particle decay given by Equation 11-3 we can conserve both momentum and energy only if the pi-plus goes off with a *fixed* energy and the pi-zero also goes off with a *fixed* energy. Thus, if the kay-plus decays in the two-step process, the energy distribution of the outgoing positive pions will look like Figure 11-12a. On the other hand, if the kay-plus decays directly to *three* particles, a pi-plus and two photons, then the outgoing positive pions can have a continuous range of energies, momentum and energy being conserved in each decay. The energy distribution of the outgoing pi-plus meson in a direct decay of the kay-plus would look like Figure 11-12b. (Recall that in alpha decay, which is a decay to *two* particles, the alpha particles are *monoenergetic*, whereas in beta decay, which is a decay to *three* particles, the beta particles have a *continuum* of energies.) We can, therefore, easily distinguish between the two possible decay modes of the kay-plus by measuring the energy distribution of the outgoing pi-plus mesons. The experimental results are consistent with Figure 11-12a; thus, although the pi-zero does not live long enough to move a perceptible distance, it does live long enough to be identified as a distinct particle. Similar arguments establish the existence of the short-lived sigma zero and anti-sigma zero.

Compared with particles decaying by the electromagnetic interaction, those decaying by the weak interaction have lifetimes that are 10^6 times longer or more. They will, therefore, travel 10^6 times farther before decaying. If, for example, a lambda-zero has a speed of $\frac{1}{10}c$, before decaying it will travel a distance of

$$x = \frac{1}{10}c \times (10^{-10} \text{ sec}) = (3 \times 10^7 \text{ m/sec})(3 \times 10^{-10} \text{ sec}) = 1 \text{ cm}$$

One can thus distinguish between the point of creation and the point of decay of the lambda particle (see Figure 11-10).

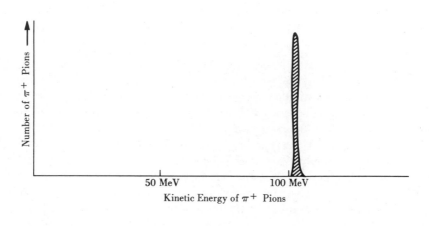

(a)

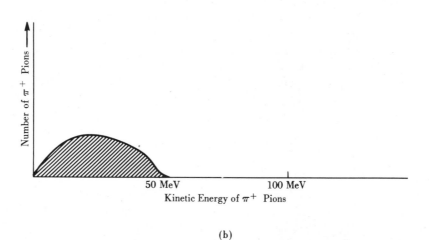

(b)

Figure 11-12. Kinetic-energy distribution of π^+ mesons in the decay of K^+ mesons: (a) the expected distribution if the K^+ decays to $\pi^+ + \pi^0$ and then the π^0 decays to $\gamma + \gamma$; (b) the expected distribution if the K^+ decays directly to $\pi^+ + \gamma + \gamma$.

PARTICLES UNSTABLE IN THE STRONG INTERACTION   Most of the unstable fundamental particles discussed so far decay by the weak interaction
with lifetimes long compared with the time of nuclear interaction ($\approx 10^{-23}$
sec). The others decay by the electromagnetic interaction, with lifetimes of
about 10^{-16} sec; their existence is inferred from the energy distribution of
the product particles.

Many particles with lifetimes even shorter than 10^{-16} sec have been discovered in recent years. With lifetimes comparable to the nuclear-interac-
tion time, $\approx 10^{-23}$ sec, they certainly do not live long enough to leave
measurable tracks, so their existence must be inferred from observations of
the energy distributions of the observable decay products. Since these distributions produce curves similar to that of Figure 11-12a—a curve with a
sharp peak, or resonance—the particles inferred from them are called
resonance particles. Before listing the many resonance particles that have
been identified since 1960, we first ask how it is possible to discern their
existence.

Consider the decay of a particle ultimately to three other particles, like
the decay of the kay-plus (Equations 11-3, 11-4, and 11-5). If the particle
decays directly to three particles, the energy distribution of any one of
the outgoing particles will be continuous and broad, as shown in the curve
of Figure 11-12b. If, on the other hand, the particle first decays to two
particles and then one of these in turn decays to two other particles, the
distribution of the particle not decaying will be sharp, as in the solid curve
of Figure 11-12a. Because of the uncertainty principle, $\Delta E \Delta t \geq \hbar$, it will
not be infinitely sharp, however; there will be a spread ΔE in energies.
For the distribution in kinetic energy of the pi-plus in the kay-plus decay,
the lifetime of the pi-zero is $\approx 10^{-16}$ sec; therefore,

$$\Delta E = \hbar/\Delta t = (10^{-34} \text{ J-sec})/(10^{-16} \text{ sec}) = 10^{-18} \text{ J} = 6 \text{ eV}$$

The kinetic energy of the pi-plus is about 100 MeV. Thus,

$$\Delta E/E = (6 \times 10^{-6} \text{ MeV})/(10^2 \text{ MeV}) = 6 \times 10^{-8}$$

and the line is, indeed, quite sharp.

It is obvious that, the shorter the lifetime of the intermediate particle,
the greater the spread in kinetic energy. Ultimately the energy spread
becomes so great that the energy distribution in intermediate-particle
decay (Figure 11-12a) has a curve that blends into that of the direct decay
(Figure 11-12b); at this limit one cannot ascertain the existence of the
intermediate particle.

For lifetimes of 10^{-23} sec the spread in energy of the particle is

$$\Delta E = (10^{-34} \text{ J-sec})/(10^{-23} \text{ sec}) = 10^{-11} \text{ J} = 60 \text{ MeV}$$

If the outgoing particle has an average kinetic energy of 100 MeV the energy distribution curves of the direct decay and the intermediate decay look like Figure 11-13. This broad resonance curve is still distinguishable from the direct three-particle decay, and we can account for its width by assuming the existence of a very short-lived, intermediate particle.

Table 11-8 lists some of the resonance particles in the meson family (integral angular momentum $\hbar$); Table 11-9 gives some in the baryon family (half-integral angular momentum $\hbar$). Such of their properties as mass, spin, lifetime, and modes of decay have been measured and are given in the tables. A number of theoretical schemes have been proposed to account for and classify the resonance particles,† but none has been completely successful. How these resonance particles fit into the scheme of the elementary particles is one of the pressing, unsolved problems of elementary-particle physics today.

11-5 A thirty-four-particle universe   A thirteen-particle model of the universe was described in Section 11-3. All thirteen particles were *assumed* to be stable when free, none to decay in any interaction. The conservation

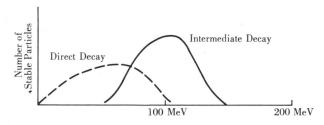

Kinetic Energy of Stable Particle

Figure 11-13. Kinetic-energy distributions of a direct three-particle decay and a two-step decay. The intermediate resonance particle's lifetime is approximately 10^{-23} sec. This results in a broad resonance curve, which is nevertheless distinguishable from the direct decay.

† Some of the models proposed for the classification of resonance particles are described in references listed at the end of this chapter.

Table 11-8

Meson Resonance Particles

RESONANCE PARTICLE	MASS, m_e	REST ENERGY, MeV	MEAN LIFE, $\times 10^{-23}$ sec	ANGULAR MOMENTUM, $\times \hbar$	MOST PROBABLE DECAY
f′	2,963	1,514	0.86	2	$K + \overline{K}$
A2	2,554	1,305	0.67	2	$\rho\pi + 3\pi$
f	2,466	1,260	0.43	2	2π
φ	1,994	1,019	20	1	$K^+ + K^-$
η′	1,875	958	<15	0	$\eta + \pi + \pi$
ω	1,532	783	5.0	1	$\pi^+ + \pi^- + \pi^0$
ρ	1,497	765	0.48	1	$\pi + \pi$
η	1,074	549	3×10^4	0	$\gamma + \gamma$
K*	1,748	893	0.12	1	$K + \pi$
K_v	2,777	1,419	0.67	2	$K + \pi$

laws of mass-energy, linear momentum, angular momentum, electric charge, baryon number, and lepton number held in the strong and electromagnetic interactions. Observations show, however, that this simple model is inadequate. Four of the thirteen particles decay by the weak interaction (neutron, antineutron, pi-plus, and pi-minus) and one decays by the electromagnetic interaction (pi-zero). In addition, a host of other elementary particles have been found, all of which decay by one of the fundamental interactions (excluding the gravitational interaction). A more general model is needed to describe the numerous particles and interactions described in Section 11-4. Many theories have been proposed, but at present no satisfactory single model of elementary particles exists. Here we shall describe a particularly simple model that encompasses all the particles except the very short-lived ones, the resonance particles. It was developed in 1953 by M. Gell-Mann and independently by T. Nakano and K. Nishijima. It allows one to determine the types of nuclear reaction that can take place, and the predictions are in good agreement with experiment.

Table 11-10 lists all the known baryons that are either stable or decay by the weak or the electromagnetic interaction. They are grouped according to mass and electric charge. For each baryon there is an antibaryon of identical mass and lifetime and of opposite electric charge. We note that all baryons and antibaryons have either a single unit of charge or zero charge.

The particles cluster themselves into five distinct groupings according to mass: the doublet consisting of neutron and proton, the singlet lambda, the triplet sigma, the doublet xi, and the singlet omega. Insofar as the strong nuclear interaction is concerned, the members of any one group may be taken to be different states of a single particle. For example, the neutron and proton are considered two different states of the particle "nucleon."

Table 11-9

Baryon Resonance Particles

RESONANCE PARTICLE	REST MASS, m_e	REST ENERGY, MeV	LIFETIME, $\times 10^{-23}$ SEC	TOTAL ANGULAR MOMENTUM, $\times \hbar$	MOST PROBABLE DECAY[a]
Ξ^0	2,994	1,530	8.6	3/2	$\Xi + \pi$
Σ^-	3,972	2,030	0.50	7/2	$\Lambda + \pi$
Σ^+	3,464	1,770	0.63	5/2	$N + \overline{K}$
Σ	2,710	1,385	1.6	3/2	$\Lambda + \pi$
Λ	4,109	2,100	0.43	7/2	$N + \overline{K}$
Λ	3,581	1,830	0.79	5/2	$\Sigma + \pi$
Λ	3,552	1,815	0.81	5/2	$N + \overline{K}$
Λ	3,307	1,690	1.3	3/2	$\Sigma + \pi$
Λ	3,268	1,670	3.3	1/2	$N + \overline{K}$
Λ	2,974	1,520	3.8	3/2	$N + \overline{K}$
Λ	2,749	1,405	1.2	1/2	$\Sigma + \pi$
Δ	3,757	1,920	0.27	7/2	$N + \pi$
Δ	3,209	1,640	0.33	1/2	$N + \pi$
Δ	2,418	1,236	0.50	3/2	$N + \pi$
N	4,288	2,190	0.24	7/2	$N + \pi$
N	3,346	1,710	0.20	1/2	$N + \pi$
N	3,303	1,688	0.46	5/2	$N + \pi$
N	3,287	1,680	0.35	5/2	$N + \pi$
N	3,033	1,550	0.46	1/2	$N + \eta$
N	2,984	1,525	0.52	3/2	$N + \pi$
N	2,876	1,470	0.29	1/2	$N + \pi$

[a] N refers to a nucleon (proton or neutron).

This multiplicity of states is quite analogous to the several magnetic substates of a particle having a given total angular-momentum quantum number l (Section 7-4). Indeed, the analogy has led to the concept of total *isotopic spin* (or, sometimes, *isospin*) and associated isotopic spin states. For example, in analogy with the $2l + 1$ magnetic states of a particle with total angular-momentum quantum number l the two states of a nucleon (proton and neutron) may be represented by assigning to the nucleon a total isotopic spin quantum number $\frac{1}{2}$; then the proton may be described as having the isotopic spin "component" $+ \frac{1}{2}$ and the neutron the component $- \frac{1}{2}$. In a similar fashion a total isotopic spin may be assigned to each of the baryon groups. Each particle within a group is then specified by one component of the isotopic spin. The total isotopic spin number of each of the five baryon groups is shown in Table 11-10.

In like manner all mesons decaying by the weak or electromagnetic interaction may be grouped according to mass; see Table 11-11. The pion group

Table 11-10

MASS, m_e	ISOTOPIC SPIN	BARYON ELECTRIC CHARGE			ANTIBARYON ELECTRIC CHARGE		
		$-e$	0	$+e$	$-e$	0	$+e$
3,270	0	Ω^-					Ω^+
2,580	$\frac{1}{2}$	Ξ^-	Ξ^0			$\overline{\Xi}^0$	$\overline{\Xi}^+$
2,330	1	Σ^-	Σ^0	Σ^+	$\overline{\Sigma}^-$	$\overline{\Sigma}^0$	$\overline{\Sigma}^+$
2,180	0		Λ^0			$\overline{\Lambda}^0$	
1,840	$\frac{1}{2}$		n	p^+	p^-	$\overline{n}$	
		-3 -2 -1 0			0 $+1$ $+2$ $+3$		
		strangeness			strangeness		

contains three particles; thus, it has a total isotopic spin of 1; the kaon group has two particles, kay-plus and kay-zero, and is therefore assigned a total isotopic spin of $\frac{1}{2}$. We recall that the mesons are basically different from the baryons in that they have integral values of angular momentum (in units of $\hbar$), the baryons having half-integral values. Furthermore, the pi-zero is its own antiparticle; therefore, the center of the pion group is at the line separating the particles from the antiparticles.

To describe the many strange events that were being observed (and not being observed) in the creation of the hyperons and the K mesons, A. Pais in 1953 introduced a new quantum number, which is called the strangeness number, S. He then found that in any nuclear reaction the total strangeness was always conserved. One year later Gell-Mann and Nishijima showed that the strangeness concept was closely related to that of isotopic spin. Because it is somewhat simpler to use strangeness conservation, we shall

Table 11-11

MASS, m_e	ISOTOPIC SPIN	MESON ELECTRIC CHARGE			
		$+e$	0		$-e$
970	$\frac{1}{2}$	K^+	K^0	$\overline{K}^0$	K^-
270	1	π^+	π^0		π^-
		$+1$	0	-1	
		strangeness			

illustrate the restrictions placed on nuclear reactions in terms of strangeness rather than of isotopic spin.

A strangeness number is assigned to each of the five groups of the baryon family and to each of the two groups of the meson family, according to the amount by which its center of charge is displaced from the center of charge of the normal (nonstrange) group of each family. The normal (nonstrange) group of the baryon family obviously is the proton-neutron pair, whose center of charge is at $+\frac{1}{2}$. The next group in the baryon family is the singlet lambda-zero with center of charge 0. The lambda is displaced to the left $\frac{1}{2}$ charge unit from the proton-neutron group and thereby assigned a strangeness of $S_\lambda = 2 \times$ (charge displacement from normal group) $= 2(-\frac{1}{2}) = -1$ (the factor 2 is introduced merely to make the strangeness numbers integral rather than half-integral). The triplet sigma has the same center of charge as the lambda-zero, namely 0, and thus is assigned strangeness $S_\Sigma = -1$. The doublet xi has its center of charge at $-\frac{1}{2}$, and thus its strangeness is $S_\Xi = 2(-1) = -2$. Finally, the singlet omega has center of charge -1 and strangeness $S_\Omega = 2(-\frac{3}{2}) = -3$. The strangeness numbers of all baryon groups are zero or are negative; those of all antibaryon groups are zero or are positive.

In the two meson groups the pions, the normal (or nonstrange) group, with center of charge 0, are arbitrarily assigned strangeness 0. The kaons, with center of charge at $+\frac{1}{2}$, has strangeness $S_K = 2(+\frac{1}{2}) = +1$. The antikaons, with center of charge at $-\frac{1}{2}$, have strangeness $S_{\overline{K}} = 2(-\frac{1}{2}) = -1$.

With the strangeness conservation law for the strong interactions it becomes possible to organize many experimental observations. The following example illustrates this.

Example 11-2

(a) *Associated production.* When accelerators producing particles with energies measured in giga electron volts were built, it became possible to create many hyperons and kaons. Some of the interactions that were expected on the basis of all other conservation laws were not found. For example, the reaction

$$p + n \rightarrow p + \Lambda^0$$

might be expected to be found with sufficiently energetic incoming protons. Energy-mass, linear momentum, angular momentum, charge, and baryon number are all conserved in this process, yet the reaction was not found. We can see why when we consider the law of the conservation of strangeness:

$$p + n \rightarrow p + \Lambda^0$$
strangeness: $0 + 0 \rightarrow 0 - 1$

The total incoming strangeness is zero; the total outgoing strangeness is -1. Similarly, reactions involving the creation of kay-plus mesons alone did not occur.

One possible reaction might have been

$$p + p \rightarrow p + n + K^+$$

Although allowed on the basis of the previously known conservation laws, the reaction does not occur. Again, the explanation is that it violates strangeness conservation:

$$p + p \rightarrow p + n + K^+$$
strangeness: $\quad 0 + 0 \rightarrow 0 + 0 + 1$

Since nuclear collisions are usually produced by accelerating zero-strangeness particles incident on zero-strangeness targets, the total strangeness going into the interaction is zero. This requires that more than one strange particle be produced in the reaction; Pais called this *associated production*. An example of associated production shown in Figure 11-10 is

$$p + p \rightarrow \quad \Lambda^0 + K^0 + p + \pi^+$$
strangeness: $\quad 0 + 0 \rightarrow -1 \ + 1 \ + 0 + 0$

Here two strange particles of opposite strangeness, the lambda-zero with $S = -1$ and the kay-zero with $S = +1$, are produced in the interaction. Strangeness is conserved.

After their production, the lambda-zero and kay-zero separate and become freely moving particles. According to all other conservation laws, both these particles can decay into other particles. For example, one might suppose the lambda-zero to decay as follows:

$$\Lambda^0 \rightarrow p + \pi^-$$

This process, however, does not conserve strangeness,

$$\Lambda^0 \rightarrow p + \pi^-$$
$$-1 \ \rightarrow 0 + 0$$

and therefore is not expected to occur. If strangeness were conserved in *all* interactions, the lambda-zero would be a completely stable particle. As Figure 11-10 shows, it *does* decay into a proton and negative pion, but in the relatively long time corresponding to the weak interaction.

It appears, then, that strangeness conservation applies in some interactions but is violated in others. This has been confirmed by many experiments. In strong and electromagnetic interactions strangeness is always conserved; in weak interactions it is not.

(b) *Ratio of K^- to K^+ production.* It is observed that a larger number of kay-plus mesons than of kay-minus mesons are created when high-energy accelerators produce protons that strike suitable targets. For example, two possible reactions producing kay-plus mesons when sufficiently energetic protons strike a proton target are

$$p + p \rightarrow p + \Lambda^0 + K^+$$
$$p + p \rightarrow p + \Sigma^0 + K^+$$

In both reactions the change ΔS in strangeness is zero. On the other hand, producing kay-minus mesons requires at least four outgoing particles. For example,

$$p + p \rightarrow p + p + K^+ + K^-$$

This reaction also conserves strangeness. For this second reaction to occur, however, bombarding protons of higher kinetic energy are necessary, and thus kay-minus production has a higher threshold energy than kay-plus production. At a given energy there is a smaller probability of producing kay-minus than kay-plus mesons.

The conservation of strangeness prevents the hyperons and kaons from decaying in nuclear times. They must, therefore, decay through the much longer weak interaction time, for which total strangeness may change. There is a general rule, found from experiment, for the change in strangeness number: in weak-interaction decays the change in strangeness is zero or one unit.

$$\text{strong or electromagnetic interaction:} \quad \Delta S = 0$$
$$\text{weak interaction:} \quad \Delta S = 0 \text{ or } \pm 1$$

For example, the kay-minus mesons decays (Figure 11-8a) as follows:

$$\mathrm{K}^- \to \pi^- + \pi^0$$
$$\text{strangeness:} \quad -1 \ \to 0 \ + 0$$
$$\Delta S = +1$$

In Figure 11-9 the anti-lambda-zero decays as follows:

$$\overline{\Lambda^0} \to \mathrm{p} + \pi^-$$
$$\text{strangeness:} \quad +1 \ \to 0 + 0$$
$$\Delta S = -1$$

An example of a weak-interaction decay with $\Delta S = 0$ is the decay of the pion:

$$\pi^- \to \mu^- + \overline{\nu}_\mu$$
$$\text{strangeness:} \quad 0 \ \to 0 \ + 0$$
$$\Delta S = 0$$

Table 11-12 summarizes all the observed elementary particles, except the resonance particles, and their most important properties.

The following conservation laws hold for *any* of the fundamental interactions:

(1) Conservation of baryons
(2) Conservation of leptons (the conservation of electrons and their associated neutrinos and the conservation of muons and their associated neutrinos hold separately)
(3) Conservation of angular momentum
(4) Conservation of charge
(5) Conservation of mass-energy

Table 11-12

Name	Particle	Antiparticle[a]	Strangeness	Spin $\times \hbar$	Elec. chge. e	Rest mass m_e	Rest energy MeV	Mean life, sec	Principal decay mode
BARYON FAMILY									
Hyperons:									
omega	Ω^-	$\bar{\Omega}^+$	-3	$\frac{1}{2}$	-1	3,272	1,672	1.1×10^{-10}	$\Xi^0 + \pi^-$, or $\Xi^- + \pi^0$
xi	Ξ^-	$\bar{\Xi}^+$	-2	$\frac{1}{2}$	-1	2,586	1,321	1.7×10^{-10}	$\Lambda^0 + \pi^-$
	Ξ^0	$\bar{\Xi}^0$	-2	$\frac{1}{2}$	0	2,573	1,315	2.9×10^{-10}	$\Lambda^0 + \pi^0$
sigma	Σ^-	$\bar{\Sigma}^+$	-1	$\frac{1}{2}$	-1	2,343	1,197	1.7×10^{-10}	$n + \pi^-$
	Σ^0	$\bar{\Sigma}^0$	-1	$\frac{1}{2}$	0	2,334	1,192	$<10^{-14}$	$\Lambda^0 + \gamma$
	Σ^+	$\bar{\Sigma}^-$	-1	$\frac{1}{2}$	$+1$	2,327	1,190	0.81×10^{-10}	$p + \pi^0$, or $n + \pi^+$
lambda	Λ^0	$\bar{\Lambda}^0$	-1	$\frac{1}{2}$	0	2,183	1,115	2.5×10^{-10}	$p + \pi^-$, or $n + \pi^0$
Nucleons:									
neutron	n	$\bar{n}$	0	$\frac{1}{2}$	0	1,839	939.5	1.0×10^{3}	$p + e^- + \bar{\nu}_e$
proton	p^+	p^-	0	$\frac{1}{2}$	$+1$	1,836	938.3	∞	
MESON FAMILY									
kaon	K^0	$\bar{K}^0$	$+1$	0	0	974	498	0.87×10^{-10}	$\pi^+ + \pi^-$
								0.53×10^{-8}	$\pi^+ + e^- + \bar{\nu}_e$
	K^+	K^-	$+1$	0	$+1$	966	494	1.2×10^{-8}	$\mu^+ + \nu_\mu$
pion	π^+	π^-	0	0	$+1$	273	140	2.6×10^{-8}	$\mu^+ + \nu_\mu$
	π^-	π^+	0	0	-1	273	140	2.6×10^{-8}	$\mu^- + \bar{\nu}_\mu$
	π^0	π^0 (self)	0	0	0	264	135	1.8×10^{-16}	$\gamma + \gamma$
LEPTON FAMILY									
muon	μ^-	μ^+	0	$\frac{1}{2}$	-1	207	106	2.2×10^{-6}	$e^- + \bar{\nu}_e + \nu_\mu$
electron	e^-	e^+	0	$\frac{1}{2}$	-1	1	0.51	∞	
μ-neutrino	ν_μ	$\bar{\nu}_\mu$	0	$\frac{1}{2}$	0	0	0	∞	
e-neutrino	ν_e	$\bar{\nu}_e$	0	$\frac{1}{2}$	0	0	0	∞	
PHOTON	γ	γ (self)	0	1	0	0	0	∞	

[a] The antiparticle has the same rest mass, angular momentum, and lifetime as the particle. Its baryon number, lepton number, strangeness number and electric charge are of opposite sign to that of the particle.

(6) Conservation of linear momentum

The following conservation laws hold strictly for the strong and the electromagnetic interactions:

(7) Conservation of strangeness

(8) Conservation of parity

Although both strangeness and parity conservations are violated in the weak interactions, there are some selection rules for these violations. For example, one finds that in any weak interaction the total strangeness number changes according to

$$\Delta S = 0 \qquad \text{or} \qquad \pm 1$$

This selection rule explains why the xi-particle does not decay directly into a nucleon but, rather, cascades downward in two separate decay events.

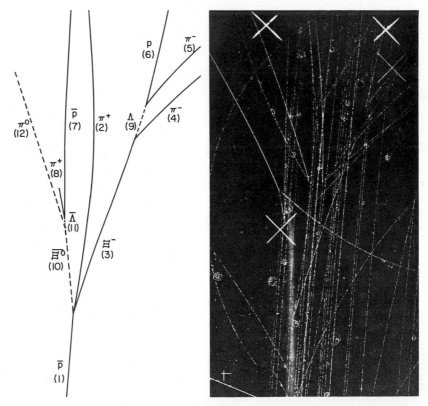

Figure 11-14. A liquid hydrogen bubble chamber photograph and sketch of a 2.8 GeV antiproton colliding with a stationary proton to produce a hyperon-antihyperon pair and a charged pion. Subsequent decays of the hyperons can also be seen on the photograph. (Courtesy of Brookhaven National Laboratory.)

This is illustrated by the decays of two xi-particles in Figure 11-14. For example, the decay of the xi-minus takes place in two steps:

$$\Xi^- \to \Lambda^0 + \pi^- \qquad \text{with} \quad \Delta S = +1$$

$$\Lambda^0 \to p + \pi^- \qquad \text{with} \quad \Delta S = +1$$

It is for this reason that the xi-particles are commonly referred to as cascade particles. An even more dramatic example of a cascade appears in the decay of the omega-minus, which has strangeness -3 (see Figure 11-11). First, it decays to a lambda-zero and a kay-minus:

$$\Omega^- \to \ \Lambda^0 + \ K^-$$

$$\text{strangeness:} \ -3 \to -1 + -1 \qquad \text{with} \quad \Delta S = +1$$

This is followed by the decays of the lambda-zero and the kay-minus:

$$\Lambda^0 \to p + \pi^-$$

$$\text{strangeness:} \ -1 \to 0 + 0 \qquad \text{with} \ \Delta S = +1$$

and possibly
$$K^- \to \mu^- + \overline{\nu_\mu}$$

$$\text{strangeness:} \ -1 \to 0 \ + \ 0 \qquad \text{with} \ \Delta S = +1$$

The kay-minus does not decay in the region of the photograph.

BIBLIOGRAPHY

FILM *Strangeness Minus Three*. New York: P. M. Roeback and Company, New York, BBC-TV production. This film, capturing the spirit of physics in discovery, is concerned with the prediction and later experimental finding of the omega-minus particle with strangeness of -3. Narrated by R. P. Feynman.

Ford, K., *The World of Elementary Particles*. New York: Blaisdell Publishing Company, 1963. A presentation of the concepts and ideas of elementary-particle physics for the general reader. Chapter 7 describes the fundamental interactions among elementary particles in terms of space-time diagrams.

Frisch, D. H., and A. M. Thorndike, *Elementary Particles*. Princeton, New Jersey: D. Van Nostrand Company, Inc., 1964. This paperback, written for the general physics student, gives an elementary account of the basic experiments and theoretical ideas of elementary-particle physics.

Swartz, C., *The Fundamental Particles*. Reading, Massachusetts; Addison-Wesley Publishing Co., Inc., 1965. Chapter 6 discusses the important conservation laws in particle interactions: Chapter 7 characterizes the particles according to their properties.

PROBLEMS

11-1   Draw graphs on a space-time diagram for the following processes: (a) an electron and positron attract one another and finally are annihilated, and photons are produced; (b) an antiproton and proton attract one another and finally are annihilated, and pions are produced.

11-2   Figure 11-15 shows four space-time graphs. (a) Describe the sequence of events (reading from past to future) for each graph. (b) Now imagine each graph to be rotated 90° relative to the space-time axes (the photon lines adjusted to the correct angle with respect to the vertical), and again describe the sequence of events for each graph.

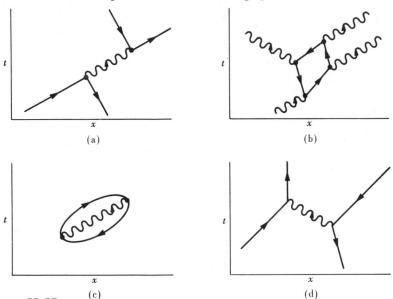

(a)   (b)

(c)   (d)

Figure 11-15

11-3   Consider a proton at rest. If the proton transforms spontaneously into a neutron and pi-plus, (a) what is the change ΔE in the energy (in MeV) of the system, and (b) over what time interval Δt can this energy be "borrowed"? (c) Show this on a space-time diagram.

11-4   Consider a neutron at rest. If the neutron transforms spontaneously into a proton and a kaon-minus, (a) what is the change ΔE in energy (in MeV) of the system, and (b) over what time interval Δt can this energy be borrowed? (c) Show this on a space-time diagram.

11-5   Wave-mechanical calculations, excluding considerations of quantum field theory, show that for a free hydrogen atom the $2^2S_{1/2}$ and $2^2P_{1/2}$ states are degenerate (see Figure 7-8). The two states, although alike in energy, differ in angular momentum and in the spatial distribution of the wave functions. In actuality these states of hydrogen (and other analogous states of hydrogen) are *not* degenerate: experiment shows they differ slightly in energy (the so-called *Lamb shift*), the difference corresponding to the energy of a photon of microwave radiation. Calculations of the energy difference by means of electromagnetic-field theory are in complete accord with observation, thereby giving a stringent proof of field-theory calculations. Show qualitatively that one expects the $2^2S_{1/2}$ and $2^2P_{1/2}$ states of hydrogen to differ in energy by virtue of the creation, annihilation, and exchange of virtual photons between the electrically charged nucleus and the electron. (*Hint:* Virtual photons may spontaneously be annihilated and so produce an electron-positron pair, and these virtual particles may interact with the atomic electron.)

11-6   One method of measuring the mass difference between the pi-minus and the pi-zero is to observe the capture of low-energy pi-minus mesons by protons. One possible reaction is $\pi^- + p \rightarrow n + \pi^0$, where both incident particles are initially at rest. The neutron leaves the reaction with a kinetic energy 0.6 MeV. (a) Using the known masses of the proton and neutron (Table 11-12) and approximating the pion mass as 1/7 of the nucleon mass, determine the mass difference between the pi-minus and pi-zero, and compare it with the data of Table 11-12.

11-7   A 50 MeV pi-zero quickly decays into two photons. If the photons move off in directions parallel and antiparallel to the direction of motion of the pion, what will be the energy of each photon, as observed in the laboratory frame of reference?

11-8 *   A free, negatively charged pion, initially at rest, can decay directly into an electron and neutrino, or it can decay to a muon and neutrino and the muon can then decay to an electron and two neutrinos (see Tables 11-2 and 11-5). (a) Calculate the kinetic energy of the electron in the direct decay of the pi-minus. (b) What is the maximum kinetic energy an electron can have in the two-step decay of the pi-minus?

11-9   In Figure 11-7 the track of the pi-plus is much longer than that of the mu-plus. Thus, the pi-plus lives longer than the mu-plus. Why does this not contradict the fact that the mean lifetime of a pi-plus is much shorter than that of a mu-plus (see Table 11-12)?

11-10   Compare the track lengths of the kay-zero and lambda-zero in Figure 11-10 and estimate the ratio of their respective lifetimes. How does this compare with the ratio of the mean lifetimes of these two particles?

11-11   For a kay-plus initially at rest, what is the spread in energy of the mu-plus mesons in the decay $K^+ \rightarrow \mu^+ + \nu$?

11-12 *   (a) Sketch the kinetic-energy distributions of pi-plus mesons produced when kay-plus mesons initially at rest, decay by the mode $K^+ \rightarrow \pi^+ + \pi^0$ and when they decay by the mode $K^+ \rightarrow \pi^+ + \pi^- + \pi^+$. (b) What is the spread in energies (in MeV) of the pi-plus mesons in each of these decay modes?

11-13 *   What experimental evidence shows that the sigma-minus is not the antiparticle of the sigma-plus, that is, that the sigma-minus and anti-sigma-minus (Σ^- and $\overline{\Sigma^-}$) are distinct elementary particles?

11-14   If you were given a beam of sigma-zero particles (Σ^0) and a second beam of anti-sigma-zero ($\overline{\Sigma^0}$) of particles, how could you determine which beam contained the sigma-zeros?

11-15 Given a beam of kay-zero particles and a beam of anti-kay-zero particles, how could you identify the kay-zero beam?

11-16 * A beam of kay-minus mesons strike a stationary proton target. What is the threshold energy for the production of omega-minus particles?

11-17 A beam of 6.0 GeV protons strikes a stationary target of protons. State which of the following reactions cannot occur and what conservation law precludes the reaction in each situation:

(a) $p + p \rightarrow \Sigma^+ + K^+$

(b) $p + p \rightarrow \Sigma^+ + \Sigma^+$

(c) $p + p \rightarrow \Sigma^+ + p + K^+$

(d) $p + p \rightarrow n + \Lambda^0 + K^+ + \pi^+$

(e) $p + p \rightarrow \Xi^+ + p + n + n + \overline{K^0} + \overline{K^0}$

11-18 (a) Show that, if a particle has electric charge q (in units of the elementary charge e), baryon number B, isotopic spin component T, and strangeness number S, the following relation applies: $S = 2(q - B/2 - T)$. (b) What is the isotopic spin component T of the sigma-minus, sigma-zero, and sigma-plus?

11-19 Consider an omega-minus particle decaying in a vacuum. (a) Write down one possible set of decay equations by which the particle might decay to stable particles. (b) Identify the kind and number of stable particles.

11-20 Table 11-10 lists all observed baryons whose lifetimes are longer than the time of a strong interaction in five groups, the baryons in each group having the same strangeness number. Two singlet groups, the lamba-zero and the omega-minus, are represented. (a) Speculate about the existence of a third singlet having $+1$ charge, and give its strangeness number and possible modes of decay. (b) How would this particle be distinguished from the antiparticle of the omega-minus?

TWELVE

MOLECULAR AND SOLID-STATE PHYSICS

Some simpler aspects of atomic and nuclear structure can be understood on the basis of a few fundamental principles of the quantum theory, often without recourse to the formal mathematical procedures of wave mechanics. This happy situation does not, however, obtain when one deals with more complicated systems, such as molecules or solids, which consist of many interacting particles. These many-body systems can be treated adequately only by a thoroughgoing wave-mechanical analysis combined with the statistical methods of handling very large numbers of particles. For this reason our discussion of molecular structure and the physics of the solid state will be of a somewhat qualitative nature, and certain results of wave mechanics and statistical mechanics will be given without detailed proof. We shall illustrate the nature of some fundamental problems in molecular and solid-state physics with a few simple examples: molecular binding, rotation, and vibration, the classical and quantum distribution laws, lasers, the quantum theory of specific heats of gases and solids, blackbody radiation, the free-electron theory of metals, and the properties of conductors, semiconductors, and insulators.

12-1 Molecular binding Consider the ways in which a simple diatomic molecule, consisting of two atoms held together by an attractive force, may be bound. We know that if the molecule is to exist as a stable bound system, the energy of the two atoms when close together must be *less* than the energy of the two atoms when separated by a great distance, and to show that molecular binding occurs we have merely to establish that the total energy of the atoms is reduced when they are brought sufficiently close together.

The two important ways in which molecules are bound are by *ionic*, or *heteropolar*, *binding* and by *covalent*, or *homopolar*, *binding*. An example of a molecule bound almost completely by ionic binding is sodium chloride, $NaCl$; an example of covalent binding is the hydrogen molecule, H_2.

IONIC BINDING We wish to show that $NaCl$ can exist as a stable molecule, the total energy of the system being less than the total energy of the two atoms separated. The element sodium, $_{11}Na$, is in the alkali-metal group, the first column of the periodic table (see Table 7-3); as such, it has one electron outside a closed subshell. Its electron configuration in the ground state is $1s^2 2s^2 2p^6 3s^1$. The single $3s$ electron is relatively weakly bound to the atom; it can be removed by adding 5.1 eV, thereby ionizing the atom and leaving it with a net electric charge of $+1e$. The alkali metals are said to be *electropositive*, because they are easily ionized to form positive ions, with a resulting electron configuration consisting of closed electron shells, like those of the inert gases.

The element chlorine, $_{17}Cl$, is a halogen element, falling in the seventh column of the periodic table; all elements in this column lack one electron of completing a closed p subshell. The electron configuration of chlorine in the ground state is $1s^2 2s^2 2p^6 3s^2 3p^5$. The neutral chlorine atom lacks one electron of filling a tightly bound, complete $3p$ subshell and, indeed, its energy is *lowered* by 3.8 eV when an electron is added to it, forming a negative ion of charge $-1e$. The halogen elements are said to be *electronegative*, and the *electron affinity energy* of $_{17}Cl$ is 3.8 eV. It follows that 3.8 eV of energy must be added to the Cl^- ion to remove the last electron, leaving the neutral atom.

Suppose that one begins with a neutral sodium atom and a neutral chlorine atom, infinitely separated. To remove one electron from Na, thereby forming Na^+, costs 5.1 eV, but when this electron is imagined to be transferred to Cl, thereby forming Cl^-, 3.8 eV of this energy is repaid; overall, the energy required is only $5.1 - 3.8 = 1.3$ eV; the energy differences are shown in Figure 12-1. We now have a positive ion and a negative ion, still separated. These ions will attract one another by the Coulomb electrostatic force, the Coulomb potential energy being $-ke^2/r$, where r is the distance between the centers of the two ions. When the sodium and chlorine

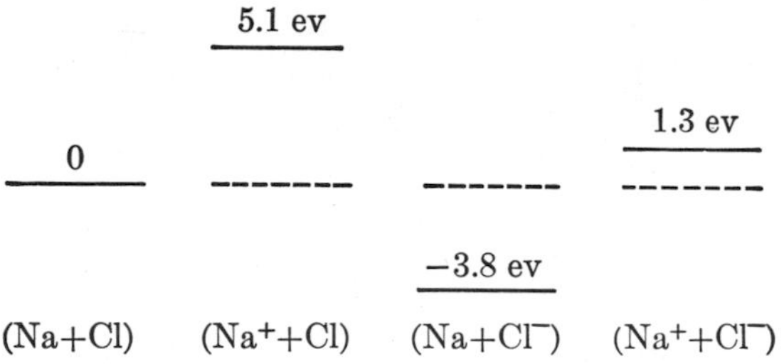

5.1 ev
_____

1.3 ev
_____

0
_____   - - - - - -   - - - - - -   - - - - - -

−3.8 ev
_____

(Na+Cl)   (Na$^+$+Cl)   (Na+Cl$^-$)   (Na$^+$+Cl$^-$)

Figure 12-1. Energy differences of sodium and chlorine atoms and ions.

ions are brought together, the total energy of the system decreases, since the force is attractive and the potential energy is negative. If r is chosen as, say, 4.0 Å, which is larger than the sum of the radii of the closed sub-shells of the respective ions, the Coulomb energy is easily found to be −1.8 eV. Thus, when the ions are separated by 4.0 Å, the total energy, $1.3 − 1.8 = −0.5$ eV, is clearly less than that of a sodium atom and chlorine atom infinitely separated. The net cost of forming two ions is more than repaid by the electrostatic attraction.

We have seen that sodium and chlorine atoms will attract one another when their nuclei are separated by less than about 4 Å. When the separation between the nuclei is decreased still further, a repulsive force begins to act between the ions. The ions repel one another when the electron clouds of the two ions, each of which may be regarded as spherical, begin to overlap. The Pauli exclusion principle governs the number of electrons that can be accommodated in any given atomic electron shell. Both ions have their full electron quotas, and further electrons can be accommodated only if they occupy relatively high energy states. Consequently, as the interatomic distance is reduced, the electron shells are prevented from overlapping by the Pauli exclusion principle. The electrons must go to higher available states, and the total energy of the molecule is then increased. Because the atoms attract one another at large distances but repel one another at sufficiently small distances, there exists an equilibrium interatomic separation distance r_0 at which the total potential energy of the system is a minimum, as shown in Figure 12-2.

The *dissociation energy* of a molecule is its binding energy, the energy that must be added to it in its lowest energy state to separate it into its component atoms. The molecule NaCl has a dissociation energy of 4.24 eV, and an equilibrium separation distance r_0 of 2.36 Å. Since the molecule is held together by ionic binding, the end containing the Na nucleus represents a region of positive electric charge, and the end containing the Cl nucleus represents a region of negative electric charge. Thus, an ionic molecule is a *polar molecule*, with a permanent *electric dipole moment*. For this reason, ionic binding is known as *heteropolar binding*.

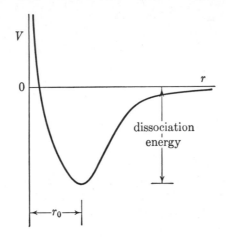

Figure 12-2. Molecular potential as a function of interatomic distance.

COVALENT BINDING   A simple example of covalent binding is found in the hydrogen molecule, H_2. Before discussing this molecule, however, we shall first consider a still simpler system, the hydrogen molecule ion, H_2^+. We can imagine it as being formed when a neutral hydrogen atom (an electron bound to a proton) is brought together with an ionized hydrogen atom (a bare proton). When the protons are far apart, the electron will be bound to the one proton alone, but when the protons are separated by a distance of approximately 1 Å, the electron can be imagined to jump from one proton to the other, making, as it were, orbits about one or the other of the protons or about both.

Using wave mechanics it is possible to solve in detail for the wave function ψ of the single electron; the probability of the electron's being at any position is proportional to ψ^2. The results are shown in Figure 12-3. We see that there is a relatively high probability of the single electron's being in the region between the two nuclei compared with that of its being at either "end" of the molecule. When it is between the protons, the electron attracts both protons by the Coulomb electrostatic force; when it is at

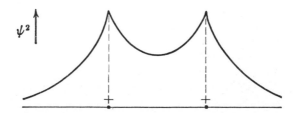

Figure 12-3. Quantum-mechanical probability for finding the electron in the hydrogen molecule ion, H_2^+.

some exterior location, the protons are less strongly attracted to the electron, and their mutual repulsion becomes more important. Because the mutual repulsive force between the two nuclei increases as r (their separation) decreases, the H_2^+ molecule has a minimum in the potential energy. It is found that the equilibrium separation is $r_0 = 1.06$ Å, and the dissociation energy is 2.65 eV.

Now consider the hydrogen molecule, H_2, formed when two neutral hydrogen atoms are brought close together. The binding together of two neutral, identical atoms is completely inexplicable in classical terms. The binding of the hydrogen molecule can be understood only on the basis of wave mechanics and the Pauli exclusion principle. When the two hydrogen atoms are separated by a distance that is large compared with the size of the first Bohr orbit (0.5 Å), each electron is clearly identified with its own parent nucleus, but when they are separated by a distance comparable to the size of either atom, there is, one must recognize, absolutely no way of distinguishing between the two electrons, and it is no longer possible to associate one electron with one particular nucleus.

There are, however, two distinct ways in which the two hydrogen atoms can be brought together: with the two electron spins aligned in the same direction, or with the electron spins antialigned, or in opposite directions. Wave mechanics shows that, when the hydrogen atoms are brought together, the total energy of the system increases when the electron spins are aligned but decreases when they are antialigned, as shown in Figure 12-4. This difference in energy arises from the operation of the Pauli exclusion principle.

The force binding the (two-electron) neutral hydrogen molecule, which is not present in the (one-electron) hydrogen molecule ion, is associated

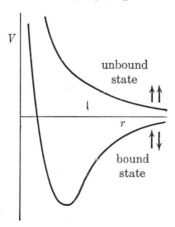

Figure 12-4. Potential between two hydrogen atoms with aligned and anti-aligned spins.

with the so-called exchange energy. The occurrence of *electron exchange* is a strictly wave-mechanical phenomenon, for which there is no exact classical analogue. Nevertheless, one can visualize the exchange of two identical, indistinguishable electrons through the behavior of their spins. We have noted that the hydrogen molecule is bound, with a sharing of the two electrons by the two nuclei, only when the electrons have their spins antialigned, but it is possible for this bound state to persist even when the two electrons exchange their spin orientations; that is, if the electron with spin up becomes an electron with spin down, and the electron with spin originally down simultaneously becomes an electron with spin up. Indeed, this exchange of electron spins is the principal contribution to the binding of the molecule. Inasmuch as two antialigned electrons can both be found simultaneously in the region between the protons, the two electrons can exert attractive forces on both protons. Roughly speaking, the two nuclei of the hydrogen molecule share the two electrons so that each nucleus can, at least for a part of the time, have both electrons filling a closed shell about it.

Because of the exchange phenomenon the total energy of the two hydrogen atoms is reduced as the atoms approach one another with antialigned spins. Eventually, however, the mutual repulsion of the nuclei exceeds the binding due to exchange. Thus, a minimum energy exists, corresponding to the equilibrium configuration of the molecule. For the hydrogen molecule the equilibrium association is $r_0 = 0.74$ Å and the dissociation energy is 4.48 eV.

The chemical binding of two identical, nonpolar atoms is called *covalent binding*, inasmuch as it is the sharing of valence electrons that is basically responsible for the attractive force. A molecule such as H_2 has no permanent electric dipole moment and is said to be nonpolar. For this reason covalent binding is also referred to as *homopolar binding*.

A bound hydrogen molecule can exist with two atoms but not with three or more. The valence forces operating in covalent binding show *saturation*, in that the number of atoms that can be bound together is limited. The saturation of covalent chemical forces arises from the phenomenon of electron exchange.

We wish to show that it is impossible for the molecule H_3 to exist as a bound system. First consider, for simplicity, the forces acting between a neutral helium atom and a neutral hydrogen atom. When helium is in its ground state, the two electrons complete the $1s$ shell, the configuration being $1s^2$. The two electrons must, by the Pauli principle, have their spins antialigned ($\downarrow \uparrow$), the total spin of the atom being zero. Now suppose that a hydrogen atom (with electron spin $\frac{1}{2}$) approaches a helium atom (with total electron spin 0). If there is to be chemical binding between the two atoms it must arise from the exchange of electron spins. There are only two possible ways in which the single electron (↑) in the hydrogen atom can interact with the helium atom: by exchanging spins with one electron (↑) or with the other (↓). Suppose that the hydrogen electron (↑) exchanges spins with the (↑) helium electron. The two spins are then aligned (↑ ↑), and the exchange force between the atoms is, as in the case of the hydrogen molecule, repulsive. Suppose now that the hydrogen electron (↑) exchanges spins with the (↓) helium electron; this would result in a binding between the two atoms, except that the electron spins of the helium atom would then be aligned (↑ ↑), which is prohibited by the Pauli exclusion principle. Thus, this exchange is impossible. Therefore, the only possible exchange force between a hydrogen atom and a helium atom is repulsive, and the molecule HHe does not exist.

We can easily extend this argument to the interaction between a hydrogen molecule, H_2, and a hydrogen atom, H_1. The molecule H_2, like the He atom, has its electron spins antialigned. The only possible electron exchange between H_2 and H_1 leads to a repulsive force, and the chemical homopolar bond between hydrogen atoms is saturated with two electrons. The molecule H_3 is not formed. The homopolar binding of atoms can be extended to more complicated structures; it is found that the binding in all organic molecules is of this type. Most inorganic molecules are, however, bound by a mixture of both ionic and covalent binding, one or the other type typically dominating.

A third type of force, the only one operating in the interaction between closed-shell atoms of inert gases, is the *Van der Waals force*. This force is responsible for the cohesion in the liquid and solid state of rare gases. When two such atoms approach one another, the "center" of the negative charge is displaced from the positive nucleus. The atoms then weakly interact through the electric dipoles induced by the charge displacement.

The ionic and homopolar binding processes can hold atoms together to form crystalline solids. An example of an ionic crystal is NaCl (shown in Figure 5-1), an alkali halide, in which the Na^+ and Cl^- ions are found alternately on the corners of a cubic lattice. An example of a covalent crystal is diamond (carbon, C), where there are carbon nuclei at the center and corners of a tetrahedron in the elementary cell structure. A third type of crystalline binding, for which there is no counterpart in molecules, is metallic binding. This type of binding, arising from the Coulomb interaction between the fixed positive ions and the free electrons of the metal, is of wave-mechanical origin.

12-2 Molecular rotation and vibration The atoms of a diatomic molecule can rotate about the molecule's center of mass and vibrate along the interatomic axis. The energies both of molecular rotation and of vibration are quantized, and this leads to distinctive molecular rotational and vibrational spectra. Moreover, the quantization of rotational and vibrational energy relates importantly to the specific heats of gases and solids.

MOLECULAR ROTATION   The angular momentum L associated with the orbital motion of an atomic electron is quantized according to the rule

[7-1] $$L = \sqrt{l(l + 1)}\hbar$$

where l is the orbital angular momentum quantum number with possible values $0, 1, 2, \ldots, n - 1$. Similarly, the angular momentum L_r associated with the rotational of a molecule as a whole, in the fashion of a rigid dumbbell, about an axis passing through the molecule's center of mass, is quantized according to the rule

$$\boxed{L_r = \sqrt{J(J + 1)}\hbar}$$ [12-1]

where the rotational quantum number J has the possible integral values $J = 0, 1, 2, \ldots$.

The quantization of molecular rotational angular momentum implies a quantization of the molecule's energy of rotation, inasmuch as the kinetic energy E_k of any rotating object with angular velocity ω, moment of inertia I, and angular momentum $L = I\omega$, all relative to the same rotation axis, is given by†

$$E_k = \tfrac{1}{2}I\omega^2 = (I\omega)^2/2I = L^2/2I$$

Substituting Equation 12-1 in the relation above yields

$$\boxed{E_r = J(J + 1)\hbar^2/2I}$$ [12-2]

The rotational kinetic energy is quantized, the possible values of E_r being $0, 2, 6, 12, \ldots$ times $\hbar^2/2I$, a constant for a given rigid rotator. An energy-level diagram of pure rotation is shown in Figure 12-5. Because the nuclear masses of a diatomic molecule are always large compared with the masses of atomic electrons, the only appreciable molecular moment of inertia is about an axis at right angles to the interatomic axis joining the two nuclei. For such an axis of rotation passing through the molecule's center of mass, as shown in Figure 12-6, the moment of inertia I is given by‡

$$I = \sum m_i r_i^2 = m_1 r_1^2 + m_2 r_2^2$$ [12-3]

where r_1 and r_2 are the respective distances of the atomic masses m_1 and m_2 from the center of mass. The masses and distances are related through

---

† See Equation 14-13, Weidner and Sells, *E. C. P.*
‡ See Equation 14-5, Weidner and Sells, *E. C. P.*

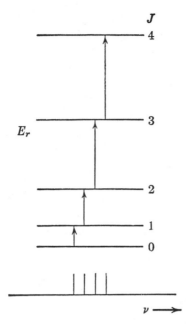

Figure 12-5. Rotational energy-level diagram of a diatomic molecule, together with the pure rotational spectrum.

the definition of center of mass† by $m_1r_1 = m_2r_2$. Equation 12-3 can also be written in the form

$$I = [m_1m_2/(m_1 + m_2)](r_1 + r_2)^2 \qquad [12\text{-}4]$$

We recognize the quantity within the brackets to be the molecule's reduced mass μ (see Problem 6-37) and $r_1 + r_2$ to be the separation distance r_0 between the nuclei of the two atoms. Therefore, the molecular moment of inertia may be written more simply as

$$I = \mu r_0^2 \qquad [12\text{-}5]$$

Transitions between the quantized molecular rotational energy states of a polar molecule give rise to the molecule's *pure rotational spectrum*. The selection rule governing allowed transitions is $J = \pm 1$. The photon frequencies ν are found, through the general quantum relation $h\nu = \Delta E$ and Equation 12-2, to be given by $\nu = (\hbar/2\pi I)(J + 1)$, where J is the rotational quantum number of the lower energy state. Thus, the pure rotational spectrum consists, as shown in Figure 12-5, of equally spaced lines, which typically are found in the far infrared or microwave regions of the electromagnetic spectrum. Observation of the frequencies of the

† See Equation 8-18, Weidner and Sells, *E. C. P.*

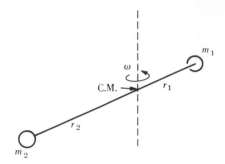

Figure 12-6. A rotating diatomic molecule.

pure rotational spectra permits the moment of inertia I and, therefore, the interatomic separation distance $r_0 = (I/\mu)^{1/2}$ to be computed. Poly-atomic spectra are more complicated, since the molecules are characterized by more than one nonzero molecular moment of inertia.

MOLECULAR VIBRATION   A simple harmonic oscillator is characterized by a potential energy of

$$E_p = \tfrac{1}{2}kx^2 \qquad [12\text{-}6]$$

where x is the displacement from the equilibrium position and k is a measure of the stiffness with which the particle is bound to its surroundings. Classically, for a particle of mass m subject to a restoring force $F = -kx$ the natural frequency of oscillation f is given by

$$f = (1/2\pi)\sqrt{k/m} \qquad [12\text{-}7]$$

So long as the curve of potential energy versus displacement is strictly parabolic, $E_p \propto x^2$, the oscillation frequency f is independent of the oscilla-tion amplitude and depends only on the inertia m and elasticity k of the oscillator.

The problem of the quantum-mechanical simple harmonic oscillator, that of finding the permitted wave functions and quantized energies, is solved by using the potential-energy function given in Equation 12-6 in the Schrödinger wave equation. The results for the allowed vibrational energies E_v (see Figure 5-26b and Problem 5-46) are as follows:

$$\boxed{E_v = (v + \tfrac{1}{2})\hbar \sqrt{k/m} = (v + \tfrac{1}{2})hf} \qquad [12\text{-}8]$$

where the vibrational quantum number v takes on the integral values $v = 0, 1, 2, \ldots.$

An energy-level diagram of a quantum simple harmonic oscillator is shown in Figure 12-7. The energies are equally spaced, with a separation of hf between adjacent levels. Note especially that the energy of the lowest

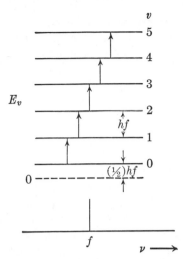

Figure 12-7. Vibrational energy-level diagram of a diatomic molecule, together with the vibrational spectrum.

vibrational level, that of $v = 0$, is not zero but $E_0 = \frac{1}{2}hf$. This corresponds to the so-called *zero-point vibration*. In quantum mechanics, an oscillator is never at rest, zero-point vibration taking place even in the ground state; in classical mechanics the particle can, of course, be imagined to have zero total energy and be exactly at rest. The occurrence of zero-point vibration is a particularly striking manifestation of the uncertainty principle, which requires that the product of the uncertainties in a particle's momentum and in its associated position coordinate be of the order of h, or $\Delta p_x \Delta x \approx h$. For, if the particle of an oscillator were to be exactly at rest, with $\Delta p_x = 0$, then the uncertainty in the particle's position would be infinite; conversely, if the particle were localized within a finite region of space, its momentum and, hence, energy could not be zero.

The atoms of a diatomic molecule undergo simple harmonic motion along the interatomic axis joining them. As shown in Figure 12-2, the interatomic potential energy is nearly parabolic in the vicinity of the minimum, at which the equilibrium separation distance is r_0. At separation distances not greatly different from r_0 the potential energy of a diatomic molecule may be written approximately as

$$V = V_0 + \tfrac{1}{2}k(r - r_0)^2 \qquad\qquad [12\text{-}0]$$

which is the potential-energy function of a simple harmonic oscillator. Thus, the nuclei of the two atoms are subject to an attractive restoring force at $r > r_0$ and a repulsive restoring force at $r < r_0$. Each of the two atoms undergoes oscillations relative to the molecule's center of mass. The quantized energies of molecular vibration are thus given by Equation

12-8. We recognize, however, that since both atoms oscillate relative to the molecule's center of mass, the mass m appearing in Equations 12-7 and 12-8 must represent the molecule's reduced mass, $\mu = m_1 m_2 / (m_1 + m_2)$.

The allowed transitions for a polar molecule undergoing vibrations are those following the selection rule $\Delta v = \pm 1$; transitions are between adjacent energy levels. Thus, the photon frequency ν for transitions between vibrational levels is given by $h\nu = \Delta E_v = hf$, or

$$\nu = f \qquad [12\text{-}10]$$

Photons absorbed or emitted in transitions between equally spaced vibrational levels thus have a *single* frequency. Moreover, the photon frequency is exactly the corresponding classical frequency of oscillation. The vibrational spectrum of a typical diatomic molecule (really just a single line, omitting rotation) falls in the infrared region of the electromagnetic spectrum. The vibrating diatomic molecule is but one example of a quantum-mechanical simple harmonic oscillator. Atoms in a solid are also bound by an interatomic potential, which is closely parabolic for small atomic displacements, and the allowed energies for interatomic oscillations are therefore also given by Equation 12-8.

Spectrum of a Diatomic Molecule.   The vibrational spectrum of a polar diatomic molecule differs from that of an ideal harmonic oscillator (the potential of which is strictly parabolic at all displacements), because the molecular potential shows departure from the parabolic shape at high degrees of vibrational excitation above the ground state. For this reason the vibrational energy levels are not equally spaced for high quantum numbers; instead, they crowd together near the dissociation limit. For such an *anharmonic* oscillator, transitions for which v changes by $2, 3, \ldots$, as well as by 1 are allowed.

The vibrational frequencies of diatomic molecules fall in the infrared portion of the electromagnetic spectrum, at roughly 100 times the rotational frequencies of molecules. The differences in energy between vibrational energy states are, therefore, approximately 100 times larger than the differences in energy between rotational states. Thus, for each vibrational state there is a whole set of possible rotational states, as shown in Figure 12-8. Because of the rotational fine structure of the vibrational states the absorption or emission spectra from diatomic molecules consist, not of single vibrational lines, but of groups of very closely spaced rotational lines crowded near the frequency of the vibrational transition. The infrared spectra of diatomic molecules reflect changes in both the vibrational and the rotational states of the molecule and are called *vibrational-rotational spectra*. The vibrational-rotational lines of the molecule HCl, for example, are found to be centered about a wavelength of 3.3×10^{-4} cm.

In our discussion of molecular vibration and rotation we have been primarily concerned with the rotational and vibrational motions of the nuclei of atoms and not with the motions of electrons. It is proper to assume that there is no change in the state of the electrons in a molecule during vibration or rotation, because the molecular motions take place so much more slowly than the motions of electrons that the latter are able to follow the nuclei. However, changes in the electronic

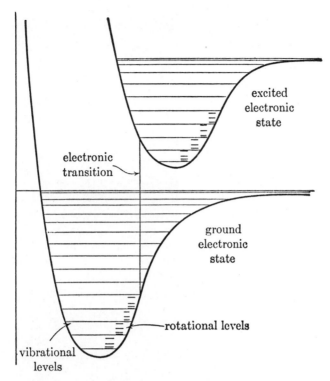

Figure 12-8. Energy-level diagram showing some of the electronic, vibrational, and rotational levels of a diatomic molecule.

structure of a molecule can take place when an electron in the molecule changes its state or orbit. Such an electronic transition results in the emission or absorption of a molecular *electronic spectrum* in the visible or ultraviolet portion of the electromagnetic spectrum.

The lowest electronic state and an excited electronic state of a diatomic molecule are shown in Figure 12-8. The potential curve of the molecule in an excited electronic state is displaced upward by an amount that is large compared with either the vibrational or the rotational energy differences. The molecular electronic excited state may be thought of as that in which one of the electrons of the atom has been raised to an excited state. As a consequence the equilibrium position r_0 may be displaced.

The electronic spectra of molecules are enormously complicated, because for a single electronic transition there are many possible rotational and vibrational states between which transitions can occur. The molecular spectrum in the visible or ultraviolet region consists, then, not of a relatively small number of sharply defined lines, as in atomic spectra, but of many groups of very closely spaced lines, which with moderate resolution appear as nearly continuous *bands*, as shown in Figure 12-9.

12-3 The statistical distribution laws Many problems arising in physics are concerned with the behavior of systems composed of very large num-

Figure 12-9. A portion of the band spectrum of cyanogen (CN) in the ultra-violet. (Courtesy of RCA Laboratories, Princeton, New Jersey.)

bers of weakly interacting, identical particles. The statistical methods of handling large numbers of particles whose mechanics are known are called *statistical mechanics*.

A familiar example of a system that can be treated by the methods of statistical mechanics is that of an ideal gas composed of a large number of identical point particles obeying Newton's laws of motion. Although it is possible in principle to describe in detail the motion of every particle of such a system, the problem is so mathematically formidable as to be virtually beyond solution. Actually, what is of interest is *not* the *detailed behavior* of every particle of the system but, rather, the *average behavior* of the microscopic particles and their influence on macroscopic measured quantities. Thus, it is possible to predict the pressure (a macroscopic quantity) of a gas on its container in terms of the mass and average speed of the molecules (microscopic quantities). Furthermore, it is possible to relate another macroscopic quantity, the absolute temperature T of a gas, to a microscopic quantity, the average kinetic energy $\bar{\epsilon}$ of the molecules $(\bar{\epsilon} = \frac{3}{2}kT)$.†

In such a system as a gas of particles, interacting only weakly with one another, an equilibrium distribution results. The molecules interact with one another and with the walls by collisions, whose duration is short compared with the time between collisions. Some molecules will have small kinetic energy, and others will have large kinetic energy; in short, there will be a distribution of the energies (and, thus, of the speeds) over a considerable range. If the molecules are in equilibrium and their number is very large, the relative number of molecules of any particular energy will be essentially constant, although the energy of any one molecule will, of course, change with time through collisions.

Statistical mechanics allows one to determine the energy distribution of *any* system of weakly interacting particles in thermal equilibrium, whether the particles obey classical or quantum mechanics. Although a rigorous development of statistical mechanics is beyond the scope of this book, we shall state and briefly discuss some important results. We shall then apply these results to several physical problems of interest in molecular and solid-state physics.

It is assumed that each particle in a system composed of a very large number of identical, weakly interacting particles has available to it a discrete set of quantum states, the energy of each state i being designated by ϵ_i. In a classical system there is a continuum of allowed energies, and the separation between adjacent energies can be taken to be zero. Inasmuch as the particles are imagined to interact only weakly with one another, each particle has its own set of states, and if the particles are all identical, they will all have identical sets of states available to them for occupancy.

† See Sections 21-3 and 21-4, Weidner and Sells, *E. C. P.*

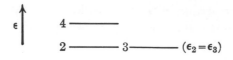

Figure 12-10. Quantized energy states available to a particle.

A very simple hypothetical example is shown in Figure 12-10, where each particle must at any one time exist in one of the four possible states. We notice that the states 2 and 3 have identical energies: $\epsilon_2 = \epsilon_3$. Whenever two or more distinct states, such as 2 and 3, have the same energy, the states are said to be *degenerate*. (Degeneracy can, however, be removed by some external disturbance; for example, the Zeeman degeneracy is removed by a magnetic field, as shown in Section 7-5.) Now the question is "How are the particles of the system distributed among the various available states?"

Statistical mechanics predicts the most probable distribution of the particles among the various states in three kinds of systems met in physical problems. Because most systems of interest have a large number of particles, the most probable distribution becomes overwhelmingly more probable than any other distribution and thus represents (with almost complete certainty) the actual distribution. In Table 12-1 are listed the three types

Table 12-1

	MAXWELL-BOLTZMANN	BOSE-EINSTEIN	FERMI-DIRAC
Characteristics determining the statistics	Identical but distinguishable particles	Identical, indistinguishable particles of integral spin	Identical, indistinguishable particles of half-integral spin, obeying Pauli exclusion principle
Distribution function $f(\epsilon_i)$	$f_{\mathrm{MB}}(\epsilon_i) = Ae^{-\epsilon_i/kT}$	$f_{\mathrm{BE}}(\epsilon_i) = \dfrac{1}{e^{\alpha}e^{\epsilon_i/kT} - 1}$	$f_{\mathrm{FD}}(\epsilon_i)$ $= \dfrac{1}{e^{(\epsilon_i - \epsilon_F)/kT} + 1}$
Examples of systems obeying statistics	Essentially all gases at all temperatures	Liquid helium (spin 0) Photon gas (spin 1) Phonon gas (spin 0)	Electron gas (spin $\frac{1}{2}$)

of probability distributions: Maxwell-Boltzmann, Bose-Einstein, and Fermi-Dirac statistics. Also included in the table are the characteristic properties defining the statistical behavior and examples of physical systems that obey the various distributions.

The *distribution function* $f(\epsilon_i)$ in Table 12-1 *represents the average number of particles in the state* i. Inasmuch as $f(\epsilon_i)$ depends only on the energy of the state, the average number of particles in states having the same energy, such as states 2 and 3 in Figure 12-10, will be the same; for example, $f(\epsilon_2) = f(\epsilon_3)$. The distribution functions are derived from the *fundamental postulate of statistical mechanics*:

> *Any particular distribution of particles among the various available states of a system is just as likely as any other distribution.*

Any particular distribution must, of course, be consistent with the characteristics of the particles and with such conservation laws as the conservation of energy and of particles.

THE MAXWELL-BOLTZMANN DISTRIBUTION   The Maxwell-Boltzmann distribution, a classical distribution, applies to a system of *identical particles* which are, nevertheless, *distinguishable* from one another (for example, a collection of billiard balls of identical mass and diameter but painted red, blue, etc.). The average number f_{MB} of particles in a state i with energy ϵ_i is

$$f_{\mathrm{MB}}(\epsilon_i) = Ae^{-\epsilon_i/kT}$$ [12-11]

where A is a constant, k is the Boltzmann constant, 1.38×10^{-23} J/K°, and T is the absolute temperature of the system of particles, always assumed to be in equilibrium. It is the *average* behavior of a gas of atoms or molecules which is described by the Maxwell-Boltzmann distribution law. This distribution function, $f_{\mathrm{MB}}(\epsilon_i)$, is plotted in Figure 12-11 for two different temperatures.

THE BOSE-EINSTEIN DISTRIBUTION   The Bose-Einstein distribution law applies to a system of *identical particles* that are *indistinguishable*, each having an *integral spin*. Such particles are called *bosons*. The average number of particles occupying a particular state i of energy ϵ_i is given by

$$f_{\mathrm{BE}}(\epsilon_i) - \frac{1}{e^{\alpha}e^{\epsilon_i/kT} - 1}$$ [12-12]

The Bose-Einstein distribution is plotted in Figure 12-12 for $\alpha = 0$. It can be shown that for a system of photons or for a system of phonons (to be defined in Section 12-8) the constant α must always be zero (thus, $e^{\alpha} = 1$). This arises from the fact that the total number of photons (or phonons) in a system is not conserved. It can be seen both from Equation

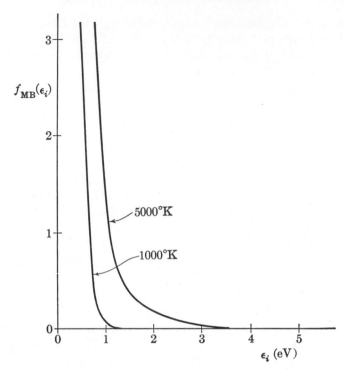

Figure 12-11. Maxwell-Boltzmann distribution function.

12-12 and Figure 12-12·that the distribution function $f_{BE}(\epsilon_i)$ approaches the Maxwell-Boltzmann distribution $f_{MB}(\epsilon_i)$ when $\epsilon_i \gg kT$ (with $\alpha = 0$). At low energies, or $\epsilon_i \ll kT$, the term -1 in the denominator of Equation 12-12 becomes important and has the effect of making $f_{BE}(\epsilon_i)$ much larger than $f_{MB}(\epsilon_i)$ for the same energy.

THE FERMI-DIRAC DISTRIBUTION   The Fermi-Dirac distribution applies to a system of *identical particles* that are *indistinguishable* but each having a *half-integral spin*. Particles of half-integral spin (*fermions*), such as the electron, proton, or neutron, obey the Pauli exclusion principle. This prevents two or more particles from existing in the same state at the same time. The Pauli principle represents, so to speak, a very strong interaction between identical Fermi particles, preventing any two from occupying the same state. Although the Maxwell-Boltzmann and Bose-Einstein distribution laws impose no restriction on the number of particles that can occupy the same state, the Fermi-Dirac statistics allows, at most, only one particle in a particular state. The average number of particles in a particular quantum state i with energy ϵ_i is given by

$$f_{FD}(\epsilon_i) = \frac{1}{e^{(\epsilon_i - \epsilon_F)/kT} + 1}$$ [12-13]

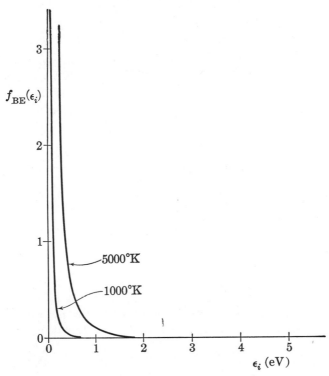

Figure 12-12. Bose-Einstein distribution function.

The quantity ϵ_F, called the *Fermi energy,* is a constant for many problems of interest and is nearly independent of temperature.

The physical meaning of the Fermi energy can be seen from Equation 12-13. The average number of particles in a state in which $\epsilon_i = \epsilon_F$ is $\frac{1}{2}$; that is, the probability that a state of energy ϵ_F is occupied is just $\frac{1}{2}$. For those states with energies much less than ϵ_F the exponential term in the denominator of Equation 12-13 is essentially zero, and $f_{FD} = 1$; thus, all such states have their full quota of particles, one per state, and are filled. For states with energies much greater than the Fermi energy the exponential term becomes much greater than $+1$, and f_{FD} reduces to the Maxwell-Boltzmann distribution, Equation 12-11. At the absolute zero of temperature the Fermi-Dirac distribution f_{FD} is 1 for all states up to ϵ_F and zero for all states with energies greater than ϵ_F; see Figure 12-13.

Now, it must be noted that for all three types the distribution function $f(\epsilon_i)$ gives only the *average* number of particles occupying a *state i* of energy ϵ_i and *not* the number $n(\epsilon_i)$ of particles *with the energy* ϵ_i. This is so because there may be two or more states with the same energy. Therefore, we introduce the quantity $g(\epsilon_i)$, called the *statistical weight,* which gives the number of states with the same energy ϵ_i; for instance, in Figure 12-10 $g(\epsilon_i) = 1$,

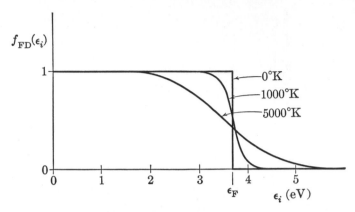

Figure 12-13. Fermi-Dirac distribution function.

$g(\epsilon_2) = 2$, and $g(\epsilon_4) = 1$. It follows that

$$n(\epsilon_i) = f(\epsilon_i)\, g(\epsilon_i)$$ [12-14]

In many situations the energy levels are so closely spaced as to be regarded as continuous. One then wishes to know the number of particles, $n(\epsilon)\, d\epsilon$, having energies between ϵ and $\epsilon + d\epsilon$. Equation 12-14 then is written as

$$n(\epsilon)\, d\epsilon = f(\epsilon)\, g(\epsilon)\, d\epsilon$$ [12-15]

where $g(\epsilon)$, the *density of states*, gives the number of states per unit energy.

Equation 12-15 will form the basis of all our discussions in this chapter; for, if one knows the applicable distribution function $f(\epsilon)$, and if the density of states $g(\epsilon)$ can be computed for a particular system, then one will know the (most probable) number $n(\epsilon)\, d\epsilon$ of particles within the range ϵ to $\epsilon + d\epsilon$. Given the energy distribution of the system's particles, such properties of the system as its average energy, specific heat, etc., can be computed.

12-4 Maxwell-Boltzmann statistics applied to an ideal gas Consider a classical, ideal gas composed of N identical atoms or molecules assumed to be point particles obeying Newton's laws of motion. We wish to calculate the number $n(\epsilon)\, d\epsilon$ of atoms within the energy range $d\epsilon$. Inasmuch as this system obeys the Maxwell-Boltzmann statistics, Equation 12-15 becomes

$$n(\epsilon)\, d\epsilon = f_{MB}(\epsilon)\, g(\epsilon)\, d\epsilon$$
$$n(\epsilon)\, d\epsilon = A e^{-\epsilon/kT} g(\epsilon)\, d\epsilon$$ [12-16]

The quantity $g(\epsilon)$ for this system is most easily evaluated as follows. The only energy these particles possess (strictly, the only energy that can change) is translational kinetic energy, and any one particle has available to it a whole continuum of energy states ranging from zero upward. The state of such a particle is specified by giving the three components of its momentum, $(p_x,\ p_y,\ p_z)$. This specification of the free particle's state gives no information about the particle's location within the container, but we need not know this, inasmuch as the energy depends *only* on the momentum, the potential energy being zero.

It is convenient to represent the states available to a particle by points in *momentum space*, where the coordinates in this space are the three components $p_x,\ p_y,$ and p_z of the momentum. Then each point in classical momentum space corresponds to a possible available state, and all points in momentum space are allowed.

We now have a means of finding the number $g(\epsilon)\,d\epsilon$ of states in the energy range $d\epsilon$, where ϵ represents the total energy (and here also the kinetic energy) of any one particle. We write

$$\epsilon = \tfrac{1}{2}mv^2 = p^2/2m$$

$$d\epsilon = p\,dp/m \qquad\qquad [12\text{-}17]$$

so that the magnitude of the momentum $\boldsymbol{p}$ is

$$p = (p_x^2 + p_y^2 + p_z^2)^{1/2}$$

Furthermore, $\qquad\qquad g(\epsilon)\,d\epsilon = g(p)\,dp \qquad\qquad [12\text{-}18]$

where $g(p)\,dp$ gives the number of states with a momentum magnitude between p and $p + dp$. This number is proportional to the volume of a spherical shell in momentum space, that is, to $4\pi p^2\,dp$, as shown in Figure 12-14. Thus,

$$g(p)\,dp \propto p^2\,dp \qquad\qquad [12\text{-}19]$$

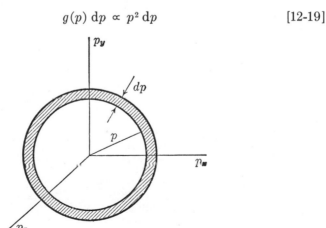

Figure 12-14. Momentum states between p and $(p + dp)$.

Using Equations 12-17 and 12-18 in Equation 12-19, we have

$$g(\epsilon)\, d\epsilon \propto g(p)\, dp \propto p^2\, dp \propto p\, d\epsilon$$

$$g(\epsilon)\, d\epsilon \propto \epsilon^{1/2}\, d\epsilon \qquad\qquad [12\text{-}20]$$

Finally, the most probable number of particles with energies between ϵ and $\epsilon + d\epsilon$ is, from Equation 12-16,

$$\boxed{\, n(\epsilon)\, d\epsilon = Ce^{-\epsilon/kT}\epsilon^{1/2}\, d\epsilon \,} \qquad\qquad [12\text{-}21]$$

where C is a proportionality constant. The distribution of the particles as a function of energy is shown in Figure 12-15. The constant C may be evaluated by applying the conservation of particles, their total number N being fixed:

$$N = \int_0^\infty n(\epsilon)\, d\epsilon = C \int_0^\infty \epsilon^{1/2} e^{-\epsilon/kT}\, d\epsilon \qquad\qquad [12\text{-}22]$$

Each of the $n(\epsilon)\, d\epsilon$ particles within $d\epsilon$ has an energy ϵ; therefore, the total energy E of the gas is

$$E = \int_0^\infty \epsilon n(\epsilon)\, d\epsilon = C \int_0^\infty \epsilon^{3/2} e^{-\epsilon/kT}\, d\epsilon$$

Then, integrating this equation by parts and using Equation 12-22, we have

$$E = \tfrac{3}{2}NkT$$

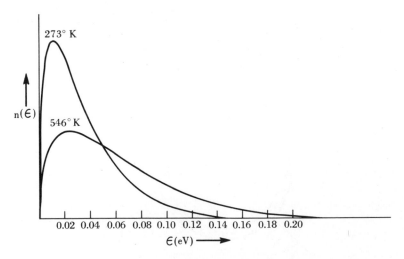

Figure 12-15. Energy distribution of the molecules of an ideal gas.

The average energy $\bar{\epsilon}$ per atom is then

$$\bar{\epsilon} = E/N = \tfrac{3}{2}kT \qquad\qquad [12\text{-}23]$$

The average translational kinetic energy per atom, $\bar{\epsilon} = \tfrac{3}{2}kT$, may be considered to be divided equally among the three translational *degrees of freedom*. A degree of freedom is defined as one of the independent coordinates needed to specify the position of the particle. Therefore, the average energy per degree of freedom may be taken to be $\tfrac{1}{2}kT$.

The molar specific heat C_v of a gas at a constant volume is defined as the energy necessary to increase the temperature of 1 mole of gas 1 K°, the volume of the gas being fixed; that is,

$$C_v \equiv (1/n)\ dE/dT = (N_A/N)\ dE/dT \qquad\qquad [12\text{-}24]$$

where n is the number of moles and N_A is the number of particles per mole (Avogadro's number). Using Equation 12-23, we obtain $dE/dT = \tfrac{3}{2}kN$, and Equation 12-24 becomes

$$\boxed{C_v = \tfrac{3}{2}kN_A = \tfrac{3}{2}R} \qquad\qquad [12\text{-}25]$$

where the gas constant R is kN_A. Thus, the molar specific heat C_v of a classical ideal gas composed of atoms or molecules regarded as point particles (that is, as having no internal structure) is predicted to be $\tfrac{3}{2}R$. The measured specific heats of *monatomic* gases are in excellent agreement with this theoretical value; for example, C_v is $1.50R$ for both helium and argon. On the other hand, the measured C_v values of diatomic or polyatomic gases are greater than $\tfrac{3}{2}R$; for example, at room temperature C_v for H_2 is $2.47R$ and C_v for N_2 is $2.51R$.†

12-5 Maxwell-Boltzmann statistics applied to the specific heat of a diatomic gas In the last section the specific heat at constant volume of a classical ideal gas imagined to consist of point masses was computed to be $\tfrac{3}{2}R$, in good agreement with the measured values of *monatomic* gases. Of course, the atoms of a monatomic gas are *not* simple point masses; they have a complicated internal structure and follow the laws of the quantum theory. Their translational kinetic energy, however, is *not* quantized, and for moderate temperatures the electron configuration is always that of the ground state. Thus, the atoms of a monatomic gas behave (at moderate temperatures) *as if* they were point masses.

Now consider the specific heat of a gas of diatomic molecules. There are three contributions to the total energy of such molecules: the (unquantized) *translational kinetic energy* of the center of mass, the (quantized) *rotational kinetic energy* of the molecule as a whole about the center of mass, and the (quantized) *vibrational energy* of the atoms of the molecule.

† See Sections 21-6 and 21-7, Weidner and Sells, *E. C. P.*

The molecules' translational kinetic energy contributes to the total energy of the gas at all finite temperatures, but there are contributions to the total energy from rotation and vibration only if an appreciable fraction of the molecules exist in excited rotational or vibrational states.

If all molecules were in the lowest rotational state ($J = 0$), the rotational kinetic energy would be zero, and if all molecules were in the lowest vibrational state ($v = 0$), there would be no contribution from vibrational energy (except for the ever-present zero-point vibration). We can determine under what circumstances molecular rotation and vibration make significant contributions to the total energy of a diatomic gas by applying the Maxwell-Boltzmann statistics to find the temperatures for which excited rotational and vibrational states are appreciably occupied.

The number $n(E_r)$ of molecules, each with a rotational kinetic energy E_r, can be found by using Equation 12-14 and the Maxwell-Boltzmann distribution function, Equation 12-11. The density $g(E_r)$ of states for pure rotation is $2J + 1$, where J is the rotational (angular momentum) quantum number. This corresponds to the Zeeman degeneracy for the orbital angular-momentum quantum number l, as given in Section 7-5. Therefore,

$$n(E_r) = (2J + 1)Ae^{-E_r/kT} \qquad [12\text{-}26]$$

where
$$E_r = J(J + 1)\hbar^2/2I$$

from Equation 12-2. The number of molecules occupying some particular rotational state J depends only on the moment of inertia I of the molecules and the temperature T of the gas.

Consider the population of the rotational states for the hydrogen molecule H_2, which has a relatively small moment of inertia, $I = 4.64 \times 10^{-48}$ kg-m^2. Figure 12-16 shows the relative number of molecules in the first several rotational states for the temperatures 56, 170 and 340 °K, computed from Equation 12-26. It is clear that at 56 °K most of the hydrogen molecules are in the lowest ($J = 0$) rotational state; at this temperature most of the molecules do not rotate, and there is very little contribution to the total energy of the gas from molecular rotation. On the other hand, at a temperature of 340 °K a large fraction of the molecules are rotating. In short, there is a large increase in the rotational energy of this gas from 56 to 340 °K, because the higher rotational states become more populated as the temperature of the gas is raised.

We can make a similar computation for the relative population of the vibrational states. For vibration we have $g(E_v) = 1$, and the number $n(E_v)$ of molecules, each having a vibration energy E_v, is then given by

$$n(E_v) = Ae^{-E_r/kT} \qquad [12\text{-}27]$$

where
$$E_v = (v + \tfrac{1}{2})hf \qquad \text{and} \qquad f = \frac{1}{2\pi}(k/\mu)^{1/2}$$

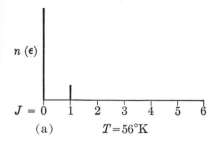

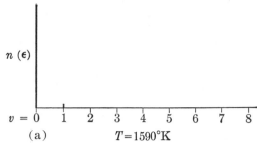

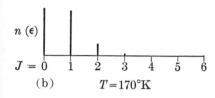

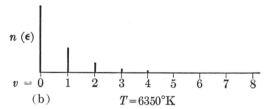

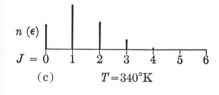

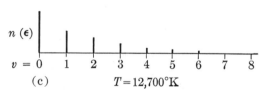

Figure 12-16. The relative number of H_2 molecules occupying rotational states at three different temperatures.

Figure 12-17. The relative number of H_2 molecules occupying vibrational states at three different temperatures.

from Equations 12-7 and 12-8. For the hydrogen molecule H_2 we have $f = 1.32 \times 10^{14}$ sec^{-1}. Figure 12-17 shows the relative number of hydrogen molecules in the lowest several vibrational states for the temperatures 1,590, 6,350, and 12,700 °K, computed from Equation 12-27.

It is clear that at temperatures of less than about 1,600 °K essentially all molecules are in the ground state ($v = 0$ vibrational state) and that at temperatures of 10,000 °K or more a substantial fraction of the molecules are in excited vibrational states. Thus, for $T < 1,600$ °K appreciable vibration does not occur, whereas for $T > 10,000$ °K the hydrogen gas has a significant contribution to its total energy from molecular vibration.

We have seen that there is an energy of $\frac{1}{2}kT$ per molecule associated with each of the three degrees of freedom for translation, the total translational kinetic energy being $\frac{3}{2}kT$ per molecule. *Two* degrees of freedom are associated with molecular rotation of diatomic molecules, one for each of the two mutually perpendicular directions with respect to the interatomic axis about which rotation can take place. Thus, at temperatures at which a substantial fraction of the molecules are rotating the rotational energy per molecule is $2 \times \frac{1}{2}kT = kT$. For the single vibrational degree of freedom there are two contributions to the vibrational energy, one for the kinetic energy and one for the potential energy, each $\frac{1}{2}kT$; therefore, again at sufficiently high temperatures, the vibrational energy per molecule is also kT.

We have seen that for $T < 50$ °K only translational energy is important for hydrogen gas; therefore, the total energy per molecule is $\frac{3}{2}kT$ in this region, as for a monatomic gas. Molecular rotation of H_2 becomes significant at temperatures of a few hundred degrees and the total energy per molecule is then $(\frac{3}{2}) + \frac{2}{2}kT = \frac{5}{2}kT$. Finally, at a few thousand degrees molecular vibration, besides rotation and translation takes place, and the total energy per molecule is then $(\frac{3}{2} + \frac{2}{2} + \frac{2}{2})kT = \frac{7}{2}kT$. The corresponding molar specific heats (at constant volume) for the three temperature regions are $\frac{3}{2}R$, $\frac{5}{2}R$, and $\frac{7}{2}R$, respectively. The observed values of the specific heat of a hydrogen gas are shown in Figure 12-18. Clearly, observed variation of the specific heat with temperature demonstrates the quantization of molecular vibration and rotation and is in complete accord with theoretical expectation.

12-6   The laser   The relative population of the quantized states of atomic systems enters crucially in the operation of a *laser*, an acronym for "light amplification by the stimulated emission of radiation." Such a device produces unidirectional, monochromatic, intense, and—most importantly —coherent visible light.† The corresponding device for operation in the microwave region of the electromagnetic spectrum is the *maser*.

Consider first the several processes by which the energy of a free atom can change in a quantum transition with the emission or absorption of a

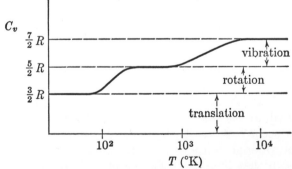

Figure 12-18. Molar specific heat of molecular hydrogen (H_2) as a function of temperature, showing the specific-heat contributions arising in consequence of translation, rotation, and vibration.

† For a discussion of coherent and incoherent sources of light see Section 45-5, Weidner and Sells, *E. C. P.*

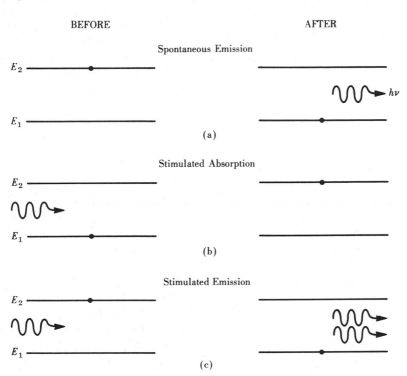

Figure 12-19. Processes in which the quantum state is changed by the absorption or emission of photons; (a) Spontaneous emission: (b) Stimulated absorption: (c) Stimulated emission.

photon, as shown in Figure 12-19; these processes are spontaneous emission, stimulated absorption, and stimulated emission.

In *spontaneous emission* an atom is initially in an excited state and decays to a lower energy state with the emission of a photon of energy $h\nu = E_2 - E_1$. The excited atom, initially at rest and having no preferred direction in space, can emit the photon in any direction. After emission the atom, now in a lower energy state, recoils in a direction opposite to that of the emitted photon. Like the radioactive decay of unstable nuclei, the decay of unstable atoms is governed by an exponential decay law (Equation 9-17) with a characteristic half-life or mean life. Typically, an excited atomic state has a lifetime of the order of 10^{-8} sec; that is, the time, on the average, for an atom in an excited state to decay spontaneously with the emission of a photon is only 10^{-8} sec. Some few atomic transitions are, however, much slower. For such so-called metastable states the atomic lifetime may be as long as 10^{-3} sec. (The *spontaneous* transition of an atom from a lower to a higher energy state is, of course, ruled out by energy conservation.)

In *stimulated absorption* an incoming photon stimulates an atom to make an upward transition, and the photon is thereby absorbed. After absorption the atom recoils in the same direction as that of the incoming photon.

In *stimulated emission* an incoming photon stimulates, or induces, an atom initially in an excited state to make a downward transition. The atom emits a photon as its energy is lowered, this photon being *in addition* to the photon inducing the transition: one photon approaches the atom in an excited state, and two photons leave, the atom, now being in the lower energy state. Moreover, the two photons both leave in the same direction as that of the incoming photon, and they are exactly in phase relative to one another; that is, they are coherent. We may see that stimulated emission produces coherent radiation simply by noting that, if the two photons were out of phase by any amount, they would at least partially interfere destructively, in violation of energy conservation. The stimulated-emission process produces light amplification, or photon multiplication. The trick in constructing a laser is to make the stimulated-emission process dominate competing processes.

The probability of decay by spontaneous emission is characterized by the mean life of the excited state. Similarly, one can assign probabilities P_a and P_e to the respective processes of stimulated absorption and stimulated emission. Detailed quantum-mechanical analysis shows that

$$P_a = P_e \qquad [12\text{-}28]$$

That is, given a photon energy and type of atomic system, stimulated emission is just as probable as stimulated absorption. Thus, if a certain number of photons directed at a collection of atoms all initially in a lower energy state cause, say, a tenth of the atoms to undergo stimulated absorption, then the same number of photons directed at the same collection of atoms in the upper energy state will cause a tenth of the atoms to undergo stimulated emission.

The three processes of spontaneous emission, stimulated absorption, and stimulated emission apply to free atoms interacting with photons. If a system consisting of many interacting atoms is in thermal equilibrium, still other so-called *relaxation processes* may operate to change the quantum state of an atom without, however, emission or absorption of photons. For example, an atom in an excited state may make a nonradiative transition to a lower energy state, the excitation energy going into the thermal energy of the system rather than into the creating of a photon; conversely, an atom may be raised to a higher energy state as the thermal energy of a system decreases.

Consider a collection of atoms in thermal equilibrium at some temperature T for which $\epsilon_i > kT$, where ϵ_i is the energy of an atom. The distribution of the atoms among the available energy states can be given to a good approximation by the classical Maxwell-Boltzmann distribution. The statistical weight $g(\epsilon_i)$ will depend upon the detailed characteristics of the atoms but typically will not differ drastically between one quantum state and another. Then we have, using Equation 12-14,

$$n(\epsilon_i) \propto f_{\mathrm{MB}} \propto e^{-\epsilon_i/kT} \qquad \qquad [12\text{-}29]$$

Some atoms are in the ground state, others occupy the first excited state, and still others are in higher energy states. The relative number of atoms in the various possible states is controlled by the system's temperature T according to the Boltzmann factor $e^{-\epsilon/kT}$. If the numbers of atoms in progressively higher energy states 1, 2, and 3 are n_1, n_2, and n_3, respectively, where $n_1 \propto e^{-E_1/kT}$, $n_2 \propto e^{-E_2/kT}$, and $n_3 \propto e^{-E_3/kT}$, then, since $E_1 < E_2 < E_3$, it follows that $n_1 > n_2 > n_3$. The ground state is more heavily populated than the first excited state, and the number of atoms occupying higher states is still less.

Suppose that we have a collection of atoms that have only two energy states and are in thermal equilibrium (for example, atoms with free or nearly free electrons, whose spin direction may be aligned or antialigned with an external magnetic field). There are more atoms n_1 in the lower energy state than there are atoms n_2 in the upper energy state; see Figure 12-20. Suppose further that a beam of photons, each of energy $h\nu = E_2 - E_1$, illuminates the atoms. Ignoring for the moment spontaneous emission and the relaxation processes within the system (or taking these processes to be characterized by low probability or long mean life), we concentrate on

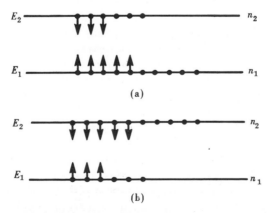

(a)

(b)

Figure 12-20. Changes in the occupancy of quantized states through the processes of stimulated absorption and stimulated emission only. (a) In thermal equilibrium stimulated absorption dominates stimulated emission, and the number of photons is reduced. (b) For a population inversion stimulated emission dominates stimulated absorption, and the number of photons is enhanced.

the processes of stimulated absorption and stimulated emission only, which have the same probability. Stimulated absorption depopulates the lower energy state and reduces the number of photons. Stimulated emission depopulates the upper energy state and increases the number of photons. What is the net effect on the total number of photons?

The number of photons disappearing by virtue of stimulated absorption is proportional to $P_a n_1$, and the number of additional photons created by virtue of stimulated emission is proportional to $P_e n_2 = P_a n_2$, from Equation 12-28. But for thermal equilibrium we have $n_1 > n_2$, so there is net absorption. Absorption dominates emission simply because more atoms occupy the lower energy state than the upper one. Moreover, the net absorption is accompanied by a tendency to equalization of the populations of the two states.

Now, if we were somehow to produce a *population inversion*, in which the number of atoms occupying the upper energy state *exceeded* the number in the lower state, then emission would dominate over absorption; see Figure 12-20. With a population inversion incoming light would be amplified coherently, since the number of additional photons produced through stimulated emission would more than compensate for the number of photons decreased through stimulated absorption. Such population inversions have been achieved in a wide variety of materials by a number of clever procedures, most of them involving a relatively slow relaxation process. What follows below is a brief description of the first laser operating with a crystal of ruby.

Ruby consists of aluminum oxide, Al_2O_3, with a few scattered atoms of Cr replacing Al; the chromium atoms are the ones responsible for the laser behavior. Figure 12-21 shows the important energy levels of chromium C level 3 actually consists of a number of closely spaced levels). The excited state E_2 is metastable; the lifetime for spontaneous decay to the ground state is unusually long, about 3×10^{-3} sec. Suppose that the atoms, initially in thermal equilibrium, with $n_1 > n_2 > n_3$, are "optically pumped" by the sending of light of wavelength 5,500 Å (yellow-green) at the atoms. Atoms make transitions from state 1 to state 3 by absorbing photons of this wavelength, and almost immediately afterwards are de-excited by transitions to state 2. Atoms brought to excited state 2 remain in this state for relatively long times. The optical pumping depletes the population of state 1 and enhances the population of state 2. Indeed, n_1 is decreased to such a degree that $n_2 > n_1$; population inversion is achieved. Now, if a few photons of 6,943 Å (ruby-red light) appear, possibly from the spontaneous decay from state 2 to state 1, they will stimulate transitions in which emission dominates absorption. Thus, the light is amplified, each photon joining the train being exactly in phase, or coherent, with the initial beam.

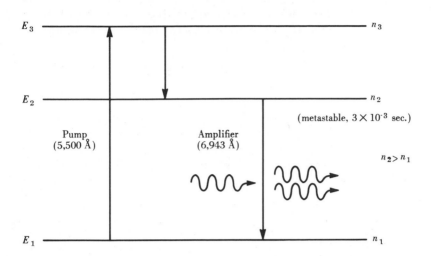

Figure 12-21. Energy levels of Cr in a ruby laser. The pumping radiation, between states 1 and 3, depletes the population of state 1 and increases that of state 2. The radiation between states 2 and 1 is amplified because of the population inversion with $n_2 \geq n_1$.

In practice the light is sent through the ruby crystal many times by being reflected from optically flat and parallel ends, as in Figure 12-22. At the ends some light escapes and the remainder is reflected back into the ruby crystal. But only that light which is precisely perpendicular to the reflecting ends will traverse the crystal in many round trips; photons traveling obliquely to the crystal axis escape from the crystal before substantial photon multiplication can take place. The amplified light is highly monochromatic, unidirectional, intense, and coherent.

The technological applications of lasers are many; they all derive from the fact that with lasers one can produce intense electromagnetic radiation in the visible region having the coherence properties heretofore available

Figure 12-22. Laser cell with flat, parallel reflecting ends. Only those photons traveling perpendicular to the end plates undergo appreciable photon multiplication: oblique photons escape through the sides before they have an opportunity to stimulate many emissions.

only in radio waves. In addition to solid-state lasers, such as the ruby laser described above, there are gas lasers and liquid lasers. Descriptions of these may be found in the bibliography at the end of this chapter.

12-7 Blackbody radiation   A physical system illustrating the Bose-Einstein distribution law is that of a blackbody and its radiation.† Actually, it was the successful theoretical explanation of the electromagnetic radiation from a solid, given by Max Planck in 1900, that marked the beginning of the quantum theory. We have, however, postponed until now a discussion of this phenomenon because an interpretation of the radiation from solids involves not only the quantum theory but also the statistical distribution of particles in a many-particle system.

All substances at a finite temperature radiate electromagnetic waves. The radiation spectra from atomic gases, in which the atoms are far apart and interact only feebly with one another, consist of discrete frequencies or wavelengths. The spectra of molecules, with contributions from rotational and vibrational transitions besides electronic transitions, again consist of discrete lines. The molecular lines in the visible region appear, on casual observation, as continuous bands. A solid represents a still more complex radiator or absorber, and it may be regarded in some ways as an enormous molecule with a correspondingly increased number of degrees of freedom. The radiation emitted by solids consists of a *continuous spectrum*, *all* frequencies or wavelengths being radiated. An adequate theory of blackbody radiation must account for how the radiation is distributed among the various frequency components and how it varies with the temperature of the emitting surface.

Consider first what is meant by the term *blackbody*. Any solid will absorb a certain fraction of the radiation incident on its surface, the remainder being reflected. An ideal blackbody is defined as a material that absorbs *all* of the incident radiation, reflecting none. From the point of view of the quantum theory a blackbody is, then, a material that has so many quantized energy levels, spaced over so wide a range of energy differences, that *any* photon, whatever its energy or frequency, is absorbed when incident on it. Inasmuch as the energy absorbed by a material would increase its temperature if no energy were emitted, a perfect absorber, or blackbody, is also a perfect emitter.

A very good approximation to an ideal blackbody, one that can be achieved in the laboratory, is a hollow container, completely closed except for a small hole, through which radiation can enter or leave. Any radiation entering the container through the hole has a very small probability of being immediately reflected out again. Instead, the radiation is absorbed

† See Section 23-8, Weidner and Sells, *E. C. P.*

or reflected repeatedly at the inner walls, so that effectively all radiation incident through the hole is absorbed in the container. By the same token, the radiation leaking out through the hole is representative of the radiation in the interior.

When the container is maintained at some fixed temperature T, the inner walls emit and absorb photons at the same rate. Under these conditions the electromagnetic radiation may be said to be in thermal equilibrium with the inner walls; in different language, the *photon gas* may be said to be in thermal equilibrium with the system of particles (in the walls) creating and absorbing the photons.

The observed frequency distribution of the radiation from a blackbody, analyzed by measuring the radiation escaping through the hole, is shown in Figure 12-23 for two fixed temperatures. Some general features of blackbody radiation may be seen from the figure, as follows.

(a) For a fixed temperature the energy $E(\nu)\,d\nu$ emitted in the small frequency interval $d\nu$ between the frequencies ν and $\nu + d\nu$,

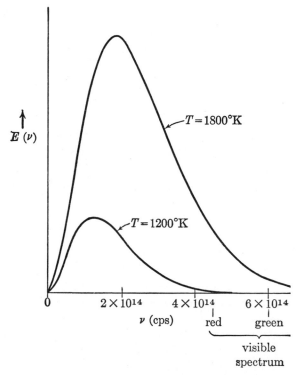

Figure 12-23. Energy distribution as a function of frequency of electromagnetic radiation emitted by a blackbody for two temperatures.

first increases with frequency, then reaches a maximum, and finally decreases at still higher frequencies.

(b) $E(\nu)\,d\nu$ increases with the temperature T at any frequency; consequently, the total energy

$$E_{\mathbf{T}} = \int_{0}^{\infty} E(\nu)\,d\nu$$

increases with T. Before Planck's development of the theory of blackbody radiation $E_{\mathbf{T}}$ was known to vary as T^4; this is the so-called *Stefan-Boltzmann law*.

(c) A larger fraction of the emitted radiation is carried by the higher-frequency components as the temperature of the radiating body is increased. The wavelength corresponding to the peak in the radiation spectrum is found to be inversely proportional to the absolute temperature; this relation is known as the *Wien displacement law*.

(d) The blackbody radiation spectrum is independent of the material of which the radiator is constructed.

All attempts to deduce the observed radiation curves from classical theory failed, and agreement with experiment was first achieved only when Planck introduced the quantum concepts. We shall not follow Planck's original arguments, which were based primarily on the energy quantization of particles in the emitting or absorbing material; instead we shall use a somewhat simpler approach, in which our concern will be with the electromagnetic radiation, regarded as a photon gas. Photons, having a spin of 1, will, of course, obey the Bose-Einstein statistics.

We may regard the equilibrium radiation within the blackbody enclosure in either of two ways: in terms of electromagnetic waves or in terms of particle-like photons:

(a) When the radiation is treated as a collection of electromagnetic waves, the waves may be imagined to be repeatedly reflected from the walls of the container, producing standing waves.

(b) When the radiation is treated as a collection of electromagnetic particles, the photons may be imagined to interact only with the container walls and to be in thermal equilibrium with the container.

We wish to find the number of photons with energies between ϵ and $\epsilon + d\epsilon$; since $\epsilon = h\nu$, we may, equivalently, find the number of photons with frequencies between ν and $\nu + d\nu$. This number is the product of the number $g(\epsilon)$ of available energy states between ϵ and $\epsilon + d\epsilon$ and the Bose-Einstein distribution function $f_{\mathrm{BE}}(\epsilon) = 1/(e^{\epsilon/kT} - 1)$, which gives the average number of photons in a particular state of energy ϵ.

The strategy for finding the number of available photon states (which is to say, the number of possible electromagnetic waves) is the following.

We imagine plane electromagnetic waves to be confined within a cube (for simplicity) of edge L. Then we count the number of stationary, or standing, wave patterns that can exist within the cube. This procedure is not unduly restrictive, for the cube may be imagined arbitrarily large, so that even the longest waves can be accommodated.

The state of a photon is completely specified by giving the three components of its linear momentum, p_x, p_y, and p_z, and its two possible polarization directions. Thus, there are two states for each particular set of p_x, p_y, and p_z values. The procedure for fitting stationary electromagnetic waves within a three-dimensional enclosure is analogous to that used in Section 5-9 for finding the permitted quantum states of a particle confined to a unidimensional potential-energy well. Only certain values of p_x, p_y, and p_z will lead to stationary states.

Figure 12-24 shows one particular electromagnetic wave, traveling obliquely with respect to the sides of the box, its direction of propagation being given by the momentum vector $\boldsymbol{p}$. The wave fronts, to which $\boldsymbol{p}$ is

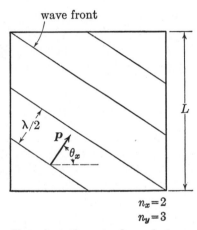

Figure 12-24. An allowed stationary place electromagnetic wave in a cubical box.

perpendicular, are one half wavelength apart, where $\lambda = h/p$. For stationary waves to exist within the cubical box, the projection of any side along the direction of propagation must be an integral number of half-wavelengths. Thus, for the side parallel to the p_x direction we must have

$$L \cos \theta_x = n_x(\lambda/2) \tag{12-30}$$

where n_x is an integer and θ_x is the angle between $\boldsymbol{p}$ and the p_x axis. For photons we have $p = h/\lambda$ and, therefore,

$$p_x = p \cos \theta_x = h \cos \theta_x/\lambda \tag{12-31}$$

Combining this with Equation 12-30, we find, for the permitted values of the p_x component of $\boldsymbol{p}$,

$$p_x = (h/2L)n_x$$

Similarly,   [12-32]

$$p_y = (h/2L)n_y \quad \text{and} \quad p_z = (h/2L)n_z$$

Figure 12-25 shows the allowed values of (p_x, p_y, p_z) in momentum space. Each point actually represents two possible states, because of the two possible polarization directions (the heavy dot in the figure corresponds to the state illustrated in Figure 12-24). For a macroscopic length L the separation between the adjacent points, $h/2L$, is very small compared with the momentum of all photons except those of the longest wavelengths. For example, if the cube is as small as 5 cm, electromagnetic waves with wavelengths of less than 10 cm (in the microwave radio region) and essentially all wavelengths in the visible region ($\approx 10^{-7}$ m) can be accommodated within the box.

We are interested in the number of states within the small energy range ϵ to $\epsilon + d\epsilon$, where $\epsilon = pc$ and $p = (p_x^2 + p_y^2 + p_z^2)^{1/2}$. It can be found by computing the number of states within a shell of radius p and of thickness dp, counting only the positive values of p_x, p_y, and p_z. Then

$$g(p)\, dp = \frac{2(\tfrac{1}{8})(4\pi p^2\, dp)}{(h/2L)^3} \tag{12-33}$$

The factor 2 accounts for the two polarization directions, the factor $\tfrac{1}{8}$ is introduced because only one octant of the spherical shell may be included

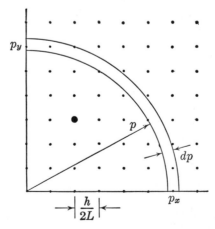

Figure 12-25. Allowed values of p_x, p_y, and p_z in momentum space. The heavy dot corresponds to the state ($n_x = 2$, $n_y = 3$) illustrated in Fig. 12-24.

(only *positive* values of n_x, n_y, and n_z are permitted), and the factor $(h/2L)^3$ represents the volume associated with each point in momentum space. With $p = \epsilon/c$ and $L^3 = V$, the total volume of the box, Equation 12-33 becomes

$$g(p)\,dp = g(\epsilon)\,d\epsilon = \frac{8\pi V \epsilon^2\,d\epsilon}{h^3 c^3} \qquad [12\text{-}34]$$

The quantity $g(\epsilon)\,d\epsilon$ represents the number of states available for occupancy by photons in the energy range ϵ to $\epsilon + d\epsilon$. Multiplying $g(\epsilon)\,d\epsilon$ by the average number of photons per state, $f_{BE}(\epsilon)$, gives the number of photons in the infinitesimal energy range $d\epsilon$. Since each photon has an energy $\epsilon = h\nu$, we obtain for $E(\nu)\,d\nu$, the radiation energy per unit volume within the frequency interval $d\nu = d\epsilon/h$, the following:

$$E(\nu)\,d\nu = \frac{h\nu\, g(\epsilon)\,d\epsilon}{V(e^{\epsilon/kT} - 1)} = \frac{(h\nu)8\pi V(h\nu)^2(h\,d\nu)}{V h^3 c^3 (e^{\epsilon/kT} - 1)}$$

$$\boxed{E(\nu)\,d\nu = \frac{8\pi h\nu^3}{c^3} \cdot \frac{1}{e^{h\nu/kT} - 1}\,d\nu} \qquad [12\text{-}35]$$

This is the *Planck radiation equation*, giving the blackbody radiation spectrum. It is in complete agreement with the observed experimental curves, such as Figure 12-23.

It is of interest to note that the Planck equation reduces for low frequencies, $h\nu/kT \ll 1$, to the classical *Rayleigh-Jeans radiation formula*:

$$\text{for low } \nu: \qquad E(\nu)\,d\nu = (8\pi\nu^2 kT/c^3)\,d\nu \qquad [12\text{-}36]$$

The classical Rayleigh-Jeans relation fails, of course, in the high-frequency region, because Equation 12-36 predicts an infinite value of $E(\nu)$ as ν approaches infinity; this failure is known as the *ultraviolet catastrophe*. For high frequencies $h\nu/kT \gg 1$, the Planck relation reduces to the *Wien formula*:

$$\text{for high } \nu: \qquad E(\nu)\,d\nu = \left(\frac{8\pi h\nu^3}{c^3}\, e^{-h\nu/kT}\right)d\nu \qquad [12\text{-}37]$$

This relation fails, of course, for low frequencies.

Finally, we write the energy distribution in terms of the wavelength λ rather than the frequency ν, and we set $dE(\lambda)/d\lambda = 0$, to find the peak in the energy distribution as a function of wavelength; we arrive at the *Wien displacement law*:

$$\lambda_{max}T = \text{constant}$$

$$\lambda_{max}T = 2.898 \times 10^7 \text{ Å-K}°$$

where λ_{max} is the wavelength corresponding to the maximum of $E(\lambda)$. The Wien displacement relation shows that when the temperature of a blackbody is changed, the wavelength peak in the radiation spectrum is displaced inversely as the absolute temperature, a blackbody becoming progressively red, white, and blue as its temperature is raised.

The total energy E_T radiated from a blackbody is obtained by integrating $E(\nu) \, d\nu$ in Equation 12-35 over the entire range of emitted frequencies:

$$E_T = \int_0^\infty E(\nu) \, d\nu = CT^4$$

where C is a constant. The power P radiated from a unit area of a blackbody is given by $P = \sigma T^4$, where σ is 5.67×10^{-8} W/m^2 = $^\circ K^4$.

12-8   The quantum theory of the specific heats of solids   Another application of the quantum statistics is to the specific heat of solids. In this section we first review the partially successful classical theory and then give the quantum theory, again utilizing the Bose-Einstein statistics.

Consider a crystalline solid composed of N atoms, each atom bound in the crystal lattice by forces arising from its neighboring atoms. When any one atom is displaced from its equilibrium position, it is subject, in a first approximation, to a restoring force proportional to its displacement. Thus, any atom displaced from its equilibrium position will undergo simple harmonic motion. However, when one atom is displaced from its equilibrium position, so too are the neighbors with which it is coupled by interatomic binding forces. Consequently, if one atom undergoes simple harmonic motion, it causes neighboring atoms also to oscillate and the disturbance or deformation to be propagated through the crystal as an elastic wave.

At temperatures below the melting point the total energy content of the solid which may change with temperature consists of the following contributions from each atom: the kinetic energy of the essentially free, outer, valence electrons and the energy of vibration of the remainder of the atom, namely the nucleus plus the tightly bound, inner electrons. At all moderate temperatures the quantum state of any of the bound electrons is unchanged. For this reason the nucleus plus the bound electrons may be treated as a single, inert, vibrating particle. If the internal energy of the solid changes, so too does the temperature, and the change in the internal energy of the crystal per unit change in temperature is the specific heat of the solid. The total specific heat of the solid consists of the *electronic specific heat* and the *lattice* (vibrational) *specific heat*. For all temperatures except the very lowest the electronic specific heat is negligible (Section 12-9); in this section we shall discuss the contributions arising from the lattice vibrations only.

We first compute the specific heat of a solid by using the classical theory, attributing the lattice-energy content to N simple harmonic oscillators. For each degree of freedom of a simple harmonic oscillator there is $\frac{1}{2}kT$ of energy associated with potential energy and $\frac{1}{2}kT$ associated with kinetic energy (see also Section 12-5). Therefore, for oscillations in three dimensions the total vibrational energy E is the number of degrees of freedom, $3N$, times the energy per degree of freedom, kT,

$$E = (3N)(kT) = 3NkT$$

and the classical lattice specific heat per mole, C_v, is

$$C_v = \frac{1}{n}\left(\frac{dE}{dT}\right) = 3\left(\frac{N}{n}\right)k = 3N_Ak = 3R \qquad [12\text{-}38]$$

where n is the number of moles, N_A is Avogadro's number, and R is the constant of the general gas law. This classical relation is known as the *Dulong-Petit law*.† The equation, predicting that the molar specific heat of any solid is the same constant, $3R$, independent of the material and of the temperature, is in agreement with experiment at *high* temperatures. The classical theory is, however, incapable of explaining the observed decrease in the specific heat at low temperatures, as shown in Figure 12-26.

The first successful theoretical treatment of the lattice specific heat for *all* temperatures was given by A. Einstein in 1906. This early quantum treatment was improved upon by P. Debye in 1912 and is usually referred to as the *Debye theory of specific heats*.

The essential quantum feature of lattice vibrations is the quantization of the atoms' vibrational energies. In this view, any one atom gains or loses energy in discrete amounts and transfers energy to neighboring atoms in discrete amounts, the amount of the mechanical energy transferred being hf, where f is the classical frequency of vibration of the atom about its equilibrium position (Equation 12-10). Because the energy propagated through the lattice in the form of elastic deformations is quantized, we may speak of the propagation of quasiparticle quanta of vibrational energy, called *phonons*. Phonons are created and absorbed by quantized lattice vibrators upon changing their quantum states, just as photons are created or absorbed by the atoms of a blackbody. The phonons represent the thermal-energy content of a crystalline lattice, just as the photons represent the equilibrium electromagnetic radiation content of a blackbody. The Bose-Einstein statistics imposes no limit on the number of photons that can occupy any one available energy state. Similarly, the number of possible phonons is unrestricted, their distribution being governed also by the Bose-Einstein statistics. By analogy with a photon, the energy of a

See Section 23-4, Weidner and Sells, *E. C. P.*

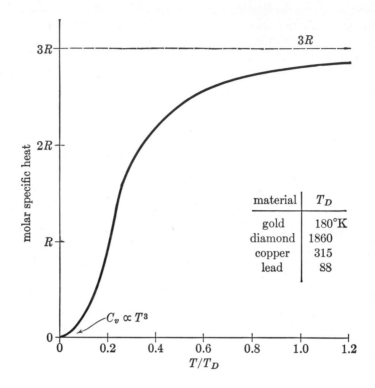

material	T_D
gold	180°K
diamond	1860
copper	315
lead	88

Figure 12-26. Observed molar specific heat of solids as a function of temperature. The temperatures are given in units of T_D, the Debye temperature (Equation 12-43).

phonon is given by $\epsilon = hf$, and its momentum is given by $p = \epsilon/v_s$, where v_s is the speed of phonon propagation, the speed of sound.

Because of the close analogy between a photon gas in equilibrium with a blackbody and a *phonon gas* in equilibrium with the quantized simple harmonic oscillators of an elastic solid the quantum lattice specific heat of the solid is closely related to the radiation distribution of a blackbody. Modifications must be made, however, because of the difference between a photon and a phonon.

Again we wish to find the number $n(\epsilon)\, d\epsilon$ of states available within the energy interval $d\epsilon$. To do this we again find the number of waves, now elastic rather than electromagnetic, that can be fitted as stationary waves between the boundaries of the medium, now the crystal boundaries rather than the walls of a blackbody. Thus, replacing the speed c with the speed v_s in Equation 12-34 and removing the factor 2 for the two photon polarization directions, we have, for the density of states,

$$g(\epsilon)\, d\epsilon = \frac{4\pi V \epsilon^2\, d\epsilon}{h^3 v_{\mathrm{s}}^3}$$

or, since $\epsilon = hf$,

$$g(f)\, df = \left(\frac{4\pi V}{v_{\mathrm{s}}^3}\right) f^2\, df$$

Two distinct types of elastic wave are propagated through the medium: (1) a transverse wave traveling at a speed v_t and having two possible, mutually perpendicular polarization directions, and (2) a longitudinal wave traveling at a different speed, v_l. The number of elastic modes of vibration, or the total number of available phonon states, in the frequency interval df is then

$$g(f)\, df = 4\pi V \left(\frac{2}{v_t^3} + \frac{1}{v_l^3}\right) f^2\, df \qquad [12\text{-}39]$$

The total number of vibrational modes is limited, however, to the total number $3N$ of degrees of freedom of the crystal. One of Debye's contributions consisted in recognizing this restriction. The elastic vibrations are cut off at the frequency f_D, called the *Debye frequency*, as follows:

$$\text{total number of modes} = \int_0^{f_D} g(f)\, df = 4\pi V \left(\frac{2}{v_t^3} + \frac{1}{v_l^3}\right) \int_0^{f_D} f^2\, df = 3N$$

Therefore,

$$f_D^3 = \frac{9N}{4\pi V} \left(\frac{2}{v_t^3} + \frac{1}{v_l^3}\right)^{-1} \qquad [12\text{-}40]$$

Equation 12-39 may now be written in terms of the Debye frequency f_D:

$$g(f)\, df = \frac{9N}{f_D^3} f^2\, df \qquad [12\text{-}41]$$

Because the elastic vibrations are quantized, but the number of phonons in any particular state is not restricted by the exclusion principle, the phonon distribution is given by the Bose-Einstein statistics, where again $\alpha = 0$ in Equation 12-12. Therefore, the number of phonons in the frequency range between f and $f + df$ is

$$n(f)\, df = g(f) \frac{1}{e^{hf/kT} - 1}$$

Since the energy per phonon is hf, the total vibrational energy content of the crystal is

$$E = \int_0^{f_D} hf \frac{g(f)\, df}{e^{hf/kT} - 1} = 9N \left(\frac{kT}{hf_D}\right)^3 kT \int_0^{x_m} \frac{x^3\, dx}{e^x - 1} \qquad [12\text{-}42]$$

where we have used Equation 12-41 for $g(f)$ and defined $x \equiv hf/kT$ and $x_m \equiv hf_D/kT$.

It is convenient to define a characteristic temperature, called the *Debye temperature* T_D, as that temperature for which $hf_D = kT_D$. Then,

$$T_D = hf_D/k \qquad \text{and} \qquad x_m = T_D/T \qquad [12\text{-}43]$$

Equation 12-42 may then be written

$$E = 9N \left(\frac{T}{T_D}\right)^3 kT \int_0^{x_m} \frac{x^3 \, dx}{e^x - 1} \qquad [12\text{-}44]$$

The integral in this equation must be evaluated numerically.

The molar specific heat C_v immediately follows from the definition $C_v = (1/n)(dE/dT)$. Although one cannot easily evaluate C_v for all temperatures (because x and x_m in Equation 12-44 are functions of T), it is possible to find expressions for E and C_v for high temperatures and low temperatures.

In the high-temperature limit we have $kT \gg hf_D$ and $x \ll 1$ and, therefore, $e^x \approx 1 + x$. Equation 12-44 becomes, at high temperatures,

$$E \approx 9N \left(\frac{T}{T_D}\right)^3 kT \int_0^{x_m} x^2 \, dx = 9N \left(\frac{T}{T_D}\right)^3 (kT) \left(\frac{T_D^3}{3T^3}\right)$$

$$E = 3NkT$$

and the molar specific heat is

$$C_v = \frac{1}{n}\left(\frac{dE}{dT}\right) = 3N_A k = 3R$$

In the high-temperature limit the quantum theory of lattice specific heat gives exactly the same result, $C_v = 3R$, as the classical theory, Equation 12-38.

Consider now the low-temperature limit, where $kT \ll hf_D$ and $x_m \to \infty$. The integral in Equation 12-44 may be evaluated in closed form to yield

$$\int_0^\infty \frac{x^3 \, dx}{e^x - 1} = \frac{\pi^4}{15}$$

and Equation 12-44 becomes, at low temperatures,

$$E \approx \tfrac{3}{5}\pi^4 NkT \left(\frac{T}{T_D}\right)^3$$

and the molar specific heat is

$$C_v = \frac{1}{n}\left(\frac{dE}{dT}\right) = \left(\frac{12\pi^4 R}{5T_D^3}\right) T^3$$

The lattice specific heat is thus seen to vary as T^3 in the low-temperature region, again in accord with observation; see Figure 12-26.

The observed temperature dependence of the specific heats for solids, *whether insulators or conductors*, are found to be in good agreement with the Debye theory, as shown in Figure 12-26. This is, at first sight, rather surprising, inasmuch as the Debye theory takes into account the internal energy arising from the lattice vibrations but *not* the contribution to the specific heat of the conduction electrons. An electric or thermal insulator is a material in which there are essentially no free electrons. It is to be expected, then, that the specific heat of an insulator would have contributions from the lattice vibrations alone, in agreement with experiment and the Debye theory, but that a conductor would have, in addition, a contribution to the specific heat from the free electrons.

A good conductor is imagined to have a large number of unbound, free electrons, which can wander throughout the material (these conduction electrons will show a net flow in one direction when a temperature gradient or external electric field is applied, accounting qualitatively for the high thermal and electrical conductivities of metals). Let us compute the electronic specific heat of a solid under the assumption that each of the N atoms of the solid has one free, or conduction, electron and that the N free electrons may be regarded as classical particles of a Maxwell-Boltzmann gas. Three degrees of freedom are associated with the translational motion of each particle and, if these free electrons are regarded as classical particles wandering throughout the solid conductor, much as molecules in a gas, then the total electronic energy is $E_e = N(\frac{3}{2}kT)$. The electronic contribution to the molar specific heat would be $C_{v,e} = (1/n)(dE_e/dT) = \frac{3}{2}(Nk/n) = \frac{3}{2}R$. But at the high-temperature, classical limit of the Debye theory the lattice specific heat is $3R$. Thus, if the conduction electrons of a conductor were to behave as classical free particles, the conductor's *total* molar specific heat at relatively high temperatures would be $3R + \frac{3}{2}R$, or $\frac{9}{2}R$, whereas the observed value of C_v for both insulators and conductors is $3R$ (for $T > T_D$).

A classical treatment of electronic specific heat is clearly untenable. It fails because a gas of free electrons is *not* a collection of classical particles but, rather, a system of particles obeying the Pauli exclusion principle and the Fermi-Dirac statistics. The almost negligible electronic specific heat of metallic conductors, which is inexplicable with the classical free-electron theory, is understood on the basis of the quantum free-electron theory of a metal, to which we now turn.

12-9 The free-electron theory of metals   The simple free-electron model of a metal, first developed by W. Pauli and A. Sommerfeld in 1927, is an example of a system of particles subject to the Pauli exclusion principle and obeying the Fermi-Dirac statistics.

In the free-electron model a metallic crystal is imagined to consist of two components: the nuclei together with their tightly bound electrons, and the weakly bound valence electrons, which may be considered to belong to the entire crystalline solid rather than to any particular atom. The valence electrons are assumed to be free in the sense that any one of them experiences no net force from the remaining ones or from the nuclei and bound electrons of the lattice. Therefore, it is assumed that in the interior of the solid each valence electron experiences a *constant* electrostatic potential energy $-E_i$ which is independent of its location within the crystal. The electric potential rises markedly at the boundaries of the crystal to zero; this corresponds to the net electrostatic attraction on a valence electron at the boundary. A plot of the potential energy of a free electron is shown in Figure 12-27. In the free-electron model of a metal

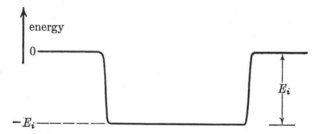

Figure 12-27. Average potential energy of a free electron in a conducting solid.

we have, therefore, a collection of a large number of free particles confined to a box—that is, to the interior of the metal. The *electron gas* is not, however, an ordinary gas, whose distribution is given by the Maxwell-Boltzmann statistics; rather, the free electrons exist in states restricted by the Pauli exclusion principle, and their distribution among available states is governed by the Fermi-Dirac statistics.

We wish to find the number $n(\epsilon)\, d\epsilon$ of free electrons with energies in the range ϵ to $\epsilon + d\epsilon$, where $n(\epsilon) = g(\epsilon)\, f_{\mathrm{FD}}(\epsilon)$. With a knowledge of the energy distribution of the free electrons we shall be able to interpret some aspects of the macroscopic behavior of a metal.

The density $g(p)\, dp$ of states in the momentum range p to $p + dp$ is computed by considering the total number of ways in which N free electrons, regarded as waves, can be fitted within a three-dimensional box of side L. This problem is exactly analogous to that of finding the total number of ways in which N photons, regarded as electromagnetic waves, can be arranged within boundaries to form stationary wave patterns. Therefore Equation 12-33, derived in the section on blackbody radiation, may be used directly:

$$g(p)\, dp = \frac{8\pi V p^2\, dp}{h^3} \qquad\qquad [12\text{-}45]$$

The factor 2, which was earlier introduced to account for the two possible polarization directions, is retained; it now accounts for the two electrons, one with spin up and the other with spin down, which have the same momentum components. For simplicity we measure electron energies upward from the constant potential in the interior of the metallic crystal, now taking the potential energy to be zero in the interior of the metal. Then the total energy ϵ of a free electron is purely kinetic, and we can write

$$\epsilon = \tfrac{1}{2}mv^2 = p^2/2m$$

$$d\epsilon = (p/m)\,dp = (\sqrt{2m\epsilon}/m)\,dp$$

Equation 12-45 then becomes

$$g(p)\,dp = \frac{8\pi V}{h^3}\,(2m\epsilon)\sqrt{\frac{m}{2\epsilon}}\,d\epsilon = g(\epsilon)\,d\epsilon$$

$$g(\epsilon)\,d\epsilon = C\epsilon^{1/2}\,d\epsilon \qquad [12\text{-}46]$$

where $$C = 8\sqrt{2}\pi Vm^{3/2}/h^3 \qquad [12\text{-}47]$$

Note that $g(\epsilon)$ varies as ϵ^2 for photons and phonons (both bosons) but as $\epsilon^{1/2}$ for molecules obeying the Maxwell-Boltzmann statistics and for electrons (fermions).

The distribution function for a collection of fermions is given by

[12-13] $$f_{\text{FD}} = \frac{1}{e^{(\epsilon - \epsilon_F)/kT} + 1} \qquad [12\text{-}48]$$

where $$n(\epsilon)\,d\epsilon = f_{\text{FD}}(\epsilon)\,g(\epsilon)\,d\epsilon$$

Using Equation 12-46, we have

$$n(\epsilon)\,d\epsilon = \frac{C\epsilon^{1/2}\,d\epsilon}{e^{(\epsilon - \epsilon_F)/kT} + 1} \qquad [12\text{-}49]$$

This equation gives the energy distribution of free electrons in equilibrium with a material at a temperature T. The significance of the quantity ϵ_F, called the Fermi energy, is best seen by considering the distribution of electron energies in a metal at the zero of absolute temperature.

METALS AT ZERO ABSOLUTE TEMPERATURE   A plot of the energy distribution of an electron gas, Equation 12-49, is shown in Figure 12-28 for $T = 0$. The plot is based on the product of two energy-dependent terms: the factor $\epsilon^{1/2}$, which accounts for the parabolic rise in $n(\epsilon)$ from $\epsilon = 0$ upward, and the factor $1/(e^{(\epsilon - \epsilon_F)/kT} + 1)$, the Fermi-Dirac probability distribution function (Figure 12-13), which for $T = 0$ has the value of 1 from $\epsilon = 0$ to $\epsilon = \epsilon_F$ and zero at $\epsilon \geq \epsilon_F$.

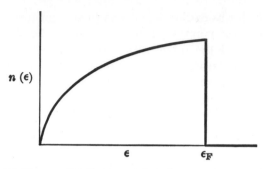

Figure 12-28. Energy distribution of free electrons is a metal at $T = 0°K$.

Figure 12-28 shows that the free electrons do *not* all have zero kinetic energy at the zero of absolute temperature, as would the particles in a classical gas; rather, there are electrons with finite energies up to a maximum energy, the Fermi energy ϵ_F. The electrons have finite energies and are in motion, even at $T = 0$, because of the Pauli exclusion principle, to which electrons are subject: no more than two electrons, one for each of the two possible electron-spin orientations, are permitted in any particular energy state; hence, all of the lowest states become filled, until the most energetic electrons reach $\epsilon = \epsilon_F$. At zero absolute temperature the Fermi energy is the kinetic energy of the most energetic electrons, all states of lesser energy being filled and all states of greater energy being empty.

The value of the Fermi energy ϵ_F can be computed quite directly. The total number N of free electrons is

$$N = \int_0^{\epsilon_F} n(\epsilon)\, d\epsilon = C \int_0^{\epsilon_F} \epsilon^{1/2}\, d\epsilon = \tfrac{2}{3} C \epsilon_F^{3/2} \qquad [12\text{-}50]$$

Using the value of C from Equation 12-47, we have

$$\epsilon_F = \frac{h^2}{2m} \left(\frac{3n}{8\pi}\right)^{2/3} \qquad [12\text{-}51]$$

where n is the number of free electrons per unit volume and m is the electron mass. For copper, with a valence of 1 and one free electron per atom, the Fermi energy is computed from this equation to be 7.0 eV; for the conductor sodium 3.1 eV. The values of ϵ are typically of the order of a few electron volts. Thus, the most energetic electrons of a conductor have a kinetic energy of several electron volts even at the lowest possible temperature.

The average kinetic energy $\bar{\epsilon}$ of a free electron at absolute zero may be found directly, as follows.

$$\bar{\epsilon} = \frac{1}{N} \int_0^{\epsilon_F} \epsilon n(\epsilon)\, d\epsilon = \frac{C}{N} \int_0^{\epsilon_F} \epsilon^{3/2}\, d\epsilon = \frac{2C\epsilon_F^{5/2}}{5N}$$

But $C\epsilon_{\mathrm{F}}^{3/2} = \tfrac{3}{2}N$, from Equation 12-50, and hence

$$\bar{\epsilon} = \tfrac{3}{5}\epsilon_{\mathrm{F}} \qquad [12\text{-}52]$$

The relatively high average kinetic energy, a few electron volts, of a free electron in a metal at $T = 0$ °K may be contrasted with the average kinetic energy per classical free particle, $\tfrac{3}{2}kT$, which is a mere 0.04 eV at room temperature and zero, of course, at $T = 0$ °K. This extraordinary behavior, in which electrons of a material at $T = 0$ °K have a sizable kinetic energy, is, like the zero-point vibration of a simple harmonic oscillator, strictly a quantum phenomenon.

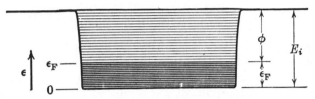

Figure 12-29. Occupation of the energy levels by the free electrons of a metal at $T = 0$°K.

An energy-level diagram showing the occupied energies of the free electrons of a metal at absolute zero is shown in Figure 12-29. The electrons occupy energy states continuously up to the Fermi energy; all higher states are unfilled. The binding energy of the least tightly bound electrons of the metal (those at the Fermi surface) is, of course, the work function ϕ (Section 4-2); hence,

$$E_i = \epsilon_{\mathrm{F}} + \phi \qquad [12\text{-}53]$$

Since all three quantities in this equation can be determined independently, the simple features of the quantum free-electron model can be verified. The work function ϕ can be measured in experiments involving the photoelectric effect. The Fermi energy ϵ_{F} is evaluated by means of Equation 12-51. The difference in potential energy E_i between the interior and the exterior of the crystal produces a change in the speed of an electron upon entering the crystal. This results in a refraction of electrons at the surface, and this refraction is manifest in turn in the *diffraction* of electrons by the crystal lattice. In this way E_i can be measured and Equation 12-53 verified. For example, the conductor lithium, with one valence electron, has $E_i = 6.9$ eV, $\epsilon_{\mathrm{F}} = 4.7$ eV, and $\phi = 2.2$ eV, in agreement with Equation 12-53. We shall see that the values of ϵ_{F} and E_i are nearly temperature-independent and that Equation 12-51 holds for all moderate temperatures.

METALS AT A FINITE TEMPERATURE   We now inquire into the changes that occur when the temperature of the conductor is raised. A plot of the energy distribution for a finite temperature is shown in Figure 12-30,

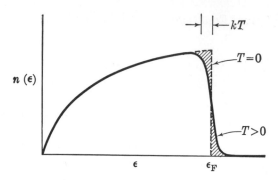

Figure 12-30. Energy distribution of free electrons in a metal at a finite temperature.

following Equation 12-49. The energy distribution at a moderate temperature is quite similar to that at $T = 0\,°K$; the only significant difference is that the corners of the plot, at $\epsilon = \epsilon_F$, are now slightly rounded. The rounding of the corners at the Fermi energy is a result that follows from the change in the Fermi-Dirac distribution function $f_{FD}(\epsilon)$, shown in Figure 12-13.

At room temperature kT is about 0.03 eV, an energy that is much less than the typical Fermi energy ϵ_F, which is always a few electron volts. Therefore, the Fermi-Dirac distribution function $f_{FD}(\epsilon)$ is unchanged from $f_{FD}(\epsilon)$ at $T = 0$ except for an electron energy ϵ close to the Fermi energy ϵ_F. For $kT \ll \epsilon_F$:

$$f_{FD}(\epsilon) = \frac{1}{e^{(\epsilon - \epsilon_F)/kT} + 1} \approx 1, \qquad \text{when} \quad \epsilon \ll \epsilon_F$$

$$\approx 0, \qquad \text{when} \quad \epsilon \gg \epsilon_F$$

There is a difference between the energy distributions $n(\epsilon)$ at a finite temperature T and at $T = 0\,°K$ only within the small energy range in which $|\epsilon - \epsilon_F| \approx kT$; that is, the energy distributions differ significantly only within the range kT of the Fermi energy. We see from Equation 12-48 that, when $\epsilon = \epsilon_F$, then $f_{FD}(\epsilon) = \frac{1}{2}$; thus, for a finite temperature the Fermi energy corresponds to that energy for which there is a one-to-one chance that the state will be occupied. It can be shown that ϵ_F may be assumed to be a constant independent of the temperature for temperatures less than a few thousand degrees.

The distribution in energy of the free electrons of a metal at a finite temperature (Figure 12-30) has an interesting interpretation. Those electrons whose energy is much less than the Fermi energy remain in the low energy states that they occupy at $T = 0\,°K$. Only the most energetic electrons, those within the range kT of the Fermi energy, have available to them unoccupied higher energy states, to which they can be excited by thermal excitation. The low-energy electrons are, so to speak, locked in their energy states when the metal is excited thermally, there being no unoccupied states available to them within an energy range kT, either above or below their states, at $T = 0$ °K. Roughly speaking, a fraction of the electrons within the energy range kT of ϵ_F are promoted to states on the high side of the Fermi energy, again within the range kT of the Fermi energy. Thus, as the temperature of a conductor is raised, only a very small fraction of all of the free electrons can move to higher states and thereby increase the electronic energy content of the solid.

We see from Figure 12-30 that the electronic energy $E_e(T)$ of the metal at some finite temperature T is greater than its energy $E_e(0)$ at $T = 0$ °K because of the shifting of a small fraction of the electrons (shaded areas) from below to above the Fermi energy. The number of electrons promoted to higher energies is proportional to kT. Furthermore, the average increase in the energy of each promoted electron is approximately kT. Therefore, we may write

$$E_e(T) = E_e(0) + A(kT)^2$$

where A is a constant. The molar *electronic specific heat* $C_{v,e}$ is then given by

$$\boxed{C_{v,e} = (1/n)[dE_e(T)/dT] = \gamma T} \qquad [12\text{-}54]$$

where γ is a constant. The quantum free-electron theory thus predicts that the electronic contribution to the specific heat of a conductor is directly proportional to the absolute temperature. A more detailed analysis shows that $\gamma = (\pi^2/2)z(k/\epsilon_F)R$, where z is the number of valence electrons per atom. Therefore, Equation 12-54 becomes

$$C_{v,e} = \left(\frac{\pi^2}{2}\right) z \left(\frac{kT}{\epsilon_F}\right) R \qquad [12\text{-}55]$$

In copper, a typical conductor, $z = 1$, $\epsilon_F = 7.0$ eV, and $kT = 0.03$ eV at room temperature. Using Equation 12-55, we find that $C_{v,e} \approx 0.02R$ for copper at room temperature. The *lattice* molar specific heat for copper is nearly $3R$ at this temperature, so that the electronic contribution to the specific heat is negligible at moderate temperatures.

The electronic specific heat becomes comparable to the lattice specific heat only at the very lowest temperatures (a few degrees Kelvin). That the electronic contribution is very small follows from the fact that only a very small number of the free, or valence, electrons are able to participate in an energy change when the temperature of a metal is changed.

If the temperature of a conductor is raised to several thousand degrees, so that kT becomes comparable to the work function of the metal, some of the free electrons will have enough energy to escape from the metal surface, their kinetic energy ϵ then equaling or exceeding the internal potential energy E_i (see Figure 12-29). Thus, severe thermal excitation of free electrons can result in their emission from the metal. This process is known as *thermionic emission*.

Although the quantum free-electron theory of metals is capable of accounting for such properties as the electronic specific heat and thermionic emission, it cannot account for other important properties of solids, properties that depend on the fact that the electrons, even the valence electrons, in a metal are *not* completely free. In the next section we shall discuss a more realistic model of solids, in which the electrons experience a nonconstant potential within the metal.

12-10　The band theory of solids: conductors, insulators, and semiconductors

The *band theory* of solids is the basis for understanding such phenomena as electrical and thermal conductivities and the distinction between conductors, insulators, and semiconductors. The band theory is able to account for the tremendous range in electrical resistivities from a good insulator to a good conductor, the ratios of which may be as large as 10^{30}. Although a detailed, quantitative treatment of the band theory of solids involves a rigorous application of wave mechanics, it is possible to understand some of the important qualitative features of this highly successful theory without mathematical analysis. There are two approaches to the band theory:

(a) The theory of F. Bloch (1928) emphasizes the fact that a valence electron in a metal does *not* see a constant potential in its motion through the crystal but, rather, experiences a periodic potential, corresponding to the periodicity of the crystalline structure.

(b) The theory of W. Heitler and F. London (1927) considers the effects on the electron wave functions when isolated atoms are brought close together to form a crystalline solid.

Consider first a perfect crystal with nuclei located at fixed lattice positions (called *sites*) within the crystal. These nuclei form a geometrically ordered array, small groups of nuclei being repeated throughout the crystal. Associated with them are the electrons, whose total number is such that the crystal as a whole is electrically neutral. An inner electron is tightly bound to an individual nucleus and must, therefore, remain at all times with this nucleus. On the other hand, an outer, or valence, electron is weakly bound to any one nucleus and may wander from one nucleus to another. A wandering valence electron, according to the Bloch theory, is considered to belong to the entire crystal rather than to any one nucleus. Furthermore, a valence electron sees a periodic electric potential arising from the fixed nuclei and the remaining electrons.

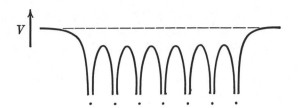

Figure 12-31. Periodic potential seen by an electron in a crystalline solid.

A representation of a simple periodic potential seen by an electron in a crystal is shown in Figure 12-31. Now, the problem of determining the allowed states and energies of valence electrons basically is that of determining what electron wavelengths are possible within the crystal. Thus, one is confronted with the problem of finding what electron wavelengths can be fitted to the periodic potential that characterizes the interaction between a valence electron and the remainder of the crystal, a very complicated problem indeed.

The second approach to the band theory of solids, that of Heitler and London, lends itself more easily to a qualitative description. We consider N identical, isolated (noninteracting) atoms. Each free atom has its own particular set of energy levels, and the permitted states of some one atom are identical with those of any other atom. For an example the energy-level diagram of a lithium atom is shown in Figure 12-32a together with the number of available states for each allowed energy. Since the energy-level diagrams of all atoms are identical, the combined energy-level dia-

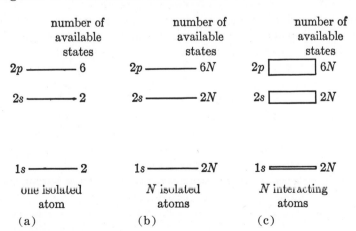

Figure 12-32. Schematic representation of the energy levels and states available to (a) one isolated lithium atom, (b) N isolated lithium atoms, and (c) N interacting lithium atoms.

gram of the N atoms, all separated far from one another, is simply that of the single atom, except that the number of available states for each energy level is now increased by a factor of N. A single atom can accommodate 2 electrons in an s energy level and 6 electrons in a p energy level (see Section 7-8), but N atoms have room for $2N$ electrons in the s energy level and $6N$ electrons in the p energy level, as shown in Figure 12-32b.

When the N atoms are brought together so that the separation between adjacent atoms is comparable to the separation of the atoms in a crystalline solid, they interact fairly strongly with one another. A consequence of the interaction is to broaden the energy levels of the system so that those states which were earlier degenerate, with the same energy, now have slightly different energies (we saw an example of this splitting in Figure 12-4, in the case of two hydrogen atoms that were brought together to form H_2). The effect of bringing together a very large number of the originally isolated atoms (Figure 12-32b) to form a bound system is shown schematically in Figure 12-32c. The $2N$ available states for the $1s$ energy level are no longer coincident but are spread essentially continuously throughout the $1s$ *energy band*. Similarly, there are $2N$ available states in the $2s$ energy band and $6N$ available states in the $2p$ energy band. The regions between the available energy bands cannot be occupied by any electron at all and are known as *forbidden bands*. The width and separation of the energy bands depends, of course, on the particular crystalline material with which they are associated.

We have, up to this time, discussed only the *available* states in the energy bands of a solid but not how the electrons occupy them. To illustrate the distribution of the electrons among the various energy bands of the crystal we first consider the conductor sodium in the ground state at $T = 0$ °K. We shall, for simplicity, assume at first that the several energy bands do not overlap. The electron configuration of an isolated sodium atom in the ground state is $1s^2 2s^2 2p^6 3s^1$; thus, all electron shells are filled up to the $3s$ shell, which contains only one electron. Therefore, the sodium crystal has energy bands for each of the electron shells of the atom, as shown in Figure 12-33a. The $1s$, $2s$, and $2p$ bands are all filled with $2N$, $2N$, and $6N$ electrons, respectively. The $3s$ band, which has $2N$ available states, is only half filled, with N $3s$ electrons. Note that the $1s$ band, corresponding to inner electrons, is quite narrow compared with higher bands; this band is relatively narrow because the inner electrons are strongly attracted to their parent nuclei and are less influenced by neighboring electrons and nuclei.

The fact that the uppermost energy band of a conductor, such as sodium, is only partially filled is responsible for the high electrical conductivity of these materials. Consider what happens to the occupation of the energy bands when an electric field is applied to the metal. It is then possible for the electrons in the partially filled band to gain small amounts of energy by

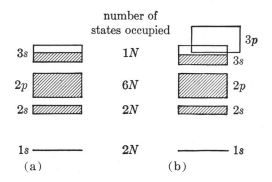

Figure 12-33. Schematic representation of the energy bands and their occupancy by electrons in sodium. The dark regions correspond to occupied states.

the action of an external electric field and so be promoted to the continuum of available states lying immediately above. One accounts similarly for the high thermal conductivity of metallic crystals.

The distribution of the electrons among the available states at some finite temperature differs only slightly from the distribution at absolute zero. The shift in occupation of electrons is controlled here, as in the simple free-electron theory, by the Fermi-Dirac statistics. Consequently, the signicant change in the distribution occurs only for those very few electrons which lie within a region of energy kT about the uppermost filled level (the Fermi level) at $T = 0$ °K.

The energy bands of sodium shown in Figure 12-33a do not include the unoccupied $3p$ band, which comes immediately after the $3s$ band. Not only is the $3p$ band quite broad, but also it overlaps the $3s$ band, as shown in Figure 12-33b. Thus, the number of unoccupied levels available to the electrons in the $3s$ shell is increased further, and this leads to a very high electrical conductivity.

The very low electrical conductivity of an insulator, such as diamond, $_6C$, can also be understood on the basis of the band theory. The electron configuration of carbon in its ground state is $1s^2 2s^2 2p^2$. Because the $2p$ energy band is only partially filled, with $6N$ available states but only $2N$ electrons, it might at first appear that diamond would be an electrical conductor. There are, however, two distinct $2p$ energy bands, separated from each other by a forbidden region of 6 eV, as shown in Figure 12-34. This separation of the $2p$ band arises from the nature of the crystalline structure of diamond. The lower $2p$ band is filled completely with $2N$ electrons in the $2N$ available states. At room temperature kT is about 0.03 eV; thus, the gap width for diamond is so much greater than the thermal excitation energy kT that virtually no electrons occupy the upper $2p$ band. When an

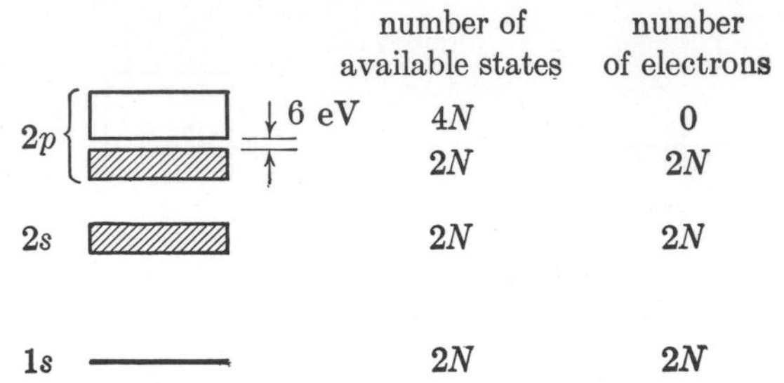

	number of available states	number of electrons
$2p$	$4N$	0
	$2N$	$2N$
$2s$	$2N$	$2N$
$1s$	$2N$	$2N$

$\downarrow 6\ eV$

Figure 12-34. Schematic representation of the energy bands and their occupancy in diamond. Note the sizeable forbidden region between the two $2p$ bands.

external electric field is applied, electrons cannot gain enough energy to be promoted to the upper, unoccupied $2p$ band. Thus, an external field cannot cause a net electron flow, or electric current. In short, a substance such as diamond is a good insulator in that there is a sizable energy gap between a filled band, called the *valence band*, and the next empty (but available) energy band, called the *conduction band*.

Similarly, the electrons in the valence band of an insulator cannot have their energies raised by the absorption of photons whose energy is less than the gap width. This means that in diamond all visible-light photons are transmitted through the crystal without absorption, which is to say that diamond is perfectly transparent to visible light. By the same token, conductors are opaque; this follows from the fact that a continuum of unfilled energy states lies immediately above the filled states, to which electrons in a conductor can be promoted by the absorption of photons over a continuum of wavelengths.

Some crystalline solids, such as silicon and germanium, have a filled valence band and an empty conduction band, like diamond, but a much *smaller* forbidden region separating the bands, as shown in Figure 12-35. The energy gap between the valence and conduction bands is 1.1 eV for silicon and 0.70 eV for germanium, both an order of magnitude smaller than that of the insulator diamond. At very low temperatures the thermal excitation of the valence electrons is so small that essentially none of these elec-

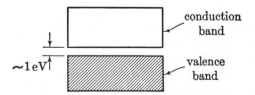

Figure 12-35. Energy bands for semiconductors, such as silicon or germanium, with a small, forbidden energy gap separating the valence and conduction bands.

trons are excited to states in the conduction band, and thus at low temperatures these materials behave as insulators.

Consider now, however, the occupation of states in the conduction band at higher temperatures. If the gap width is small, there will be some electrons occupying available states within the conduction band, and under the influence of an external electric field they can participate in a net electron flow through the material. At the same time the unfilled states in the valence band, called *holes*, also contribute to the electric current. The conductivity of such materials lies between the very low values for insulators and the very high values for conductors and so are known as *semiconductors*. The type of semiconductor described above, which consists strictly of atoms of a single type and depends for its semiconductivity on those electrons in the conduction band which have been thermally excited across the energy gap, is known as an *intrinsic semiconductor*.

A second type of semiconductor, called an *extrinsic*, or *impurity, semiconductor*, depends for its semiconductivity upon the presence within a semiconducting crystal of a few atoms, called *impurity atoms*, of a type different from those of the crystal. Before we discuss the influence of the impurity atoms on the energy-band structure, we must first examine the bonding of atoms and impurity atoms within the crystal. Silicon and germanium both lie in the fourth column of the periodic table, their outermost shells having $3s^2 3p^2$ and $4s^2 4p^2$ electron configurations, respectively. Each silicon or germanium atom in the crystalline solid is bound to its four nearest neighbors by covalent bonds, each saturated bond representing the sharing of two valence electrons, as shown schematically in Figure 12-36. This structure is called the diamond structure, since it is like that of the diamond crystal ($_6$C with $2s^2 2p^2$ electrons).

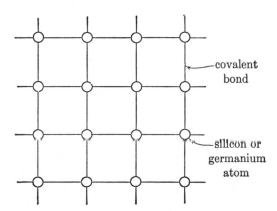

Figure 12-36. Covalent bonding of the atoms in a crystalline solid of silicon or germanium. Each line between nearest neighboring atoms represents a saturated covalent bond, with the sharing of two valence electrons.

Now consider the effect of a few atoms of arsenic in a silicon crystal. The element $_{33}$As lies in the fifth column of the periodic table, its ground-state electron configuration being $4s^2 4p^3$. Thus, a neutral atom of arsenic has one more electron than a neutral atom of silicon, and when an arsenic atom replaces a silicon atom in the crystal, there is one additional electron that is not bonded covalently (see Figure 12-37). The unpaired electron

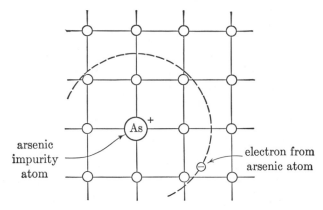

arsenic impurity atom

electron from arsenic atom

Figure 12-37. An example of a donor impurity atom in silicon, producing n-type semiconductivity.

from the impurity atom may be imagined to move in an orbit of very great size (because of the high dielectric constant in the crystal's interior) about the nucleus of the arsenic atom. The electron consequently is very weakly bound, and one may regard the impurity atom as having donated a carrier of negative electric charge to the crystal. Therefore, impurity atoms in the fifth column of the periodic table are *donors* and produce *n-type impurity semiconductors*.

Suppose now that the impurity atoms are from elements in the third column of the periodic table, such as gallium, $_{31}$Ga, with an electron configuration of only *one p* electron. Then the covalent bonding around an impurity atom in the crystal is not complete. One incomplete bond is associated with each impurity atom (see Figure 12-38). The covalent bonding around such an impurity atom is completed by the impurity atom's accepting an electron from the valence band, thereby producing one vacancy, or hole, in the valence band. This hole may be imagined to move in an orbit about the now negatively charged impurity ion. When one speaks of the motion of a hole, imagined as an equivalent positive charge, one is, in effect, describing the motion in the opposite direction of electrons. An impurity atom, which accepts an electron for complete bonding, is known as an *acceptor*, and a semiconductor containing such impurities (and, hence, holes), is known as a *p-type impurity semiconductor*.

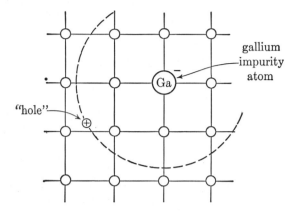

Figure 12-38. An example of an acceptor impurity atom in silicon, producing *p*-type semiconductivity.

The effect on the energy-band structure of impurities in silicon is shown in Figure 12-39. The n-type impurities introduce additional, closely spaced energy levels lying just below the top of the conduction band, these levels being occupied by the weakly bound electrons contributed by the donor atom. The electrons in these discrete energy levels may be excited to the available states in the conduction band, which lie immediately above. The p-type impurities introduce closely spaced levels just above the valence band. Therefore, electrons from the valence band, just below, can be excited upward and occupy these available impurity states, thereby accounting for the slight conductivity of the semiconductor. The conductivity of an impurity semiconductor may be controlled by the relative concentration of the impurity atoms.

Impurity semiconductors have a number of significant technological applications: used singly or in combination, they may form rectifiers, ampli-

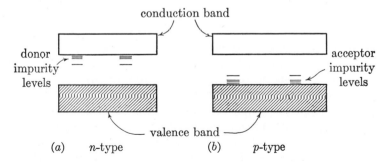

Figure 12-39. Energy-level diagram of a silicon crystal modified by (a) donor impurities and (b) acceptor impurities.

fiers, detectors, transistors, and other solid-state devices. One such device, the p-n junction, is described below.

Consider the junction between a p-type semiconductor, with positive charge carriers, or holes, and an n-type semiconductor, with negative charge carriers, or electrons; see Figure 12-40. The boundary is not produced

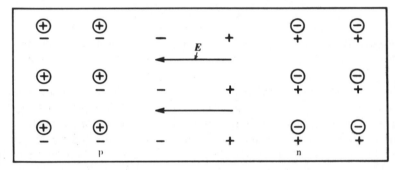

Figure 12-40. A p-n junction. The charge carriers from impurity atoms, positive on the p-side and negative on the n-side, are shown encircled.

merely by pressing together the two semiconductor types; rather, the boundary changes continuously from p-type to n-type through so-called "doping" procedures, in which impurity atoms are diffused in controlled fashion through the material. There is a concentration of holes within the p-type material on the left and a concentration of electrons within the n-type material on the right. Both sides of the junction are electrically neutral. At the junction itself the mobile electrons and holes combine. Thus, the n-type side adjoining the junction has, through a loss of electrons, a net positive charge, while the p-type side adjoining the junction has, through a loss of holes, a net negative charge. The charge layers on either side of the junction thereby produce an internal electric field from the n-type to the p-type side (toward the left in Figure 12-40).

Consider the effects of this internal electric field. It produces a force to the left on the holes on the p-type side (strictly, of course, the force is on electrons, which move to fill vacancies), and the internal electric field produces a force to the right on the electrons on the n-type side, thereby preventing further recombination of electrons and holes at the junction.

Suppose now that an *external* electric field is applied across the junction through an electric potential difference across the electrodes attached to the p-type and n-type sides. If the p-type side is negative and the n-type side positive, the external electric field is to the left and in the same direction as the internal electric field. Then the electrons and holes are further prevented from moving or recombining, and the electric current through the junction under these circumstances is small, arising solely from thermally generated electrons and holes at the junction. This condition is referred to as the *reverse bias* of a p-n junction.

When the polarity of the potential difference is reversed, so that the p-type side is positive and the n-type side negative, the external applied electric field is to the right. This condition is known as *forward bias*. The external electric field to the right exceeds the internal electric field to the left, and holes are driven to the right and electrons to the left. Both types of charge carrier contribute to a conventional current to the right, which may be substantial. In short, the p-n junction is a good conductor for forward bias but a poor conductor for reverse bias. The junction acts as a rectifier, passing current easily in one direction but not in the other. Moreover, the junction is a nonlinear, or nonohmic circuit element: its current–voltage characteristic is not a straight line corresponding to Ohm's law.

12-11 Summary The two principal types of molecular binding are ionic (heteropolar) binding, resulting from the electrostatic attraction of ions, and covalent (homopolar) binding, resulting from the sharing of valence electrons.

The rotational and vibrational energies of a diatomic molecule are quantized. The photons absorbed or emitted in transitions between rotational states or vibrational states are in the far-infrared and infrared regions of the electromagnetic spectrum, respectively. The application of quantum mechanics to the rotational and vibrational motions of a diatomic molecule leads to the results shown in Table 12-2.

Table 12-2

	ROTATION	VIBRATION
Allowed energies of molecule	$E_r = \dfrac{J(J+1)\hbar^2}{2I}$ where $J = 0, 1, 2, \ldots$ and $I = \mu r_0^2$	$E_v = (v + \frac{1}{2})\hbar f$ where $v = 0, 1, 2, \ldots$ and $f = \left(\dfrac{1}{2\pi}\right)\sqrt{k/\mu}$
Allowed transitions	$\Delta J = \pm 1$	$\Delta v = \pm 1$
Frequency of photons	$\nu = (\hbar/2\pi I)(J_l + 1)$	$\nu = f$

The three kinds of probability distributions for dealing with large numbers of weakly interacting particles are the Maxwell-Boltzmann, the Bose-Einstein, and the Fermi-Dirac. The properties of these distribution functions are summarized in Table 12-1.

The number $n(\epsilon_i)$ of particles with an energy of ϵ_i is given by $n(\epsilon_i) = f(\epsilon_i) g(\epsilon_i)$, where $f(\epsilon_i)$, the distribution function, is the average number of particles in the state i, and $g(\epsilon_i)$ is the number of states with the energy ϵ_i. For very closely spaced energy levels one may write $n(\epsilon)\, d\epsilon = f(\epsilon) g(\epsilon)\, d\epsilon$ where $g(\epsilon)$, the density of states, gives the number of states per unit of energy, and $n(\epsilon)$ is the number of particles per unit energy. See Table 12-3.

Characteristics of Various Solids

Conductors. The uppermost band containing electrons is only partially occupied.

Insulators. The uppermost band holding electrons is completely filled; the next available, higher-lying (conduction) band is separated from the filled (valence) band by a forbidden gap of a few electron volts.

Intrinsic semiconductors. The conduction and valence bands are separated by a narrow forbidden gap, and semiconductivity arises from the electrons thermally excited to the conduction band.

Impurity semiconductors. Traces of impurities introduce available states into the region of the forbidden gap. The donor impurity atoms of an n-type semiconductor introduce discrete states lying just below the conduction band, and semiconductivity results from electron transport. The acceptor impurity atoms of a p-type semiconductor introduce discrete states lying just above the valence band, and semiconductivity results from the transport of holes.

BIBLIOGRAPHY

Kittel, C., *Elementary Solid State Physics*. New York: John Wiley & Sons, Inc., 1962. This is a short and elementary version of the author's standard text *Introduction to Solid State Physics*, which contains detailed references to original papers and numerical values of many physical properties of solids.

McKelvey, J. P., *Solid State and Semiconductor Physics*. New York: Harper & Row, 1966. An analytical treatment, at a fairly elementary level, of fundamental problems in solid state physics, together with a thorough treatment of the quantum theory required.

A. L. Schalow, "Optical Masers," *Scientific American*, June, 1961; "Advances in Optical Lasers," A. L. Schalow, *Scientific American*, July, 1963; "Liquid Lasers," A. Lempicki and H. Samelson, *Scientific American*, June, 1967.

Sproull, R. L., *Modern Physics*, 2nd edition. New York: John Wiley & Sons, Inc., 1963. A large part of this book is devoted to solid state physics, particularly semiconducting devices.

Table 12-3

	$f(\epsilon)$	PARTICLES	$g(\epsilon)$	RESULTS
Ideal gas	f_{MB}	Point particles	$g(\epsilon) \propto \epsilon^{1/2}$ $(\epsilon = p^2/2m)$	$\bar{\epsilon} = \frac{3}{2}kT$ $C_v = \frac{3}{2}R$
Diatomic gas	f_{MB}	Diatomic molecules	$g(E_r) = (2J + 1)$ $g(E_v) = 1$	Low temperatures: $\bar{\epsilon} \approx \bar{\epsilon}_{tr} = \frac{3}{2}kT$ $C_v \approx (C_v)_{tr} = \frac{3}{2}R$
				Intermediate temperatures: $\bar{\epsilon} \approx \bar{\epsilon}_{tr} + \bar{\epsilon}_r = \frac{5}{2}kT$ $C_v \approx (C_v)_{tr} + (C_v)_r = \frac{5}{2}R$
				High temperatures: $\bar{\epsilon} \approx \bar{\epsilon}_{tr} + \bar{\epsilon}_r + \bar{\epsilon}_v = \frac{7}{2}kT$ $C_v \approx (C_v)_{t,r} + (C_v)_r + (C_v)_v = \frac{7}{2}R$
Blackbody radiation	f_{BE}	Photons	$g(\epsilon) \propto e^2$ $(\epsilon = pc)$	Planck radiation equation: $E(\nu)\, d\nu = \left(\dfrac{8\pi h\nu^3}{c^3}\right)\left(\dfrac{1}{e^{h\nu/kT} - 1}\right) d\nu$
Lattice specific heat of solids	f_{BE}	Phonons	$g(\epsilon) \propto \epsilon^2$ $(\epsilon = pv_s)$	$E(f)\, df = \left(\dfrac{9Nhf^3}{f_D{}^3}\right)\left(\dfrac{1}{e^{hf/kT} - 1}\right) df$ $E = 9N\left(\dfrac{T}{T_D}\right)^3 (kT)\displaystyle\int_0^{x_m} \dfrac{x^3\, dx}{e^x - 1}$
				For high temperatures: $T \gg T_D$ $(C_v)_{lattice} = 3R$
				For low temperatures: $T \ll T_D$ $(C_v)_{lattice} \propto T^3$
Electronic specific heat	f_{FD}	Electrons	$g(\epsilon) \propto \epsilon^{1/2}$ $(\epsilon = p^2/2m)$	Fermi energy $\epsilon_F = \dfrac{h^2}{2m}\left(\dfrac{3n}{8\pi}\right)^{2/3}$ $(C_v)_{electronic} \propto T$
Band theory of solids	f_{FD}	Electrons	Not calculated. $(\epsilon = p^2/2m + V)$, where V is the periodic potential energy between an electron and the crystalline lattice	Available states for electron occupancy are bands ($1s$, $2s$, $2p$ band, etc.) with possible forbidden gaps between the bands

Troup, G. J. F., *Masers and Lasers*, 2nd edition. London: Methuen & Company, Ltd., 1963. A very short book giving the basic principles of maser and laser operation.

PROBLEMS

12-1 Show that the moment of inertia, $I = m_1 r_1^2 + m_2 r_2^2$, of a diatomic molecule about an axis perpendicular to the interatomic axis and passing through the center of mass may also be written as $I = \mu r_0^2$, where the reduced mass is $\mu = m_1 m_2/(m_1 + m_2)$ and $r_0 = r_1 + r_2$ is the interatomic distance.

12-2 Show that in the correspondence limit of large rotational quantum numbers the photon frequency for quantum transitions between adjacent rotational energy levels of diatomic molecules is the same as the classical frequency of rotation of the molecule about its center of mass.

12-3 Choosing order-of-magnitude values for the parameters involved, show that the pure rotational spectra of molecules are expected to be found in the far infrared and microwave regions of the electromagnetic spectrum.

12-4 Show that the frequencies of the lines in the pure rotational spectrum are given by $\nu = (\hbar/2\pi I)(J + 1)$, where J is the rotational quantum number of the lower energy state.

12-5 A typical interatomic potential curve, such as Figure 12-2, has its minimum at a few angstroms and a depth, relative to infinite separation, of a few electron volts. From these parameters arrive at a typical value of the force constant k for molecular vibration, and show that the vibration spectrum is expected to be found in the near-infrared region of the electromagnetic spectrum.

12-6 Compute the ratio of the vibrational frequencies of the $^1H^{35}Cl$ and $^1H^{37}Cl$ molecules, assuming the interatomic force constant to be the same for both molecules.

12-7 (a) What is the zero-point vibrational energy of a simple pendulum 1.0 m long with a mass of 1.0 kg? (b) What is the vibrational quantum number when the pendulum oscillates with an amplitude of 1.0 mm?

12-8 An electronic transition in the molecule CO produces bands of lines in the visible region (6,000 Å) of the spectrum. What is the approximate separation in wavelength between adjacent rotational lines of the bands, if the interatomic distance for CO is 1.128 Å? This illustrates the apparently continuous band spectrum of molecules in the visible region.

12-9 Show that the Bose-Einstein and Fermi-Dirac distribution functions approach the Maxwell-Boltzmann distribution in the high-energy limit $(\epsilon \gg kT)$.

12-10 (a) Show that the ratio of the statistical weights of the $n = 2$ state to the $n = 1$ state of free hydrogen atoms is 4. (b) A gas of atomic hydrogen is at room temperature: what is the ratio of the number of atoms in the $n = 2$ state to that in the $n = 1$ state?

12-11 * Show that the Maxwell-Boltzmann velocity distribution of an ideal gas of classical point particles is given by $n(v) = Av^2 e^{-mv^2/2kT}$, where $A = (4/\sqrt{\pi})(m/2kT)^{3/2}$. Hint: $n(v)\,dv = n(\epsilon)d\epsilon$.

12-12 At what temperature will 2 percent of the molecules of a CO gas be found in the first rotational state, assuming the remainder to be in the zeroth rotational state? The interatomic distance of carbon monoxide is 1.128 Å.

12-13 * The temperature T of a system of particles may be defined in terms of the relative occupancy of the allowed energy states. Suppose that the particles of a two-level system have energies E_1 and E_2, where $E_2 > E_1$. The corresponding number of particles in the two states are n_1 and n_2. If $n_2 > n_1$, a population inversion has been achieved. (a) Show that under these circumstances the system may be said to have a *negative* absolute temperature equal to $(E_2 - E_1)/[k \ln (n_1/n_2)]$ (take the number of particles with energy E to be proportional to the Boltzmann factor $e^{-E/kT}$). (b) Suppose that a system of particles with two energy levels, such as a collection of protons whose spins are aligned with or against an external magnetic field, has initially a population inversion and therefore a negative absolute temperature. The system is isolated from external influence, but internal relaxation processes may change the relative population of the two allowed states, until the system finally achieves thermal equilibrium with its surroundings. Show that the system's temperature first *rises* to an infinite negative value, then becomes infinitely positive, and finally decreases to a finite positive value.

12-14 The particles of a certain system have three possible energies: E_1, E_2, and E_3, where $E_1 < E_2 < E_3$. The corresponding number of particles in the three states are n_1, n_2, and n_3, where for thermal equilibrium $n_1 > n_2 > n_3$. The system is irradiated by pumping radiation, each photon having an energy $h\nu = E_3 - E_1$. Under high-intensity pumping radiation the populations of the two participating states become equal. Show that there must then exist a population inversion between the states of one other pair, with either $n_3 > n_2$ or $n_2 > n_1$.

12-15 Compute the relative number of hydrogen molecules occupying the first several rotational states at 170 °K, and compare your results with Figure 12-16.

12-16 Compute the relative number of hydrogen molecules occupying the first several vibrational states at 6,350 °K, and compare your results with Figure 12-17.

12-17 Show that the molar specific heat at constant *pressure* of H_2 is $\frac{5}{2}R$, $\frac{7}{2}R$, and $\frac{9}{2}R$ for the three temperature regions shown in Figure 12-18.

12-18 What is the number of modes of electromagnetic waves between the wavelengths of 4,000 Å and 4,100 Å in a black box 10 cm on a side?

12-19 * (a) Calculate the momentum and energy of photons in a box 10 cm on a side, in the available states for which (n_x, n_y, n_z) is $(1, 0, 0)$ and $(1, 1, 0)$. (b) What is the difference in energy between these two states compared with the energy of the lower state? (c) Repeat parts (a) and (b) for the states $(100, 0, 0)$ and $(100, 1, 0)$.

12-20 A blackbody is at a temperature of 1,000 °K. (a) What is the radiation energy per unit volume in the visible region from 4,000 Å to 4,100 Å (assume that $E(\nu)$ is constant over this range of wavelengths)? (b) What is the radiation energy per unit volume in the same wavelength band at the radio frequency 1.0 Mc/sec.

12-21 (a) Show that the Rayleigh-Jeans radiation formula, Equation 12-36, is the low-frequency approximation to the Planck radiation formula. (b) Show that the Wien formula, Equation 12-37, is the high-frequency approximation to the Planck radiation formula.

12-22 * Verify that the Stefan-Boltzmann radiation law follows from the Planck radiation relation.

12-23 * Verify that the Wien displacement law is a consequence of the Planck radiation relation.

12-24 The Debye temperature of diamond is 1,860 °K. What is the molar specific heat of diamond at room temperature? Use Figure 12-26.

12-25 The molar specific heats of copper and beryllium are $2.8R$ and $1.7R$, respectively, at room temperature. Which material has the higher Debye temperature?

12-26 Show that the Fermi energy of a typical metal is of the order of magnitude of a few electron volts.

12-27 Show that the fractional number of conduction electrons in copper (valence 1) that have energies greater than the Fermi energy at room temperature is of the order of 10^{-3}.

12-28 The element gold has a Debye temperature of 180 °K. What is the specific heat of gold (in cal/g-K°) at room temperature?

12-29 * Show that if the atoms of a lattice are assumed to be arranged in a cubical array (as in Figure 5-1), the Debye frequency corresponds to an elastic wave for which the distance between adjacent atoms is approximately one half-wavelength. Assume, for simplicity, that $v_t = v_l$.

It is assumed in the Debye theory that the elastic waves are propagated through an essentially continuous medium, for which the wavelength is long compared with the interatomic distance. The Debye cut-off occurs when the wavelength is so short that elastic waves cannot be propagated.

12-30 Verify that the electronic specific heat of a typical conductor is very small compared with the lattice specific heat at room temperature.

12-31 For the element copper the Debye temperature is 315 °K, the Fermi energy is 7.0 eV, and the number of valence electrons per atom is 1. At what temperature are the contributions from the lattice and the electronic specific heats equal?

12-32 * For barium the work function is 2.51 eV, the internal potential energy seen by a free electron is 6.31 eV, the atomic weight is 138, and the density is 3.78 g/cm³. Calculate the number of free electrons per atom in barium.

12-33 (a) When an impurity atom from the fifth column of the periodic table, such as arsenic, replaces a silicon atom in a silicon crystal, the unbonded electron sees a charge of e located at the arsenic atom. The dielectric constant of silicon is 12. Assuming for simplicity that the unbonded electron moves in a Bohr orbit about the positive charge in silicon, compute the radius of the first Bohr orbit and compare it with the distance of 2.35 Å between nearest neighboring atoms in silicon. (b) Compute the corresponding orbital radius of arsenic impurity atoms in germanium, which has a dielectric constant of 16. The distance between nearest neighbors in germanium is 2.44 Å.

THE ATOMIC MASSES

Given here are the masses of the neutral atoms of all stable nuclides and a few of the unstable nuclides (designated by an asterisk following the mass number A). Masses are given in unified atomic mass units (u) where M is exactly 12 u for $^{12}_{6}C$, by definition.

These data are derived from J. H. E. Mattauch, W. Thiele, and A. H. Wapstra, *Nuclear Physics*, *67*, 1 (1965). The uncertainties are less than 0.000001 u for many nuclides of low mass number and as large as 0.001500 u for some nuclides of high mass number.

Element	A	Atomic mass u	Element	A	Atomic mass u
$_0$n	1*	1.008 665		17	16.999 133
$_1$H	1	1.007 825		18	17.999 160
	2	2.014 102		19*	19.003 578
	3*	3.016 050	$_9$F	17*	17.002 095
$_2$He	3	3.016 030		18*	18.000 937
	4	4.002 603		19	18.998 405
	6*	6.018 893		20*	19.999 987
$_3$Li	6	6.015 125		21*	20.999 951
	7	7.016 004	$_{10}$Ne	18*	18.005 711
	8*	8.022 487		19*	19.001 881
$_4$Be	7*	7.016 929		20	19.992 440
	9	9.012 186		21	20.993 849
	10*	10.013 534		22	21.991 385
$_5$B	8*	8.024 609		23*	22.994 473
	10	10.012 939	$_{11}$Na	22*	21.994 437
	11	11.009 305		23	22.989 771
	12*	12.014 354	$_{12}$Mg	23*	22.994 125
$_6$C	10*	10.016 810		24	23.990 962
	11*	11.011 432		25	24.989 955
	12	12.000 000		26	25.991 740
	13	13.003 354	$_{13}$Al	27	26.981 539
	14*	14.003 242	$_{14}$Si	28	27.976 930
	15*	15.010 599		29	28.976 496
$_7$N	12*	12.018 641		30	29.973 763
	13*	13.005 738	$_{15}$P	31	30.973 765
	14	14.003 074	$_{16}$S	32	31.972 074
	15	15.000 108		33	32.971 462
	16*	16.006 103		34	33.967 865
	17*	17.008 450		36	35.967 090
$_8$O	14*	14.008 597	$_{17}$Cl	35	34.968 851
	15*	15.003 070		36*	35.968 309
	16	15.994 915		37	36.965 898

Element	A	Atomic mass u	Element	A	Atomic mass u
$_{18}$Ar	36	35.967 544	$_{32}$Ge	70	69.924 252
	38	37.962 728		72	71.922 082
	40	39.962 384		73	72.923 463
$_{19}$K	39	38.963 710		74	73.921 181
	40*	39.964 000		76	75.921 406
	41	40.961 832	$_{33}$As	75	74.921 597
$_{20}$Ca	40	39.962 589	$_{34}$Se	74	73.922 476
	41*	40.962 275		76	75.919 207
	42	41.958 625		77	76.919 911
	43	42.958 780		78	77.917 314
	44	43.955 49		80	79.916 528
	46	45.953 689		82	81.916 707
	48	47.952 531	$_{35}$Br	79	78.918 330
$_{21}$Sc	41*	40.969 247		81	80.916 292
	45	44.955 919	$_{36}$Kr	78	77.920 403
$_{22}$Ti	46	45.952 632		80	79.916 380
	47	46.951 769		82	81.913 482
	48	47.947 951		83	82.914 132
	49	48.947 871		84	83.911 504
	50	49.944 786		86	85.910 616
$_{23}$V	48*	47.952 259	$_{37}$Rb	85	84.911 800
	50*	49.947 164		87*	86.909 187
	51	50.943 962	$_{38}$Sr	84	83.913 431
$_{24}$Cr	48*	47.953 760		86	85.909 285
	50	49.946 055		87	86.908 893
	52	51.940 514		88	87.905 641
	53	52.940 653	$_{39}$Y	89	88.905 872
	54	53.938 882	$_{40}$Zr	90	89.904 700
$_{25}$Mn	54*	53.940 362		91	90.905 642
	55	54.938 051		92	91.905 031
$_{26}$Fe	54	53.939 617		94	93.906 314
	56	55.934 937		96	95.908 286
	57	56.935 398	$_{41}$Nb	93	92.906 382
	58	57.933 282	$_{42}$Mo	92	91.906 811
$_{27}$Co	59	58.933 190		94	93.905 091
	60*	59.933 814		95	94.905 839
$_{28}$Ni	58	57.935 342		96	95.904 674
	60	59.930 787		97	96.906 022
	61	60.931 056		98	97.905 409
	62	61.928 342		100	99.907 475
	64	63.927 958	$_{44}$Ru	96	95.907 598
$_{29}$Cu	63	62.929 592		98	97.905 289
	65	64.927 786		99	98.905 936
$_{30}$Zn	64	63.929 145		100	99.904 218
	66	65.926 052		101	100.905 577
	67	66.927 145		102	101.904 348
	68	67.924 857		104	103.905 430
	70	69.925 334	$_{45}$Rh	103	102.905 511
$_{31}$Ga	69	68.925 574	$_{46}$Pd	102	101.905 609
	71	70.924 706		104	103.904 011
				105	104.905 064

Element	A	Atomic mass u	Element	A	Atomic mass u
	106	105.903 479		138	137.905 000
	108	107.903 891	57La	138*	137.906 910
	110	109.905 164		139	138.906 140
47Ag	107	106.905 094	58Ce	136	135.907 100
	109	108.904 756		138	137.905 830
48Cd	106	105.906 463		140	139.905 392
	108	107.904 187		142	141.909 140
	110	109.903 012	59Pr	141	140.907 596
	111	110.904 189	60Nd	142	141.907 663
	112	111.902 763		143	142.909 779
	113	112.904 409		144*	143.910 039
	114	113.903 361		145	144.912 538
	116	115.904 762		146	145.913 086
49In	113	112.904 089		148	147.916 869
	115*	114.903 871		150	149.920 915
50Sn	112	111.904 835	62Sm	144	143.911 989
	114	113.902 773		147*	146.914 867
	115	114.903 346		148	147.914 791
	116	115.901 745		149	148.917 180
	117	116.902 959		150	149.917 276
	118	117.901 606		152	151.919 756
	119	118.903 314		154	153.922 282
	120	119.902 199	63Eu	151	150.919 838
	122	121.903 442		153	152.921 242
	124	123.905 272	64Gd	152	151.919 794
51Sb	121	120.903 817		154	153.920 929
	123	122.904 213		155	154.922 664
52Te	120	119.904 023		156	155.922 175
	122	121.903 066		157	156.924 025
	123	122.904 277		158	157.924 178
	124	123.902 842		160	159.927 115
	125	124.904 418	65Tb	159	158.925 351
	126	125.903 322	66Dy	156	155.923 930
	128	127.904 476		158	157.924 449
	130	129.906 238		160	159.925 202
53I	127	126.904 470		161	160.926 945
54Xe	124	123.906 120		162	161.926 803
	126	125.904 288		163	162.928 755
	128	127.903 540		164	163.929 200
	129	128.904 784	67Ho	165	164.930 421
	130	129.903 509	68Er	162	161.928 740
	131	130.905 086		164	163.929 287
	132	131.904 161		166	165.930 307
	134	133.905 398		167	166.932 060
	136	135.907 221		168	167.932 383
55Cs	133	132.905 355		170	169.935 560
56Ba	130	129.906 245	69Tm	169	168.934 245
	132	131.905 120	70Yb	168	167.934 160
	134	133.904 612		170	169.935 020
	135	134.905 550		171	170.936 430
	136	135.904 300		172	171.936 360
	137	136.905 500			

Element	A	Atomic mass u	Element	A	Atomic mass u
	173	172.938 060		193	192.963 012
	174	173.938 740	$_{78}$Pt	190*	189.959 950
	176	175.942 680		192	191.961 150
$_{71}$Lu	175	174.940 640		194	193.962 725
	176*	175.942 660		195	194.964 813
$_{72}$Hf	174	173.940 360		196	195.964 967
	176	175.941 570		198	197.967 895
	177	176.943 400	$_{79}$Au	197	196.966 541
	178	177.943 880	$_{80}$Hg	196	195.965 820
	179	178.946 030		198	197.966 756
	180	179.946 820		199	198.968 279
$_{73}$Ta	181	180.948 007		200	199.968 327
$_{74}$W	180	179.947 000		201	200.970 308
	182	181.948 301		202	201.970 642
	183	182.950 324		204	203.973 495
	184	183.951 025	$_{81}$Tl	203	202.972 353
	186	185.954 440		205	204.974 442
$_{75}$Re	185	184.953 059	$_{82}$Pb	204	203.973 044
	187*	186.955 833		206	205.974 468
$_{76}$Os	184	183.952 750		207	206.975 903
	186	185.953 870		208	207.976 650
	187	186.955 832	$_{83}$Bi	209	208.981 082
	188	187.956 081	$_{90}$Th	232*	232.038 124
	189	188.958 300	$_{92}$U	234*	234.040 904
	190	189.958 630		235*	235.043 915
	192	191.961 450		238*	238.050 770
$_{77}$Ir	191	190.960 640			

ANSWERS

to odd-numbered numerical problems

2-3 (a) 1.3×10^{-6} sec $+ 1.3 \times 10^{-10}$ sec; (b) 1.3 sec $+ 1.3 \times 10^{-4}$ sec
2-5 (a) 0.20 mm; (b) $(0.20 + 3 \times 10^{-8})$ mm
2-9 (a) $+0.9978\ c$; (b) $-0.9978\ c$; (c) $-0.80\ c$; (d) $+0.98\ c$
2-13 $0.9996\ c$, $11.5°$ South of East
2-15 (a) $\nu_2 = \nu_1[1 - (v/c)]/[1 - (v/c)^2]^{1/2}$
     $\lambda_2 = \lambda_1[1 - (v/c)^2]^{1/2}/[1 - (v/c)]$
2-19 (a) S_1 has 50 min, S_2 has 250 min; (b) S_2 has 10 min, S_1 has 50 min.
2-21 (a) $0.3\ c$; (b) $x_1 = 0$, $t_1 = 0$; $x_1 = 1.15$ km, $t_1 = 2.10 \times 10^{-6}$ sec
2-23 (a) Wave front is sphere of radius 3.0×10^8 m with center at the origin of S_1. The
     origin of S_2 is at $x_1 = 2.9 \times 10^8$ m;
     (b) Wave front is sphere of radius 3.0×10^8 m with center at the origin of S_2. The
     origin of S_1 is at $x_1 = 2.9 \times 10^8$ m;
     (c) Both S_1 and S_2 would observe a spherical wave front of 3.0×10^8 m radius
     with center at the origin of S_1.
2-25 (a) Labelling the corners A, B, C, and D starting at the origin and going
     counter-clockwise, the coordinates (x_1, y_1) are: $A(0, 0)$, $B(L_0[1 - (v/c)^2]^{1/2}, 0)$,
     $C(L_0[1 - (v/c)^2]^{1/2}, L_0)$, and $D(0, L_0)$;
     (b) Values of t: $A(0)$, $B(L_0[1 - (v/c)^2]^{1/2}/c)$, $C\left(\dfrac{L_0[2 - (v/c)^2]}{c}\right)^{1/2}$, and $D(L_0/c)$
2-27 $\lambda = \lambda_0[1 - (v/c)^2]^{-1/2}$
2-29 (a) $0.26\ c$; (b) 3.8×10^{-8} sec; (c) zero

3-1 3.5×10^{-8} per cent
3-3 (a) 3.0 keV; (b) 2.0×10^6 m/sec
3-5 (a) 200 MeV/c to 2.00 GeV/c; (b) 22 MeV to 1.3 MeV
3-7 (a) $0.99999\ c$; (b) 3.2 MW
3-9 4.3×10^{-13}
3-11 9.4×10^{10} V
3-15 (a) 1.0 GeV/c; (b) 5.0 GeV/c
3-17 (a) 19 μA; (b) 6.4×10^{-4} N
3-19 (a) $0.116\ c$; (b) 3.5 keV; (c) 6.3 MeV
3-21 (a) 7.3; (b) 2.5
3-23 (a) 1.4×10^{22} J; (b) 1.6×10^5 kg; (c) 1.6×10^7 kg
3-31 (a) 5.5×10^{-15} kg; (b) 1 kg mass increases by 4.4×10^{-15} kg; 4 kg mass increases
     by 1.1×10^{-15} kg
3-33 1.0 MeV
3-35 $35°$

4-1 (a) 4.23 eV; (b) 1.97 eV
4-3 (a) 2.3 eV; (b) 5.2×10^{-15} J-sec/C
4-5 (a) 7×10^{-30} J/sec; (b) 3×10^3 yr (experimentally $\sim 10^{-9}$ sec)
4-11 1.6×10^{-6} m
4-13 3.1×10^5 Å

4-15 $\alpha 1/r^2$

4-17 (a) minimum of 2.04 eV; (b) 172 keV; (c) 28 keV

4-19 (a) 1240 Å; (b) 3.9 Å

4-21 (a) 2.0 keV; (b) x-ray

4-23 (a) 3.3×10^{-8} kg-m/sec; (b) 5.0×10^{23}

4-25 3.33×10^{-7} N/m²

4-27 (a) 4.7×10^{-6} N/m²; (b) 6.0×10^{8} N

4-29 (a) 0.0367 Å; (b) 0.0610 Å; (c) 0.66 MeV; (d) 0.80 MeV

4-31 40 keV

4-35 55 MeV

4-37 (a) $1/\sqrt{3}$; (b) $\sqrt{3}$; (c) unchanged; (d) $1/\sqrt{3}$; (e) $1/\sqrt{3}$

4-39 (a) 1.24 MeV; (b) 1.24 MeV (unmodified Compton), 0.51 MeV (annihilation photons), 0.36 (modified Compton)

4-41 0.27 MeV/c in forward direction

4-43 4.8×10^{-3} Å

4-45 (a) 0.59 MeV, 0.59 MeV/c; (b) 120°

4-49 0.135 cm⁻¹

CHAPTER 5

5-1 (a) 1.24×10^{-12} m; (b) 7.09×10^{-13} m; (c) 2.86×10^{-14} m

5-3 $\dfrac{\lambda_1}{\lambda_2} = \sqrt{m_2/m_1}$

5-5 (a) 6.2×10^{-17} m; (b) 6.2×10^{-18} m

5-7 (a) 8.2×10^{-2} eV; (b) 0.19 GeV

5-11 h/QBr

5-13 3.14 Å

5-15 (a) 23°; (b) 46°

5-19 (a) 1.68 Å; (c) 51°

5-23 (a) $h/\Delta x$; (b) $\Delta x + (2h\,\Delta t/m\,\Delta x)$

5-25 larger

5-27 $\sim$1 m/sec

5-29 (a) 4.1×10^{-10} eV; (b) 4.1×10^{-11}; (c) 4.1×10^{-20}

5-31 (a) 60 m; (b) 3.0×10^{11} m $\simeq$ dia. of Earth's orbit; (c) 1 cm; (d) 10^{-8} m

5-33 (b) It can not be localized

5-35 (a) 3×10^{-23} sec; (b) 10^{-15} m

5-37 (a) 3.8 keV, 62 keV/c; (b) 62 keV, 62 keV/c; (c) Particles have smaller energy for same wavelength and momentum

5-41 (a) $E + (\pi^2 h^2/2m)[(n_1/L)^2 = (n_2/W)^2]$, with n_1 and n_2 = 1,2,3, . . .; (b) 10^{-49} eV

CHAPTER 6

6-1 (a) 6.3×10^{4}; (b) 2.5×10^{5}

6-3 $(Z_1/Z_2)^2/(w_1/w_2)$

6-5 (a) 7.80 per cent; (b) 100 per cent; (c) 0.055 per cent

6-7 10 per cent

6-11 No

6-13 $\sim$$1.4 \times 10^{-18}$ m²

6-15 1.89 eV

6-19 (a) 6; (b) 11,000

6-21 24 days

6-23 $\sim$0.5 Å

6-25 1.09×10^{-8}

6-27 (a) 10.2 eV; (b) 10.2 eV/c; (c) 1210 Å; (d) 5.6×10^{-8} eV

6-29 (a) 10^{-7} eV; (b) 10^{-7}; (c) complete uncertainty

6-31 $A = a^{3/2}/\sqrt{\pi}$

6-33 6.4×10^5

6-35 0.12 keV

6-41 (a) 12.1 eV; (b) 13.6 eV

6-43 (a) $(3/8)E_I$; (b) $(3/2)E_I$

6-45 10^5 °K

6-47 4.14×10^{-15} J-sec/C

CHAPTER 7

7-3 4.9 eV

7-9 (a) 10^{-5} eV

7-13 1.76×10^{11} C/kg

7-15 0.6 Wb/m²

7-17 (a) 2×10^{25} sec⁻¹ (Note that, on this classical model, the equatorial speed $\sim$200 c!); (b) $(\sqrt{3}/2)(eh/2m)$, one-half of the correct quantum value.

7-21 (b) 8.4×10^9 Hz

7-29 (a) $(\sqrt{3}/2)h$ and $(1/\sqrt{3})(eh/2m)$, using the results of Problem 7-27; (b) $(\sqrt{3}/2)h$ and $\sqrt{3}(eh/2m)$

7-31 Quantum numbers (n, ℓ, m_l, m_s): (a) $(1, 0, 0, -\frac{1}{2})$, $(1, 0, 0, \frac{1}{2})$, and $(2, 0, 0, -\frac{1}{2})$; (b) $(2, 0, 0, \frac{1}{2})$ and $(2, 1, 0, -\frac{1}{2})$

7-33 $1s^2 2s^2 2p^6 3s^2 3p^5$

7-37 0.20 Å

7-39 (a) 5.5×10^{-4} eV; (b) 6.9×10^{-8}

CHAPTER 8

8-1 (a) 2.0×10^5; (b) 3.2×10^{-14} C; (c) 1.6 V

8-3 (a) 2.4×10^{-2} cm; (b) 1.3 cm

8-5 17 V

8-7 (a) 248 V; (b) 225 V; (c) 146 V

8-9 3×10^{-8} sec

8-11 0.53 GeV

8-17 (a) parabola; (b) helix

8-21 (a) 4.5 MeV; (b) 13 keV

8-23 $[E_0^2 + (eBxc/2)^2]^{1/2} - E_0$

8-25 (a) 31°; (b) 1.2 GeV/c; (c) 5 m; (d) 5.6×10^{-8} sec

8-27 (a) 98.9 per cent ^{12}C, 1.1 per cent ^{13}C; (b) 12.011

8-33 (a) 1.09 m; (b) 0.15 m; (c) 98; (d) $\sim$40 m

8-35 (a) 3.2×10^{-8} per cent; (b) $\sim$3 inches; (c) 9×10^{13} electrons/sec

8-37 $f_p = 2f_d$

8-39 (a) 31 MHz; (b) 16 MHz; (c) 16 MHz; (d) 48 MeV; (e) 24 MeV; (f) 48 MeV

8-41 (a) 30.5 MHz; (b) 29.6 MHz

8-43 (a) 4.1×10^6; (b) 3.9×10^5 km; (c) 3.1 MHz

8 45 $\sim$200 per cent

8-47 (a) 3×10^{15} eV; (b) 4 G.N.P. (1970); (c) $\sim$2000 A.D.

8-49 2700 GeV

CHAPTER 9

9-3 12.8 MHz

9-5 (a) 11.01145 u; (b) 11.01143 u

9-7 (a) 84°; (b) 3.0 MeV; (c) 8.2 MeV

9-13 (a) $^{24}_{12}$Mg : 11.7 MeV, $^{23}_{11}$Na : 8.8 MeV, $^{22}_{10}$Ne : 10.4 MeV, $^{21}_{10}$Ne : 6.8 MeV, $^{20}_{10}$Ne : 12.8 MeV, and $^{19}_{9}$F : 8.0 MeV; (b) larger; (c) proton and neutron levels are filled with two nucleons alternately.

9-17 (a) $Z = 50$ with 10 stable isotopes; (b) $N = 82$ with 7 stable isotones; (c) $^{4}_{2}$He, $^{16}_{8}$O, $^{40}_{20}$Ca, $^{48}_{20}$Ca, $^{208}_{82}$Pb

9-19 2.3×10^{-2} sec^{-1}

9-25 2.2×10^{-4} g

9-29 6×10^{-7} m/sec down

9-31 (a) β^-, β^+, electron capture; (b) electron capture; (c) β^+, electron capture; (d) β^-, electron capture

9-33 6.1 μW

9-35 20.8 keV

9-37 (a) 0.41 MeV; (b) ~0.41 MeV; (c) 2.2 eV; (d) 5.4×10^{-6}

9-39 (a) 0.33 keV; (b) 0.78 MeV; (c) 0.78 MeV

9-41 circa O A.D.

Chapter 10

10-1 (a) β^-; (b) β^+ and electron capture; (c) β^-; (d) β^+ and electron capture

10-3 (a) $^{13}_{6}$C(n, γ)$^{14}_{6}$C, $^{13}_{6}$C(d, p)$^{14}_{6}$C, $^{14}_{7}$N(n, p)$^{14}_{6}$C; (b) $^{12}_{6}$C(α, n)$^{15}_{8}$O, $^{14}_{7}$N(d, n)$^{15}_{8}$O, $^{15}_{7}$N(p, n)$^{15}_{8}$O, $^{16}_{8}$O(p, d)$^{15}_{8}$O; (c) $^{57}_{26}$Fe(α, p)$^{60}_{27}$Co, $^{60}_{28}$Ni(n, p)$^{60}_{27}$Co, $^{59}_{27}$Co(n, γ)$^{60}_{27}$Co

10-5 9.02 MeV, 6.85 MeV, 5.62 MeV, 5.35 MeV

10-7 2.3 MeV

10-9 22.0 MeV

10-11 (a) 4.35 MeV; (b) 1.6 MeV; (c) 5.7 MeV

10-13 (a) 0.33 MeV; (b) 2.0 MeV

10-15 decreased

10-19 (a) 1.99×10^3 barn; (b) 1.99×10^2 barn

10-21 22 MeV

10-25 $^{15}_{7}$N(γ, $^{14}_{7}$N(n, $^{11}_{5}$B(α, $^{13}_{6}$C(d

10-27 ~10^{-14} sec

10-29 (a) ~200 MeV; (b) the same

10-31 (a) 3×10^{-3} MeV; (b) 3×10^2 fermi

10-33 (a) 2×10^{38} neutrinos/sec; (b) 8×10^{14} neutrinos/m²-sec; (c) 3×10^6 neutrinos/m³ = 3 neutrinos/cm³

Chapter 11

11-3 (a) 141 MeV; (b) 0.44×10^{-23} sec

11-7 155 MeV (parallel), 30 MeV (anti-parallel)

11-11 5×10^{-8} eV

11-13 Σ^- and $\overline{\Sigma^-}$ have *different* rest energies, mean-lives, decay products, and strangeness number

11-15 A beam of $\overline{K^0}$ mesons striking a proton target may produce the reaction $\overline{K^0} + p \rightarrow \Lambda^0 + \pi^+$, whereas a beam of K^0 mesons could not because it would violate the conservation of strangeness.

11-17 (a) baryon number; (b) strangeness number; (c) electric charge; (e) mass-energy

11-19 (b) $2\gamma + 2e^- + 2\bar{\nu}_e + 2\nu_\mu + 2\bar{\nu}_\mu + p$

Chapter 12

12-5 ~10^2 N/m

12-7 (a) 1.0×10^{-15} eV; (b) ~10^{28}

12-15 43, 46, 10, and 1 per cent

12-19 (a) For $(1, 0, 0)$ 6.2×10^{-6} eV/c and 6.2×10^{-6} eV, and for $(1, 1, 0)$ 8.8×10^{-6} eV/c and 8.8×10^{-6} eV; (b) 41 per cent; (c) for $(100, 0, 0)$ 6.2×10^{-4} eV/c and 6.2×10^{-4} eV, and for $(100, 1, 0)$ 6.2×10^{-4} eV/c and 6.2×10^{-4} eV; 0.005 per cent

11-25 Beryllium

11-31 $3°$ K

11-33 (a) 6.4 Å; (b) 8.5 Å

INDEX

**PHYSICAL
CONSTANTS
COMMONLY
NEEDED IN
COMPUTATIONS**

→